OBSERVER'S HANDBOOK 2011

The Royal Astronomical Society of Canada is dedicated to the advancement of astronomy and its related sciences; this Handbook espouses the scientific method, and supports dissemination of information, discoveries, and theories based on that well-tested method.

EDITOR
PATRICK KELLY

ONE-HUNDRED-AND-THIRD YEAR OF PUBLICATION

© THE ROYAL ASTRONOMICAL SOCIETY OF CANADA
203–4920 DUNDAS STREET WEST, TORONTO ON M9A 1B7
2010

ISSN 0080-4193
ISBN 978-0-9813292-5-3

MIX
Paper from
responsible sources
FSC® C017783
www.fsc.org

PRINTED IN CANADA
BY THISTLE PRINTING LIMITED

TABLE OF CONTENTS

Key to Marginal Chapter Symbols

Basic Data 1₂³

Time ⌛

Optics and Observing 🔭

The Sky Month by Month

Eclipses and Transits �<

The Moon ☽

The Sun ☼

Planets and Satellites ○⌐

Asteroids ☌

Meteors, Comets, and Dust

Stars ★

Nebulae and Galaxies ○

Ⓘ Special for 2011 edition   Ⓝ New section with this edition
Ⓐ Annual update   Ⓡ Revised significantly with this edition
Ⓔ Expanded from previous edition   Ⓣ Tabular data updated annually

LIST OF CONTRIBUTORS

JAY ANDERSON, Prairie Storm Prediction Centre, Winnipeg, Manitoba....................................
(Frequency of Nighttime Cloud Cover, Star-Party Weather, Weather for Eclipses)

J. RANDY ATTWOOD, Mississauga, Ontario.............................(Voyages in our Solar System)

ROY BISHOP, Avonport, Nova Scotia...(Binoculars, Eclipse Patterns,
Electromagnetic Spectrum, Expired Stars, Filters, Interplanetary Dust
Mars oppositions diagram, Map of Moon, Maps of the Night Sky,
Midnight Twilight and Midnight Sun, Orbital Motion, Rainbows, Saturn ring diagram,
Some Astronomical and Physical Data, Telescope Exit Pupils, Telescope Parameters,
Tides and the Earth–Moon System, Time and Time Scales,
left-hand pages of The Sky Month by Month (text))

LARRY D. BOGAN, Cambridge Station, Nova Scotia ..... (Configurations of Jupiter's Galilean
satellites, Configurations of Saturn's Brightest Satellites)

RANDALL BROOKS, Canada Science and Technology Museum, Ottawa, Ontario...................
(Astronomical Twilight and Sidereal Time)

PETER BROWN, University of Western Ontario, London, Ontario ....(Meteors)

IAN CAMERON, University of Manitoba, Winnipeg, Manitoba...................(Pluto finder chart)

MARGARET CAMPBELL-BROWN, University of Calgary, Calgary, Alberta...........(Meteors)

DAVID L. CRAWFORD, Kitt Peak National Observatory, Tucson, Arizona.....(Light Pollution)

ROBERT DICK, Carleton University & University of Ottawa, Ottawa, Ontario........................
(Light-Pollution Abatement in Canada)

DAVID W. DUNHAM, International Occultation Timing Association, Greenbelt, Maryland..........
(Occultations by the Moon, Planetary and Asteroidal Occultations)

MICHEL DUVAL, Montréal, Québec..(Coloured Double Stars)

ALAN DYER, Telus World of Science, Calgary, Alberta .... (Deep-Sky Challenge Objects,
Deep-Sky Observing Hints, The Finest NGC Objects, The Messier List)

JAMES EDGAR, Melville, Saskatchewan (Selected Observatories, Star Parties, and Planetaria)

LEO ENRIGHT*, Sharbot Lake, Ontario ....(David Levy's Deep-Sky Gems)

FRED ESPENAK, NASA/Goddard Space Flight Centre, Greenbelt, Maryland..... (Eclipses in 2011)

REV. ROBERT EVANS, Hazelbrook, New South Wales, Australia...(Amateur Supernova Hunting)

ROBERT F. GARRISON, University of Toronto, Toronto, Ontario..................(The Brightest Stars)

PHILIP GEBHARDT, Pickering, Ontario .... (Radio Detection of Meteors)

PAUL GRAY, Fredericton, New Brunswick...(Dark Nebulae)

RAJIV GUPTA, University of British Columbia, Vancouver, British Columbia........................
(Polar Alignment, Times of Moonrise and Moonset, Times of Sunrise and Sunset, Twilight,
right-hand pages of The Sky Month by Month (librated lunar graphics))

KIM HAY, Yarker, Ontario ....(Solar Observing)

ARNE A. HENDEN, American Association of Variable Star Observers, Cambridge, Massachusetts..
(Variable Stars)

TODD J. HENRY, Georgia State University, Atlanta, Georgia ....(The Nearest Stars)

WILLIAM HERBST, Wesleyan University, Middletown, Connecticut...................(Galactic Nebulae)

CHRISTOPHER D.K. HERD, University of Alberta, Edmonton, Alberta . (Meteorite Identification)

RICHARD K. HERD, Geological Survey of Canada, Ottawa, Ontario...... (Meteorite Identification)

*Deceased, 2009 Aug. 11.

ALAN HILDEBRAND, University of Calgary, Calgary, Alberta..............................(Fireballs)

PETER JEDICKE, Fanshawe College, London, Ontario................. (Happy Birthday, Neptune!, Star Clusters)

LEE JOHNSON, Vancouver, British Columbia .....(Magnification and Contrast in Deep-Sky Observing, ...2011 Observer's Challenge)

TOOMAS KARMO University of Toronto, Toronto, Ontario ....(The Brightest Stars)

DAVE LANE, Saint Mary's University, Halifax, Nova Scotia ....
(finder charts for Neptune, Uranus, and Ceres, left-hand pages of The Sky Month by Month (tables), nebular filter transmission chart)

DAVID H. LEVY, Vail, Arizona.................(David Levy's Deep-Sky Gems, Observing Comets)

ALISTER LING, Edmonton, Alberta .... (Deep-Sky Challenge Objects, 2011 Observer's Challenge)

BARRY F. MADORE, Caltech, Pasadena, California ....(Galaxies: Brightest and Nearest, Galaxies with Proper Names)

PAUL MARKOV, Toronto, Ontario..(The Observing Logbook)

BRIAN G. MARSDEN, Smithsonian Astrophysical Observatory, Cambridge, Massachusetts ....
(Asteroidal osculating elements and ephemerides, Comets in 2011)

BRIAN D. MASON, U.S. Naval Observatory, Washington, D.C. ....(Double and Multiple Stars)

BRUCE MCCURDY, Edmonton, Alberta .... (Lunar Observing)

ANTHONY MOFFAT, Université de Montréal, Montréal, Québec...................... (Star Clusters)

PHILIP D. NICHOLSON, Cornell University, Ithaca, New York ...(Natural Satellites of the Planets)

RON OSTROMECKI, Erie, Pennsylvania..(Carbon Stars)

MURRAY PAULSON, St. Albert, Alberta... (The Planets for 2011)

DOUGLAS PITCAIRN, Dartmouth, Nova Scotia...................................(Limiting Magnitudes)

ALLAN RAHILL, Canadian Meteorological Centre, Dorval, Québec...
(Weather Resources on the Internet)

EBERHARD RIEDEL, München, Germany..................................... (Occultations by the Moon)

WILLIAM ROBERTS, Vancouver, British Columbia ....
(Magnification and Contrast in Deep-Sky Observing)

JOSHUA ROTH, Amateur Telescope Makers of Boston, Arlington, Massachusetts....................
(Night Myopia and Stargazing Glasses)

JOHN SPRAY, University of New Brunswick, Fredericton, New Brunswick...............................
(Meteorite Impact Craters of North America)

JAMES STAMM, International Occultation Timing Association, Tucson, Arizona.....................
(Planetary and Asteroidal Occultations)

KEN TAPPING, Dominion Radio Astrophysical Observatory, Penticton, British Columbia........
(Radio Sources, Solar Activity)

HEATHER THEIJSMEIJER, CASCA Education Coordinator, Kagawong, Ontario ....
(Teaching and the *Observer's Handbook*)

ELIZABETH O. WAAGEN, American Association of Variable Star Observers, Cambridge, Massachusetts.
(Variable Stars)

ALAN WHITMAN, Penticton, British Columbia................ (Southern Hemisphere Splendours)

THE *OBSERVER'S HANDBOOK*

The *Observer's Handbook* is one of Canada's oldest scientific publications. Created by C.A. Chant, Professor of Astronomy at the University of Toronto, it first appeared over a century ago as *The Canadian Astronomical Handbook for 1907*, a small (13 × 17 cm), 108-page publication. A second edition covered the year 1908, but for the following two years most of the information that would have appeared was published instead in installments in the *Journal of the RASC*. The Council of the Society decided to return to a separate publication for 1911 with a new name—the *Observer's Handbook*—and it has been published annually ever since.

Each year some 10 000 copies of the Handbook are distributed to many countries throughout the world, to amateur and professional astronomers, to educators at school and university levels, and to many observatories, planetaria, and libraries. The Handbook is the main source of income for The Royal Astronomical Society of Canada. Since the first edition in 1907, the various editors, assistant editors, editorial assistants (see p. 8), and contributors (see pp. 4–5) have voluntarily contributed their time and expertise to produce this unique book.

EDITORS OF THE *OBSERVER'S HANDBOOK*

		Position	Editions	RASC President
C.A. Chant	(1865–1956)	Editor	1907–1957	1903–1907
Frank Hogg	(1904–1951)	Assistant Editor	1939–1951	1940–1942
Ruth Northcott	(1913–1969)	Assistant Editor	1952–1957	1962–1964
		Editor	1958–1970	
John Percy	(1941–	Editor	1971–1981	1978–1980
Roy Bishop	(1939–	Editor	1982–2000	1984–1986
Rajiv Gupta	(1958–	Editor	2001–2006	2002–2004
Patrick Kelly	(1958–	Editor	2007–2011	

The *Observer's Handbook* is intended to be "a companion which the observer would wish always to have in his pocket or on the table before him."

C.A. Chant, Toronto, 1906

"We believe that the *Observer's Handbook* is a truly significant contribution that Canadian astronomy in general and our Society in particular has been making to the dissemination of astronomical knowledge for half a century. I trust that it will still occupy the same position of respect after the first hundred years."

Ruth Northcott, Ottawa, 1964

"The more one knows, the more one can benefit from the Handbook. It inspires all who leaf through its pages to learn and question what the tables, graphs and data mean, perhaps to speculate on the mysteries of the Universe, and above all, to get out and look beyond our world. You have in your hands a key to the Universe—a key which will fit many doors. Please use it well and treasure it."

Peter Broughton, Toronto, 1992
Author of *Looking Up, A History of the RASC*

"The *Observer's Handbook* is the single most useful publication for the observational astronomer. Its combination of authoritative data, informative diagrams, and concise text is unique. Anyone interested in astronomy, beginner or expert, amateur or professional, student or teacher, will find the *Observer's Handbook* indispensable. Its international reputation for quality is a credit both to its many contributors and to Canadian astronomy."

Roy Bishop, Halifax, 2000

HOW TO USE THIS HANDBOOK

This Handbook is a concise, high-density compilation of information that is of interest to observers. By reading the following points, you will allow yourself to reap maximum benefit from it.

(1) The Handbook is composed of various *sections*. Related sections are grouped into chapters, as listed in the CONTENTS. Chapter titles are given in large dark-grey boxes and section titles against light background shades, both of which extend to the edge of the page. The section title and chapter title are given in headers at the top of the pages. In addition, staggered marginal symbols (see p. iii for a key) mark the edges of the pages in each chapter. These various identifiers are meant to facilitate the quick location of desired material.

(2) References to other sections are given in SMALL CAPITAL TYPE, and this type is generally reserved for this purpose. Internet email addresses and Web sites are also given in a distinctive font.

(3) The GLOSSARY and INDEX at the back contains a listing of definitions and keywords.

(4) Alternate blocks of rows are shaded in most tables, in order to make the location of entries easier. Every table has a shaded header with the titles of the various columns given in bold type. Detailed explanation of the meaning of the columns is usually given in accompanying text.

(5) SI symbols and abbreviations are used throughout. See pp. 33 and 36 in the section SOME ASTRONOMICAL AND PHYSICAL DATA for the most common abbreviations. The letter "m" is used to denote both minutes of right ascension and metres; the meaning will be clear from the context. Minutes of time are usually abbreviated "min".

(6) The time scale Universal Time is generally used. Times of day are usually given in the 24-hour clock, using numerals separated by colons. The section TIME AND TIME SCALES on p. 43 explains the various time scales used in astronomy.

(7) The section TERMINOLOGY AND SYMBOLS on p. 20 lists Greek letters (and other symbols) and defines some basic terms.

(8) The section TEACHING AND THE *OBSERVER'S HANDBOOK* on p. 17 gives an overview of the contents of this Handbook.

(9) The Web site of the Handbook is **www.rasc.ca/handbook**. Resources related to the Handbook, including a page of links to all Web sites cited in the Handbook, are given at this site, and any updates and corrections will also be posted there.

Cover photos

"Picard, you are about to move into areas of the galaxy containing wonders more incredible than you can possibly imagine—and terrors to freeze your soul." The Star Trek *character Q could be describing Orion in the days of film, with the Orion Nebula as a wonder, and the Horsehead as a terror. The digital revolution has magnified the glory and reduced the terror, as you can see by this year's cover images.*

The front-cover image of M42, the Orion Nebula, was taken by Leslie Marczi (Niagara Centre) from his observatory in Welland, Ontario. He used a Canon Hutech-Modified 300D camera attached to a Takahashi Sky 90 II f/5.6 telescope (operating at f/4.5) on an Astro-Physics 900 GTO mount. A total of 57 images (20 300-s exposures, 25 125-s exposures, and 12 15-s exposures were taken with a Baader LPS filter and combined using Images Plus, Noise Ninja, and Photoshop CS3. Mask layering techniques were used in Photoshop to preserve the bright core around the Trapezium.

The back cover photo of the area around the Horsehead Nebula was taken by Todd Benko (Calgary Centre) using a Skywatcher Equinox 80 telescope on a EQ6 mount. Fifteen 300-s colour exposures taken one night, were combined with 12 1200-s Hα exposures taken the following night. Software used in processing consisted of Nebulosity, Images Plus, FITS Liberator, Noise Ninja, and Photoshop CS4.

The objects are numbers 42 and 3, respectively, in the THE MESSIER CATALOGUE and DARK NEBULAE sections on pages 319 and 334 of this Handbook.

EDITOR'S COMMENTS

This edition of the Handbook is the thickest yet. There are two new sections, Ron Ostromecki's CARBON STARS looks at these very interesting objects, while Joshua Roth has contributed a section called NIGHT MYOPIA AND STARGAZING GLASSES, which may surprise you as much as it did me. Other sections have been expanded with new material, as you can see from the table of contents. In most cases, this required more pages, especially in THE PLANETS FOR 2011. One section has had a name change as Roy Bishop has added the green flash to the section on rainbows. Calling it RAINBOWS, HALOS, SUNDOGS, PILLARS, CORONAE, GLORIES, HUILIGENSCHEIN AND THE GREEN FLASH was a bit much, given that the Handbook is supposed to be concise, so it is now RAINBOWS AND SOME OTHER SKY PHENOMENA.

The 2011 edition will be my last as editor, as my five-year term has come to an end. It has been an incredible experience, and I have met a lot of amazing and dedicated people as a result. All of the contributors, past and present, have been a pleasure to work with. I would especially thank Roy Bishop, James Edgar, Bruce McCurdy, and Betty Robinson, who have served on the editorial "committee." One thing I have learned is that when it comes to spotting errors, more eyes are always better!

Without the readers, the Handbook would be of little use. The scope of the letters, questions, comments, and suggestions that have come in have shown me that there are a lot of people who read the Handbook in great detail. It is always encouraging to know that one is helping to produce something on which so many people not only rely, but care about deeply.

Seeing the Handbook go from a layout on the computer screen, to printed "blues" from the press to be proofed, still does not prepare me for that amazing feeling when I open up the box with the final product. Computers screens are nice, and PDF files may be convenient, but the power of the printed page still has a draw all of its own. That is especially true when one lives in a part of the country that has had its major star party cancelled two years in a row by hurricanes and power outages. One can still read the Handbook by candlelight and dream of the skies that might have been.

The next Handbook editor will be David Chapman who is a member of both the Halifax and Dave Centres. (See www.rasd.ca for details; he is Dave XVII and has a link to his own Web site.) I have known David since joining the RASC in the early 1980s, and he has always been active in the Centre, taking on projects ranging from being president of the Centre (Halifax, not Dave), to being one of the people instrumental in the establishment of Nova Scotia's first dark-sky preserve at Kejimkujik National Park. Dave is very well suited to the task. I am sure that he will find the experience to be as challenging and rewarding as mine has.

chalmey Huv.

Patrick Kelly
handbookeditor@rasc.ca
Falmouth, Nova Scotia
2010 Sep. 27

THE OBSERVER'S HANDBOOK

EDITOR
Patrick Kelly

EDITOR'S ASSISTANT AND PROOFREADER
James Edgar

PROOFREADER
Bruce McCurdy
Roy Bishop

In addition to the 54 contributors listed on pp. 4 & 5, several other individuals and organizations played a rôle in the production of this Handbook.

Some of the data contained herein comes from the publications *Astronomical Phenomena for the Year 2011* and *The Astronomical Almanac 2011*, both prepared jointly by the U.S. Naval Observatory's Nautical Almanac Office and Her Majesty's Nautical Almanac Office.

Corrections or suggestions for improvement that were incorporated in this edition were provided by Tom Annard, Roy Bishop, Matthew Buynoski, Rob Dick, Douglas Gies, Steve Gottlieb, Clark Muir, Walter Nissan, Michael Spencer, and John Westfall.

HAPPY BIRTHDAY, NEPTUNE!

BY PETER JEDICKE

Parents gush with pride when their offspring attain noteworthy milestones, such as birthdays. Ask astronomers about the significance of a birthday and they will explain that it celebrates the completion of a full orbit around the Sun. Of all the interesting 2011 events noted in the *Observer's Handbook*, surely Neptune's first birthday must be the most compelling cause for festivities.

By what reasoning do we say that Neptune's first birthday will fall in this Earthly calendar year? We could recognize September 23 as the anniversary of the discovery of Neptune each year, since it was late in the evening on that date in 1846 (or perhaps just after midnight on the 24th) when astronomer Johann Galle at the Berlin Observatory, assisted by student Louis d'Arrest, found it. The story of how a mathematical astronomer, Urbain J.J. Le Verrier in Paris, predicted where to look to make the discovery is a famous triumph of modern astronomy.

In fact, the story took a rather scandalous twist in 1998, when contemporary documents related to the discovery were uncovered. The documents were withheld, apparently deliberately and with the connivance of successive Astronomers Royal, for a century and a half! For all that time, John Couch Adams of Cambridge, England, has been listed alongside Le Verrier as co-discoverer of Neptune. Based on those documents, RASC Honorary Member William Sheehan and his co-authors wrote in *Scientific American* (Dec 2004, Vol. 291, Issue 6, pp. 92–99) "that Adams' British contemporaries gave him more credit than was due him, even though he had performed some remarkable calculations."

Surely the discovery is the appropriate moment to call Neptune's birth, but why not use Neptune's own orbit to determine its birthday? As you will find on page 23 of this Handbook, a Neptunian year corresponds to about 165 of yours or mine, so Neptune will complete its first orbit in 2011, thus giving astronomers on our own blue planet a superb opportunity to focus on that other blue planet.

To settle on a specific date that can be entered into your iPhone or Android calendar app, we need to investigate Neptune's orbit more carefully. You could try the **tropical year** for Neptune, which is the time it takes to travel around the ecliptic between two successive crossings of the zero point of the coordinate system which is called the First Point of Aries. So we need to refer Neptune's position at the time of discovery to the zero point. This number is called the heliocentric ecliptic longitude. It seems reasonable to neglect that Neptune will be a tad above or below the ecliptic each time it comes around. More importantly, the First Point of Aries itself is not fixed, but precesses slowly westward around the ecliptic by 50.29 arcseconds each year, according to page 34 of the Handbook. In fact, on 2010 Jun. 27, Neptune already passed the point where it made the same angle (326.9611° of heliocentric ecliptic longitude, for those who want to check) with the precessing zero point.

This hardly seems fair! Neptune's birthday should not depend on precession, which is caused by the changing orientation of Earth's axis. What we really need is a coordinate system that is fixed beyond Earth, or any other solar system reference. The current method to establish the background for the sidereal coordinates uses 1448 extragalactic radio targets as primary sources, and is called the International Celestial Reference Frame (ICRF2) When Neptune circles the solar system and returns to the same angle as measured in ICRF2, that is called Neptune's **sidereal year**, and surely is the definition to use.

To avoid skewing things by precession, astronomers commonly pick some convenient moment in time, which is called the Epoch, and refer all their calculations to the First Point of Aries on that date. Nowadays, instead of looking at some musty table, we can access the Jet Propulsion Laboratory's website (www.jpl.nasa.gov/horizons.cgi) where they have made their full-fledged model of the solar system, called DE405, available to all. On 1846 Sep. 23/24 at midnight, Neptune was 329.1022° from the spot where the First Point of Aries was at the beginning of the year 2000—the Epoch most widely used today.

According to JPL's calculator, Neptune will return to ecliptic longitude 329.1022 at 22:27 UT on 2011 Jul. 12, a Tuesday. The time of discovery being uncertain by a half hour anyway, readers will have plenty of time to catch the bartender's attention and order a suitable celebratory libation. Perhaps RASC Centres can negotiate a special Neptunian discount for that day at their favourite restaurant.

[Thanks to Roy Bishop, David L. Clark, Brian Fenerty, Randy Kissack, and Bruce McCurdy for discussions on the technical aspects of this article.]

THE ROYAL ASTRONOMICAL SOCIETY OF CANADA

The beginnings of The Royal Astronomical Society of Canada go back to the mid-1800s. Then, in 1890, the Society was incorporated within the province of Ontario, received its Royal Charter from King Edward VII in 1903, and was federally incorporated in 1968. The National Office of the Society (containing the business office and historical archives) is located at 203–4920 Dundas Street West, Toronto ON M9A 1B7; telephone: (416) 924-7973 or (888) 924-7272 from within Canada; email: nationaloffice@rasc.ca; Web site: www.rasc.ca.

The RASC has approximately 4200 members, who are from many countries and all walks of life. Members receive the *Observer's Handbook* (published every fall for the next calendar year) and electronic access to the bimonthly *Journal of the RASC*, which contains review articles, research papers on historical and contemporary topics, education notes, general notes of astronomical interest, book reviews, news items concerning the Society and its Centres, informal articles, and letters. (A print version of the *Journal of the RASC* is available at a modest extra cost.) Also included in membership is *SkyNews*, Canada's popular bimonthly astronomy magazine.

Membership fees are $70 per year, with a reduced rate for persons under 21 years of age. For members outside of Canada, these figures are to be read as U.S. dollars, and there is an additional fee ($16 for U.S. addresses; $45 for international addresses) to cover higher mailing costs. An applicant may affiliate with one of the Centres of the Society across Canada or join the Society directly as an unattached member. Membership in some Centres will require a higher membership fee.

The Society currently has 29 Centres located throughout Canada, in every province and in most major Canadian cities. See the inside front cover for mailing addresses. Most Centres hold monthly meetings at which prospective members are welcome. Details on each Centre's activities as well as contact information for the Centre are available at its Web site; for links to the Centres' Web sites, visit www.rasc.ca.

REPORTING OF ASTRONOMICAL DISCOVERIES

To report a possible significant discovery (e.g. a new comet, nova, or supernova), a message should be sent to the International Astronomical Union's Central Bureau for Astronomical Telegrams. Send electronic mail to cbat@cfa.harvard.edu. Messages are monitored at all times. If this preferred method of communication is unavailable, a telephone call may be made to (617) 495-7244 or -7440 or -7444, but telephone calls are discouraged and these numbers will not be answered at all times. Also, a follow-up letter should be sent to the Central Bureau at 60 Garden St, Cambridge MA 02138, USA. Inexperienced observers should have their observation checked before contacting the Central Bureau.

For any new object, specify the date and time of observation, RA and Dec (with equinox), magnitude, and some physical description. For photographic and CCD discoveries, confirmation with a second image is highly desirable. In the case of a new comet, the rate of motion in RA and Dec should also be indicated.

Reports may instead be filled out at www.cfa.harvard.edu/iau/cbat.html. Recent IAU circulars and subscription information are also available at this URL.

RECOMMENDED READING AND ATLASES

Astronomy, a nontechnical monthly magazine for amateur astronomers (Canada and U.S.: (800) 533-6644; www.astronomy.com).

The Backyard Astronomer's Guide (3rd ed.), by Terence Dickinson and Alan Dyer. Firefly Books (Canada: (800) 387-6192, United States: (800) 387-5085), 2002; www.fireflybooks.ca). The best guide to equipment and techniques for amateur astronomers, by two experienced observers.

Catalog of the Astronomical Society of the Pacific ((415) 337-1100; www.astrosociety.org), an excellent source of astronomical educational resources such as books, slides, videos, globes, posters, software, teachers' classroom activity guides, and more.

Catalogue of Sky Publishing, a good source of books, atlases, globes, slide sets, software, and posters ((866) 644-1377; www.shopatsky.com).

Exploring the Night Sky, by Terence Dickinson. Firefly Books (see above), 1987. A guide to stargazing, recommended for children.

A Field Guide to the Stars and Planets, by Jay M. Pasachoff. Houghton Mifflin Company, New York, 2000. In the Petersen Field Guides series, this classic work (currently in its 4th edition) is packed with star maps and accessible information.

Nightwatch (4th ed.), by Terence Dickinson. Firefly Books (see above), 2006. An excellent introductory observing guide.

Sky & Telescope, a monthly magazine widely read by both amateur and professional astronomers ((866) 644-1377; www.skyandtelescope.com).

SkyNews, the Canadian magazine of astronomy and stargazing, published bimonthly ((866) 759-0005; www.skynewsmagazine.com).

Starlight Nights, by Leslie Peltier (1900–1980), 1965. Sky Publishing. Anyone who enjoys the night sky should read this book.

Atlas of the Moon, by Antonín Rükl, Gary Seronik (Editor). Sky Publishing, 2007. A first-rate lunar atlas for amateur astronomers.

Bright Star Atlas 2000.0, by Wil Tirion. Introductory atlas containing 9000 stars to magnitude 6.5 and 600 clusters, nebulae, and galaxies on 10 charts.

Millennium Star Atlas, by Roger Sinnott and Michael Perryman. A comprehensive atlas based on data from the *HIPPARCOS* satellite. Three volumes, each covering 8 hours in RA. Contains more than 1 000 000 stars to magnitude 11 and more than 10 000 clusters, nebulae, and galaxies on 1548 charts.

Sky Atlas 2000.0 (2nd ed.), by Wil Tirion and Roger Sinnott, 1998. Large format and well done. Contains 81 000 stars to magnitude 8.5 and 2700 clusters, nebulae, and galaxies on 26 charts; laminated version available.

Uranometria 2000.0 Deep Sky Atlas, by Wil Tirion, Barry Rappaport, and Will Remaklus. A second edition of the popular atlas, with stellar data from the *HIPPARCOS* satellite. Contains more than 280 000 stars to magnitude 9.75 and 30 000 clusters, nebulae, and galaxies on 220 double-page charts.

Computer-based Planetarium Programs: Several are available, for example, *ECU (Earth Centered Universe)*, *MegaStar*, *RedShift 5*, *Starry Night*, *TheSky*, and *Voyager 4*. For more information, see the catalogues listed above or do an Internet search at, for example, www.google.com.

Many of these items are available from Sky Publishing, A New Track Media Company, 90 Sherman Street, Cambridge MA 02140, USA; (866) 644-1377, www.skyandtelescope.com.

SELECTED OBSERVATORIES, STAR PARTIES, AND PLANETARIA
BY JAMES EDGAR

Some observatories and selected *star parties* with URL, latitude and longitude to nearest minute, and elevation in metres and feet are given below, ordered by longitude from east to west.

Location	Lat.	Long.	Alt. (m/ft.)
Anglo-Australian Observatory—Siding Spring, Australia www.aao.gov.au	31°17′S	149°04′E	1164/3819
Mount Stromlo Observatory—Canberra, Australia www.mso.anu.edu.au/home.php	35°19′S	149°00′E	767/2516
Perth Observatory—Bickley, Australia www.wa.gov.au/perthobs	32°00′S	116°08′E	380/1247
Effelsberg Radio Telescope—Effelsberg, Germany www.mpifr-bonn.mpg.de/div/effelsberg	50°31′N	6°53′E	319/1046
Greenwich Observatory—Greenwich, England www.rog.nmm.ac.uk	51°29′N	0°00′	31/102
Lovell Radio Telescope—Jodrell Bank, England www.jodrellbank.manchester.ac.uk	53°14′N	2°18′W	89/292
Armagh Observatory—Armagh, Northern Ireland www.arm.ac.uk/home.html	54°21′N	6°39′W	43/144
"Leviathan" Great Telescope—Birr, Ireland www.birrcastle.com/index.asp	53°05′N	7°54′W	59/194
Isaac Newton Telescope—La Palma, Canary Islands www.ast.cam.ac.uk/ING	28°45′N	17°53′W	2327/7634
Butterpot Star Party—Butter Pot Prov. Park, Newfoundland www.sji.ca/rasc/star-party.html	47°23′N	53°04′E	164/538
Nova East—Smileys Provincial Park, Nova Scotia halifax.rasc.ca/ne/home.html	45°01′N	63°58′W	150/492
St. Croix Observatory—St. Croix, Nova Scotia halifax.rasc.ca/sco.html	44°57′N	64°02′W	65/213
Arecibo Observatory—Arecibo, Puerto Rico www.naic.edu/index.htm	18°21′N	66°45′W	307/1007
Paranal Observatory (ESO)—Cerro Paranal, Chile www.eso.org/paranal/site/paranal.html	24°38′S	70°24′W	2635/8645
Las Campanas Observatory—Cerro Las Campanas, Chile www.lco.cl	29°00′S	70°42′W	2282/7486
Gemini South Observatory—Cerro Pachon, Chile www.gemini.edu	30°14′S	70°44′W	2722/8930
La Silla Observatory (ESO)—Cerro La Silla, Chile www.ls.eso.org/index.html	29°15′S	70°44′W	2400/7980
Cerro Tololo Inter-American Observatory—Cerro Tololo, Chile www.ctio.noao.edu	30°10′S	70°49′W	2200/7220
Mont Mégantic Observatory—Mont Mégantic, Québec www.astro.umontreal.ca/omm	45°27′N	71°09′W	1114/3654
Stellafane—Springfield, Vermont www.stellafane.com	43°16′N	72°31′W	393/1290
Van Vleck Observatory—Middletown, Connecticut www.astro.wesleyan.edu	41°33′N	72°40′W	65/213
CAFTA—St-Timothée, Québec membres.lycos.fr/cdadfs/cafta.html	45°26′N	73°44′W	24/79

Location	Lat.	Long.	Alt. (m/ft.)
Helen Sawyer Hogg Observatory—Ottawa, Ontario www.sciencetech.technomuses.ca	45°24′N	75°37′W	70/230
SMARTScope—Ottawa, Ontario ottawa.rasc.ca/smartscope/smartscope.html	45°21′N	75°53′W	68/223
Algonquin Adventure—Algonquin Park, Ontario toronto.rasc.ca/content/aaa11.shtml	45°57′N	78°31′W	404/1325
David Dunlap Observatory—Richmond Hill, Ontario www.theDDO.ca	43°52′N	79°25′W	244/800
Green Bank Telescope—Green Bank, West Virginia www.gb.nrao.edu/gbt	38°26′N	79°50′W	803/2634
Hamilton Centre Observatory—Waterdown, Ontario www.hamiltonrasc.ca	43°23′N	79°55′W	269/882
Allegheny Observatory—Pittsburgh, Pennsylvania www.pitt.edu/~aobsvtry	40°29′N	80°01′W	380/1247
Carr Astronomical Observatory—Collingwood, Ontario toronto.rasc.ca/content/CAO.shtml	44°30′N	80°23′W	422/1384
Starfest—Mount Forest, Ontario www.nyaa.ca/starfest.htm	44°04′N	80°50′W	400/1312
Winter Star Party—Camp Wesumkee, Florida www.scas.org/wsp.html	24°39′N	81°19′W	1/4
Sudbury Neutrino Observatory—Creighton, Ontario www.sno.phy.queensu.ca	46°46′N	81°20′W	−2073/−6800
Manitoulin Star Party—Gordon's Park, Ontario www.gordonspark.com/astronomy.html	45°40′N	81°58′W	235/771
Hallam Observatory—Comber, Ontario www.rascwindsor.com/pages/history.php	42°14′N	82°31′W	181/594
Astrofest—Kankakee, Illinois www.astronomynow.com/astrofest	41°09′N	87°51′W	194/636
Yerkes Observatory—Williams Bay, Wisconsin astro.uchicago.edu/yerkes	42°34′N	88°33′W	314/1030
Texas Star Party—Fort Davis, Texas www.texasstarparty.org	30°36′N	103°57′W	1542/5057
McDonald Observatory—Fort Davis, Texas www.as.utexas.edu/mcdonald/mcdonald.html	30°40′N	104°01′W	2065/6773
Kalium Observatory—Regina, Saskatchewan telescope.ras.sk.ca	50°26′N	104°36′W	577/1894
Apache Point Observatory—Sunspot, New Mexico www.apo.nmsu.edu	32°47′N	105°49′W	2788/9147
Sleaford Observatory—Saskatoon, Saskatchewan homepage.usask.ca/~ges125/rasc/sleaford.html	52°06′N	105°57′W	565/1853
Very Large Array—Socorro, New Mexico www.vla.nrao.edu	34°05′N	107°37′W	2123/6965
Saskatchewan Summer Star Party—Cypress Hills Park, Sask. homepage.usask.ca/~ges125/rasc/starparty.html	49°39′N	109°31′W	1272/4174
Steward Observatory—Tucson, Arizona skycenter.arizona.edu	32°26′N	110°47′W	2510/8230
Fred Lawrence Whipple Observatory—Amado, Arizona www.sao.arizona.edu/FLWO/whipple.html	31°41′N	110°53′W	2554/8379
Kitt Peak National Observatory—Tucson, Arizona www.noao.edu/kpno	31°57′N	111°36′W	2078/6816
Lowell Observatory—Flagstaff, Arizona www.lowell.edu	35°12′N	111°40′W	2206/7236

U.S. Naval Observatory—Flagstaff, Arizona www.nofs.navy.mil	35°11′N 111°44′W	2262/7421
TELUS World of Science—Edmonton, Alberta www.edmontonscience.com/pages/PlanVisit/Observatory.aspx	53°34′N 113°34′W	677/2221
Wilson Coulee Observatory—Okotoks, Alberta calgary.rasc.ca/tourrequest.htm	50°46′N 114°02′W	1127/3697
Alberta Star Party—Caroline, Alberta calgary.rasc.ca/asp.htm	52°08′N 114°43′W	1072/3517
Riverside Telescope Makers Conference—Camp Oakes, Calif. www.rtmcastronomyexpo.org	34°14′N 116°45′W	2316/7600
Palomar Observatory—San Diego, California www.astro.caltech.edu/palomar	33°21′N 116°52′W	1706/5597
Mt. Wilson Observatory—Pasadena, California www.mtwilson.edu	34°13′N 118°03′W	1740/5700
Dominion Radio Astrophysical Observatory—Penticton, B.C. www.nrc-cnrc.gc.ca/eng/services/hia/drao-visitors.html	49°19′N 119°37′W	545/1788
Mount Kobau Star Party—Osoyoos, British Columbia www.mksp.ca	49°07′N 119°40′W	1860/6102
Oregon Star Party—Ochoco National Forest, Oregon www.oregonstarparty.org	44°18′N 120°08′W	1499/4918
Fall Star Quest—Loon Lake, British Columbia www.merrittastronomical.com	49°53′N 120°30′W	1159/3802
Table Mountain Star Party—Ellensburg, Washington www.tmspa.com	47°15′N 120°35′W	1937/6357
Goldendale Observatory—Goldendale, Washington www.perr.com/gosp.html	45°51′N 120°47′W	640/2100
Pine Mountain Observatory—Pine Mountain, Oregon pmo-sun.uoregon.edu	43°47′N 120°57′W	1905/6250
Lick Observatory—San Jose, California mthamilton.ucolick.org	37°20′N 121°39′W	1290/4232
Prince George Centre Observatory—Prince George, B.C. www.vts.bc.ca/pgrasc/tour.html	53°45′N 122°51′W	691/2296
Gordon Southam Observatory—Vancouver, B.C. www.hrmacmillanspacecentre.com/observatory.htm	49°16′N 123°09′W	6/21
Dominion Astrophysical Observatory—Victoria, B.C. www.nrc-cnrc.gc.ca/eng/ibp/hia.html	48°31′N 123°25′W	238/780
RASCALS Star Party—Malahat, British Columbia victoria.rasc.ca/events/StarParty	48°33′N 123°34′W	345/1132
James Clerk Maxwell Telescope—Mauna Kea, Hawaii www.jach.hawaii.edu/JCMT	19°49′N 155°28′W	4092/13 426
Canada-France-Hawaii Telescope—Mauna Kea, Hawaii www.cfht.hawaii.edu	19°49′N 155°28′W	4204/13 793
Gemini North—Mauna Kea, Hawaii www.gemini.edu/public	19°49′N 155°28′W	4213/13 824

A selection of North American planetaria with URL, phone number, and related information, ordered alphabetically by city, is given below.

Planetarium	Notes
Lodestar Astronomy Center—Albuquerque www.naturalhistoryfoundation.org/planetarium_sched.html (505) 841-5955	Part of University of New Mexico outreach; Infinity Express multimedia program; astronomy store; astrophoto contests
Fiske Planetarium—Boulder fiske.colorado.edu (303) 492-5001	Evening shows and weekend matinees; observatory available following shows for stargazing; school groups welcome

TELUS World of Science—Calgary www.calgaryscience.ca (403) 268-8300	Join "Seymour Sky" at the Planetarium dome; several programs, multimedia shows, and kits available for kids of all ages
Adler Planetarium—Chicago www.adlerplanetarium.org/home.shtml (312) 922-7827	Historic, first in Western Hemisphere; large collection of historic instruments; Doane Observatory on-site
Christa McAuliffe Planetarium—Concord www.starhop.com/contact-us (603) 271-7827	Dedicated to first "Teacher In Space" who tragically died in shuttle *Challenger* disaster 1986 Jan. 28
TELUS World of Science—Edmonton www.edmontonscience.com/pages/WhatsOn (780) 451-3344	Observatory; IMAX theatre; exhibit galleries; science camps and courses, planetarium shows, computer lab; robotics lab, gift shop
Burke Baker Planetarium—Houston www.hmns.org/see_do/planetarium.asp (713) 639-4629	One of the Challenger Centres; dome is used for training astronauts to identify star fields; SkyScan digital stars; theatre seats 232
Samuel Oschin Planetarium—Los Angeles www.griffithobservatory.org/bsoplanet.html (213) 473-0800	Newly renovated with state-of-the-art tech- nology; 300-seat theatre; Zeiss Mark IX star projector; and Digistar 3-laser system
ASTROLab du Mont Mégantic—Mont Mégantic www.astrolab-parc-national-mont-megantic.org (819) 888-2941	Cosmic Rhythms multimedia show; dark skies; astronomy evenings; on-site lodging; open house for teachers; school programs
Planétarium de Montréal—Montréal www.planetarium.montreal.qc.ca (514) 872-4530	Programs for all ages and groups; activity sheets; classroom kits; advanced workshop for teachers and educators
Mystic Seaport Planetarium—Mystic www.mysticseaport.org (860) 572-5315	Celestial navigation workshops; 30-foot dome; specialized group programs; history of navigation exhibit; GPS workshop
Hayden Planetarium—New York www.amnh.org/rose (212) 769-5100	At American Museum of Natural History; programs, courses, and lectures; Zeiss Mark IX Universarium Star Projector
Harry C. Kendall Planetarium—Portland www.omsi.edu/planetarium (503) 797-4610	Fifty-two-foot domed theatre with Digistar 3 projection; presentations on astronomy, space science, and lasers; school programs
James S. McDonnell Planetarium—St. Louis www.slsc.org (314) 289-4400	The 80-foot dome houses a Zeiss Model IX; includes exhibits about living and working in space; camp-ins for the whole family
Ontario Science Centre—Toronto www.ontariosciencecentre.ca (416) 696-1000	In central Toronto; OMNIMax theatre; kids' sleepovers; summer day camps; home of the RASC Toronto Centre
MacMillan Planetarium—Vancouver www.spacecentre.ca (604) 738-7827	Close to downtown Vancouver; special laser shows in summer; numerous programs for school groups of all ages; teacher packages
Centre of the Universe—Victoria www.nrc-cnrc.gc.ca/eng/services/hia/centre-universe.html (250) 363-8262	Interactive exhibits; Starlab planetarium; multimedia shows; family-friendly weekend events; Plaskett (1.8 m) Telescope
Albert Einstein Planetarium—Washington www.nasm.si.edu/visit/theaters/planetarium (202) 633-1000	At National Air and Space Museum; café; IMAX theatre; special exhibits commemo- rate 100th year of powered flight
Northern Lights—Watson Lake, Yukon www.northernlightscentre.ca (867) 536-7827	Canada's only all-dome video planetarium; daily shows; programs concentrate on aurora borealis and northern experience
Aldrin Planetarium—West Palm Beach www.sfsm.org/planetarium.html (561) 832-1988	Laser shows; telescopes; exhibits; science camps; teachers' programs; birthday party programs
Manitoba Planetarium—Winnipeg www.manitobamuseum.ca /pl_info.html (204) 956-2830	In central Winnipeg; science centre, museum, and planetarium in one site; school programs; Guide/Scout badge program

SELECTED INTERNET RESOURCES

The World Wide Web is an important source of astronomical information. A selection of Web sites together with a reference to a page number in this Handbook (if any) is given below. A listing of all Web sites mentioned in this Handbook, with URL links to the various sites, is available at:

www.rasc.ca/handbook/links.shtml

URL	Description
www.aavso.org	American Association of Variable Star Observers (p. 291)
www.alpo-astronomy.org	Association of Lunar and Planetary Observers
www.astrosociety.org	Astronomical Society of the Pacific (p. 19)
www.astronomy.com	*Astronomy* magazine (p. 11)
www.cascaeducation.ca	Canadian Astronomical Society's education Web site (p. 17)
www.space.gc.ca	Canadian Space Agency
www.cleardarksky.com/csk	Clear Sky Chart, by Attilla Danko (p. 83)
www.MrEclipse.com	Eclipse photography and safety (p. 137)
heritage.stsci.edu	Hubble Heritage Site, access to HST images
www.cfa.harvard.edu/iau/cbat.html	International Astronomical Union Central Bureau (p. 10); see also www.iau.org
www.darksky.org	International Dark-Sky Association (p. 89)
www.imo.net	International Meteor Organization (p. 250)
www.lunar-occultations.com/iota	International Occultation Timing Association (p. 162)
www.jpl.nasa.gov	Jet Propulsion Laboratory, activities for adults and kids
miac.uqac.ca	Meteorites and Impacts Advisory Committee, Canadian Space Agency (p. 252)
cdsads.u-strasbg.fr	NASA Astrophysics Data System (ADS); bibliographic database, access to millions of articles
eclipse.gsfc.nasa.gov	NASA eclipse site (p. 128)
nedwww.ipac.caltech.edu	NASA/IPAC Extragalactic Database (p. 325)
spaceflight.nasa.gov	NASA space flight site giving current information on Space Shuttle missions and ISS activities
www.rasc.ca/handbook	*Observer's Handbook* Web site (p. 6)
planetary.org	Planetary Society—contains over 2000 pages of information about space exploration
www.rasc.ca	Royal Astronomical Society of Canada (p. 10)
www.saguaroastro.org	Saguaro Astronomy Club, includes observing list database (p. 95)
www.heavens-above.com	Satellite tracking information, including International Space Station and Space Shuttle
simbad.u-strasbg.fr/simbad	SIMBAD astronomical database
www.skyandtelescope.com	*Sky & Telescope* and Sky Publishing (p. 11)
www.skynewsmagazine.com	*SkyNews*—Canada's astronomy magazine (p. 11)
www.stsci.edu	Space Telescope Science Institute; access to Digitized Sky Survey
seds.lpl.arizona.edu	Students for the Exploration and Development of Space
vizier.hia.nrc.ca/viz-bin/VizieR	VizieR service; access to most astronomical catalogues

TEACHING AND THE *OBSERVER'S HANDBOOK*
BY HEATHER THEIJSMEIJER

You are holding in your hand a valuable resource for teaching astronomy. Every user of this Handbook, whether amateur or professional astronomer or teacher in any setting, at any level, can contribute to education in astronomy; see *JRASC, 96* (October 2002), p. 196, (also found at www.cascaeducation.ca/files/outreach_paper.html) for information on how you can too.

As a result of curriculum renewal in Canada, the United States, and other countries, astronomy is now taught in many elementary and secondary schools; see *JRASC, 96* (June 2002), p. 114. The Canadian Astronomical Society, in partnership with the RASC and other organizations, has now embarked on a major education and public outreach initiative and has created a Canadian astronomy education Web site: www.cascaeducation.ca. The RASC has published *Skyways*, by Mary Lou Whitehorne, an excellent astronomy guide for teachers; a French version, *Explorons l'astronomie*, is also available.

Countering Misconceptions
Surveys show that many basic astronomical concepts are misunderstood by most people. Examples of common misconceptions include the relative sizes and distances within the solar system, the "reason for the seasons," and the cause of lunar phases. Poor understanding of these physical systems is often based in false logic (i.e. it is warmer in the summer because the Earth is closer to the Sun) and misleading diagrams (with a poorly-chosen, or no existing scale) in common reference books. There is an excellent review and explanation of these and other misconceptions at the Private Universe Project: www.learner.org/teacherslab/pup—certainly worth checking out.

Many of these concepts are so basic that it is worth taking the time to teach them correctly. During learning activities, students' preconceptions can be monitored through interviews and discussions. As teachers, we can make sure that these concepts are understood, and that the students can explain them from personal understanding — not just from memorization. This section of the Handbook is designed to do just that.

Each topic below is divided into two sections: *Minds-on* will show you where to get information and background pertaining to the specific topic for the classroom, and how it relates to teaching. *Hands-on* will suggest teaching activities to reinforce the concepts discussed in *Minds-on*, along with other resources.

The Sun
Minds-on: The Sun appears in the sky as a perfect "ball of burning gas." Students are often amazed to learn that the surface of the Sun is quite turbulent and always changing. The SOLAR OBSERVING section (p. 189) describes in detail the types of "blemishes" that can be seen on the surface of the Sun, as well as safe methods of observing the Sun (see also www.cascaeducation.ca/files/solar_observing.html). The SOLAR ACTIVITY section (p. 192) explains the effects that an unstable solar atmosphere can have on the Earth, while Roy Bishop's section on rainbows, halos, etc. (p. 197) examines some of the more common visual phenomena caused by the interaction of sunlight with water droplets and ice crystals in our own atmosphere.
Hands-on: Students can track the motion of the Sun throughout the course of the day, or the position of the Sun at the same time of day throughout the year. Likewise, Sun rise and set times can be charted to try to find patterns (sunrise and sunset times can be found on pages 208-210). Building a sundial (www.mos.org/sln/wtu/activities/patterns.html) can give students a sense of how the Sun is linked to our 24-hour clock. Viewing the Sun by projection is an easy way to search for sunspots in a classroom setting. See the link above or the Handbook section VIEWING A SOLAR ECLIPSE – A WARNING (p. 151) for a description of these methods. However, **NEVER** observe the Sun directly, especially by looking through binoculars or a telescope. Permanent eye damage could result. Daily images of the Sun are available at sohowww.nascom.nasa.gov.

The Moon

Minds-on: When asked what can be seen in the night sky, students will often first answer with the Moon. Four hundred years ago, the Moon was one of Galileo's first telescopic targets. It is one of the easiest objects to observe as a class, and can even sometimes be found in the daytime sky! A detailed map of the Moon can be found on page 152, with historical and geographical details. The sections on TIMES OF MOONRISE AND MOONSET (p. 154) and LUNAR OBSERVING (p. 162) can be used to help coordinate when the Moon can best be seen. The sections ECLIPSES IN 2011 (p. 130) and THE SKY MONTH BY MONTH (p. 98) can be referenced to learn if there are any special celestial events involving the Moon. Finally, the section TIDES AND THE EARTH–MOON SYSTEM (p. 182) gives an excellent review of the Moon's effects on the Earth, to which many Canadian students can relate.

Hands-on: Like the Sun, students can sketch the position of the Moon from night to night throughout the lunar month. The appearance of the Moon can also be sketched, as seen with the naked eye or through binoculars or a telescope. Using the maps in this Handbook, students can then try to identify any of the prominent lunar features they saw. Building a scale model (**tinyurl.com/earthmoonscale**) can help dispel misconceptions about the relative sizes and distances from the Earth to the Moon. These scale models, with the addition of a light source to act as the Sun, can also be used to explain the phases of the Moon and eclipses. An extension to the rest of the solar system would be to compare the size of Earth's Moon with the moons of other planets (pp. 25–30). Ours is one of the largest!

The Night Sky

Minds-on: In a sense, astronomy is the easiest strand of science to practice — simply go outside at night and look up! No lab equipment needed for the true beginner. Star charts can be found in many books and magazines (see p. 11), as well as in the MAPS OF THE NIGHT SKY section (p. 343). Aside from finding the Moon, many people can identify constellations and asterisms, a listing of which can be found on pages 276-277, and with images at **www.seds.org/Maps/Const/constS.html**. THE SKY MONTH BY MONTH (p. 98) will also give you a concise overview of what's up in the night sky during a particular time of the year.

Hands-on: Have the students create a planisphere, which they can use to locate objects in the sky (**tinyurl.com/cdnplanisphere**). This can also be used to teach the proper way to read a star chart. Students can practice the science of observation by drawing what they see in the night sky, including the horizon and compass points, and by keeping an observing logbook (p. 96). Even the study of light pollution (pp. 92-97) can be an educational experience, relating astronomy to the environment; see *JRASC, 96* (February 2002), p. 24, and **www.astrosociety.org/education/publications/tnl/44/lightpoll.html**.

The Solar System, Including Comets and Asteroids

Minds-on: The solar system is our celestial neighbourhood. Our planet neighbours are discussed below, but what else can be found in the "immediate" vicinity? The PRINCIPAL ELEMENTS OF THE SOLAR SYSTEM (p. 22) and the VOYAGES IN OUR SOLAR SYSTEM (p. 40) sections of the Handbook are an excellent introduction into the history of exploration of our solar system, as well as what types of objects are believed to be typical in stellar systems. THE BRIGHTEST ASTEROIDS section (p. 250) can be used to find asteroids in the night sky (only binoculars are needed), while a table of sizes and distances from the Sun can be found on page 23. The section on METEORITE IMPACT CRATERS OF NORTH AMERICA (p. 266) brings the idea of meteorite impacts a little closer to home for students.

Hands-on: The toilet-paper solar system (**www.nthelp.com/eer/HOAtpss.html**) and the Earth as a peppercorn model (**www.noao.edu/education/peppercorn/pcmain.html**) are both excellent, hands-on activities for modelling the vast distances

in the solar system. Likewise, students can design their own scale model using www.exploratorium.edu/ronh/solar_system. Students can simulate meteoric impacts in the class with the "crazy craters" activity (www.cascaeducation.ca/files/students_crazycraters.html) and can even build a comet out of dry ice, sand, and other organic materials, with instructions found at www.noao.edu/education/crecipe.html.

The Planets
Minds-on: Learning about "another world" in the classroom and then seeing that planet in the night sky serves to stimulate student interest and fire up their imaginations. THE SKY MONTH BY MONTH (p. 98) tells us when the various planets are visible, and these are sure to be the highlight of any outdoor observing session with students. THE PLANETS FOR 2011 (p. 214) gives more information about each planet, as does the tabled data on pages 22-23. A history of the theories pertaining to the motion of the planets is provided in the ORBITAL MOTION section (p. 31).
Hands-on: Using the information summarized from THE PLANETS FOR 2011 (p. 214), students can "design an alien" that could live on a particular planet, given the surface temperature, atmospheric composition, surface features, etc. This could also be adapted for older students by having them design a human colony on another planet. It is certainly true that a picture can be worth a thousand words — many of the resources listed on pp. 11 and 16 help bring these other worlds into the classroom. Finally, Exploratorium has calculators for one's age and weight on other planets at www.exploratorium.edu/ronh, as well as other activities

Is a Telescope Necessary?
Binoculars and telescopes can be useful but are not essential; much interesting astronomy can be done with the unaided eye. However, binoculars are often available and should be used when helpful. See the section BINOCULARS (p. 65) for a guide to their selection and use. The inexpensive, make-it-yourself *Project STAR* telescopes are highly recommended. See TELESCOPE PARAMETERS (p. 55) and TELESCOPE EXIT PUPILS (p. 56) for a summary of some quantitative aspects of telescopes.

Resources
In addition to the list of reading material below, and the RASC's *Skyways*, you may be able to make use of the following:
(1) See the SELECTED OBSERVATORIES, STAR PARTIES, AND PLANETARIA section in this Handbook (p. 12). Take your students to visit one of these.
(2) The Royal Astronomical Society of Canada is the largest organization of amateur astronomers in Canada. Their 29 Centres across Canada (see the section THE ROYAL ASTRONOMICAL SOCIETY OF CANADA on p. 10) offer a wide variety of activities that might be interesting to you and your students. For example, a member of the RASC might be willing to visit your class and demonstrate a telescope. The Astronomical Society of the Pacific's *Project ASTRO How-To Manual* can facilitate such visits. See www.astrosociety.org/education/astro/project_astro.html.

Astronomical Society of the Pacific, 390 Ashton Ave, San Francisco CA 94112, USA; (415) 337–1100. In addition to their excellent educational material, the ASP publishes a free quarterly teachers' newsletter; download current and back issues from www.astrosociety.org/education/publications/tnl/tnl.html.

Project STAR Hands-on Science Materials, Science First/STARLAB, 86475 Gene Lasserre Blvd, Yulee FL 32097, USA; (800) 537-8703; www.starlab.com. Unique, high-quality, low-cost materials for introducing students (and teachers) to astronomy.

SkyNews, Box 10, Yarker ON K0K 3N0; (866) 759-0005; www.skynewsmagazine.com. Bimonthly. General astronomy from a Canadian perspective. Included with RASC membership.

The Universe at Your Fingertips, and *More Universe at Your Fingertips*, edited by Andrew Fraknoi, et al. Astronomical Society of the Pacific, 390 Ashton Ave, San Francisco CA 94112, USA. Another excellent collection of teaching activities and resources for grades 3–12. See also www.astrosociety.org/education/activities/astroacts.html.

BASIC DATA
TERMINOLOGY AND SYMBOLS
COORDINATE SYSTEMS

Astronomical positions are usually measured in a system based on the *celestial poles* and *celestial equator*, the intersections of Earth's rotation axis and equatorial plane, respectively, and the infinite sphere of the sky. *Right ascension* (RA or α) is measured in hours (h), minutes (m), and seconds (s) of time, eastward along the celestial equator from the vernal equinox (see below). *Declination* (Dec or δ) is measured in degrees (°), minutes ('), and seconds (") of arc, northward (N or +) or southward (S or –) from the celestial equator toward the north or south celestial pole.

Positions can also be measured in a system based on the *ecliptic*, the intersection of Earth's orbital plane and the infinite sphere of the sky. The Sun appears to move eastward along the ecliptic during the year. *Longitude* is measured eastward along the ecliptic from the vernal equinox; *latitude* is measured at right angles to the ecliptic, northward or southward toward the north or south ecliptic pole. The *vernal equinox* is one of the two intersections of the ecliptic and the celestial equator; it is the one at which the Sun crosses the celestial equator moving from south to north.

An object is *in conjunction with the Sun* if it has the same longitude as the Sun and *at opposition* if its longitude differs from that of the Sun by 180°. Mercury and Venus are in *superior* conjunction when they are more distant than the Sun and in *inferior* conjunction when they are nearer than the Sun (see the diagram at the right). An object is *stationary* when it reaches an extreme longitude.

Two *nonsolar* objects are in conjunction if they have the same RA. Generally, but not always, close mutual approaches correspond to conjunctions; following Jean Meeus, we use the term *quasi-conjunction* to denote close (< 5°) nonconjunctional approaches.

If an object crosses the ecliptic moving northward, it is at the *ascending node* of its orbit; if it crosses the ecliptic moving southward, it is at the *descending node*.

Elongation is the geocentric angle between an object and the Sun, or between a satellite and its primary, measured in the plane formed by Earth and the other two bodies.

SYMBOLS
Sun, Moon, and Planets

☉ Sun	☾ Last Quarter	⊕ Earth	♅ Uranus
🌑 New Moon	☾ Moon generally	♂ Mars	♆ Neptune
☺ Full Moon	☿ Mercury	♃ Jupiter	♇ Pluto
☽ First Quarter	♀ Venus	♄ Saturn	

Signs of the Zodiac

♈ Aries....................0°	♌ Leo ....120°	♐ Sagittarius ....240°
♉ Taurus................30°	♍ Virgo ....150°	♑ Capricornus.....270°
♊ Gemini ....60°	♎ Libra................180°	♒ Aquarius..........300°
♋ Cancer...............90°	♏ Scorpius ....210°	♓ Pisces ....330°

The Greek Alphabet

A, α.......alpha	H, η.......eta	N, ν.......nu	T, τ........tau
B, β.......beta	Θ, θ, ϑ...theta	Ξ, ξ.......xi	Υ, υ.......upsilon
Γ, γ.......gamma	I, ι.........iota	O, o.......omicron	Φ, φ.......phi
Δ, δ.......delta	K, κ.......kappa	Π, π.......pi	X, χ.......chi
E, ε........epsilon	Λ, λ.......lambda	P, ρ........rho	Ψ, ψ ......psi
Z, ζ........zeta	M, μ ......mu	Σ, σ ....sigma	Ω, ω ......omega

SOLAR SYSTEM GEOMETRY

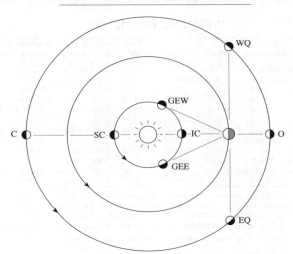

The diagram is a simplified view of our solar system, from the north side. Earth is shown (middle orbit) together with an inferior planet (i.e. Mercury or Venus) and a superior planet (e.g. Mars). Four special geometrical configurations of the inferior planet relative to Earth are shown; in counterclockwise chronological sequence they are inferior conjunction (IC), greatest elongation west (GEW), superior conjunction (SC), and greatest elongation east (GEE). Four special configurations of the superior planet relative to Earth are also shown; in clockwise chronological sequence they are opposition (O), eastern quadrature (EQ), conjunction with the Sun (C), and western quadrature (WQ).

HELIOCENTRIC LONGITUDES FOR 2011

The heliocentric longitude of a planet is the angle between the vernal equinox and the planet, as seen from the Sun. It is measured in the ecliptic plane, in the direction of the orbital motion of the planet (counterclockwise as viewed from the north side of the ecliptic plane). Knowing these heliocentric longitudes and the distances of the planets from the Sun (see p. 23), one can construct a diagram or model showing the relative positions of the Sun and planets on any date.

UT	Me °	V °	E °	Ma °	J °	S °	U °	N °	P °
Jan. 1.0	156	139	100	294	8	191	360	328	275
Feb. 1.0	259	189	132	313	11	192	0	328	275
Mar. 1.0	352	234	160	331	13	193	0	328	276
Apr. 1.0	165	283	191	351	16	194	1	329	276
May 1.0	262	331	220	9	19	195	1	329	276
Jun. 1.0	11	20	250	28	22	196	1	329	276
Jul. 1.0	178	68	279	46	24	197	2	329	276
Aug. 1.0	273	118	308	63	27	198	2	329	276
Sep. 1.0	33	168	338	79	30	199	2	330	277
Oct. 1.0	193	217	7	94	33	200	3	330	277
Nov. 1.0	285	266	38	109	36	201	3	330	277
Dec. 1.0	51	314	68	122	38	202	3	330	277
Jan. 1.0	207	3	100	136	41	203	4	330	277

PRINCIPAL ELEMENTS OF THE SOLAR SYSTEM

PHYSICAL ELEMENTS

Object (Pronun.)	Equatorial Diameter km	Oblate- ness	Mass Earth=1*	Den- sity t/m³	Grav- ity† Earth=1	Escape Speed† km/s	Rotation Period d	Inclina- tion‡ °	Albedo
Sun	1 392 530	0	332 946.0	1.41	27.9	617.5	25–35††	—	—
Mercury (mûr'kū–rē)	4 879	0	0.055 274	5.43	0.38	4.2	58.646	0.0	0.11
Venus (vē'nŭs)	12 104	0	0.815 005	5.24	0.90	10.4	243.019	2.6	0.65
Earth (ûrth)	12 756	1/298	1.000 000	5.52	1.00	11.2	0.9973	23.4	0.37
Moon	3 475	0	0.012 300	3.35	0.17	2.4	27.3217	6.7	0.12
Mars (märz)	6 792	1/148	0.107 447	3.94	0.38	5.0	1.0260	25.2	0.15
Jupiter (jōō'pĭ–tēr)	142 980 ‡‡	1/15.4	317.833	1.33	2.53	59.5	0.4101†††	3.1	0.52
Saturn (săt'ûrn)	120 540 ‡‡	1/10.2	95.163	0.69	1.06	35.5	0.4440	26.7	0.47
Uranus^A (yŭr'à–nŭs)	51 120 ‡‡	1/43.6	14.536	1.27	0.90	21.3	0.7183	82.2	0.51
Neptune^B (nĕp'tyōōn)	49 530 ‡‡	1/58.5	17.149	1.64	1.14	23.5	0.6712	28.3	0.41
Pluto^C (plōō'tō)	2 390	0	0.002 2	1.8	0.08	1.3	6.3872	57.5	0.3

* 5.972×10^{24} kg †At the equator ‡Inclination of equator to orbital plane †† Depending on latitude
‡‡At 1 atmosphere (101.325 kPa) ††† For the most rapidly rotating part, the equatorial region
^{A}Discovered by Sir William Herschel, 1781 Mar. 13 ^{B}Discovered by Johann G. Galle, 1846 Sep. 23
^{C}Discovered by Clyde Tombaugh, 1930 Feb. 18. In 2008, the IAU reclassified Pluto as a plutoid.

Pronunciation guide: à gàgà; ē wē; ĕ mĕt; ē makēr; ĭ bĭt; ō gō; ōō mōōn; ū ūnite; ŭ sŭn; û ûrn

OSCULATING ORBITAL ELEMENTS FOR 2011

The tables at the right give the orbital elements of the planets and 30 largest main-belt asteroids, the latter provided by Dr. Brian Marsden. At any given time or "epoch," six basic quantities determine each body's elliptical orbit, for example:

(1) the mean distance from the Sun, a, equal to the semimajor axis of the ellipse;
(2) the eccentricity e of the ellipse;
(3) the inclination i of the orbital plane to the ecliptic;
(4) the longitude Ω of the ascending node of the orbital plane on the ecliptic;
(5) the longitude $\tilde{\omega}$ of perihelion;
(6) the body's mean longitude L at the given epoch.

The date of the ecliptic and equinox used to measure the last four quantities must also be specified, and may be different from the given epoch. Other, equivalent parameters may be substituted: the distance q of perihelion in place of a; the argument of perihelion, $\omega = \tilde{\omega} - \Omega$, in place of $\tilde{\omega}$; or the mean anomaly, $M = L - \tilde{\omega}$, or time T of perihelion in place of L. Once six fundamental quantities are known, all other attributes of the orbit of the body, such as the sidereal period P and synodic period S, can be derived.

If the body followed a perfectly elliptical orbit as predicted by classical orbital mechanics, then for a fixed ecliptic and equinox the first five quantities above would be constant over time. However, because of perturbations caused by the gravitational influence of other bodies, the orbits are not perfectly elliptical; hence the orbital elements depend on the epoch. The given *osculating* elements can be used to determine an elliptical orbit that is a close approximation to the actual path of the body for times near the given epoch. Two epochs, corresponding to Feb. 8 and Aug. 27, are provided for the planets; the elements for these epochs can be linearly interpolated to other epochs in 2011 for precision of a few arcseconds (typically 1″ or 2″). For the asteroids one epoch, corresponding to Aug. 27, is given, with resulting precision of about 1′.

HELIOCENTRIC OSCULATING ORBITAL ELEMENTS FOR 2011
REFERRED TO THE MEAN ECLIPTIC AND EQUINOX OF J2000.0

Planet	Epoch Julian Date 245	Mean Distance a au	Eccen- tricity e	Incli- nation i °	Long. of Asc. Node Ω °	Long. of Perihelion $\tilde{\omega}$ °	Long. at Epoch L °	Sidereal Period P a	Synodic Period† S d
Mercury	5600.5	0.387098	0.205627	7.0043	48.3163	77.4728	288.7311	0.2409	115.88
	5800.5	0.387099	0.205626	7.0044	48.3159	77.4710	27.1986	0.2409	115.88
Venus	5600.5	0.723328	0.006748	3.3946	76.6463	131.633	199.4176	0.6152	583.93
	5800.5	0.723329	0.006730	3.3946	76.6456	131.602	159.8461	0.6152	583.93
Earth‡	5600.5	1.000004	0.016672	0.0016	173.9	103.1171	137.6047	1.0000	—
	5800.5	0.999983	0.016706	0.0016	175.0	103.0656	334.7254	1.0000	—
Mars	5600.5	1.523602	0.093348	1.8489	49.5240	336.1756	320.6644	1.8807	780.03
	5800.5	1.523645	0.093471	1.8488	49.5246	336.1006	65.3558	1.8808	779.99
Jupiter	5600.5	5.202752	0.048891	1.3038	100.5121	14.4874	11.3430	11.8620	398.89
	5800.5	5.202858	0.048910	1.3038	100.5120	14.4652	27.9424	11.8624	398.89
Saturn	5600.5	9.509322	0.054778	2.4877	113.6226	89.2006	185.7382	29.3070	378.16
	5800.5	9.510149	0.055213	2.4876	113.6126	89.3722	192.4038	29.3108	378.16
Uranus	5600.5	19.24936	0.044307	0.7720	74.0189	170.0166	0.8440	84.4038	369.64
	5800.5	19.24378	0.044714	0.7721	73.0366	169.4428	3.2419	84.3671	369.64
Neptune	5600.5	30.16459	0.010956	1.7682	131.7685	31.381	329.2958	165.5665	367.48
	5800.5	30.13595	0.010926	1.7684	131.7708	37.085	330.5368	165.3186	367.48
Pluto	5600.5	39.43235	0.247093	17.1362	110.3121	224.2796	255.2523	247.4601	366.74
	5800.5	39.36863	0.246272	17.1458	110.3034	224.0423	256.0257	246.8606	366.74

Elements are for epochs 2011 Feb. 8 and 2011 Aug. 27 respectively.

*1 au = 1.496×10^{11} m † Synodic period = (product of Ps of two planets) ÷ (difference of the Ps).
Tabular values are relative to Earth. ‡ Values are actually for the Earth-Moon barycentre.

Asteroid	Diameter km	Mean Distance a au	Eccen- tricity e	Incli- nation i °	Long. of Asc. Node Ω °	Long. of Perihelion $\tilde{\omega}$ °	Long. at Epoch L °	Sidereal Period P a	Synodic Period* S d
(1) Ceres	957	2.766547	0.078563	10.5859	80.3791	152.8265	352.1440	4.6016	466.67
(2) Pallas	524	2.771149	0.231242	34.8416	173.1264	123.1898	304.8912	4.6131	466.35
(4) Vesta	512	2.361216	0.088312	7.1346	103.9043	253.7861	310.1889	3.6283	504.23
(10) Hygiea	444	3.138991	0.116462	3.8409	283.4150	236.4269	251.7235	5.5614	445.33
(704) Interamnia	329	3.059279	0.151308	17.2962	280.3524	16.3700	320.1322	5.3509	449.21
(511) Davida	326	3.164744	0.186904	15.9422	107.6362	85.8143	288.6798	5.6300	444.15
(15) Eunomia	320	2.644072	0.188602	11.7353	293.2197	30.8928	33.0325	4.2994	475.96
(52) Europa	302	3.097482	0.106778	7.4800	128.7439	112.7330	202.7640	5.4515	447.31
(3) Juno	274	2.671174	0.255163	12.9809	169.9103	58.0976	180.4212	4.3657	473.78
(87) Sylvia	261	3.493357	0.083400	10.8583	73.2370	339.3985	5.6447	6.5293	431.32
(31) Euphrosyne	256	3.157142	0.223539	26.3223	31.1591	92.4197	47.4093	5.6097	444.49
(16) Psyche	239	2.920732	0.137422	3.0993	150.2992	17.2574	115.8588	4.9916	456.76
(88) Thisbe	232	2.766671	0.165019	5.2151	276.7061	312.8674	122.8190	4.6019	466.66
(65) Cybele	230	3.426146	0.109547	3.5628	155.6553	258.4104	84.3338	6.3417	433.63
(324) Bamberga	228	2.685860	0.336962	11.1031	327.9801	11.9784	194.6212	4.4017	472.63
(451) Patientia	225	3.062678	0.077647	15.2180	89.3358	68.1068	14.4923	5.3598	449.03
(19) Fortuna	225	2.442822	0.157758	1.5732	211.2302	33.4686	227.4057	3.8180	494.87
(107) Camilla	223	3.494772	0.072641	10.0381	173.0832	120.6708	22.9806	6.5332	431.27
(48) Doris	222	3.110246	0.075003	6.5562	183.7412	79.6952	3.2580	5.4852	446.69
(45) Eugenia	215	2.724474	0.081215	6.6027	147.8755	234.9994	19.4037	4.4970	469.71
(29) Amphitrite	212	2.556026	0.073433	6.0931	356.4860	58.6233	28.2753	4.0865	483.60
(7) Iris	211	2.386267	0.230543	5.5231	259.6508	44.9136	156.4492	3.6862	501.23
(121) Hermione	209	3.447997	0.135270	7.5970	73.1585	11.3805	159.1098	6.4025	432.87
(423) Diotima	209	3.068004	0.039034	11.2310	69.5035	271.9344	176.8614	5.3738	448.77
(9) Metis	209	2.385545	0.122745	5.5755	68.9492	75.1930	323.6354	3.6845	501.32
(13) Egeria	208	2.576580	0.085368	16.5456	43.2701	123.4166	4.2858	4.1359	481.73
(532) Herculina	207	2.770482	0.177782	16.3140	107.5885	183.9873	290.3768	4.6114	466.40
(94) Aurora	204	3.160458	0.088860	7.9647	2.6842	62.6769	240.4443	5.6186	444.34
(702) Alauda	195	3.194763	0.020753	20.6043	289.9468	283.2650	211.0087	5.7103	442.80
(6) Hebe	190	2.424712	0.202253	14.7502	138.7265	18.0155	94.2478	3.7756	496.85

Elements are for epoch Julian Date 245 5800.5 (2011 Aug. 27)

NATURAL SATELLITES OF THE PLANETS
BY PHILIP D. NICHOLSON

Of the 169 natural satellites listed in the table, all but 6 orbit the giant planets Jupiter (62), Saturn (61), Uranus (27), and Neptune (13). With a few exceptions, these moons may be divided into three groups, which presumably reflect their different origins. Closest to the planets are small ring moons, 20 km to 200 km in diameter and with strong evolutionary and dynamical connections to the planetary ring systems. Most of these objects were discovered during the *Voyager* flybys of 1979–1989, and all are very difficult to observe from Earth. These include the shepherd satellites Prometheus, Pandora, Cordelia, Ophelia, and Galatea; the co-orbital satellites Janus and Epimetheus; and Pan, which orbits within the Encke Gap in Saturn's A ring.

Next come the larger "regular" satellites in near-circular orbits in or near the planets' equatorial planes, thought to have been formed in situ via accretion in circumplanetary disks at the dawn of the solar system. The dividing line between the first two groups is fuzzy, but the regular satellites may be considered to start beyond about three planetary radii, that is, at Amalthea, Mimas, Puck, and Proteus. This group extends out to Callisto, Iapetus, Oberon, and Proteus but probably does not include Triton, which is now thought to have been captured. There are numerous orbital resonances among the regular satellites, for example, Io:Europa:Ganymede (1:2:4), Mimas:Tethys (1:2), Enceladus:Dione (1:2), and Titan:Hyperion (3:4); the origin of the orbital resonance is generally ascribed to orbital expansion driven by tidal interaction with Jupiter or Saturn. Temporary capture in similar resonances in the past may have been responsible for the anomalously large inclinations of Miranda and (perhaps) Naiad. Tidal-energy dissipation within Io is responsible for this moon's spectacular volcanic activity, and similar heating at a lower level may still occur within Europa and Enceladus.

The third and outermost group—and the group whose numbers have increased so much in recent years—comprises the "irregular" satellites. These generally small bodies (2 km to 200 km in diameter, except for 340-km Nereid) move in quite eccentric orbits at large inclinations to the planets' orbital planes. Their orbits are not random; rather, they fall into several more-or-less tight clusters in semimajor axis and inclination: three or four at Jupiter (all but one retrograde) centred on Himalia, Ananke, Pasiphae, and Carme and three at Saturn (one retrograde) centred on Albiorix, Siarnaq, and Phoebe. These clusters are believed to be due to collisional disruptions of a smaller number of original objects captured from heliocentric orbits. The situation at Uranus and Neptune remains unclear, although there are now nine Uranian irregulars (all but one retrograde) and six Neptunians (three retrograde). The orbits of the irregular satellites, along with that of Earth's Moon, are subject to strong solar gravitational perturbations, and thus maintain approximately fixed inclinations to their respective planet's orbital planes rather than to their equators.

Jupiter's S/2003 J17 has been officially named L Herse. That leaves twelve Jovian satellites, all discovered in 2003, unnamed. Eight Saturnian satellites, four discovered in 2004, and two discovered in both 2006 and 2007, also remain unnamed.

TABLE OF NATURAL SATELLITES OF THE PLANETS

Name (Pronunciation)	Diameter km	Mass[A] 10^{18} kg	Density t/m^3	Visual Mag.[B]	Albedo	Mean Dist. from Planet 10^3 km	Orbital Period d	Eccentricity	Orbit Incl.[C] °	Discovery
Satellite of Earth										
Moon* (mōōn)	3475.	73 490. (10)	3.34	−12.7	0.11	384.4	27.322	0.0554	5.16	—
Satellites of Mars										
I Phobos* (fō'bŏs)	22.	0.0107 (0.00002)	1.87	11.4	0.07	9.38	0.319	0.0151	1.1	A. Hall, 1877
II Deimos* (dī'mŏs)	12.	0.0022 (0.0002)	2.3	12.5	0.07	23.46	1.262	0.0002	1.8v	A. Hall, 1877
Satellites of Jupiter										
XVI Metis (mē'tĭs)	43.	—	—	17.5	0.06	128.0	0.295	0.0012	0.02	*Voyager 2*, 1979
XV Adrastea (ă-drăs'tē-ă)	16.	—	—	18.7	≈0.05	129.0	0.298	0.0018	0.39	*Voyager 1*, 1979
V Amalthea* (ăm'ʼl-thē'ă)	167.	—	—	14.1	0.09	181.4	0.498	0.0031	0.39	E. Barnard, 1892
XIV Thebe** (thē'bē)	99.	—	—	16.0	0.05	221.9	0.675	0.0177	1.07	*Voyager 1*, 1979
I Io*[D] (ī'ō)	3643.	89 330. (10)	3.53	5.0	0.62	421.8	1.769	0.0041	0.04	Galileo, 1610
II Europa*[D] (ū-rō'pa)	3122.	48 000. (10)	3.01	5.3	0.68	671.1	3.551	0.0094	0.47	Galileo, 1610
III Ganymede*[D] (găn'ē-mēd')	5262.	148 200. (10)	1.94	4.6	0.44	1 070.	7.155	0.0011	0.17	Galileo, 1610
IV Callisto* (ka-lĭs'tō)	4820.	107 600. (10)	1.83	5.6	0.19	1 883.	16.689	0.0074	0.19	Galileo, 1610
XVIII Themisto (thē-mĭs'tō)	4.[E]	—	—	21.0	—	7 284.	130.	0.24	43.	C. Kowal, 1975[F]
XIII Leda (lē'dă)	≈20	—	—	19.5	—	11 165.	241.	0.16	27.	C. Kowal, 1974
VI Himalia*** (hĭm'ă-lī-ă)	185.	—	—	14.6	0.03	11 461.	251.	0.16	27.	C. Perrine, 1904
X Lysithea*** (lĭs'ĭ-thē'ă)	≈35	—	—	18.3	—	11 717.	259.	0.11	28.	S. Nicholson, 1938
VII Elara (ē'lar-a)	85.	—	—	16.3	0.03	11 741.	260.	0.22	26.	C. Perrine, 1905
XLVI Carpo (kar'po)	3.[G]	—	—	23.0	—	16 989.	456.	0.43	51.	S. Sheppard et al., 2003
S/2003 J12	1.[G]	—	—	23.9	—	17 582.	490.	0.51	151.	S. Sheppard et al., 2003

Pronunciation guide: ă tăp; ā dāte; à câre; ä gäga; ĕ wĕ; ē mēt; ĭ ice; ī bĭt; ŏ gŏ; ō hŏt; ŏ ŏrb; oo book; ōō mōōn; ŭ ŭp; ū cūte; û ûrn

For some background on the satellites' names, visit planetarynames.wr.usgs.gov/Page/Planets.

Visual magnitudes are at mean opposition distance.

* synchronous rotation; ** probably synchronous; *** asynchronous; **** chaotic rotation; (no asterisk) rotation unknown

[A] The numbers in parentheses are possible errors.

[B] Jovian, Saturnian, and Uranian irregular satellites discovered in 1997–2001 are CCD-R magnitudes (675 nm); the solar V–R is 0.53.

[C] Inclinations of inner satellites (those closer than 100 planetary radii) are relative to the planet's *equator*. As customary, inclinations for outer satellites (those beyond Jupiter IV, Saturn VIII, Uranus IV, and Neptune I) are relative to the planet's *orbital plane*. Iapetus is an intermediate case. For our Moon, the inclination relative to Earth's orbital plane is 5°; relative to Earth's equator it varies between 18° and 29° in an 18.61-year cycle. A value >90° indicates retrograde motion.

[D] Laplace resonance; longitudes satisfy $L(\text{Io}) - 3L(\text{Europa}) + 2L(\text{Ganymede}) \approx 180°$. Also, the mean motions are such that the three periods are nearly 1:2:4.

[E] Diameters assume an albedo of 0.06.

[F] Initially detected in 1975 and then lost; recovered in 2000 by S. Sheppard and D. Jewitt.

[G] Diameters assume an albedo of 0.04.

TABLE OF NATURAL SATELLITES OF THE PLANETS (continued)

Name (Pronunciation)	Diameter km	Mass^A 10^18 kg	Density t/m^3	Visual Mag.^B	Albedo	Mean Dist. from Planet 10^3 km	Orbital Period d	Eccentricity	Orbit Incl.^C °	Discovery
Satellites of Jupiter (continued)										
XXXIV Euporie (ū-pôr'ī-ē)	2.^E	—	—	23.1	—	19304.	551.	0.14	146.	S. Sheppard et al., 2001
S/2003 J3	2.^G	—	—	23.4	—	20221.	584.	0.20	148.	S. Sheppard et al., 2003
S/2003 J18	2.^G	—	—	23.4	—	20514.	597.	0.02	146.	B. Gladman et al., 2003
XXXV Orthosie (ôr-thô-sī'ē)	2.^E	—	—	23.1	—	20720.	623.	0.28	146.	S. Sheppard et al., 2001
XXXIII Euanthe (ū-an'thē)	3.^E	—	—	22.8	—	20797.	620.	0.23	149.	S. Sheppard et al., 2001
XXII Harpalyke (här-pā-lē'kē)	3.^E	—	—	22.2	—	20858.	623.	0.23	149.	S. Sheppard et al., 2000
XXXVII Praxidike (prāk-sī'dī-kē)	5.^E	—	—	21.2	—	20907.	625.	0.23	149.	S. Sheppard et al., 2000
XXIX Thyone (thī'ō-nē)	3.^E	—	—	22.3	—	20939.	627.	0.23	149.	S. Sheppard et al., 2001
S/2003 J16	2.^G	—	—	23.3	—	20957.	616.	0.22	149.	B. Gladman et al., 2003
XXIV Iocaste (ī-ō-kăs'tē)	4.^E	—	—	21.8	—	21061.	632.	0.22	149.	S. Sheppard et al., 2000
XL Mneme (nē'mē)	2.^G	—	—	23.3	—	21069.	620.	0.23	149.	B. Gladman, S. Sheppard, 2003
XXX Hermippe (hēr-mī'pē)	4.^E	—	—	22.1	—	21131.	634.	0.21	151.	S. Sheppard et al., 2001
XXX Thelxinoe(thĕl-kī'nō-ē)	2.^G	—	—	23.4	—	21162.	628.	0.22	151.	S. Sheppard et al., 2004
XLV Helike (hĕl'ī-kē)	4.^G	—	—	22.6	—	21263.	635.	0.16	155.	S. Sheppard et al., 2003
XII Ananke*** (à'nän-kē)	≈30	—	—	18.8	—	21276.	630.	0.24	149.	S. Nicholson, 1951
S/2003 J15	2.^G	—	—	23.5	—	22627.	690.	0.19	147.	S. Sheppard et al., 2003
XXXII Eurydome(ū-rĭd'ō-mē)	3.^E	—	—	22.7	—	22865.	717.	0.28	150.	S. Sheppard et al., 2001
S/2003 J17 = L Herse (hûr'-sē)	2.^G	—	—	23.4	—	22922.	714.	0.24	165.	B. Gladman et al., 2003
XLIII Arche (ar'kē)	3.^G	—	—	22.8	—	22931.	724.	0.26	165.	S. Sheppard et al., 2002
XXXVIII Pasithee (pă-sī'thē)	2.^E	—	—	23.2	—	23004.	719.	0.27	165.	S. Sheppard et al., 2001
S/2003 J10	2.^G	—	—	23.6	—	23041.	716.	0.43	165.	S. Sheppard et al., 2003
XXI Chaldene (kăl'dē-nē)	3.^E	—	—	22.5	—	23100.	724.	0.25	165.	S. Sheppard et al., 2000
XXVI Isonoe (ī-sō'nō-ē)	3.^E	—	—	22.5	—	23155.	726.	0.25	165.	S. Sheppard et al., 2000
XXV Erinome (ē-rĭn'ō-mē)	3.^E	—	—	22.8	—	23196.	729.	0.27	165.	S. Sheppard et al., 2000
XXXVII Kale (kā'lē)	2.^E	—	—	23.0	—	23217.	729.	0.26	165.	S. Sheppard et al., 2001
XXXI Aitne (ā-īt'nē)	3.^E	—	—	22.7	—	23229.	730.	0.26	165.	S. Sheppard et al., 2001
XX Taygete (tā-ij'ē-tē)	4.^E	—	—	21.9	—	23280.	732.	0.25	165.	S. Sheppard et al., 2000
S/2003 J9	1.^G	—	—	23.7	—	23384.	733.	0.26	165.	S. Sheppard et al., 2003
XI Carme (kär'mē)	≈45	—	—	17.6	—	23404.	734.	0.25	165.	S. Nicholson, 1938
XXXVI Sponde (spōn'dē)	2.^E	—	—	23.0	—	23487.	748.	0.31	151.	S. Sheppard et al., 2001
XIX Megaclite (mĕg-ā-klī'tē)	4.^E	—	—	21.7	—	23493.	753.	0.42	153.	S. Sheppard et al., 2000
S/2003 J5	4.^G	—	—	22.4	—	23495.	739.	0.25	165.	S. Sheppard et al., 2003
S/2003 J19	2.^G	—	—	23.7	—	23533.	740.	0.26	165.	B. Gladman et al., 2003
S/2003 J23	2.^G	—	—	23.5	—	23563.	732.	0.27	146.	S. Sheppard et al., 2004

TABLE OF NATURAL SATELLITES OF THE PLANETS (continued)

Name (Pronunciation)	Diameter km	Mass[A] 10^{18} kg	Density t/m³	Visual Mag.[B]	Albedo	Mean Dist. from Planet 10^3 km	Orbital Period d	Eccentricity	Orbit Incl.[C] °	Discovery
Satellites of Jupiter (continued)										
XXIII Kalyke (kǎ-lē'kē)	4.[E]	—	—	21.8	—	23 566.	742.	0.25	165.	S. Sheppard et al., 2000
VIII Pasiphae (pa-sǐf'a-ē')	≈60	—	—	17.0	—	23 624.	744.	0.41	151.	P. Melotte, 1908
XLVII Eukelade (ū-kě-lā'dē)	4.[G]	—	—	22.6	—	23 661.	746.	0.27	165.	S. Sheppard et al., 2003
S/2003 J4	2.[G]	—	—	23.0	—	23 930.	755.	0.36	150.	S. Sheppard et al., 2003
XXXIX Hegemone (hě-jě'mō-nē)	3.[G]	—	—	22.8	—	23 947.	740.	0.33	155.	S. Sheppard et al., 2003
XLVIII Cyllene (sǐ-lē'nē)	2.[G]	—	—	23.2	—	23 951.	752.	0.41	150.	S. Sheppard et al., 2003
XLI Aoede (ā-ō'dē)	4.[G]	—	—	22.5	—	23 981.	762.	0.43	158.	S. Sheppard et al., 2003
IX Sinope*** (sǐ-nō'pē)	≈38	—	—	18.1	—	23 939.	759.	0.25	158.	S. Nicholson, 1914
XLIX Kore (kōr'-ē)	2.[G]	—	—	23.6	—	24 011.	779.	0.34	145.	S. Sheppard et al., 2003
XLIV Kallichore (kǎ-lǐ-kō'rē)	2.[G]	—	—	23.7	—	24 043.	765.	0.26	166.	S. Sheppard et al., 2003
XXVIII Autonoe (ô-tôn'ō-ē)	3.[B]	—	—	22.0	—	24 046.	761.	0.32	152.	S. Sheppard et al., 2001
XVII Callirrhoe (kǎ-lǐr'ō-ē)	7.[E]	—	—	20.7	—	24 103.	759.	0.28	147.	J. Scotti, T. Spahr, 1999
S/2003 J2	2.[G]	—	—	23.2	—	29 541.	980.	0.23	161.	S. Sheppard et al., 2003
Satellites of Saturn										
XVIII Pan[H] (pǎn)	26.	—	—	19.4	≈0.5	133.6	0.575	0.0002	0.007	M. Showalter, 1990
XXXV Daphnis (dǎf'-nǐs)	7.	—	—	23.4[I]	—	136.5	0.594	≈0.	≈0.	Cassini ISS team, 2005
XV Atlas (ăt'lǎs)	20.	—	—	19.0	0.4	137.7	0.602	0.0012	0.01	Voyager 1, 1980
XVII Prometheus**[J] (prō-mē'thē-ūs)	94.	0.19	0.44	15.8	0.6	139.4	0.613	0.002	0.006	Voyager 1, 1980
XVI Pandora**[J] (pǎn-dôr'a)	81.	0.15	0.53	16.4	0.5	141.7	0.629	0.004	0.052	Voyager 1, 1980
XI Epimetheus*[K] (ěp'a-mē'thē-ūs)	120.	0.5 (0.1)	0.61	15.6	0.5	151.4	0.694	0.010	0.35	J. Fountain, S. Larson, 1978
X Janus*[K] (jā'nūs)	180.	1.9 (0.1)	0.66	14.4	0.6	151.5	0.695	0.007	0.17	A. Dollfus, 1966
LIII Aegaeon (ē-gē'-ăn)	≈0.5	—	—	—	—	167.5	0.808	0.0002	0.001	Cassini ISS team, 2008
I Mimas* (mī'mǎs)	397.	38. (1)	1.16	12.8	0.6	185.6	0.942	0.0206	1.57	W. Herschel, 1789
XXXII Methone (měth-ō'nē)	3.	—	—	25.1	—	194.2	1.010	0.0000	0.013	Cassini ISS team, 2004
XLIX Anthe (ăn'-thē)	≈2[E]	—	—	≈26	—	197.7	1.037	0.0012	0.017	Cassini ISS team, 2007
XXXIII Pallene (pǎ-lā'nē)	4.	—	—	24.5	—	212.3	1.154	0.0040	0.181	Cassini ISS team, 2004
II Enceladus* (ěn-sěl'a-dūs)	499.	65. (2)	1.61	11.8	1.0	238.1	1.370	0.0001	0.01	W. Herschel, 1789
III Tethys* (tē'thǐs)	1060.	627. (5)	0.96	10.3	0.8	294.7	1.888	0.0001	0.168	J. Cassini, 1684

[H] Orbits within the Encke Gap. Discovered in Voyager images (1980–81).
[I] Orbits within the Keeler Gap.
[J] Prometheus and Pandora are shepherds of the F ring.
[K] Co-orbital satellites that "exchange orbits" every 4.0 years.
[L] Telesto librates about the trailing (#5) Lagrangian point of Tethys's orbit.
[M] Calypso librates about the leading (#4) Lagrangian point of Tethys's orbit.

TABLE OF NATURAL SATELLITES OF THE PLANETS (continued)

Name (Pronunciation)	Diameter km	Mass[A] 10^18 kg	Density t/m^3	Visual Mag.[B]	Albedo	Mean Dist. from Planet 10^3 km	Orbital Period d	Eccentricity	Orbit Incl.[C] °	Discovery
Satellites of Saturn (continued)										
XIII Telesto (tǎ-lēs'tō)	25.	—	—	18.5	0.7	294.7	1.888[L]	~0.	1.16	B. Smith et al., 1980
XIV Calypso** (kà-līp'sō)	19.	—	—	18.7	1.0	294.7	1.888[M]	~0.	1.47	D. Pascu et al., 1980
IV Dione* (dī-ō'nē)	1120.	1097.(2)	1.46	10.4	0.6	377.4	2.737	0.0002	0.002	J. Cassini, 1684
XII Helene (ha-lēn')	30.	—	—	18.4	0.6	377.4	2.737[N]	~0.	0.21	P. Laques, J. Lecacheux, 1980
XXXIV Polydeuces (pŏl-i-dü'sēz)	3.5	—	—	24.8	—	377.4	2.737[O]	0.018	0.17	Cassini ISS team, 2004
V Rhea* (rē'a)	1530.	2308.(60)	1.23	9.7	0.6	527.1	4.518	0.0009	0.327	J. Cassini, 1672
VI Titan** (tī't'n)	5150.[P]	134570.(20)	1.88	8.4	0.2	1221.9	15.945	0.0288	0.33	C. Huygens, 1655
VII Hyperion**** (hī-pēr'ī-ŏn)	266.	5.6	0.57	14.4	0.3	1464.1	21.276	0.0175	0.57	W. Bond, G. Bond, W. Lassell, 1848
VIII Iapetus* (ī-ǎp'ē-tŭs)	1469.	1809	1.09	11.0v	0.08–0.4	3560.8	79.331	0.0284	7.57	J. Cassini, 1671
XXIV Kiviuq (kē-vyook')	14.[E]	—	—	21.9	—	11365.	449.	0.33	46.	B. Gladman et al., 2000
XXII Ijiraq (ē-jē-rǎk')	10.[E]	—	—	22.5	—	11442.	451.	0.32	47.	J. Kavelaars et al., 2000
IX Phoebe*** (fē'bē)	213.	8.2	1.63	16.5	0.08	12944.3	548.	0.1644	175.	W. Pickering, 1898
XX Paaliaq (pä-lyak')	19.[E]	—	—	21.2	—	15198.	687.	0.36	45.	B. Gladman et al., 2000
XXVII Skadi (skä'dē)	6.[E]	—	—	23.5	—	15641.	728.	0.27	153.	J. Kavelaars et al., 2000
XXVI Albiorix (ăl'bē-ôr-īks)	26.[E]	—	—	20.4	—	16394.	783.	0.48	34.	M. Holman, T. Spahr, 2000
S/2007 S2	5.[E]	—	—	24.4	—	16725.	808.	0.18	174.	S. Sheppard et al., 2007
XXXVII Bebhionn (bē-vēn')	6.[E]	—	—	24.1	—	17119.	835.	0.47	35.	S. Sheppard, D. Jewitt, 2005
XXIX Siarnaq (syar-nǎk')	32.[E]	—	—	20.0	—	17531.	896.	0.30	46.	B. Gladman et al., 2000
XXVIII Erriapus (ěr-rē-ǎp'ŭs)	8.[E]	—	—	22.9	—	17604.	871.	0.47	34.	J. Kavelaars et al., 2000
XLVII Skoll (skōl)	6.[E]	—	—	24.5	—	17665.	878.	0.46	161.	S. Sheppard et al., 2006
LII Tarqeq (tar'-kǎk)	7.[E]	—	—	23.9	—	18009.	888.	0.16	46.	S. Sheppard et al., 2007
S/2004 S13	6.[E]	—	—	24.5	—	18057.	906.	0.26	167.	S. Sheppard, D. Jewitt, 2005
LI Greip (grāp)	6.[E]	—	—	24.4	—	18206.	921.	0.33	180.	S. Sheppard et al., 2006
XXI Tarvos (tar'vōs)	13.[E]	—	—	22.0	—	18239.	926.	0.54	33.	J. Kavelaars et al., 2000
XLIV Hyrrokkin (hīr-rōk'-īn)	8.[E]	—	—	23.5	—	18437.	932.	0.33	152.	S. Sheppard et al., 2007
XXXI Narvi (när'vē)	5.[E]	—	—	24.1	—	18719.	956.	0.35	135.	S. Sheppard et al., 2003
XXV Mundilfari (mǔnd'īl-fär-ē)	6.[E]	—	—	23.7	—	18722.	952.	0.21	167.	B. Gladman et al., 2000
S/2006 S1	6.[E]	—	—	24.6	—	18790.	963.	0.12	156.	S. Sheppard et al., 2006
L Jarnsaxa (yärn-säsk'-ē)	5.[E]	—	—	24.7	—	18811.	965.	0.22	163.	S. Sheppard et al., 2006
S/2007 S3	5.[E]	—	—	24.9	—	18975.	978.	0.19	175.	S. Sheppard et al., 2007
S/2004 S17	4.[E]	—	—	25.2	—	19099.	985.	0.23	167.	S. Sheppard, D. Jewitt, 2005

[N] Helene librates about the leading (#4) Lagrangian point of Dione's orbit with a period of 769 d.
[O] Polydeuces librates about the trailing (#5) Lagrangian point of Dione's orbit with a period of 792 d.
[P] Titan's cloud-top diameter is 5550 km; as seen in the eyepiece.

TABLE OF NATURAL SATELLITES OF THE PLANETS (continued)

Name (Pronunciation)	Diameter km	Mass[A] 10^18 kg	Density t/m³	Visual Mag.[B]	Albedo	Mean Dist. from Planet 10³ km	Orbital Period d	Eccentricity	Orbit Incl.[C] °	Discovery
Satellites of Saturn (continued)										
XXXVIII Bergelmir (bår–yěl'–mir)	6.[E]	—	—	24.2	—	19372.	1007.	0.15	158.	S. Sheppard, D. Jewitt, 2005
XXIII Suttungr (süt'tŭng)	6.[E]	—	—	23.8	—	19465.	1017.	0.11	176.	B. Gladman et al., 2000
XXXVI Aegir (ī'–ēir)	6.[E]	—	—	24.4	—	19614.	1026.	0.24	167.	S. Sheppard, D. Jewitt, 2005
S/2004 S12	5.[E]	—	—	24.8	—	19906.	1049.	0.40	164.	S. Sheppard, D. Jewitt, 2005
XXXIX Bestla (běst'–lě)	7.[E]	—	—	23.8	—	19959.	1053.	0.77	148.	S. Sheppard, D. Jewitt, 2005
XXX Thrymr (thrïm)	6.[E]	—	—	23.8	—	20219.	1092.	0.49	176.	B. Gladman et al, 2000
XL Farbauti (fär–böw'–tě)	5.[E]	—	—	24.7	—	20291.	1079.	0.21	158.	S. Sheppard, D. Jewitt, 2005
XLIII Hati (hä'–tě)	6.[E]	—	—	24.4	—	20304.	1080.	0.29	163.	S. Sheppard, D. Jewitt, 2005
S/2004 S7	6.[E]	—	—	24.5	—	20577.	1102.	0.55	166.	S. Sheppard, D. Jewitt, 2005
XLV Kari (kär'–ě)	7.[E]	—	—	23.9	—	22089.	1231.	0.48	156.	S. Sheppard et al., 2006
S/2006 S3	6.[E]	—	—	24.6	—	22096.	1227.	0.40	158.	S. Sheppard et al., 2006
XLI Fenrir (fěn'–rěr)	4.[E]	—	—	25.0	—	22611.	1269.	0.13	163.	S. Sheppard, D. Jewitt, 2005
XLVIII Surtur (sür'–tär)	5.[E]	—	—	24.8	—	22704.	1297.	0.45	178.	S. Sheppard et al., 2006
XLVI Loge (lö'–gě)	6.[E]	—	—	24.6	—	23058.	1311.	0.19	168.	S. Sheppard et al., 2006
XIX Ymir (ē'měr)	16.[E]	—	—	21.6	—	23130.	1315.	0.33	173.	B. Gladman et al., 2000
XLII Fornjot	6.[E]	—	—	24.6	—	23609.	1354.	0.19	168.	S. Sheppard, D. Jewitt, 2005
Satellites of Uranus										
VI Cordelia[Q] (kôr–děl'ya)	25.[R]	—	—	24.2	—	49.8	0.335	≈0.	0.08	*Voyager 2*, 1986
VII Ophelia[Q] (ö–fēl'ya)	30.[R]	—	—	23.9	—	53.8	0.376	0.01	0.10	*Voyager 2*, 1986
VIII Bianca (bē–äng'ka)	45.[R]	—	—	23.1	—	59.2	0.435	0.001	0.19	*Voyager 2*, 1986
IX Cressida (krěs'ī–da)	65.[R]	—	—	22.3	—	61.8	0.464	≈0.	0.01	*Voyager 2*, 1986
X Desdemona (děs'da–mō'na)	60.[R]	—	—	22.5	—	62.7	0.474	≈0.	0.11	*Voyager 2*, 1986
XI Juliet (joo'lē–ět)	85.[R]	—	—	21.7	—	64.4	0.493	0.001	0.06	*Voyager 2*, 1986
XII Portia (pôr'sha)	110.[R]	—	—	21.1	—	66.1	0.513	≈0.	0.06	*Voyager 2*, 1986
XIII Rosalind (röz'a–lïnd)	60.[R]	—	—	22.5	—	69.9	0.558	≈0.	0.28	*Voyager 2*, 1986
XXVII Cupid (cū'pid)	18.	—	—	25.9	—	74.4	0.613	≈0.	≈0.	M. Showalter, J. Lissauer, 2003
XIV Belinda (ba–lïn'da)	68.[R]	—	—	22.1	—	75.3	0.624	≈0.	0.03	*Voyager 2*, 1986
XXV Perdita (pür'di–ta)	26.	—	—	23.6	—	76.4	0.638	0.003	0.07	E. Karkoschka, 1999[S]
XV Puck (pŭk)	155.	—	—	20.4	0.07	86.0	0.762	≈0.	0.32	*Voyager 2*, 1985
XXVI Mab (mäb)	24.[R]	—	—	25.4	—	97.7	0.923	0.003	0.13	M. Showalter, J. Lissauer, 2003

[Q] Cordelia and Ophelia are shepherds of the ε-ring.
[R] Diameter assumes the same albedo (0.07) as Puck.
[S] In *Voyager 2* (January 1986) images

TABLE OF NATURAL SATELLITES OF THE PLANETS (continued)

Name (Pronunciation)	Diameter km	Mass[A] 10^18 kg	Density t/m^3	Visual Mag.[B]	Albedo	Mean Dist. from Planet 10^3 km	Orbital Period d	Eccen- tricity	Orbit Incl.[C] °	Discovery
Satellites of Uranus (continued)										
V Miranda*[T] (mĭ-răn'da)	472.	66. (8)	1.2	15.8	0.32	129.9	1.413	0.0013	4.34	G. Kuiper, 1948
I Ariel*[T] (âr'ē-ĕl)	1158.	1350. (120)	1.7	13.7	0.39	190.9	2.520	0.0012	0.04	W. Lassell, 1851
II Umbriel*[T] (ŭm'brē-ĕl')	1169.	1170. (140)	1.4	14.5	0.21	266.0	4.144	0.0040	0.13	W. Lassell, 1851
III Titania*[T] (tĭ'tā'nē-a)	1578.	3520. (90)	1.7	13.5	0.27	436.3	8.706	0.0011	0.079	W. Herschel, 1787
IV Oberon* (ō'ba-rŏn)	1523.	3010. (80)	1.6	13.7	0.23	583.5	13.463	0.0014	0.068	W. Herschel, 1787
XXII Francisco (frăn'cĭs-cō)	14.[E]	—	—	25.3	—	4276.	267.	0.15	145.	M. Holman, J. Kavelaars, 2001
XVI Caliban (kăl'ĭ-băn)	60.[R]	—	—	22.4	—	7231.	580.	0.16	141.	B. Gladman et al., 1997
XX Stephano (stĕf'ă-nō)	20.[E]	—	—	24.1	—	8004.	677.	0.23	144.	B. Gladman et al., 1999
XXI Trinculo (trĭn'cŭ-lo)	14.[E]	—	—	25.3	—	8504.	749.	0.22	167.	M. Holman, J. Kavelaars, 2002
XVII Sycorax (sĭk'ō-răks)	120.[R]	—	—	20.8	—	12179.	1288.	0.52	159.	P. Nicholson et al. 1997
XXIII Margaret (măr'gà-rĕt)	15.[E]	—	—	25.2	—	14345.	1687.	0.66	57.	D. Jewitt, S. Sheppard, 2003
XVIII Prospero (prŏs'pĕr-ō)	30.[R]	—	—	23.2	—	16256.	1978.	0.44	152.	M. Holman et al., 1999
XIX Setebos (sĕt'ĕ-bōs)	35.[R]	—	—	23.3	—	17418.	2225.	0.59	158.	J. Kavelaars et al., 1999
XXIV Ferdinand (fûr'dĭn-nănd)	16.[E]	—	—	25.0	—	20901.	2887.	0.37	170.	M. Holman, J. Kavelaars, 2001
Satellites of Neptune										
III Naiad (nī'ăd)	66.	—	—	24.6	0.07	48.2	0.294	≈0.	4.74	Voyager 2, 1989
IV Thalassa (thă-lăs'a)	82.	—	—	23.9	0.09	50.1	0.311	≈0.	0.21	Voyager 2, 1989
V Despina (dĭs-pīn'a)	150.	—	—	22.5	0.09	52.5	0.335	≈0.	0.07	Voyager 2, 1989
VI Galatea (găl'ă-tē'a)	176.	—	—	22.4	0.08	62.0	0.429	≈0.	0.05	Voyager 2, 1989
VII Larissa** (la-rĭs'a)	194.	—	—	22.0	0.09	73.5	0.555	0.001	0.20	Voyager 2, 1989
VIII Proteus** (prō'tē-ūs)	420.	—	—	20.3	0.10	117.6	1.122	≈0.	0.039	Voyager 2, 1989
I Triton* (trī't'n)	2706.	21400. (50)	2.06	13.5	0.76	354.8	5.877	≈0.	157.	W. Lassell, 1846
II Nereid*** (nēr'ē-ĭd)	340.	—	—	19.7	0.16	5513.4	360.	0.75	7.23	G. Kuiper, 1949
IX Halimede (hăl'-ĭ-mē'-dē)	50.[E]	—	—	24.4	—	15686.	1875.	0.57	134.	M. Holman, J. Kavelaars, 2002
XI Sao (săy'-ō)	27.[E]	—	—	25.7	—	22452.	2919.	0.30	48.	M. Holman, J. Kavelaars, 2002
XII Laomedeia (lā̆y'-ō-mē-dē'-ē)	33.[E]	—	—	25.3	—	22580.	2982.	0.48	35.	M. Holman, J. Kavelaars, 2002
XIII Neso (nē'-sō)	43.[E]	—	—	24.7	—	46570.	8863.	0.53	132.	M. Holman, J. Kavelaars, 2002
X Psamathe (săm'ā-thē)	36.[E]	—	—	25.1	—	46738.	9136.	0.45	137.	D. Jewitt et al., 2003
Satellites of Pluto										
I Charon* (kâr'ĕn)	1208.	1620. (90)	1.65	17.3	0.37	19.57	6.387	0.00	0.0[U]	J. Christy, 1978
II Nix (nĭx)	36.[G]	—	—	23.4	—	48.68	24.856	0.02	0.0[U]	H. Weaver, S. Stern, 2005
III Hydra (hī'drā)	36.[G]	—	—	23.3	—	64.78	38.207	0.05	0.2[U]	H. Weaver, S. Stern, 2005

[T] Near resonance(?); L(Miranda) – 3L(Ariel) + 2L(Umbriel) drifts slowly (period ≈12.5 years).

[U] Nix and Hydra orbit in the same plane as the Pluto–Charon binary. Their orbital periods are in the ratio 1:4:6 (Charon:Nix:Hydra). The inclinations are with respect to Pluto's assumed equatorial plane. Most other references give these inclinations with respect to the ecliptic, which are about 96°.

ORBITAL MOTION
BY ROY BISHOP

Whether you are observing a distant galaxy, the stars in a globular cluster, the waltz of Jupiter's Galilean satellites, the drift of the Moon during an occultation, or merely uttering an expletive as an artificial satellite passes through the field of your camera, an understanding of orbital motion is central to an appreciation of the heavens.

Among early cosmologies were those of **Aristotle** (340 BC) and **Ptolemy** (published as the *Almagest*, c. AD 150), and the superior heliocentric model proposed by **Copernicus** (*De revolutionibus*, 1543). These attempts at modelling the heavens used complex systems of circles upon circles, of eccentric deferents and epicycles. John Milton, a contemporary of Galileo, wrote the following lines in his epic poem "Paradise Lost" (1674), possibly expressing his discontent with the Ptolemaic and Copernican systems of compounded circles:

> *From Man or Angel the great Architect*
> *Did wisely to conceal, and not divulge*
> *His secrets to be scann'd by them who ought*
> *Rather admire; or if they list to try*
> *Conjecture, he his Fabric of the Heav'ns*
> *Hath left to thir disputes, perhaps to move*
> *His laughter at thir quaint Opinions wide*
> *Hereafter, when they come to model Heav'n*
> *And calculate the Stars, how they will wield*
> *The mighty frame, how build, unbuild, contrive*
> *To save appearances, how gird the Sphere*
> *With Centric and Eccentric scribbl'd o'er,*
> *Cycle and Epicycle, Orb in Orb.*

Kepler, using observations accumulated by Tycho Brahe, broke with the 2000-year preoccupation with circles when he discovered that the planets move in an elegantly simple way along elliptical paths (*Astronomia nova*, 1609). Although he had discovered *how* the planets move, Kepler was unable to explain quantitatively *why* they move in this way.

Galileo strongly supported the Copernican heliocentric universe (*Dialogue on the Two Chief World Systems*, 1632) and achieved brilliant insights concerning the motion of objects (*Two New Sciences*, 1638); however, he ignored Kepler's ellipses and did not apply his mechanics to the sky.

Newton united the heavens and Earth by showing that the laws governing motions on Earth also apply to the heavens. In his *Principia* (1687), the greatest book in the physical sciences, Newton presented his three laws of motion and the first ever physical force law, his law of gravitation. He used these to explain the motions not only of bodies on Earth, but also of the planets, comets, stars, equinoxes, tides, etc. Newton was the first to realize that the Moon is falling toward Earth just as freely as does an apple, and that the elliptical orbit of the centre of mass of the Earth–Moon system is the path that results (as he described it) as these two bodies free-fall under the action of the Sun's gravitational force.

In popular-level explanations of phenomena involving rotary motion, such as spinning wheels, automobiles on corners, tides, and orbital motion, "centrifugal force" is usually invoked. This is unfortunate because centrifugal force is a fiction, and its use in a popular description of motion obscures understanding.[1]

In the case of orbits, the common misconception is that the inward gravitational force is balanced by an outward "centrifugal force." Newton's view is simpler: There

is only one force, the inward pull of gravity. There is *no physical agent* to cause an outward force. (Note that forces cause accelerations, not vice versa.) Also, if there *were* an outward supporting force, the two forces would cancel and, as Galileo realized, the body would then move along a straight line. If you choose a rotating reference frame and then ignore the rotation (mistake no. 1), you have to pretend there is a "centrifugal force" (mistake no. 2) in order to make sense of motions occurring within this frame. The two mistakes effectively cancel, but the description has been made needlessly complicated, and if you do not realize what you have done, you do not understand the motion.

Einstein's general theory of relativity (GTR) of 1915 superseded Newton's description of gravity. The arbiter of which is a good theory and which theory is wrong is nature. Newton's laws are accurate enough for most of NASA's calculations, but they do not work exactly. For example, if the computer programs used in the Global Positioning System (GPS) were based on Newton's gravitation, the system would be a multibillion-dollar boondoggle. Einstein's conception of gravitation is essential to the operation of this satellite-based navigation system. In the case of strong gravitation and/or speeds approaching the speed of light, Newton's laws fail dramatically. The GTR may be wrong too, but so far it has passed all experimental tests. Science does not hie after ultimate explanations or "truth"; its goal is a rational, coherent description of the measurable physical world, a description that has beauty in its simplicity, a description that makes sense. In the courtroom of nature, any aspect of science is falsifiable. Modern technology is making possible increasingly precise tests of general relativity (for instance, see *Sky & Telescope*, July 2004, p. 22, and August 2010, p. 29).

According to Einstein's GTR, gravitation is not a mysterious force that one mass exerts upon a distant mass; gravitation is the geometry (non-Euclidean) of the 4-dimensional spacetime within which we and the stars exist. Golf balls (if air friction is ignored), satellites, planets, stars, and light follow *geodesics*, the straightest possible, force-free paths through a spacetime whose geometry is shaped by mass–energy. The difficulty in intellectually grasping a non-Euclidean spacetime originates with us. Common sense is inadequate. This is not surprising, given that our common sense is based on the Euclidean, three-dimensional geometry of straight lines, rectangles, and spheres we learned in the crib by age two. The underlying cause of our delusion is that our senses and thought processes are constrained by the speed of neuron signals. Compared to light, neuron signals ooze along at a very slow rate, about one ten-millionth the speed of light. Consequently, to us a second of time is brief, light looks instantaneous, relativistic effects seem foreign, and time appears to be independent of space.

Gravitation is geometry. That is why no one has ever felt a force of gravity. Like the centrifugal force, it never did exist. A force of gravity was the glue Newton invented to make his naïve, Euclidean, space-plus-time model of the universe approximate reality. Newton himself was well aware of the unsatisfactory nature of several of his assumptions, far more so than most people who came after him.

When you release a coin from your hand, you see the coin "fall" because the contact force of the ground on your feet (the *only* force you feel) accelerates you the other way. An orbiting astronaut experiences no such force, so he or she remains beside a released coin. Orbital motion could not be simpler—*no* forces are involved.

What would Milton have written had he been familiar with the conjectures of Newton and Einstein?

(1) Brief descriptions of tides in the Newtonian context (without invoking the obfuscating centrifugal force!) and in the context of the general theory of relativity appear on pp. 177 and 181, respectively.

SOME ASTRONOMICAL AND PHYSICAL DATA
BY ROY BISHOP

Many of the numbers listed below are based on measurement. Exceptions include defined quantities (indicated by ≡), quantities calculated from defined quantities (e.g. m/ly, au/pc), and numbers of mathematical origin such as π and conversion factors in angular measure. Of those based on measurement, some are known to only approximate precision and the equal sign is reduced to ≈. Many others are known to quite high precision (the uncertainties occur after the last digit given), and several are from "the 2006 CODATA recommended values of the fundamental physical constants" (see physics.nist.gov/cuu/Constants/index.html). The units (Système International (SI) where possible), symbols, and nomenclature are based on recommendations of the International Astronomical Union and the International Union of Pure and Applied Physics.

LENGTH

1 metre (m) = the distance travelled by light in a vacuum in $(299\,792\,458)^{-1}$ s
1 astronomical unit (au) = $1.495\,978\,715 \times 10^{11}$ m = 499.004 786 4 light-s
1 light-year (ly) = $9.460\,536 \times 10^{15}$ m (based on average Gregorian year)
  = 63 239.8 au (63 360 inches = 1 mile)
1 parsec (pc) = $3.085\,678 \times 10^{16}$ m = 206 264.8 au = 3.261 631 ly
1 mile* ≡ 1.609 344 km
1 micron* ≡ 1 μm *Indicates deprecated unit;
1 angstrom* ≡ 0.1 nm unit on right is preferred

TIME

1 second (s) ≡ 9 192 631 770 periods of the radiation involved in the transition
  between the two hyperfine levels of the ground state of the ^{133}Cs
  atom at mean sea level

Day: Mean sidereal (equinox to equinox) = 86 164.0914 s
  Mean rotation (fixed star to fixed star) = 86 164.0998 s
  Day (d) ≡ 86 400. s
  Mean solar = 86 400.0009 s

Month: Draconic (node to node) = 27.212 221 d
  Tropical (equinox to equinox) = 27.321 582 d
  Sidereal (fixed star to fixed star) = 27.321 662 d
  Anomalistic (perigee to perigee) = 27.554 550 d
  Synodic (new Moon to new Moon) = 29.530 589 d

Year: Eclipse (lunar node to lunar node) = 346.620 075 d
  Tropical (equinox to equinox) (a) = 365.242 190 d
  Average Gregorian ≡ 365.242 5 d
  Average Julian ≡ 365.25 d
  Sidereal (fixed star to fixed star) = 365.256 363 d
  Anomalistic (perihelion to perihelion) = 365.259 635 d

EARTH

Mass, M_E = 5.972×10^{24} kg Age ≈ 4.6 Ga Central T ≈ 5000 K to 6000 K
Geocentric gravitational constant, GM_E = $3.986\,004\,42 \times 10^{14}$ m³/s²
Radius: Equatorial, a = 6378.14 km Polar, b = 6356.75 km
  Mean = $(a^2b)^{1/3}$ = 6371.00 km Of metallic core = 3475 km
Solar parallax = 8.794 143″ (Earth equatorial radius ÷ 1 au)
1° of latitude = 111.132 95 − 0.559 82 cos 2ϕ + 0.001 17 cos 4ϕ km (at latitude ϕ)
1° of longitude = 111.412 88 cos ϕ − 0.093 50 cos 3ϕ + 0.000 12 cos 5ϕ km

1 knot = 1 nautical mile ($\approx 1'$ of latitude) per hour $\equiv$ 1.852 km/h = 0.51444 m/s
Distance of sea horizon for eye h metres above sea level
  (allowing for refraction) $\approx 3.9h^{1/2}$ km $\approx 2.1h^{1/2}$ nautical miles
Atmospheric pressure: 1 atm $\equiv$ 101.325 kPa (There is $\approx$ 1 kg of air above 1 cm^2.)
Density of air at sea level (1 atm, 20 °C) = 1.2 kg/m^3
Values of atmospheric refraction for various elevations (assuming 1 atm, 10 °C):
  90°: 0′; 44°: 1′; 26°: 2′; 18°: 3′; 11°: 5′; 6°: 8′; 4°: 12′; 2°: 18′; 0°: 34′
Speed of sound in standard atmosphere = 331 m/s $\approx$ 1 km/3 s $\approx 10^{-6}\,c$
Magnetic field at surface $\approx 5 \times 10^{-5}$ T (**B** field comes out of a N-seeking pole)
Magnetic poles: 83°N, 115°W; 65°S, 138°E (as of 2005)
Standard acceleration of gravity $\equiv$ 9.806 65 m/s^2
Meteoritic flux $\approx 1 \times 10^{-15}$ kg/(m^{2}s) $\approx 10^4$ t/a over entire Earth
Obliquity of ecliptic = 23.4393° (2000.0)   Constant of aberration = 20.495 52″
Annual general precession = −50.29″ (2000.0); Precession period $\approx$ 25 800 a
Escape speed from Earth = 11.2 km/s   Mean orbital speed = 29.786 km/s
Escape speed at 1 au from Sun = 42.1 km/s ($= \sqrt{2} \times$ orbital speed)

SUN

Mass = 1.9891 $\times 10^{30}$ kg   Radius = 696 265 km   Eff. Temp. $\approx$ 5780 K
Output: Power = 3.85 $\times 10^{26}$ W, M_{bol} = 4.79
         Luminous intensity = 2.84 $\times 10^{27}$ cd, M_v = 4.82
At 1 au outside Earth's atmosphere:
         Energy flux = 1.37 kW/m^2, m_{bol} = −26.78
         Illuminance = 1.27 $\times 10^5$ lx, m_v = −26.75
Inclination of the solar equator on the ecliptic of date = 7.25°
Longitude of ascending node of the solar equator on the ecliptic of date = 76°
Period of rotation at equator $\equiv$ 25.38 d (sidereal), 27.2753 d (mean synodic)
Solar wind speed near Earth $\approx$ 450 km/s (travel time, Sun to Earth $\approx$ 4 d)
Solar velocity = 19.4 km/s toward α = 18.07h, δ = +30° (solar apex)
Location in Milky Way Galaxy: $\approx$ 27 kly from centre, $\approx$ 50 ly N of galactic
  plane, on the inner edge of the Orion arm

MILKY WAY GALAXY

Mass $\approx 10^{12}$ solar masses   Diameter $\approx$ 300 kly (including the galactic halo)
Centre: α = 17h 45.7m, δ = −29°00′; N pole: α = 12h 51m, δ = 27°08′ (2000.0)
Rotation speed at Sun $\approx$ 230 km/s, period $\approx$ 200 Ma
Velocity relative to 3 K background radiation $\approx$ 400 km/s toward $\alpha \approx$ 14h, $\delta \approx$ −30°

CONSTANTS

Speed of light, $c \equiv$ 299 792 458 m/s (This, in effect, defines the metre.)
Planck's constant, h = 6.626 069 $\times 10^{-34}$ J·s = 4.135 667 $\times 10^{-15}$ eV·s
Gravitational constant, G = 6.674 $\times 10^{-11}$ N·m^2/kg^2
Elementary charge, e = 1.602 176 $\times 10^{-19}$ C
Constant in Coulomb's law $\equiv 10^{-7}\,c^2$ (SI units) (This defines the coulomb.)
Avogadro constant, N_A = 6.022 142 $\times 10^{26}$ kmol^{-1}
Boltzmann constant, k = 1.380 65 $\times 10^{-23}$ J/K = 8.617 $\times 10^{-5}$ eV/K $\approx$ 1 eV/10^{4}K
Stefan-Boltzmann constant, σ = 5.6704 $\times 10^{-8}$ W/(m^{2}K^4)
Wien's Law: $\lambda_m T$ = 2.8978 $\times 10^{-3}$ m·K (per dλ)
Hubble constant, H = 70 ± 1 km/(s·Mpc)   Age of universe = 13.7 ± 0.1 Ga
−273.15 °C (degree Celsius) = 0 K (kelvin) (lowest thermodynamic temperature)
Volume of ideal gas at 0 °C, 101.325 kPa = 22.4140 m^3/kmol
Water: fusion at 0 °C: 0.333 MJ/kg   vapourization at 100 °C: 2.26 MJ/kg
        specific heat and density (near 20 °C): 4.18 kJ/(kg·C°) and 1.00 t/m^3
        surface tension (near 20 °C): 0.073 N/m

MASS AND ENERGY

Mass is a measure of sluggishness of response to a net force. (SI unit: kg)
Weight ($\neq$ mass) is the force required to support a body. (SI unit: N)
(1 pound-mass* = 0.453 59 kg) (1 pound-force* = 4.4482 N)

1 kilogram (kg) $\equiv$ mass of a platinum-iridium cylinder stored in Paris, France
1 atomic mass unit (u) $\equiv$ 1/12 of the mass of an atom of ^{12}C
$$= 1.660\,539 \times 10^{-27} \text{ kg} = N_A^{-1} = 931.4940 \text{ MeV}$$

1 joule (J) $\equiv$ work done by a force of 1 N acting through a distance of 1 m
$\approx$ the kinetic energy gained by this Handbook in falling freely 0.3 m
1 electron-volt (eV) $\equiv$ the kinetic energy gained by a particle carrying one unit
of elementary electrical charge (e) in falling through an
electrical potential difference of one volt (V)
$$= 1.602\,176 \times 10^{-19} \text{ J}$$

Electron mass $= 9.109\,38 \times 10^{-31}$ kg $= 548.579\,91$ μu $= 0.510\,998\,9$ MeV
Proton mass $= 1.672\,622 \times 10^{-27}$ kg $= 1.007\,276\,467$ u $= 938.2720$ MeV
Neutron mass $= 1.674\,927 \times 10^{-27}$ kg $= 1.008\,664\,916$ u $= 939.565$ MeV

Some atomic masses: ^1H (1.007 825 u) ^2H (2.014 102 u) ^4He (4.002 603 u)

Thermochemical calorie* (cal) $= 4.184$ J
1 erg*/s $= 10^{-7}$ J/s $= 10^{-7}$ W
1 BTU*/h $= 1054.35$ J/h $= 0.292\,88$ W   *Indicates deprecated unit;
1 horsepower* $= 745.7$ W   unit on right is preferred.
1 eV per event $= 23\,060$ cal/mol
$C + O_2 \rightarrow CO_2 + 4.1$ eV $4\,^1H \rightarrow {}^4He + 26.73$ MeV

Highest cosmic-ray energy (carried by protons) $\approx 10^{20}$ eV
Power output (average) of an adult human ≈ 100 W
1 kg of TNT or milkshake releases 4.2 MJ ≈ 1000 kcal ≈ 1 kWh
Fuel oil: 6.36 GJ/barrel (1 barrel $\equiv$ 42 U.S. gallons = 35.0 Imp. gallons = 159 L)

Relation between rest mass (m), linear momentum (p), total energy (E), kinetic
energy (KE), and $\gamma \equiv (1 - v^2/c^2)^{-0.5}$, where c is the speed of light and v is the
speed of the object: $E = \gamma mc^2 = mc^2 + KE = [(mc^2)^2 + (pc)^2]^{0.5}$

MAGNITUDE RELATIONS (See also p. 54 and 59.)

Log of light intensity ratio $\equiv 0.4$ times magnitude difference
Distance modulus $(D) \equiv$ apparent magnitude (m) – absolute magnitude (M)
Log of distance in ly $= 0.2\,D + 1.513\,435$ (neglecting absorption)
Magnitude of sum of magnitudes m_i is equal to $-2.5 \log \Sigma_i\, 10^{-0.4 m_i}$

Moon's apparent visual magnitude at phase angle P degrees (0° = full Moon)
when at its average distance from Earth: $-12.7 + 0.026\,|P| + (4 \times 10^{-9})\,P^4$

A light source of apparent visual magnitude m provides an illuminance
E (lux) where $E = 10^{-0.4\,(m + 13.99)}$ or $m = -13.99 - 2.5 \log E$
A diffuse (matte) surface with albedo A subject to illuminance E (lux) will have
luminance L (visual surface brightness): $L = AE \div \pi$ (cd/m^2)
To convert luminance S (magnitude/arcsecond^2) to luminance L (cd/m^2):
$L = 10^{0.4(12.59-S)}$ or $S = 12.59 - 2.5 \log L$

DOPPLER RELATIONS FOR LIGHT

$\alpha \equiv$ angle between velocity of source and line from source to observer
$\beta \equiv v/c$ $\gamma \equiv (1 - \beta^2)^{-0.5}$
Frequency: $f = f_0\,\gamma^{-1}(1 - \beta \cos \alpha)^{-1}$ $z \equiv (\lambda - \lambda_0)/\lambda_0 = \gamma\,(1 - \beta \cos \alpha) - 1$
For $\alpha = \pi$ radians: $z = (1 + \beta)^{0.5}(1 - \beta)^{-0.5} - 1$ ($\approx \beta$ if $\beta << 1$)
$\beta = [(1 + z)^2 - 1][(1 + z)^2 + 1]^{-1}$

OPTICAL WAVELENGTH DATA

Bright-adapted (photopic) visible range ≈ 400 – 750 nm ($L \approx 0.005 - 10^5$ cd/m^2)
Dark-adapted (scotopic) visible range ≈ 400 – 620 nm ($L \approx 1 - 5000$ μcd/m^2)
Wavelength of peak sensitivity of eye: ≈ 555 nm (photopic), 507 nm (scotopic)
Mechanical equivalent of light: 1 lm ≡ 1/683 W at 540 THz ($\lambda \approx 555$ nm)
   i.e. 1.46 W/klm (A 60-W incandescent light bulb emits about 1 klm = 1000 lm.
     Compared to an optimum light source that delivers all its energy as light
     at 540 THz, a 60-W incandescent light bulb is 1.46/60 ≈ 2.4% efficient.)
Colours (representative wavelength, nm):
  violet (420), blue (470), green (530), yellow (580), orange (610), red (660)

Some useful wavelengths (element, spectral designation or colour and/or
(Fraunhofer line)):

H Lyman α	121.6 nm	N_2^+ blue†	465.2	Hg yellow	579.1
Ca (K solar)	393.4	Hβ (F solar)*	486.1	Na (D_2 solar)	589.0
Ca (H solar)	396.8	O^{++} green*	495.9	Na (D_1 solar)	589.6
Hg violet	404.7	O^{++} green*	500.7	O red†	630.0
Hδ (h solar)	410.2	Hg green	546.1	He-Ne laser	632.8
Hγ (g solar)	434.0	O yel.-green†	557.7	O red†	636.4
Hg deep blue	435.8	Hg yellow	577.0	Hα (C solar)	656.3

* Strong contributor to the visual light of gaseous nebulae
† Strong auroral lines

ANGULAR RELATIONS

2π radians = 360°   π = 3.141 592 653 589 793 2… ≈ $(113 \div 355)^{-1}$
Number of square degrees on a sphere = 41 253

For 360° = 24 h, 15° = 1 h, 15′ = 1 min, 15″ = 1 s (Earth turns 360° in 86 164.1 s)

Relations between sidereal time t, right ascension α, hour angle h, declination δ,
azimuth A (measured east of north), altitude a, and latitude φ:

$h = t - α$
$\sin a = \sin δ \sin φ + \cos h \cos δ \cos φ$
$\cos δ \sin h = -\cos a \sin A$
$\sin δ = \sin a \sin φ + \cos a \cos A \cos φ$

Annual precession in α ≈ 3.0750 + 1.3362 sin α tan δ seconds   (α must be
Annual precession in δ ≈ 20.043″ cos α   in degrees)

SOME SI SYMBOLS AND PREFIXES

m	metre	N	newton (kg·m/s^2)	a	atto	10^{-18}
kg	kilogram	J	joule (N·m)	f	femto	10^{-15}
s	second	W	watt (J/s)	p	pico	10^{-12}
min	minute	Pa	pascal (N/m^2)	n	nano	10^{-9}
h	hour	t	tonne (10^3 kg)	μ	micro	10^{-6}
d	day	L	litre (10^{-3} m^3)	m	milli	10^{-3}
a	year	Hz	hertz (s^{-1})	c	centi	10^{-2}
A	ampere	C	coulomb (A·s)	h	hecto	10^2
rad	radian	V	volt (J/C)	k	kilo	10^3
mas	milliarcsecond	Wb	weber (V·s)	M	mega	10^6
sr	steradian	T	tesla (Wb/m^2)	G	giga	10^9
K	kelvin (temperature)	lm	lumen	T	tera	10^{12}
ha	hectare (10^4 m^2)	cd	candela (lm/sr)	P	peta	10^{15}
b	barn (10^{-28} m^2)	lx	lux (lm/m^2)	E	exa	10^{18}

THE ELECTROMAGNETIC SPECTRUM
By Roy Bishop

The Scottish physicist James Clerk Maxwell (1831–1879) was the first to understand the nature of light. In 1865, with elegant mathematics, Maxwell predicted that light is a self-sustaining electromagnetic wave, a quivering linkage of electric and magnetic fields in which a changing electric field generates a magnetic field, and vice versa, sustaining each other as they travel at a prodigious speed.

Four decades later Albert Einstein (1879–1955) revealed three more remarkable properties of light: (1) unlike water waves and sound waves, electromagnetic waves require no medium whatsoever in which to travel; (2) the speed of electromagnetic waves is the same for all observers, irrespective of any motion of the source of the waves; (3) when electromagnetic waves interact with matter, they do so as if composed of discrete particles, photons, whose individual energy E is proportional to the frequency f of the wave: $E = hf$, where h is Planck's constant (see p. 34).

The product of wavelength λ and wave frequency is the speed of a wave: $\lambda f = c$, where c is the usual symbol for the speed of an electromagnetic wave. The frequency (or photon energy, or wavelength) range of electromagnetic waves is unlimited, but our eyes see only a very narrow slice of this spectrum. Vision has a range of less than an octave, $\lambda \sim 400$ to 750 nm (see p. 36). We are almost blind! Nevertheless, once the physics was understood, the technologies to generate and detect all parts of the electromagnetic spectrum were soon developed. The first step in this direction occurred prior to Maxwell's work, in 1800 when astronomer Sir William Herschel (1738–1822) discovered *infrared* radiation beyond the red end of the visible spectrum.

The diagram at the end of this article summarizes the electromagnetic spectrum. The various named parts of the spectrum overlap to some extent. One part is defined by the source of the radiation rather than by wavelength or photon energy: *gamma rays* refer to electromagnetic radiation emitted by radioactive atomic nuclei. *X-rays* overlap with gamma rays but are produced by sources other than atomic nuclei — an arbitrary distinction based on the historical origins of these two terms. A detector defines another part of the spectrum: *light* is usually restricted to human vision, although occasionally this term is extended to include the adjacent *ultraviolet* portion of the spectrum.

The importance of the particle aspect at high frequencies and of the wave aspect at low frequencies is implied by the names; for instance, gamma **rays** and radio **waves.** Photon energy, not wavelength, dominates the behaviour of gamma rays. At the other end of the spectrum, the energy of individual photons is very small, obscuring the granular nature of the radiation, and frequency is usually the measured characteristic of the radiation. Vision operates between these two extremes where *both* particle and wave properties play significant roles. Events in the retina are triggered by individual photons, and wave diffraction is relevant for minimum eye pupil size and the spacing of retinal photoreceptors. For the infrared and microwave regions, wavelength has a convenient range and is usually cited. The transition across the spectrum from photon through wavelength to frequency domination is indicated in the diagram by the range of the units on the left side of each of the three scales.

Photon energy determines how electromagnetic radiation interacts with matter. Chemistry and biology involve changes in atomic and molecular structure, the energies involved being typically a few *electron-volts* (eV) per reaction (see p. 35). Retinal photochemistry operates over a very limited energy range, and thereby determines the narrow visual window on the electromagnetic spectrum. For $\lambda > 750$ nm, the photon energy is insufficient (<1.6 eV) to alter the structure of light-sensing

protein molecules in the retina, so we cannot see the infrared. For λ < 400 nm, the photon energy is high enough (>3.1 eV) to damage these delicate molecules; however, the cornea and lens of the eye absorb that radiation before it can reach the retina. Thus we cannot see the ultraviolet.

Although the energy of an infrared photon is too weak to stimulate vision, infrared photons are readily absorbed by many types of molecules, such as water, causing the molecules to move more rapidly, thereby increasing the temperature of the substance. In this manner, infrared radiation from the Sun, a fire, or a hot stove warms us. Hence infrared is often called heat radiation, although it is *not* heat that is being radiated. The heating is a secondary effect, generated in our bodies subsequent to the absorption of the photons.

Confusion of sensation with electromagnetic radiation also occurs with visible light. For instance, almost invariably we speak of colours as if they were a property of light, or of the bodies emitting the light, rather than being indescribable hue sensations arising in the brain. As Sir Isaac Newton cautioned us three centuries ago: "The rays, to speak properly, are not coloured." The light reflected by a leaf is not green, and neither is the leaf; green exists only in the neuron-based representation of the leaf in the observer's consciousness, and then only if the light is not too dim. The electromagnetic radiation from a leaf is characterized by a particular spatial and spectral distribution of radiant power. A CCD or CMOS chip finds only photons. It is we who create the colour and the brightness. The distinction between our internal visual world and the external physical world is profound but rarely appreciated. It is the distinction between how the world *looks* to us, and how it *is*.

Visual perception aside, what *is* light, a wave or a particle? Light travels like a wave (Maxwell was right) and interacts like a particle (Einstein was right). A detector finds photons, but *where* the detector finds photons is determined by a wave. When a typical backyard telescope is aimed at an average star in the night sky, at any instant there is seldom more than one photon from that star in transit through the telescope. Yet the distribution of light in the star's image at the focal plane is determined by an aperture-filling wave. In the case of a Newtonian telescope with a four-vane spider support for the secondary mirror, in some real sense, each photon passes through all four quadrants of the spider. But it is not that the spider quarters the hapless photon like a cleaver quarters a steak in a butcher shop; whole photons, not quartered photons arrive at the detector. The message of physics revealed during the first half of the last century is that it is simply *wrong* to speak of the path of a photon while in transit to a detector. Light is queerer than we can imagine. Matter is equally queer, for it too displays a wave-particle duality, a duality that is particularly obvious on the subatomic scale. Just as it is wrong to speak of the path of a photon, it is wrong to speak of the path of an electron in an atom—as if, for example, it were in orbit about the nucleus. The wave-particle puzzle is of our own making, for we try to apply naïve concepts abstracted from crude sensory experiences on the macroscopic scale of everyday life to the subatomic world. Pure waves or pure particles never did exist. Reality is more mysterious.

Despite the strange behaviour of electromagnetic radiation, we know how to describe its interaction with matter quantitatively and with astounding accuracy. The theory encompasses the work of Maxwell and Einstein, and was completed in the mid-20th century by Richard Feynman (1918–1988) and Julian Schwinger (1918–1994) of the United States, and Sin-Itiro Tomonaga (1906–1979) of Japan, for which they shared the Nobel Prize in Physics in 1965. The theory is called quantum electrodynamics. With the exception of gravitation and things that go on inside atomic nuclei, quantum electrodynamics appears to describe all phenomena in the physical world— in principle, if not in actuality, in the case of complex systems because of complexity.

THE ELECTROMAGNETIC SPECTRUM

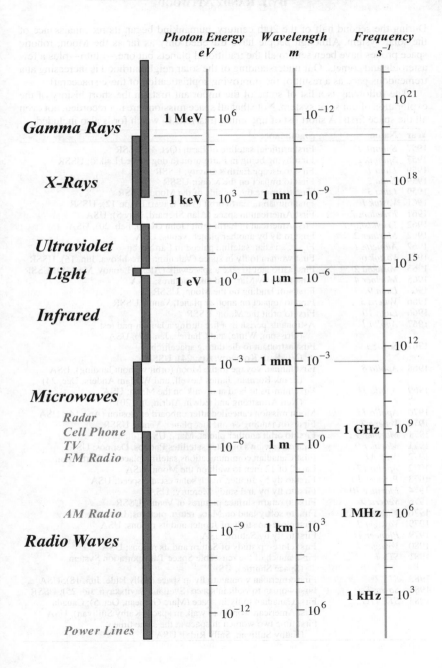

	Photon Energy eV	Wavelength m	Frequency s^{-1}

Gamma Rays — 1 MeV — 10^6 — 10^{-12} — 10^{21}

X-Rays — 1 keV — 10^3 — 1 nm — 10^{-9} — 10^{18}

Ultraviolet

Light — 1 eV — 10^0 — 1 μm — 10^{-6} — 10^{15}

Infrared — 10^{-3} — 1 mm — 10^{-3} — 10^{12}

Microwaves
Radar
Cell Phone — 1 GHz — 10^9
TV — 10^{-6} — 1 m — 10^0
FM Radio

AM Radio — 1 MHz — 10^6

Radio Waves — 10^{-9} — 1 km — 10^3

— 1 kHz — 10^3

Power Lines — 10^{-12} — 10^6

VOYAGES IN OUR SOLAR SYSTEM
BY J. RANDY ATTWOOD

During the second half of the 20th century, humankind began its reconnaissance of the solar system. Although people have travelled only as far as the Moon, robotic space probes have been sent to all the traditional planets but one—Pluto—plus a few asteroids and comets. Our understanding of the solar neighbourhood is increasing at a tremendous pace as a result of the improving sophistication of these spacecraft.

The following is a list of some of the important firsts in the short history of the exploration of our solar system. Note that all space missions are not recorded, not even all the space firsts. A short list of upcoming missions to watch for is also included.

Year	Name	Significance
1957	Sputnik 1	First artificial satellite of Earth (Oct. 4); USSR
1957	Sputnik 2	First living being in Earth orbit (a dog named Laika); USSR
1959	Luna 1	First to escape Earth's gravity; USSR
1959	Luna 2	First to impact on the Moon; USSR
1959	Luna 3	First to image the far side of the Moon; USSR
1961	Vostok 1	First human in Earth orbit (Yuri Gagarin, Apr. 12); USSR
1961	Freedom 7	First American in space (Alan Shepard, May 5); USA
1962	Friendship 7	First American in Earth orbit (John Glenn, Feb. 20); USA
1962	Mariner 2	First to fly by another planet, Venus; USA
1962	Alouette 1	First Canadian satellite palced in Earth orbit
1963	Vostok 6	First woman to fly in space (Valentina Tereshkova, Jun. 16); USSR
1965	Voshkod 2	First astronaut to take a spacewalk (Alexei Leonov, Mar. 18); USSR
1965	Mariner 4	First to fly by Mars and take pictures; USA
1966	Luna 9	First soft landing on the Moon; USSR
1966	Venera 3	First to impact on another planet, Venus; USSR
1966	Luna 10	First to orbit the Moon; USSR
1967	Apollo 1	Astronauts perish in a fire during a launch-pad test (Grissom, White, and Chaffee, Jan. 27); USA
1967	Soyuz 1	First astronaut to die during spaceflight (Vladimir Komarov, Apr. 24); USSR
1968	Apollo 8	First human voyage to the Moon (orbit without landing); USA (Frank Borman, James Lovell, and William Anders, Dec. 24)
1969	Apollo 11	First humans to land and walk on the Moon; USA (Neil Armstrong and Edwin Aldrin, Jul. 20)
1970	Apollo 13	Moon mission cancelled after onboard explosion (Apr. 14); USA
1970	Venera 7	First soft landing on another planet, Venus; USSR
1971	Mariner 9	First to orbit another planet, Mars; USA
1971	Mariner 9	First close views of outer satellites Phobos, Deimos; USA
1972	Anik A1	First Canadian communications satellite placed in Earth orbit
1972	Apollo 17	Last 2 of 12 men to walk on the Moon; USA
1973	Pioneer 10	First to fly by Jupiter, reach solar escape speed; USA
1974	Mariner 10	First to fly by and study Mercury; USA
1975	Venera 9	First to return surface pictures of Venus; USSR
1976	Viking 1	First to softly land on Mars, return pictures; USA
1979	Voyager 1	First close-up study of Jupiter and its moons; USA
1979	Pioneer 11	First to fly by Saturn; USA
1980	Voyager 1	First close-up study of Saturn and its moons; USA
1981	STS 1	First launch of the reuseable Space Transportation System (Space Shuttle); USA
1983	STS 7	First American woman to fly in space (Sally Ride, Jun. 18); USA
1984	Soyuz T-7	First woman to walk in space (Svetlana Savitskaya, Jul. 25); USSR
1984	STS 41G	First Canadian to fly in space (Marc Garneau, Oct. 5); Canada
	"	First American woman to walk in space (Kathy Sullivan); USA
	"	First time two women in space at the same time (Kathy Sullivan, Sally Ride); USA

Year	Name	Significance
1985	*International Cometary Explorer (ICE)*	
		First to study a comet; USA
1986	*Voyager 2*	First close-up study of Uranus and its moons; USA
1986	*Challenger*	First American astronauts to die during spaceflight (Jan. 28); USA
1986	*Giotto*	First images taken of a comet nucleus, Halley; ESA
1989	*Voyager 2*	First close-up study of Neptune and its moons; USA
1990	*Hubble*	Launch of the *Hubble Space Telescope*; USA
1991	*Galileo*	First flyby, close-up photos of an asteroid, 951 Gaspra; USA
1992	*STS 42*	First Canadian woman to fly in space
		(Roberta Bondar, Jan. 22); Canada
1994/95		Longest single spaceflight–437 days in Earth orbit
		(Valeri Polyakov); USSR
1995	*Ulysses*	First fly above the Sun's south/north poles; ESA
1995	*Galileo*	First probe into Jupiter's atmosphere; USA
1996	*Galileo*	First to orbit Jupiter; USA
2001	*Soyuz TM-32*	First private citizen to pay for a spaceflight (Denis Tito)
2001	*NEAR Shoemaker*	First to orbit and soft land on an asteroid, Eros; USA
2003	*Columbia*	Second Space Shuttle disaster; crew of 7 lost (Feb. 1); USA
2003	*MOST*	First Canadian space telescope launched into Earth orbit; Canada
2003	*Shenzhou V*	First Chinese taikonaut to orbit the Earth (Yang Liwei); China
2004	*Mars Rovers*	First long-range surface exploration of Mars; USA
2004	*Stardust*	First collection and return of cometary material, Wild 2; USA
2004	*Cassini*	First to orbit Saturn; USA
2005	*Huygens*	First to land on Titan; USA/ESA
2005	*Deep Impact*	First to impact on and study the interior of a comet, Tempel 1; USA
2008	*Mars Phoenix*	First spacecraft to examine Martian soil in the arctic regions,
		discovered water ice; USA
2009	*ISS*	Most people in space at one time—13 (Expedition 20/21 and
		STS 127), including two Canadians (Robert Thirsk, Julie Payette)
2010	*Hayabusa*	First asteroid-sample return mission; Japan (rendezvous completed
		in 2005, return delayed until 2010 due to spacecraft problems)
2010		Total number of people who have been in space: 513 (as of Sep. 2010)
2011	*Atlantis**	135th and last scheduled Space Shuttle flight (tentative)
2011	*NEOSSat**	First satellite to look for near-Earth asteroids on a potential
		collision course with Earth; Canada
2011	*Dawn*	First spacecraft to orbit two asteroids (Vesta and Ceres in 2015); USA
2011	*Messenger*	First spacecraft to orbit and study Mercury; USA
2012	*Curiosity**	First nuclear-powered rover/science laboratory on Mars; USA
2014	*Rosetta*	First to orbit, soft land on a comet; ESA
2014	*JWST**	Launch of the *James Webb Space Telescope*; USA/ESA
2015	*New Horizons*	First to fly by Pluto, its moons, Kuiper belt objects (2016–2020); USA
2016	*Juno**	First mission to study Jupiter from a polar orbit; USA

*Mission not yet launched

TABLE OF PRECESSION FOR ADVANCING 50 YEARS

RA for Dec – (h m)	RA for Dec + (h m)	Prec in Dec (′)	Precession in right ascension for declination in row immediately below											Prec in Dec (′)	RA for Dec + (h m)	RA for Dec – (h m)
			85° (m)	80° (m)	75° (m)	70° (m)	60° (m)	50° (m)	40° (m)	30° (m)	20° (m)	10° (m)	0° (m)			
12 00	0 00	16.7	2.56	2.56	2.56	2.56	2.56	2.56	2.56	2.56	2.56	2.56	2.56	-16.7	12 00	24 00
12 30	0 30	16.6	4.22	3.39	3.10	2.96	2.81	2.73	2.68	2.64	2.61	2.59	2.56	-16.6	11 30	23 30
13 00	1 00	16.1	5.85	4.20	3.64	3.35	3.06	2.90	2.80	2.73	2.67	2.61	2.56	-16.1	11 00	23 00
13 30	1 30	15.4	7.43	4.98	4.15	3.73	3.30	3.07	2.92	2.81	2.72	2.64	2.56	-15.4	10 30	22 30
14 00	2 00	14.5	8.92	5.72	4.64	4.09	3.53	3.22	3.03	2.88	2.76	2.66	2.56	-14.5	10 00	22 00
14 30	2 30	13.3	10.31	6.41	5.09	4.42	3.73	3.37	3.13	2.95	2.81	2.68	2.56	-13.3	9 30	21 30
15 00	3 00	11.8	11.56	7.03	5.50	4.72	3.92	3.50	3.22	3.02	2.85	2.70	2.56	-11.8	9 00	21 00
15 30	3 30	10.2	12.66	7.57	5.86	4.99	4.09	3.61	3.30	3.07	2.88	2.72	2.56	-10.2	8 30	20 30
16 00	4 00	8.4	13.58	8.03	6.16	5.21	4.23	3.71	3.37	3.12	2.91	2.73	2.56	-8.4	8 00	20 00
16 30	4 30	6.4	14.32	8.40	6.40	5.39	4.34	3.79	3.42	3.15	2.94	2.74	2.56	-6.4	7 30	19 30
17 00	5 00	4.3	14.85	8.66	6.57	5.52	4.42	3.84	3.46	3.18	2.95	2.75	2.56	-4.3	7 00	19 00
17 30	5 30	2.2	15.18	8.82	6.68	5.59	4.47	3.88	3.49	3.20	2.96	2.76	2.56	-2.2	6 30	18 30
18 00	6 00	0.0	15.29	8.88	6.72	5.62	4.49	3.89	3.50	3.20	2.97	2.76	2.56	0.0	6 00	18 00
0 00	12 00	-16.7	2.56	2.56	2.56	2.56	2.56	2.56	2.56	2.56	2.56	2.56	2.56	16.7	24 00	12 00
0 30	12 30	-16.6	0.90	1.74	2.02	2.16	2.31	2.39	2.44	2.48	2.51	2.54	2.56	16.6	23 30	11 30
1 00	13 00	-16.1	-0.73	0.93	1.49	1.77	2.06	2.22	2.32	2.39	2.46	2.51	2.56	16.1	23 00	11 00
1 30	13 30	-15.4	-2.31	0.14	0.97	1.39	1.82	2.05	2.20	2.31	2.41	2.49	2.56	15.4	22 30	10 30
2 00	14 00	-14.5	-3.80	-0.60	0.48	1.03	1.60	1.90	2.09	2.24	2.36	2.46	2.56	14.5	22 00	10 00
2 30	14 30	-13.3	-5.19	-1.28	0.03	0.70	1.39	1.75	1.99	2.17	2.31	2.44	2.56	13.3	21 30	9 30
3 00	15 00	-11.8	-6.44	-1.90	-0.38	0.40	1.20	1.62	1.90	2.11	2.27	2.42	2.56	11.8	21 00	9 00
3 30	15 30	-10.2	-7.54	-2.45	-0.74	0.13	1.03	1.51	1.82	2.05	2.24	2.41	2.56	10.2	20 30	8 30
4 00	16 00	-8.4	-8.46	-2.91	-1.04	-0.09	0.89	1.41	1.75	2.00	2.21	2.39	2.56	8.4	20 00	8 00
4 30	16 30	-6.4	-9.20	-3.27	-1.28	-0.27	0.78	1.33	1.70	1.97	2.19	2.38	2.56	6.4	19 30	7 30
5 00	17 00	-4.3	-9.73	-3.54	-1.45	-0.39	0.70	1.28	1.66	1.94	2.17	2.37	2.56	4.3	19 00	7 00
5 30	17 30	-2.2	-10.06	-3.70	-1.56	-0.47	0.65	1.25	1.63	1.92	2.16	2.37	2.56	2.2	18 30	6 30
6 00	18 00	0.0	-10.17	-3.75	-1.59	-0.50	0.63	1.23	1.63	1.92	2.16	2.36	2.56	0.0	18 00	6 00

If declination is positive, use inner RA scale; *if declination is negative, use outer RA scale and reverse the sign of the precession in declination.*
To avoid interpolation in this table, which becomes increasingly inaccurate for large |Dec|, precession formulae may be used (see p. 36).

TIME

TIME AND TIME SCALES
By Roy Bishop

Time has been said to be nature's way of keeping everything from happening at once. In 1687, Sir Isaac Newton (1642–1727) perceived time as being separate from and more fundamental than the spinning of changeable planets or the oily mechanisms of clocks: "Absolute, true, and mathematical time, of itself, and from its own nature flows equably without regard to anything external." This is the common sense or intuitive view most people have of time.

Albert Einstein (1879–1955) was the first to understand that time is but an abstraction that does not exist independently of clocks. In his special theory of relativity (1905) Einstein predicted that clocks moving relative to an observer run slower. This is called time dilation or the second-order Doppler effect. For example, relative to a clock fixed beside a road the wristwatch of a person driving past at a speed of 100 km/h loses 0.26 ps per minute (ps = picosecond = 10^{-12} s; see p. 36). A decade later, in his theory of gravitation, the general theory of relativity, Einstein predicted that clocks lower or higher than the observer in a gravitational field run slower or faster, respectively, than the observer's clock. In the case of a lower clock this is called the gravitational redshift. For example, an alarm clock on the floor a metre below your bed loses 3.1 ps per 8-h night relative to a watch on your wrist. These counterintuitive effects are not only real, but in recent years they have found their way into the consumer marketplace in the form of GPS (Global Positioning System) receivers. These handheld units receive signals from orbiting atomic clocks and rely on programs that allow for time dilation and gravitational redshift (see *Physics Today*, May 2002, p. 41). In astronomy the general theory of relativity was mostly ignored until the last few decades of the 20th century, when increasing precision of clocks and advances in theoretical astrophysics and cosmology demanded its use.

As to understanding time, Lord Kelvin (1824–1907) said that you know a physical quantity if you can measure it. Time can indeed be measured, with mind-boggling precision. For those who feel compelled to state "We still don't know what time actually is," perhaps the mystery resides merely in the meaning of this statement.

The essence of time is that isolated material changes occur in invariant ratios one with respect to another. That is, as Sir Hermann Bondi (1919–2005) put it: "Time is that which is manufactured by clocks." Thus, to deal with time, clocks must be devised and units and time scales established. Readers who wish to pursue this topic beyond the brief overview presented here should consult *The Measurement of Time*, by C. Audoin and B. Guinot, Cambridge University Press, 2001, and the *Explanatory Supplement to the Astronomical Almanac*, by P.K. Seidelmann (ed.), University Science Books, 1992. For less-technical descriptions of many aspects of time see *A Matter of Time*, a special edition of *Scientific American* (vol. 16, no. 1, 2006) that includes ten articles from the September 2002 issue of that magazine.

Periodic Time Intervals and Clocks

There are three obvious, natural, periodic time intervals on Earth: the seasonal cycle (year), the cycle of lunar phases (month), and the day–night cycle (day). The cycle of the seasons is called the *tropical year* and contains 365.242 190 days. The cycle of lunar phases is known as the *synodic month* and equals 29.530 589 days. The average day–night (diurnal) cycle is the *mean solar day* and presently contains approximately

86 400.0009 s. Other types of year, month, and day have been defined and are listed along with brief definitions and durations on p. 33.

The problem of accurately subdividing these natural intervals to make time locally available at any moment (i.e. timekeeping) was satisfactorily solved in 1657 by Christiaan Huygens, who invented the first practical pendulum clock. Through successive refinements the pendulum clock reigned supreme for nearly three centuries, until it was surpassed in precision by the quartz oscillator in the 1940s. Within another 20 years the quartz clock was, in turn, superseded by the cesium atomic clock, which, using the technique of *laser cooling* of atomic beams (see *Physics Today*, December 1997, p. 17, February 1998, p. 21, and March 2001, p. 37), today has a precision near 2 in 10^{15} (one second in 16 million years).

Earth's Rotation and Time Scales

Of the three obvious, natural, periodic time intervals on Earth (year, month, and day), the day dominates our lives and determines the various time scales we have created. The day is caused primarily by Earth's rotation on its axis. To count rotations, a reference or fiducial point is required. Four such points are of interest, and three of these are the basis of five time scales:

(1) Earth's rotation relative to the distant stars: Although the distant stars (or better, extragalactic sources) provide a reference frame to determine the "true" period of Earth's rotation (presently about 86 164.0998 s), because of Earth's orbital motion and its rotational precession, this true period is not that of either the solar day or the RA/Dec coordinate grid used to specify astronomical positions. Hence no time scales are based on Earth's true rotational period.

(2) Earth's rotation relative to the equinox: The equator and poles of the RA/Dec celestial coordinate grid are aligned with Earth's mean equator and poles. ("Mean" denotes that small, periodic variations caused by the nutation of Earth's axis have been averaged out. Nutation involves the true pole moving relative to the mean pole with an amplitude of about 9″ and a variety of short periods up to 18.6 years.) Hence the RA/Dec grid slowly shifts relative to the distant stars as Earth's rotation axis and equator precess, a motion caused primarily by the torques exerted by the Moon and Sun on Earth's equatorial bulge. The other planets make a smaller contribution to this *precession of the equator* and also cause a *precession of the ecliptic*. The sum of these two precessions is called *general precession*. General precession causes the zero point of right ascension (the "Greenwich of the skies," the vernal equinox, or "first point of Aries") to drift westward (retrograde) along the ecliptic about 50″ per year. As a result, Earth's rotation period relative to the equinox (called the *mean sidereal day*, currently is 86 164.0914 s) is 8.4 ms shorter than the time for one rotation (see p. 33). At any longitude on Earth the RA of a star on the meridian (corrected for nutation) is the *Local Mean Sidereal Time* (**LMST**) at that instant. At the Greenwich meridian (0° longitude) this is called *Greenwich Mean Sidereal Time* (**GMST**). LMST may be used to set a telescope on an object of known right ascension. The hour angle of the object equals the sidereal time less the right ascension. LMST may be available from a sidereal clock, or it can be calculated as explained in the middle of p. 50. Because Earth makes one more rotation with respect to the other stars than it does with respect to the Sun during a year, sidereal time gains relative to time scales linked to the Sun (see below) by about 3 min 56 s per day, or 2 h per month.

(3) Earth's rotation relative to the real Sun: A common misconception is that the Sun is highest in the sky and lies on the local north–south meridian at 12:00 noon. However, time based on the position of the Sun in the sky, known as local *apparent solar time* or *sundial time*, can differ by up to an hour or more from civil time (the time that we normally use). There are two reasons for this discrepancy. One reason is

that the Sun's eastward annual apparent motion around the sky is far from uniform both because of Earth's elliptical orbit and because of the inclination of the celestial equator to the ecliptic. Thus apparent solar time does not have a uniform rate (see the next paragraph). The second reason for the difference between sundial time and civil time is addressed in the penultimate paragraph of this article.

(4) Earth's rotation relative to the mean Sun: If the Sun is replaced by a fictitious mean sun moving uniformly along the celestial equator, Earth's rotation relative to this mean sun defines *Local Mean (solar) Time* (**LMT**). Apparent solar time can differ by up to 16 min from LMT depending upon the time of year (see the diagram on p. 183). Small, periodic shifts of Earth's crust relative to the axis of rotation *(polar motion)* affect astronomical time determinations through the resulting east–west shift in the meridian at latitudes away from the equator. LMT at the Greenwich meridian (0° longitude) when corrected for this polar motion is called *Universal Time* (**UT1**, or often simply **UT**). UT1 is determined using very-long-baseline interferometry, satellite laser-ranging data, lunar laser-ranging data, and GPS data (via the International GPS Service).

All the above mean time scales (LMST, GMST, LMT, and UT1), being based upon Earth's rotation, are only as uniform as this rotation. By the mid-19th century discrepancies between theory and the observed motion of the Moon indicated that, over the long term, Earth's rotation is slowing down. However, not until clocks became better timekeepers than the spinning Earth (c. 1940, when crystal-controlled clocks exceeded precisions of 1 in 10^{10}) was it realized how complex is the variable rotation of our planet. There are (i) long-, (ii) medium-, and (iii) short-term accelerations:

(i) Over many centuries there is a *secular* slowing caused by tidal friction of about 8 parts in 10^{13} per day (i.e. the day becomes one second longer about every 40 000 years).

(ii) Over a few decades there are *random* accelerations (positive and negative), apparently caused by core–mantle interactions and possibly by changes in ocean currents. These are about 10 times larger than the tidal deceleration and thus completely obscure the latter effect over time intervals of less than a century or so.

(iii) The largest accelerations in Earth's rotation rate are short-term ones: *periodic components* are associated mainly with lunar-induced tides (over two-week and monthly intervals) and seasonal meteorological factors (over semiannual and annual intervals); *nonperiodic* (chaotic) high-frequency variations are associated mainly with the global atmospheric wind and pressure distributions. These short-term accelerations are typically one or two orders of magnitude larger again than the random, decade fluctuations on which they are superimposed (see the article by John Wahr in the June 1986 issue of *Sky & Telescope*, p. 545).

Uniform Time Scales

(1) Based on orbital motion: Although Earth's axial rotation is not sufficiently predictable to serve as a precise clock, the orbital motions of our Moon, Earth, and the other planets are predictable to high accuracy. Through the dynamical equations describing these motions plus extended astronomical observations, a uniform dynamical time scale can be derived. Such a scale, known as *Ephemeris Time* (ET), was for several years (1952–1984) the basis of astronomical ephemerides. The ephemeris second, defined in 1955 as a certain fraction of the tropical year 1900.0, was the fundamental unit of time. Early in the 20th century the UT1 and ET scales coincided, but because Earth's rotation rate has been generally slower than the ET rate, by 1984 UT1 was 54 s behind ET and was losing about half a second per year. From 1985 until 1999 Earth's rotation rate was fairly steady, losing about 0.7 s per year relative to ET (actually TT, see below). During the years 2000–2005 the rotation rate increased (part of the random decade fluctuations) such that by 2005 the annual

loss was less than 0.2 s. Beginning in 2006 an abrupt slowing occurred, doubling the annual loss.

(2) Based on atomic motion: The quantum nature of matter gives atoms a permanence and stability that macroscopic objects such as quartz crystals, planets, and pendula do not possess. The idea of an atomic clock was proposed by the Austrian–American physicist Isidor Rabi in 1945. In 1967, the second was given an atomic definition: 9 192 631 770 periods of the radiation involved in the transition between the two hyperfine levels of the ground state of the cesium 133 atom. This is known as the SI (for Système International) second (abbreviation s, *not* sec). The number 9 192 631 770 was chosen so that on the rotating geoid (i.e. for clocks fixed on Earth at mean sea level), the SI second is identical to the older ET second to within the precision of measurement.

The previous sentence implies that clocks on the geoid run at the same rate. What about Earth's rotation? Clocks nearer the equator move faster, so does time dilation not make them run slower relative to clocks at higher latitudes? Ignoring the Moon and Sun, if Earth did not rotate and had an isotropic density distribution, its geoid (mean sea-level surface) would be spherical, and clocks fixed on this geoid would, by symmetry, all run at the same rate (they would all be at rest and have similar positions in Earth's gravitational field). For a rotating Earth the equatorial bulge is such that clocks away from the poles are just enough higher in Earth's gravitational field that the resulting gravitational blueshift exactly cancels the time dilation associated with their rotational speed. This simple, elegant, and convenient result is a consequence of Einstein's principle of equivalence: A body at rest in a gravitational field is equivalent to a body being accelerated in a field-free space. As described by general relativity, gravitation is geometry, not a force, which is why no one has ever felt a force of gravity. The only force acting on Earth-based clocks, or on any stationary Earth-based objects, is the electromagnetic contact force supporting them. Any two nearby clocks located on the same surface perpendicular to the direction of this contact force (the plumb-bob direction) will have identical rates. Thus *all* clocks on the geoid run at the same rate. Whether or not the planet beneath is rotating is immaterial.

Five SI-second-based time scales are in use today. One of these (UTC) merely differs an integal number of seconds from one of the other four and is described in the last section. The fundamental time scale for unambiguously dating events within the solar system and beyond (e.g. planet and interplanetary spacecraft motions, and pulsar signals) is **Barycentric Coordinate Time (TCB)**. TCB is the time base of a non-rotating coordinate system with its origin located at the centre of mass of the solar system, and it is not influenced by the gravitational fields of any bodies in the solar system. It is as if the solar system were not present.

The fundamental time scale for unambiguously dating events in the vicinity of Earth (e.g. motions of Earth-orbiting satellites) is **Geocentric Coordinate Time (TCG)**. TCG is the time base of a non-rotating coordinate system with its origin located at the centre of mass of Earth, and it is not influenced by the gravitational field of Earth. It is as if all bodies of the solar system except Earth were present.

TCG runs at a slower (and slightly variable) rate relative to TCB because of both time dilation associated with Earth's orbital motion and gravitational redshift associated with Earth's location within the Sun's gravitational well, and (to a much lesser extent) the gravitational wells of all the other bodies in the solar system (except Earth). Relative to TCB, TCG loses about 467 ms per year.

One might expect that TCG would be the time scale of choice for Earth-based observers (e.g. for dealing with apparent geocentric ephemerides); however, cesium atomic clocks at Earth's surface are deep within Earth's gravitational well and

lose about 22 ms per year relative to TCG. To avoid this inconvenience a second geocentric coordinate time scale has been devised, **Terrestrial Time (TT)**. TT is defined as having a rate exactly $1 - 6.969290134 \times 10^{-10}$ as large as the TCG rate so that the unit of the TT scale is very close to the SI second on the rotating geoid, matching the rate of Earth-based atomic clocks. Thus TT is an idealized atomic time scale on the geoid, and is a derived scale, not fundamental. The TT rate definition is based upon TCG and not the geoid because of uncertainties surrounding the realization of the geoid (the geoid would coincide with Earth's sea surface *if* the waters of the oceans were homogeneous and at rest). TT loses about $22 + 467 = 489$ ms (nearly half a second) per year relative to TCB.

TCB, TCG, and TT are theoretical, ideal time scales. Real clocks are needed for measurements. To this end, in 1972 *International Atomic Time* (TAI = Temps Atomique International) was introduced. TAI is based on a weighted average of more than 200 atomic clocks in more than 30 countries and presently is the most precise *achievable* time scale. Not even atomic clocks are perfect time keepers (they drift randomly one with respect to another), so TAI shifts unpredictably relative to the ideal TT rate by about 0.1 μs/year (a few parts in 10^{15}). The TAI scale was set to agree with UT1 on 1958 Jan. 1, which led to the definition that TT be exactly 32.184 s ahead of TAI on 1977 Jan. 1.0 (TAI) to ensure continuity of TT with ET, TT's predecessor for geocentric ephemerides.

TCB, TCG, and TT are defined to have had the same reading on 1977 Jan. 1.0 (TAI) at Earth's centre of mass, all three being exactly 32.184 s ahead of TAI at that point in spacetime. At the beginning of 2011, TT is about 0.7 s behind TCG, and 17 seconds behind TCB. TCB, TCG, and TT are realized via TAI.

Three time scales no longer in use are associated with the SI second: ET, TDT, and TDB. ET and TDT have been abandoned, and TDB is deprecated. Unfortunately they still appear in some publications so they must be mentioned. *Ephemeris Time* (ET), introduced in section (1) above, was defined and adopted by the International Astronomical Union in 1952. The transition from ET to the modern TT took place in three steps: (i) Because of several difficulties surrounding both the original concept of ET and its determination (the most serious being that it ignored relativity), and because atomic clocks had become readily available, in 1984 ET was abandoned in favour of *Terrestrial Dynamical Time* (TDT). The unit of TDT was the SI second on the rotating geoid, and its scale was chosen to agree with the 1984 ET scale; (ii) In 1991 the general theory of relativity was explicitly adopted as the theoretical background for spacetime reference systems. To emphasize that TDT was no longer derived from observations of the dynamical aspects of solar-system bodies, TDT was renamed simply Terrestrial Time (TT); (iii) Because of uncertainties surrounding the realization of the geoid (mentioned above), in 2000 TT was redefined in terms of TCG.

In 1976, *Barycentric Dynamical Time* (TDB) was introduced when it became necessary to acknowledge relativistic effects but before the general theory of relativity was accepted by astronomers. It was similar to TCB except its scale unit was adjusted to approximate ET (currently TT). TDB was needlessly complex and confusing; however, it was used extensively by the Jet Propulsion Laboratory for ephemerides in planetary exploration, so was not completely abandoned when TCB was introduced in 1991. This unsatisfactory situation was resolved in 2006 when TDB was redefined by a simple linear relation in terms of TCB. Although redundant and deprecated, TDB is now an alternative way to express TCB, with the minor convenience that it keeps nearly in step with TT at Earth's centre.

(3) Based on pulsars: Millisecond radio pulsars (old, rapidly spinning neutron stars) display extraordinary stability in their rotation. Their stability, after allowing for

	UTC	TAI	TT

SI rate ——————— 34 s ————————— 32.184 s ———

Jan. 2009 – (Fixed) $\left(\begin{array}{c}\text{ET}\\1984.0\end{array}\right)$

RATE

±0.9 s

Variable but
generally
slower rate   UT1 ◄————— LAG ———
(UT)

This diagram displays the rate and scale relations between Earth-based time scales that run at or near the SI rate at sea level and that are not longitude dependent.

spin-down, is almost as good as the best atomic clocks. However, uncertainties in predicting the spin-down rate of a pulsar and in Earth's motion relative to a pulsar, the elaborate equipment needed to observe a pulsar, and the complex data analysis required all make it unlikely that a pulsar will ever replace cesium clocks as the basis for a uniform time scale. Like quartz crystals, planets, and pendulums, pulsars do not possess the permanence and stability of atoms.

Uniform Time Scales with Steps (to track the mean Sun)

Closely related to UT1 (which follows Earth's variable rotation relative to the mean Sun) is *Coordinated Universal Time* (UTC), introduced in its present form in 1972. UTC, the basis of the world system of civil time, runs at the TAI rate and is offset an integral number of seconds from TAI so that it approximates UT1. When required (usually on Jun. 30 or Dec. 31), "leap seconds" are inserted into (or, if necessary, deleted from) UTC so that the difference UT1 – UTC = ΔUT1 does not exceed ±0.9 s. The most recent leap second occurred on 2008 Dec. 31 (the previous one occurred three years earlier), making the difference TAI – UTC = ΔAT = 34 s. Hence TT – UTC = 34 s + 32.184 s = 66.184 s exactly during 2011 (see the diagram above). At the rate Earth presently is rotating (June 2010), the next leap second will likely occur at the end of 2011. UTC is readily available via radio time signals and GPS receivers (see the diagram above). (Note: The term *Greenwich Mean Time* (GMT) over the years has had three different meanings: the same as UT1, UTC, and mean solar time at the Greenwich meridian with 0 h corresponding to noon. To avoid confusion, the term *Greenwich Mean Time* should not be used.)

Anyone in North America can keep track of Earth's varying rotation by listening to the CHU or WWV radio time signals in which is coded the difference ΔUT1 = (UT1 – UTC) (see TIME SIGNALS on p. 50). Also, see the Web site **tf.nist.gov/pubs/bulletin/leapsecond.htm**. It is interesting to record ΔUT1 about once a month and use these data to make a graphical display of (TT – UT1) as a function of time over several years. During 2011, TT – UT1 = 66.184 – (UT1 – UTC).

Local Mean (solar) Time (LMT) would suffice for the inhabitants of an isolated village, but with the advent in the 19th century of rapid travel and communication (railways, steamships, and the telegraph), it became essential that clocks over a range of longitudes indicate the same time. To keep these clocks reasonably in phase with the day–night cycle and yet avoid the inconvenience to travellers of a local time that varies continuously with longitude, in 1884, Earth was divided into 24 *Standard Time* zones, adjacent zones generally differing by one hour and each ideally 15° wide (see the time-zone map on p. 52). All clocks within the same zone read the same time. The Canadian railway surveyor and construction engineer Sir Sandford Fleming (1827–1915) was instrumental in establishing this system of standard time zones. The zero zone is centred on the Greenwich meridian (longitude 0°), and, since 1972, standard time in that zone is UTC. Thus the world system of civil time is based on

UTC and includes the "leap seconds," which keep UTC near UT1. Depending upon an observer's location within his or her standard time zone, standard time may differ by up to an hour or so from LMT (see the third paragraph on p. 202). This is the second reason why the Sun seldom, if ever, is on the observer's meridian at 12:00 noon, standard time.

Humans generally have an awake/asleep cycle that is delayed by a few hours relative to the day/night cycle. Consequently, in higher latitudes during the spring and summer when the Sun rises before humans do, more energy is needed for lighting in the evening than would be the case if the two cycles coincided. To shift the lifestyles of their citizens more in phase with the day/night cycle many countries adopt *Daylight Saving Time*, advancing clocks by one hour during the spring and summer (a better term would be *Energy Saving Time* because it is energy that is being saved, not daylight). For most of Canada and the United States[1], clocks are advanced by one hour at 02:00 local time on the second Sunday in March, and return to standard time at 02:00 local time on the first Sunday in November: *spring ahead, fall back.*

---

[1] Some regions, such as northwestern Ontario, Saskatchewan, northeastern and southeastern British Columbia, Hawaii, and most of Arizona, do not observe Daylight Saving Time. For more information see webexhibits.org/daylightsaving.

TIME SIGNALS

National time services distribute Coordinated Universal Time (UTC). UTC is coordinated through the Bureau International des Poids et Mesures (BIPM) in Sèvres, France, so that most time services are synchronized to a tenth of a millisecond. Radio time signals available in North America include:

CHU Ottawa, Ontario, Canada 3.330, 7.850, 14.670 MHz
WWV Fort Collins, Colorado, USA 2.5, 5, 10, 15, 20 MHz

For CHU, each minute starts at the *beginning* of the tone following the voice announcement, the tone for the 29th second is omitted, and the tones for seconds 31 through 39 have a different sound from the others.

The difference ΔUT1 = UT1 – UTC to the nearest tenth of a second is coded in the signals. If UT1 is ahead of UTC, second markers beginning at the 1-second mark of each minute are doubled, the number of doubled markers indicating the number of tenths of a second UT1 is ahead of UTC. If UT1 is behind UTC, the doubled markers begin at the 9-second point.

Time signals are also available by telephone from the National Research Council in Ottawa. Call (613) 745-1576 for English, and (613) 745-9426 for French; the call may be routed via one or two communications satellite hops, being delayed by 0.25 seconds per hop. Internet time services can be found at time5.nrc.ca/webclock_e.shtml and **www.boulder.nist.gov/timefreq**.

MEAN SIDEREAL TIME, 2011

The following is the Greenwich Mean Sidereal Time (GMST) in hours on day 0 at 0h UT of each month ("day 0" is the last day of the previous month):

Jan. 6.6209	Apr. 12.5348	Jul. 18.5144	Oct. 0.5597
Feb. 8.6579	May 14.5061	Aug. ... 20.5514	Nov. 2.5967
Mar. 10.4978	Jun. 16.5431	Sep. 22.5884	Dec. 4.5680

GMST (in hours) at hour t UT on day d of the month =
GMST at 0h UT on day $0 + 0.065710\,d + 1.002738\,t$
LMST (Local Mean Sidereal Time) = GMST – west longitude (or + east longitude)

LMST computed by this method is accurate to ±0.2 s provided t is stated to ±0.1 s or better and the observer's longitude is known to ±1″. Note that t must be expressed in decimal hours UT and longitude in hours, not degrees. Also, to achieve ±0.1 s accuracy in t, the correction ΔUT1 must be applied to UTC. See TIME SIGNALS above.

JULIAN DATE (JD), 2011

The Julian Date (JD) is commonly used by astronomers to refer to the time of astronomical events, because it avoids some of the annoying complexities of the civil calendar. Julian Date 0.0 was the instant of Greenwich mean noon on 4713 Jan. 1 BC (see "The Origin of the Julian Day System" by G. Moyer, *Sky & Telescope*, April 1981).

The Julian day **commences at noon** (12h) UT. To find the JD at any time during 2011, determine the day of the month and time at the Greenwich meridian, convert this to a decimal day, and add it to one of the following numbers according to the month (these numbers are the JD for 0h UT on the 0th day of each month):

Jan. ... 245 5561.5	Apr. ... 245 5651.5	Jul. 245 5742.5	Oct. 245 5834.5
Feb. ...245 5592.5	May ... 245 5681.5	Aug. ..245 5773.5	Nov. ... 245 5865.5
Mar. ..245 5620.5	Jun. ... 245 5712.5	Sep. ... 245 5804.5	Dec. ... 245 5895.5

For example, 21:36 EDT on May 18 = 1:36 UT on May 19 = May 19.07 UT = 245 5681.5 + 19.07 = JD 245 5700.57.

The JD for 0h UT Jan. 0 for the three previous years are 245 0000.5 plus: 4465 (2008), 4831 (2009), and 5196 (2010).

STANDARD TIME ZONES

The map on the following page shows the world system of standard time zones. It was prepared and provided by Her Majesty's Nautical Almanac Office. Over the open oceans, the time zones are uniformly spaced and are bounded by lines of longitude 15° apart. In populated regions, political and other considerations have considerably modified the ideal geometry.

As Earth rotates with sunlight shining from one side, at some line of longitude the day of the week must jump discontinuously ahead by one day (otherwise, Monday would be followed by Monday!). The line chosen for this jump is in the relatively unpopulated central part of the Pacific Ocean and approximates longitude 180°. It is called the International Date Line. A person travelling westward across this line has to advance the calendar date by one day, while an eastward-bound traveller moves back one day on the calendar.

The standard time zones are generally designated by letters of the alphabet. The zero time zone, centred on the longitude 0° meridian passing through the Airy Transit Circle at the Old Royal Observatory in Greenwich, England, is denoted Z. Standard time within this zone is Coordinated Universal Time (UTC). Zones A, B, C,..., M (J excluded), run eastward at one-hour intervals to the International Date Line, while zones N, O, P,..., Y run westward to the same boundary. Zones M and Y are only one-half hour wide. Also, as indicated on the map, there are several partial zones that are one-half hour different from the adjacent main zones.

In North America there are six standard time zones and one partial zone. In terms of their name (and letter designation, hours behind the Greenwich zone, and the west longitude of the reference or standard meridian), these are:

(1) Newfoundland (P*, 3 h 30 min, 52.5°)
(2) Atlantic (Q, 4 h, 60°)
(3) Eastern (R, 5 h, 75°)
(4) Central (S, 6 h, 90°)
(5) Mountain (T, 7 h, 105°)
(6) Pacific (U, 8 h, 120°)
(7) Alaska (V, 9 h, 135°)

Note: Caution is advised when relying on the time-zone information given in this map. The zones are drawn based on the best information available as of June 2005 and are subject to change. Also, local jurisdictions, especially those near depicted zone boundaries, often adopt a different time. For current official Canadian and U.S. time zones visit www.nrc-cnrc.gc.ca/eng/services/inms/time-services.html and www. time.gov respectively.

WORLD MAP OF TIME ZONES

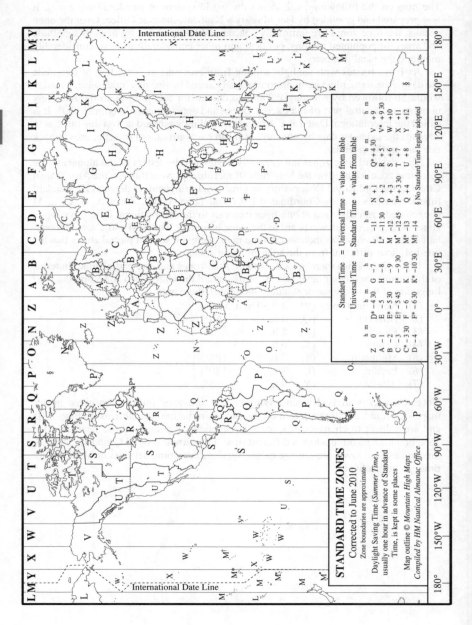

International Date Line

| Standard Time | = Universal Time − value from table |
| Universal Time | = Standard Time + value from table |

	h m		h m		h m
Z	0	D*	−4 30	L	−11
A	−1	E	−5	L*	−11 30
B	−2	E*	−5 30	M	−12
C	−3	E†	−5 45	M*	−12 45
C*	−3 30	F	−6	M*	−13
D	−4	F*	−6 30	M†	−14

	h m		h m
N	+1	Q*	+4 30
O	+2	R	+5
P	+3	S	+6
P*	+3 30	T	+7
Q	+4	U	+8

	h m
V	+9
V*	+9 30
W	+10
X	+11
Y	+12

§ No Standard Time legally adopted

STANDARD TIME ZONES
Corrected to June 2010
Zone boundaries are approximate

Daylight Saving Time (*Summer Time*),
usually one hour in advance of Standard
Time, is kept in some places

Map outline © *Mountain High Maps*
Compiled by *HM Nautical Almanac Office*

International Date Line

ASTRONOMICAL TWILIGHT AND SIDEREAL TIME
By Randall Brooks

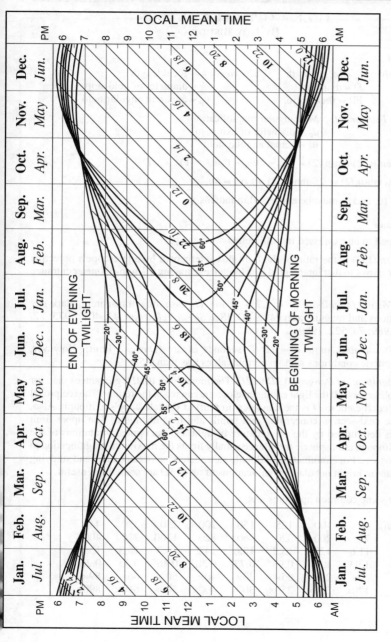

The diagram gives for any day of the year: (1) the LMT of the end and beginning of astronomical twilight at seven specified latitudes (curved lines); (2) the (LMST = right ascension at the observer's meridian) as a function of LMT (diagonal lines). Months and right ascensions shown in **boldface** are for observers in the Northern Hemisphere, those in italics are for observers in the Southern Hemisphere.

OPTICS AND OBSERVING

TELESCOPE PARAMETERS
By Roy Bishop

Equations

Objective: f_o = focal length   *Eyepiece:* f_e = focal length
D = diameter d_f = diameter of field stop
FR = focal ratio θ_p = apparent angular field

Whole Instrument: M = angular magnification
d_p = diameter of exit pupil
θ_c = actual angular field

$$M \equiv \tan(\theta_p/2)/\tan(\theta_c/2) = f_o/f_e = D/d_p \approx \theta_p/\theta_c \qquad FR = f_o/D$$

$$d_f = 2f_o \tan(\theta_c/2) = 2f_e \tan(\theta_p/2) \approx f_o\theta_c{}^* \approx f_e\theta_p{}^*$$

*(θ_c and θ_p must be expressed in radians.)

Performance

D is assumed to be expressed in millimetres.

Light Grasp (LG) is the ratio of the light flux intercepted by a telescope's objective lens or mirror to that intercepted by a human eye having a 7-mm-diameter entrance pupil.

Limiting Visual Magnitude $m \approx 2.7 + 5 \log D$, assuming transparent, dark-sky conditions and magnification $M \geq 1D$. (See *Sky & Telescope*, *45*, 401, 1973; *77*, 332, 1989; *78*, 522, 1989).

Smallest Resolvable Angle $\alpha \approx 116/D$ seconds of arc (Dawes's limit). However, atmospheric conditions seldom permit values less than 0.5″.

Useful Magnification Range $\approx 0.2D$ to $2D$. The lower limit ($0.2D$) guarantees that, for most observers, all the light exiting a telescope can reach the retina. (The reciprocal of the coefficient to D is the diameter (in mm) of the telescope's exit pupil. Also, see the next section concerning exit pupils and magnification.) The upper limit ($2D$) is determined by the wave nature of light and the optical limitations of the eye, although atmospheric turbulence usually limits the maximum magnification to 400× or less. For examination of double stars, detection of faint stars, and studying structure in bright nebulae, magnifications of up to $3D$ are sometimes useful.

Values for some common apertures are:

D (mm):	60	100	125	150	200	250	330	444
LG:	73	200	320	460	820	1300	2200	4000
m:	11.6	12.7	13.2	13.6	14.2	14.7	15.3	15.9
α:	1.93″	1.16″	0.93″	0.77″	0.58″	0.46″	0.35″	0.26″
$0.2D$:	12×	20×	25×	30×	40×	50×	66×	89×
$2D$:	120×	200×	250×	300×	400×	500×	660×	890×

TELESCOPE EXIT PUPILS
BY ROY BISHOP

The performance of a visual telescope is constrained by Earth's atmosphere, the wave aspect of light, the design of the telescope and imperfections in its optical system, and the properties of the human visual system. Telescope and eye meet at the *exit pupil* of the telescope, which is the image of the telescope's objective lens or mirror formed by its eyepiece. When a telescope is pointed at a bright area, such as the daytime sky, the exit pupil appears as a small disk of light hovering in the space just behind the eyepiece. (Insert a small piece of paper in this vicinity to prove that this disk of light *really is* located behind the eyepiece.) Since the exit pupil is the narrowest point in the beam of light emerging from the telescope, it is here that the observer's eye must be located to make optimum use of the light passing through the telescope.

The diagram on p. 57 may be used to display the relation between the diameter of the exit pupil (d_p) of a telescope and the focal lengths (f_e) of various eyepieces. Both d_p and f_e are expressed in millimetres. The numbered scale around the upper right-hand corner of the diagram indicates the focal ratio (FR) of the objective lens or mirror of the telescope. (The FR equals the focal length of the objective divided by its diameter; see p. 54.) To prepare the diagram for a particular telescope, locate the FR of the telescope's objective on the FR scale, and draw a straight diagonal line from there to the origin (the lower left-hand corner). The diagram provides a visual display of the standard relation $d_p = f_e/\text{FR}$. One can see at a glance what range of eyepiece focal lengths is suitable for a particular telescope. Concerning the "AGE" scale on the diagram, see the section Very Low (RFT) Magnifications below.

To determine, for example, the eyepiece focal length required to produce a 3-mm exit pupil on a certain telescope, locate $d_p = 3$ on the ordinate, run horizontally across to the diagonal line corresponding to the FR of that telescope, and from there drop vertically downward to the abscissa to find f_e. This procedure may, of course, be reversed: for a given f_e, find the corresponding d_p.

Magnification Ranges

The ranges H, M, L, and RFT blocked off along the ordinate of the diagram break the d_p scale into four sections, starting at 0.5 mm and increasing by factors of 2. Although this sectioning is somewhat arbitrary, it does correspond closely to what are usually considered to be the high (H), medium (M), low (L), and "richest-field telescope" (RFT) magnification ranges of any visual telescope—and the associated d_p ranges are easy to remember. Note that these magnification ranges are defined by d_p, not by the numerical value of the magnification; for example, a magnification of 100× is "high" for a telescope of aperture $D = 70$ mm, "medium" for $D = 150$ mm, "low" for $D = 300$ mm, "very low (RFT)" for $D = 600$ mm, and "ultra-low" for D larger than 0.8 m.

High Magnifications: In the case of the Moon, the planets, and all but the dimmest stars, the highest useful magnification is the point at which blurring due to diffraction (caused by the wave nature of light) becomes noticeable. This corresponds approximately to $d_p = 0.5$ mm, assuming good optics and negligible atmospheric turbulence (i.e. excellent "seeing"). Higher magnifications will not reveal any more detail in these images and will cause reductions in four desirable features: sharpness, brightness, field of view, and eye relief (the space between the eye and eyepiece). However, for double stars and for some objects requiring the use of averted vision (e.g. faint stars) very high magnifications ($d_p < 0.5$ mm) can sometimes be used to advantage.

Medium Magnifications: A problem with high magnifications is that exit-pupil diameters of about 1 mm and smaller cause "floaters" (mobile debris in the vitreous

humour of the eye in front of the retina) to interfere with vision. This problem increases with the age of the observer and with decreasing d_p. To avoid the distraction of floaters, an observer might choose to keep exit-pupil diameters no smaller than 1.5 mm (i.e. in the "medium" magnification range). For this lower limit the diagram indicates a minimum eyepiece focal length of, for example, 7 mm for a FR = 4.5 telescope, 15 mm for a FR = 10 telescope, and 24 mm for a FR = 16 telescope. With this restriction, to achieve a magnification of 250× for observing planets, a telescope would need an aperture of at least $D = M \times d_p = 250 \times 1.5 = 375$ mm. Hence, in addition to providing more light and greater resolution, a large-aperture telescope makes floaters less noticeable and magnifications in the "high" range less necessary.

With magnifications greater than very low (RFT) magnifications and also possibly greater than low magnifications, structure in dim, extended objects, such as galaxies and bright and dark nebulae, will be more easily seen. To see such objects, observers use averted vision, which places the image on the peripheral retina, which is composed primarily of the very sensitive "rod" photoreceptor cells. However, the number of rod cells far exceeds the number of nerve axons available to carry the signals to the visual centres in the brain. To accommodate this limitation and to cope with spontaneous thermal noise in the rod cells, the cells are grouped into detector units of various sizes (analogous to binning of pixels in a CCD chip). Because of the thermal noise, only those signals triggered by almost simultaneous photon hits in several rod cells are allowed to produce a conscious sensation. Thus in very dim light only large retinal detector units receive enough photon hits to respond. As a consequence, our ability to see detail is greatly reduced in dim light. Hence extra magnification helps to reveal structure in galaxies and nebulae.

Low Magnifications: Low magnifications have several advantages over certain other magnification ranges:

(1) For most observers an exit-pupil diameter between 2 mm and 4 mm results in the sharpest optical image because the combined influence of optical aberrations in the eye of the observer (which increase with increasing d_p) and blurring due to diffraction (which decreases with increasing d_p) is at a minimum. Assuming, for example, that the optimum d_p for a "typical observer" is 2.5 mm, then to realize this and achieve a magnification of 250× for observing planets, a telescope needs an aperture of $D = M \times d_p = 250 \times 2.5 = 625$ mm. Once again, the superiority of a large telescope (by amateur standards) is apparent. Another example: the reason for the crisp images provided by Canon's image-stabilized binoculars is that their d_p is in the "low magnification" range, and their optical quality is up to the challenge.

(2) Low magnifications provide greater luminance than high or medium magnifications, enabling the eye to discern contrast variations over a wider range of spatial frequencies.

(3) Viewing is more comfortable than with very low (RFT) magnifications, since the observer can move a bit (move the head and/or scan the field) without cutting into the light beam and dimming the image. As mentioned below, ultra-low magnifications have the same advantage, but light is wasted.

(4) Light entering near the edge of the pupil of the dark-adapted eye is not as effective in stimulating the rod cells in the retina—the "scotopic Stiles-Crawford effect" (see VanLoo and Enoch, *Vision Research, 15* (1975), p. 1005). Thus low magnifications make more effective use of the light than very low (RFT) magnifications.

(5) Low magnifications provide a darker sky background than very low (RFT) magnifications, producing views that some observers consider to be aesthetically more pleasing.

(text continues overleaf)

EXIT-PUPILS DIAGRAM

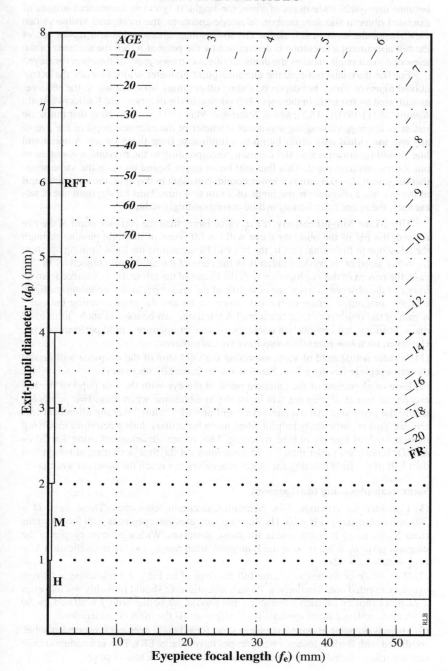

Very Low (RFT) Magnifications: Magnifications in the RFT range are useful because they yield wide fields of view, the brightest (greatest luminance) images of extended objects, and for common telescope apertures, the most stars visible in one view (hence the term *richest field*). The lowest magnification that still makes use of the full aperture of a telescope is determined by the point at which the diameter of the telescope's exit pupil matches the diameter of the *entrance pupil* of the observer's eye.

For the dark-adapted eye, the entrance-pupil diameter seldom equals the often-quoted figure of 7 mm, but depends, among other things, upon the age of the observer as indicated by the scale in the upper-left portion of the diagram (see Kadlecová et al., *Nature, 182* (1958), p. 1520; *Sky & Telescope*, May 1992, p. 502). Note that this scale indicates *average* values; the maximum diameter of the entrance pupil of the eye of any *one* individual may differ by up to a millimetre from these values. A horizontal line should be drawn across the diagram corresponding to the maximum diameter of one's own entrance pupil. This line will be an upper bound on d_p in the same sense that the line at $d_p = 0.5$ mm is a lower bound. Note that in daylight, the entrance pupil of the eye has a diameter in the range of 2 mm to 4 mm. Thus for daylight use of telescopes, the upper bound on d_p will be correspondingly reduced.

Ultra-Low Magnifications: If a d_p value larger than the entrance pupil of the eye is used, the iris of the observer's eye will cut off some of the light passing through the telescope to the retina; that is, the iris will have become the light-limiting aperture *(aperture stop)* of the system rather than the edge of the telescope's objective. In this case, the cornea of the eye together with the lenses of the telescope's eyepiece form an image of the observer's iris at the objective of the telescope; to the incoming starlight, a highly magnified image of the iris hovers as an annular skirt covering the outer region of the objective of the telescope! A telescope can be used at such "ultra-low" magnifications, but obviously a telescope of smaller aperture would perform as well. However, ultra-low magnifications have two advantages:

(1) A wider actual field of view, assuming the field stop of the eyepiece will permit this (an eyepiece having a 2-in. barrel diameter is usually necessary).

(2) Ease of alignment of the entrance pupil of the eye with the exit pupil of the telescope, an aspect of viewing that is usually troublesome when these two pupils are nearly the same size. An oversize exit pupil provides "slop," making alignment less critical. This is particularly helpful when using binoculars during activities involving motion, such as boating or bird watching. This is one advantage of using 7×50 (= $M \times D$) binoculars rather than 7×35 binoculars for daytime activities, although less than half of the light entering the larger binoculars can reach the observer's retinas.

Some examples using the diagram:

(1) Consider the common 8-in. Schmidt-Cassegrain telescopes. These have $D = 200$ mm and (usually) FR = 10. The diagram indicates that eyepieces with focal lengths from 5 mm to 55 mm are usable for most observers. With a 32-mm eyepiece, the diagram gives $d_p = 3.2$ mm, in the L magnification range, and the magnification $M = D/d_p = 200/3.2 = 62\times$.

(2) If an observer wishes to use the full aperture of an FR = 4.5 telescope, a 40-mm eyepiece is ruled out. Similarly, a 70-year-old observer should probably not use even a 27-mm eyepiece on such a telescope and should not bother with 7×50 or 11×80 binoculars, unless ease of eye/exit-pupil alignment is the main consideration.

(3) There is no point in using extremely short focal length eyepieces, especially when combined with Barlow lenses, on telescopes having large FRs. This is a common fault (among many others!) with camera/department store "junk telescopes."

MAGNIFICATION AND CONTRAST IN DEEP-SKY OBSERVING
BY LEE JOHNSON AND WILLIAM ROBERTS

One of the main challenges of deep-sky observing is to distinguish faint, extended objects from the light of the background night sky. As we shall see below, the visibility of an object is a function of its apparent size and contrast, where contrast is the ratio of the object's surface brightness (neglecting the contribution of the background sky) to that of the background sky. As an object's apparent size increases, its minimum detectable surface brightness decreases. As the background sky surface brightness decreases, so does an object's minimum detectable surface brightness. This article addresses the consequences for the visibility of faint deep-sky objects and the effect of magnification thereon.

Surface Brightness and Exit Pupils

Table 1 lists the surface brightness (luminance) of three representative deep-sky objects expressed in magnitude per square arcsecond (mag/sq″). (For more details on these objects, see, respectively, pp. 319, 309, and 319.) When these surface brightnesses are compared to those of skies corresponding to mountain-top observatories (22 mag/sq″), dark country sites (21 mag/sq″), sites with magnitude-5 stars visible (19.5 mag/sq″), and a suburban setting with magnitude-4 stars visible (18.5 mag/sq″), it is clear that the surface brightness of an object can be lower than the sky background, thus leading to very low values of contrast. A sky quality meter efficiently establishes a baseline value for any given sky background in that comparison.

TABLE 1—SURFACE BRIGHTNESS OF OBJECTS

Object	m_v	Size ′	Surface Brightness mag/sq″
NGC 7317 (galaxy)	13.6	0.5 × 0.5	20.7
M97 (planetary nebula)	9.9	3.2 × 3.2	21.1
Jones 1 (planetary nebula)	12.1	5.5 × 5.5	24.4

Sizes and magnitudes of deep-sky objects can be found in *The Deep Sky Field Guide to Uranometria 2000.0*. The surface brightnesses of several nebulae are also given in the section GALACTIC NEBULAE, p. 306. For any extended deep-sky object, the surface brightness, S, in mag/sq″ can be approximated by

$$S = m_v + 2.5 \log(2827ab),$$

where a and b are, respectively, the object's major and minor diameters in arcminutes (′), assuming an elliptical shape. (To convert magnitude per square arcminute to magnitude per square arcsecond, add 8.89.)

The exit pupil of a telescope, which equals (objective diameter)/magnification, determines the image brightness through the telescope (see TELESCOPE EXIT PUPILS, p. 55). When an extended object is magnified to the point that the exit pupil is smaller than the eye's entrance pupil—which is nominally 7 mm—its brightness decreases relative to the naked-eye view. The decrease in brightness is the same for both the object and the background sky. In other words, magnification does not alter contrast. Table 2 shows how the degree to which an object's surface brightness or that of the sky decreases as the exit pupil becomes smaller than 7 mm.

TABLE 2—DIMMING WITH RESPECT TO A 7-MM EXIT PUPIL

Exit Pupil (mm)	7	6	5	4	3	2	1	0.5
Dimming (mag)	0.0	0.3	0.7	1.2	1.8	2.7	4.2	5.7

Human binocular vision has a lower surface-brightness limit of approximately 1 μcd/m², which, when adjusted for monocular vision, is about 27 mag/sq″. When the dimming due to smaller exit pupils, as given in Table 2, is added to the sky brightness, it is apparent that the magnified sky may approach the detection limit of the eye; for example, a 1-mm exit pupil in a 22 mag/sq″ sky lowers the apparent sky brightness to 26.2 mag/sq″, which is near the eye's limit.

The Relation Between Size and Threshold Surface Brightness

Blackwell (*J. Opt. Soc. Am., 36* (1946), p. 624), in a massive World War II study that is still the only one of its kind, analyzed approximately 450 000 observations of threshold contrast under varying background illuminations. Table 3, derived from Blackwell's data, which goes down to 26 mag/sq″, gives the minimum detectable surface brightness of an object as the object's apparent size and the brightness of the sky vary. The values are corrected for monocular vision and presuppose a 50 percent probability of detection; for 90 percent probability, subtract 0.5 from the entries in the table.

TABLE 3—THRESHOLD SURFACE BRIGHTNESS FOR SIZE AND SKY BRIGHTNESS

Size (′)	Sky Surface Brightness (mag/sq″)							
	26	25	24	23	22	21	20	19
360	26.3	26.0	25.6	25.0	24.4	23.7	23.0	22.3
240	26.1	25.8	25.4	24.8	24.2	23.5	22.8	22.2
120	25.5	25.3	24.9	24.4	23.7	23.1	22.4	21.8
60	24.7	24.5	24.2	23.7	23.1	22.5	21.9	21.3
30	23.8	23.8	23.3	22.8	22.3	21.7	21.1	20.6
15	22.5	22.3	22.0	21.6	21.1	20.6	20.1	19.7

As magnification is increased, one moves up and to the left in the table. For a fixed apparent sky brightness, large objects are more easily detected than small ones of equal surface brightness. In addition, low-surface-brightness objects are more easily seen against darker backgrounds and by using higher magnifications, in agreement with experience. However, note that differences in thresholds from increases in magnification are relatively smaller toward the upper-left portion of the table. With sufficient magnification a point may be reached where a further increase in magnification reduces an object's surface brightness faster than the improvement in threshold brightness due to the increase in size. Thus the object will become more difficult to detect, although the increased magnification makes it easier to see any bright detail within the object.

It is important to note that the values in this table are guidelines only. If Table 3 suggests that the detection of an object is marginal, do not be discouraged; try anyway. Other factors that affect the detection of an object are atmospheric extinction, a telescope's efficiency of light transmission, the differences between the eye's nighttime and daytime response (see FILTERS, p. 67), and the observer's visual acuity. Typically, the cumulative effect of these factors is between –0.5 and +0.5 magnitudes; see Schaefer (*PASP, 102* (1990), pp. 213–215) for further details.

An example using Table 3

(1) Consider NGC 7317 under a 21 mag/sq″ sky. A magnification of 148× with a 445-mm telescope gives a size of 74′ and an exit pupil of 3 mm. The dimming due to a 3-mm exit pupil is 1.8 magnitudes (Table 2), which when added to both the object's and sky's surface brightness results in brightnesses of 22.5 mag/sq″ and 22.8 mag/sq″, respectively. The entry in Table 3 for a sky of surface brightness 23 mag/sq″ and

size 60′ gives a threshold surface brightness of 23.7 mag/sq″. This is more than one magnitude dimmer than the brightness of NGC 7317, which should therefore be clearly visible under the specified conditions. A 130-mm telescope with a magnification of 43×, on the other hand, gives a size of 22′ and the same surface brightnesses and exit pupil. From the interpolated value 22.2 in the fourth column of Table 3 we see that the object will likely not be visible in this smaller instrument at this magnification. Alternatively, finding the object brightness in the 23 mag/sq″ column we see that the minimum apparent size is almost 30′, and since 22′ is less than this, the object is unlikely to be seen.

Some examples using Figure 1

Figure 1 is a graphical representation of the data in Table 3, whose columns are depicted as a set of correlative curves. The y-axis represents the minimum apparent size of the object for visibility, and the x-axis is the contrast between the object and the sky. Whereas Table 3 emphasizes the visibility of the object as a function of its brightness and apparent size, Figure 1 emphasizes the visibility of the object as a function of the contrast between it and the sky in relation to its apparent size.

(2) An example with a larger object shows that magnification can be increased without dropping the object below the threshold surface brightness. Consider M97 viewed with a 200-mm aperture under a 20 mag/sq″ sky. The contrast between the object and sky surface brightnesses of 21.1 mag/sq″ and 20 mag/sq″ is 1.1 mag/sq″, which does not change with magnification. A 5-mm exit pupil (40×) gives a sky surface brightness of 20.7 mag/sq″, with a 128′ apparent size. Starting at the 1.1 mag/sq″ point on the x-axis, move vertically to the curve (21 mag/sq″) most closely corresponding to the sky surface brightness and then horizontally to get the minimum apparent object size on the y-axis (40′). Since the apparent size is greater than the minimum, M97 should be visible. If the magnification is increased to 100×, resulting in an exit pupil of 2 mm and apparent size of 320′, the sky brightness changes to 22.7 mag/sq″ and the minimum size to 80′. The object is still visible, but the apparent size is 2.5 times greater, thus resulting in a more detailed view.

The contrast of emission nebulae is a special case and can be increased with bandpass filters (see FILTERS, p. 67). Bandpass filters such as the UHC, OIII, and Hβ increase contrast by passing light near the emission wavelengths and rejecting broad-spectrum light from light pollution and natural skyglow, effectively reducing the sky's surface brightness by about 1.6 magnitudes for the UHC and about 2.6 magnitudes for the OIII and Hβ filters. The visible light from emission nebulae is mainly in the OIII and Hβ wavelengths, which lie close to the peak response of the dark-adapted eye. Filters such as the UHC pass all the light from these lines and do not significantly dim the nebulae. These filters therefore do not require an increase in exit pupils in order to maintain an object's surface brightness. OIII and especially Hβ filters, on the other hand, may pass only a portion of the light from a nebula and result in a dimming of the nebula. Here, the restoration of the object's surface brightness requires an increase in exit pupil and thus a decrease in magnification. The OIII filter passes most of the light from a typical planetary nebula and thus does not require an increase in exit pupil; it is therefore the filter of choice for these objects. The situation for other emission nebulae is not so clear.

(3) Consider viewing the planetary nebula Jones 1 with a 250-mm aperture under a 21 mag/sq″ sky. Exit pupils of 2 mm and smaller reduce the surface brightness below the eye's absolute threshold of 27 mag/sq″; larger exit pupils do not dim the sky sufficiently to make the object visible. A magnification of 50× gives an exit pupil of 5 mm, which results in a contrast of 3.4 mag/sq″, sky brightness of 21.7 mag/sq″, and

an object size of 275′. Figure 1 shows the minimum apparent size to be greater than 360′ and that Jones 1 is not visible under these conditions. An OIII filter will reduce the sky surface brightness by 2.6 magnitudes without dimming Jones 1 appreciably and results in a sky surface brightness of 24.3 mag/sq″. The contrast is now 0.1 mag/sq″, and the minimum apparent size is approximately 70′. The planetary nebula should be visible when viewed with the filter.

FIGURE 1—CRITICAL SIZE VS. CONTRAST BY SKY BRIGHTNESS

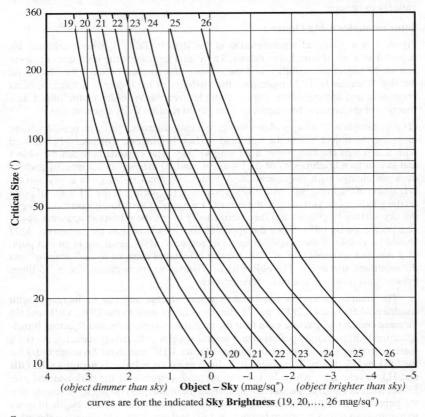

curves are for the indicated **Sky Brightness** (19, 20,…, 26 mag/sq″)

Summary

Generally, experienced deep-sky observers select eyepieces that result in exit pupils in the range of 2 mm to 3 mm when viewing a faint deep-sky object. This range of exit pupils corresponds to the middle of Table 3 and to the central sections of the middle curves in Figure 1. Larger exit pupils correspond to the lower right of the table, where small, faint objects may fall below the threshold of visibility; and smaller exit pupils to the upper left, where excessive magnification may dim the object to invisibility. At any fixed apparent size, moving from right to left across the table results in a decrease in threshold brightness, which shows the benefit of observing in increasingly dark skies or with the aid of a filter. The corresponding values for Figure 1 show that the threshold size of an object decreases in relation to the darker skies represented by curves further along the x-axis.

NIGHT MYOPIA AND STARGAZING EYEGLASSES
BY JOSHUA ROTH

For most of human history, visual astronomy relied on one and only one optical instrument: the human eye. For the past four centuries, though, we have taken to scrutinizing the heavens with optical aid, and the telescope—once a rarity—is attainable by nearly everyone in the developed world who wishes to own one. With its ability to provide more light and magnify the rings of Saturn, gaseous nebulae, and Milky Way beyond what our own eyes can do, telescopic viewing understandably has displaced naked-eye observing as the *modus operandi* of the modern visual astronomer. Nevertheless, there are many observations, some purely aesthetic, others of scientific value, that are best made with the unaided eye.

Unaided, that is, except for eyeglasses or contact lenses; and then only when warranted. But when exactly is such "unit-magnification" optical aid warranted? Most of us get glasses or contacts only when an eyecare professional diagnoses a vision defect. However, even those who were born with decent daytime vision may need eyeglasses or contact lenses to best see the stars by night; and those who *do* use eyeglasses or contact lenses by day may need a different prescription for stargazing. Are you one of those people? In what follows, I will tell you how to find out, but first, a little background on the eye as an optical instrument.

Using its varied layers and components, the eye functions like a converging lens. This means that it brings numerous light rays from a star—or any other point in the field of view—to focus at a single point in space. In practice, of course, not all of the rays that enter the eye from one point can be brought to a single focus: various aberrations conspire against this. Still, at its best the eye brings much of the light from a star to focus at a single point.

Unfortunately, in many cases that point fails to land on the retina: the pad of light-sensitive cells that functions as the eye's "CCD." In many cases, the light is focused in front of the retina, and it spreads out anew before reaching our rods and cones. We call this condition *myopia*, or nearsightedness, because a person so afflicted can see nearby objects well, even though distant ones are blurred, sometimes beyond recognition.

Needless to say, those of us who suffer from myopia typically wear our eyeglasses or contact lenses when looking at the constellations or watching for meteors. If we are purely near- or farsighted, we can do without them at the telescope, since a twist of the focus knob can correct for these visual defects. Astigmatism, on the other hand, requires us to keep using our eyeglasses or contacts at the eyepiece.

Still, many of us have been less than satisfied with our "unit-magnification" views of the night sky, straining to see 6th-magnitude stars or large, diffuse objects like the Beehive Cluster. In many cases, this is because our eyes are not bringing starlight to a focus on our retinae *even if our daytime vision is essentially perfect (be it with or without glasses or contacts)*. Rather, in many cases (though by no means all), humans become more nearsighted as their pupils dilate. This *night myopia* requires correction—above and beyond any correction that may already be in use for daylight hours—if we are to use our eyes to the fullest at night.

Eyecare professionals have debated the causes of night myopia for decades. One theory attributes the effect to the notion that humans tend to focus on their immediate surroundings when startled, frightened, or deprived of adequate visual stimulus. In recent years it has become possible to measure the human eye's optical figure precisely. In doing so, researchers have found that many peoples' eyes evince significant amounts of spherical aberration when their pupils are dilated.[1]

As a practical matter, one quick way to probe any night myopia you may have would be to borrow eyeglasses from a friend who is more myopic than you, but a better probe — and one that will quantify the effect — is to use a set of optometrists' "flippers": a pair of mounted lenses that can be held in front of your eyes (or your eyeglasses) and quickly flipped in and out of position.[2] Do-it-yourselfers can use biconcave or plano-concave lenses with focal lengths of one metre or greater (corresponding to powers of one diopter and below). Alternatively, an astronomy club could split the (admittedly modest) cost of a set of flippers.

Once you have your flippers in hand, how will you use them to establish whether or not you suffer from night myopia (and, if so, to what degree)? Ideally, lie out for at least half an hour in a setting free of light pollution, and periodically assess your night myopia as you become increasingly dark adapted. Targets such as Ursa Minor and the Pleiades, with their well-established sequences of apparent magnitudes, are ideal, but any star field you are familiar with will do. View the field through your existing eyeglasses or contact lenses (if any), then insert the various flipper lens pairs between your eyes and the night sky and take careful note of any change in limiting magnitude or image quality. Consider allowing for the possibility that each eye may have a different amount of night myopia.

If indeed you find that a particular flipper lens pair best shows you the stars, you may find that looking at the stars through your flipper is all you need to enhance your experience of the night sky. (Certainly it would suffice for a quick look through a reflex sight (e.g. *Telrad*) or to determine limiting magnitude for one's observing log.) On the other hand, you may find that you prefer to obtain a set of eyeglasses dedicated to "naked-eye" stargazing, so that you can gaze heavenward with your arms at rest. These stargazing glasses should be made of a material that separates different colors of light as little as possible (above all, do not use polycarbonate, which is very impact-resistant but also "prisms" points of light into little rainbows, especially near the edges of one's field of view). Many aficionados recommend antireflection coatings.

Anecdotal reports on Internet discussion boards suggest that correcting for night myopia has enabled many visual observers to gain a half magnitude or more in their ability to see faint stars. Such reports also suggest that the typical observer who does order a pair of stargazing eyeglasses finds him/herself correcting for ½ to ¾ diopter of night myopia (above and beyond any daytime nearsightedness that they already may be correcting with glasses or contacts). My own stargazing eyeglasses (one extra diopter) enabled me to spot Uranus "naked-eye" and a dozen or so NGC star clusters for the first time. More importantly, they improved the definition of dark nebulae and lanes in the Milky Way. I now consider them by far my most important piece of optical equipment. Systematic research on this topic by active observers among the RASC membership would be a valuable addition to the literature of visual astronomy.

References:

[1] See "Spectacles for Spectacular Skies" p. 30 in the September 2005 issue of *Sky & Telescope* for details and illustrations. As of this writing it is available free of charge in PDF format at **www.skyandtelescope.com/howto/visualobserving.**

[2] Ontario-based Optego Vision Inc. (**optego.com**) sell two affordable sets of Night Myopia Diagnostic Flippers (one with ¼ and ½ diopter of myopia correction, and another with ¾ and one diopter). Between these two sets, you can correct for night myopia as strong as 1½ diopters, as the flippers can be stacked. Optego also offer flippers with other diopter settings. 341 Deloraine Avenue, Toronto ON M5M 2B7. Tel: (416) 780–1289 or toll free (800) 678–3464

BINOCULARS
BY ROY BISHOP

For an experienced observer, binoculars are indispensable. For a beginning observer, binoculars are preferable to an astronomical telescope. For a beginner unfamiliar with the large-scale features of the sky, who cannot yet identify a dozen constellations on any clear night, a telescope's narrow field of view, confusing image orientations, and unfamiliar controls will quickly cause more frustration than fun. The beginner is at a double disadvantage because he or she also does not know enough about astronomical telescopes to distinguish those that are worthy of the name from the common camera/department-store "junk telescopes"—the $299 wonders with poor optics and wobbly mounts. How many such telescopes are gathering dust in closets, their young owners turned off astronomy and their parents a few hundred dollars poorer? Far better had the same investment been made in a good pair of binoculars. With their ease of use, wide field of view, and unreversed, upright images, binoculars are a great help in finding one's way around the sky, and provide many unique views of the heavens.

Binoculars magnifying 6 to 10 times are ideal for locating planets in the twilight, scanning the constellations, studying the larger dark nebulae and star fields of our galaxy, and viewing bright comets. Binoculars magnifying 10 to 20 times provide the best views of objects spanning a few degrees, such as the Hyades, the Pleiades, the North America Nebula, and the Andromeda Galaxy; they also give the finest view of the slender crescent Moon, or of the full Moon with broken clouds blowing by.

Binoculars permit us to view the universe with both eyes, thereby providing more advantages: an improved sense of reality and depth (although parallax is negligible when viewing the heavens); more relaxed viewing; a complete view in the sense that the blind areas of one eye (associated with blood vessels and the region where the optic nerve attaches to the retina) are compensated by the field provided by the other eye; and dim objects appear brighter when viewed with two eyes.

Sizes: Binocular sizes are specified by numbers, for example, 7 × 50 and 8 × 30. The first number, including the "×," is the angular magnification or "power"; the second number is the diameter of the front (objective) lenses in millimetres. That is, in the notation on p. 54: $M \times D$. Thus the exit pupil diameter is easily calculated from $D \div M$ (e.g. 7 × 35 binoculars have exit pupils of $35 \div 7 = 5$ mm). Another important parameter is field of view. Binoculars have apparent angular field diameters of about 50° when equipped with standard eyepieces, to near 70° with wide-angle eyepieces. The actual field of view on the sky (typically 3° to 10°) equals approximately the apparent field divided by the magnification. Thus the area of sky visible decreases rapidly with higher magnifications, making aiming binoculars at an object of interest more difficult.

What is the best binocular size for astronomical use? There is no simple answer. Almost *any* pair of binoculars will show far more than can be seen with the unaided eyes; however, for astronomical use the objective lenses should be at least 30 mm in diameter. Also, small binoculars of high quality are more enjoyable to use than a large pair of low quality.

Caveat emptor! Low-quality binoculars (and telescopes) are common. Images seen through low-quality binoculars are slightly fuzzy (usually not apparent to the inexperienced observer), one's eyes will be strained in trying to compensate for imperfectly aligned optics, and the focusing mechanism is usually flexible and crackling with an excess of grease used to mask poor workmanship. Avoid both zoom (variable magnification) binoculars and binoculars that do not have an adjustable focus—invariably these are of low quality.

Considering that binoculars contain at least 14 pieces of glass with 36 optical surfaces, antireflection coatings on (hopefully) all air-to-glass surfaces, plus two focusing mechanisms and an interpupillary adjustment, it is not surprising that top-quality instruments are in the same price range as video cameras. Such prices buy crisp, high-contrast images, accurately aligned optics, precise, rugged, dust- and moisture-proof construction, and pleasurable service for a lifetime. Nevertheless, there is a big market for $99 binoculars and $299 telescopes, and manufacturers are happy to satisfy the demand. When it comes to optical equipment, quality usually matches price.

Stability: One aspect of binocular use not often appreciated is how much more can be seen if the binoculars are mounted on a stable support, such as a camera tripod. This eliminates the constant jiggling associated with hand-holding and also supports the weight of the instrument. Adapters for attaching binoculars to a tripod are available, although usually it is not difficult to make your own. A recent major advance in binocular design is "image stabilization," an active optical system built into binoculars that compensates for the tremor associated with hand-holding. For example, the Canon company has introduced microprocessor-controlled binocular image stabilization that gives almost tripod-like stability with the convenience of hand-holding (see *SkyNews*, July/August 1998, p. 12; and *Sky & Telescope*, July 2000, p. 59). The Canon 10 × 42L model in particular, with its superb optics, convenient 6.5° diameter actual field, and close focusing ability, is the single best, hand-held set of binoculars ever created for both general daytime use and astronomy. It accepts 52-mm camera UV filters to protect the objective lenses.

Rating Binoculars

A frequently cited figure for binocular performance is "Relative Brightness," which equals the square of the diameter (in millimetres) of the instrument's exit pupils. For example, for 7 × 50 binoculars this figure is $(50 \div 7)^2 \approx 51$. Although this is a measure of the surface brightness *(luminance)* of an extended object seen through the binoculars under nighttime conditions, it is a totally inadequate measure of binocular performance on the night sky. For instance, using this figure of merit, large 14 × 100 binoculars have practically the same rating as the unaided eyes (which, when young and in dim light, are effectively 1 × 7 binoculars)!

Since seeing depends upon light, and the amount of light passing through a pair of binoculars depends primarily upon the *area* of the objective lenses (diameter D), a D^2 dependence appears reasonable. However, although the amount of light going into the point images of stars increases as D^2, assuming constant magnification the increase in the luminance of the background sky as D increases leads to a somewhat slower improvement in the visibility of these stars. A similar muted improvement occurs for dim extended images, resulting in an approximately D^1 dependence, rather than D^2.

Also, for constant D the detail that can be seen in the night sky increases with the magnification M. The resulting lower luminance of the background sky allows fainter stars to be seen, and the visibility of structure in extended images improves as M increases because the image is larger and of fixed contrast relative to the sky background.

The simplest figure of merit for the performance of binoculars in low-light conditions that combines both variables is the mathematical product $M \times D$ (which happens to look the same as the binocular size specification). In the case of two pairs of binoculars, one having twice the M and twice the D of the other, $M \times D$ indicates that "four times as much" should be visible in the larger instrument (e.g. 16 × 60 versus 8 × 30 binoculars). This is to be expected, since in the larger instrument stars will be four times brighter and extended images will have four times the area from which the eyes can glean information, with luminances being the same in both instruments.

For many decades the venerable Carl Zeiss optical company has cited $\sqrt{(M \times D)}$ as a "Twilight Performance Factor" for binoculars, its value said to be proportional to the distance at which various binoculars will show the same detail. This is equivalent to $M \times D$ being proportional to *the amount of detail that can be seen at the same distance*. The latter situation is relevant for astronomy since, unlike a bird or other object on Earth, a star or a galaxy is always at essentially the *same distance* from the observer. $M \times D$ could be called the *visibility factor*.

Binocular Performance Diagram

The diagram on the following page enables one to quickly compare binoculars in terms of their ability to reveal detail in the night sky. The vertical axis is magnification M; the horizontal axis is aperture D. The uniform grid of small dots is a guide to reading the diagram. The five straight lines indicate constant exit-pupil diameters of 3, 4, 5, 6, and 7 mm, as indicated both by numbers and by circles of these diameters near the top ends of the lines. The five curved arcs indicate constant values of $M \times D$ (the visibility factor), increasing by successive powers of 2 toward the upper right (100, 200, 400, 800, and 1600). Each large dot represents a common size of binoculars. The arrows in the lower-right corner indicate the directions on the diagram in which various quantities increase most rapidly.

Each straight line (constant exit-pupil diameter) also corresponds to constant luminance of extended areas, such as the Orion Nebula or the background sky glow, with the luminance being proportional to the square of the exit-pupil diameter (provided the entrance pupils of the observer's eyes are large enough to accommodate the exit pupils of the binoculars). However, exit pupils of 3 to 5 mm ensure that (i) all the light transmitted by the binoculars can enter the dark-adapted eyes no matter what the observer's age; (ii) alignment of exit pupils with dark-adapted eye pupils is relatively easy to achieve; (iii) the background sky glow will be subdued; and (iv) star images will be less distorted by aberrations in the observer's eyes (see TELESCOPE EXIT PUPILS, p. 55).

Examples: Some examples apparent from the diagram: for viewing the night sky 10 × 50 binoculars will show about twice as much detail as 7 × 35s; 11 × 80 and 15 × 60 binoculars are equally capable, as are 8 × 30s and 6 × 42s (assuming one's eye pupils can accommodate the exit pupils of the instrument with the larger D); 10 × 50 binoculars are appreciably better than 7 × 50s for visibility (although, assuming equal apparent angular fields, 7 × 50s will show about twice as much sky area as will 10 × 50s). Canon's image-stabilized 15 × 45 binoculars are nearly equivalent to tripod-mounted 10 × 70s, with the *triple* advantage of smaller size, accommodating observers whose pupils will not open to 7 mm, and not requiring a tripod!

The visibility factor ($M \times D$) is applicable to the usual range of binocular sizes (exit pupils between about 2 mm and 7 mm), but should not be extrapolated indefinitely. For instance, as the magnification is increased on a telescope and the exit pupil approaches 1 mm or less, a point will be reached (dependent upon the darkness of the sky) where the background sky glow is imperceptible. Also, stars will begin to show either seeing disks or diffraction disks. A further increase in M will not cause a noticeable improvement in the visibility of stars, and the perceived contrast between an extended object and the sky will decrease. In addition, the angular size of an extended object must be kept in mind. Once M is increased to the point at which the object fills the field of view of the instrument, the object may not be visible at all! For example, a large, dim comet coma may be visible in 15 × 60 binoculars ($M \times D$ = 900) but *invisible* in a 45 × 200 telescope ($M \times D$ = 9000).

BINOCULAR PERFORMANCE DIAGRAM

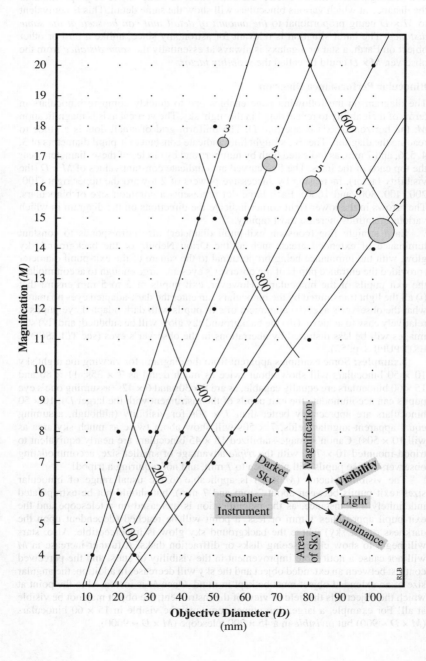

FILTERS
BY ROY BISHOP

Optical filters reflect and absorb some portion of the incident light. *Neutral-density filters* reflect and absorb light more or less uniformly across the visible spectrum. *Coloured (dye) filters* typically pass only one or two moderately broad portions of the spectrum. *Interference filters* are more selective and typically pass only one or two well-defined, narrow segments of the spectrum. All three types of filter are invaluable in astronomy.

In addition to categorization by physical type, filters may be categorized according to their intended use: lunar and planetary (neutral-density and dye filters), solar (neutral-density and interference filters), and nebular (interference filters).

Lunar and Planetary Filters

As viewed in a telescope, the Moon and the planets Venus, Mars, and Jupiter are often uncomfortably bright. A neutral-density filter, which passes only 13 percent to 25 percent of the light, solves this problem while avoiding the loss in resolution that would accompany stopping down the aperture of the telescope to decrease the brightness to the same level. With a less-glaring image, light scattering in the observer's eye is reduced and fine details are easier to see. A neutral-density filter is typically about 26 mm in diameter and is attached to the forward-facing end of an eyepiece.

Dye filters can enhance the visibility of various planetary features. For instance, a red or yellow filter will absorb bluish light scattered by the Martian atmosphere and thereby improve the contrast of features on the surface of Mars. A green filter will increase the visibility of pale red and blue areas in the atmosphere of Jupiter (although the entire image will then appear green). Also, since they absorb an appreciable fraction of the light, dye filters or polarizing filters have the same advantage as a weak neutral-density filter when viewing bright objects.

Solar Filters

A filter is essential when observing the Sun. Solar filters must be designed not only to reduce the brightness of the solar surface to a comfortable level, but to block out the invisible but damaging infrared and ultraviolet radiation. Just because a filter makes the Sun dim enough to view comfortably is no guarantee that it is not transmitting damaging amounts of invisible radiation! This is no place to experiment with do-it-yourself filter designs—use only a proper solar filter from a reputable manufacturer. *Failure to use a proper filter when observing the Sun can cause immediate and irreversible damage to vision.*

A special warning: Heavy atmospheric haze near sunrise or sunset often dims the Sun so that it appears as a dull red disk, not uncomfortably bright to the eye. At such times resist the temptation to view the Sun with a telescope without using a solar filter. The atmosphere at such times is still relatively transparent in the invisible infrared portion of the spectrum, and the great light grasp of a telescope can result in thermal retinal damage! With the unaided eyes the retinal solar image, although just as bright, is much smaller and the eye can better dissipate the heat. Also, with unaided vision, one is less apt to fixate on the Sun for a prolonged period.

For white-light views of the Sun a dark, broad-spectrum, neutral-density solar filter is needed. Aluminized Mylar and metal-coated glass are common designs, although they usually do not attenuate light uniformly across the visible spectrum (i.e. they are not perfect neutral-density filters). Aluminized Mylar gives a bluish colour to the solar image, while metal-coated glass filters usually give an orange colour.

The filter should be 50 mm or more in diameter and must be positioned to cover the *front* of the telescope. Ensure that the filter is *securely attached* so that a gust of wind or a bump cannot dislodge it. (Some small telescopes are sold with a "Sun filter" designed to attach to the eyepiece, just before the observer's eye. Sunlight concentrated by the telescope can overheat and shatter a filter of this design. Such filters should be thrown in the garbage!)

For direct viewing of the Sun (not using binoculars or a telescope) shade #14 (no other shade) rectangular welder's glass may be used; this is available for a few dollars at welding supplies shops. These filters are not suitable for attaching to the front of binoculars or a telescope simply because their poor optical quality results in a fuzzy image.

Red, flame-like prominences at the Sun's limb and much structure in its chromosphere across the solar disk can be seen in hydrogen-alpha (Hα) light, a strong spectral line emitted by atomic hydrogen. This light is totally overwhelmed by the rest of the solar spectrum, so a neutral-density filter will not work. Advances in vacuum thin-film technology have made possible interference filters, filters that operate on the same principle as Fabry-Perot interferometers, involving the interference of multiply reflected beams of light. These filters can be constructed so they are transparent only to light having an extremely narrow range of wavelengths, typically 0.15 to 0.05 nm for solar viewing, although band-passes of up to 1 nm are used in solar-prominence viewers designed to occult the solar disk. If this band-pass is centred on the Hα wavelength (656.3 nm), nearly all the Sun's light will be blocked, leaving an image in Hα light.

Hα filters are expensive, particularly for band-passes near 0.05 nm that are needed for high-contrast images of the solar disk. These filters may be located either in front of the objective of a telescope or between the objective and the eyepiece. In the latter case, because the wavelength of the centre of the narrow band-pass varies with the angle at which light rays enter the filter (a characteristic of interference filters), the focal ratio of the imaging telescope must be near f/20 for 0.15-nm band-pass filters and f/30 or higher for filters with narrower band-passes. Temperature control is usually required to keep the band-pass centred on the Hα wavelength, although some Hα filters are designed to be tilted in order to tune them to the Hα wavelength (the wavelength of peak transmittance is shifted toward shorter wavelengths when the filter is tilted away from 90° incidence).

Hα filters require a broadband "energy-rejection prefilter," located at the front of the telescope. The prefilter has a band-pass of about 100 nm in the red part of the spectrum and blocks essentially all the infrared, ultraviolet, and much of the visible part of the solar radiation from entering the telescope.

Nebular Filters

From the surface of Earth, the night sky is not completely dark. Even in the absence of light pollution (human-made and lunar), the air itself emits a feeble light called airglow. In higher latitudes, aurorae can also contribute to the glow of the atmosphere. Two other components of the light of the night sky are the zodiacal light and background starlight. The diffuse glow from all four sources reduces the contrast of celestial objects and, in the case of dim comets, galaxies, and nebulae, the object may be completely obscured by the brightness of the sky.

Filters transmit only a fraction of the incident light. Thus employing them to see faint objects may seem counterproductive. However, there are objects in the heavens that emit light only at certain wavelengths. This behaviour is characteristic of plasmas — excited gases, matter composed of separate atoms energized either by ultraviolet radiation from nearby hot stars or by collisions such as occur in supernova explosion shock fronts. Such regions are called emission nebulae and include star-forming regions,

planetary nebulae, and some supernova remnants. A filter that selectively blocks most of the background sky glow but is transparent to the wavelengths at which such objects emit most of their visible light will darken the sky background without appreciably dimming the object of interest. With narrow-band-pass interference-type filters the effect can be dramatic, improving contrast and revealing details that otherwise are completely invisible. It is the next best thing to observing these objects from above Earth's atmosphere!

Dark-adapted (scotopic) human vision responds to light having wavelengths from approximately 400 to 620 nm. In bright light (photopic vision) the spectral range extends to somewhat longer wavelengths, about 750 nm. For both types of vision the response curve (sensitivity vs. wavelength) is "bell-shaped," the wavelength of maximum sensitivity being in the middle of the visible range—near 507 nm for scotopic vision and 555 nm for photopic vision (see the figure "Nebular Filter Transmission" on the following page). The photopic sensation produced by 555-nm light is green; for scotopic vision colour is not produced, but at photopic levels 507-nm light appears blue-green.

Hydrogen is the predominant element in the universe. Atomic hydrogen, when excited by ultraviolet radiation from a nearby hot star, emits light in the visible spectrum at only four discrete wavelengths: 656, 486, 434, and 410 nm (designated as Hα, Hβ, Hγ, and Hδ, respectively, part of the *Balmer spectrum* of hydrogen). Scotopic vision is blind to 656-nm (Hα) light and relatively insensitive to the less intense 434- and 410-nm light. However, 486 nm (Hβ) lies near the 507-nm peak sensitivity of scotopic vision, and an Hβ ("H-beta") filter having a narrow band-pass at this wavelength will greatly reduce the surrounding sky brightness and reveal Hβ-emitting nebulae.

The classic example is the Horsehead Nebula, a dark, silhouetted column of dust just southeast of the east end of Orion's belt. The surrounding hydrogen gas, excited probably by the nearby hot star ζ Orionis, fluoresces dimly with Hβ light. If the obscuring airglow is blocked by an Hβ filter, the dark Horsehead can distinctly be seen in a telescope having an aperture of 400 mm or greater. However, the number of objects that can be viewed advantageously with an Hβ filter is very limited, apparently because few nebulae emit strongly in Hβ light.

Two other strong nebular emission lines lie at 496 and 501 nm, nearly at the peak sensitivity of scotopic vision. Originally detected in 1864 by the British astronomer William Huggins, the origin of these lines was unknown at that time, and they were attributed to a hypothetical new element, "nebulium." In 1927, the American astrophysicist Ira Bowen identified the lines as due to doubly ionized oxygen (O^{++} or OIII), which glows brightly when very low-density nebular gas is strongly excited (high temperature). A filter that has a narrow band-pass spanning these two wavelengths gives striking views of highly excited nebulae. A good example is the Veil Nebula, a supernova remnant in eastern Cygnus. Through an OIII filter on a dark, transparent night, the direct view of the Veil in a large amateur telescope is more spectacular than any photograph or CCD image. Planetary nebulae (fluorescing, low-density shells of gas surrounding hot central stars) also show up well with an OIII filter; examples include the Helix Nebula, the Owl Nebula (M97), the Dumbbell Nebula (M27), and the Ring Nebula (M57).

Because of their narrow band-passes, Hβ and OIII filters are sometimes called *line filters*, although their band-passes are much wider than that of an Hα filter. Filters encompassing both the Hβ and OIII lines, such as the Lumicon Ultra High Contrast (UHC) filter, are termed *narrowband filters*. These filters also enhance views of many emission nebulae, although with the wider band-pass the sky background is brighter. With a large telescope under dark skies, I find that the single most useful filter is the OIII line filter. With smaller apertures (less than about 200 mm), the narrowband

Lumicon UHC filter (or equivalent filter from other manufacturers) may be preferable since it dims the stars less.

Some other nebulae that are greatly enhanced by OIII and narrowband filters include the Omega or Loon Nebula (M17), the Trifid Nebula (M20), the Lagoon Nebula (M8), the Rosette Nebula, the Eagle Nebula (M16), the North America Nebula, and the Eta Carinae Nebula.

Nebular Filter Transmission

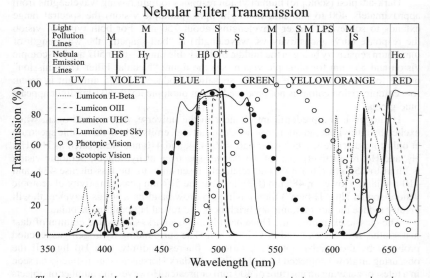

The dotted, dashed, and continuous curves show the transmission versus wavelength characteristic of four interference filters (in descending order in the legend): two line filters, a narrowband filter, and a broadband filter. The bell-shaped curves composed of small open and solid circles show the relative response of bright-adapted (photopic) vision and dark-adapted (scotopic) vision. In ascending sequence above the curves are spectral colours, nebula emission lines, and light-pollution lines (M = mercury, S = high-pressure sodium, and LPS = low-pressure sodium). High-pressure sodium light sources emit an additional broad continuum spectrum that is not shown. The two unlabelled light-pollution lines are strong airglow/auroral lines produced by atomic oxygen. (Dave Lane used a "Varian Model Cory 50 Conc. UV-Visible Spectrophotometer" owned by the Chemistry Department at Saint Mary's University to obtain the filter curves; he also prepared the diagram.)

Stars emit light across the entire visible spectrum. Thus line filters and narrowband filters impair views of single stars, reflection nebulae, star clusters, and galaxies. Filters with wide band-passes extending from about 450 to 530 nm are called *broadband filters*. Examples are the Lumicon Deep Sky filter, the Orion SkyGlow filter, and the Meade Broadband filter. These decrease the airglow somewhat and block several of the brighter wavelengths emitted by sodium- and mercury-vapour streetlights, without dimming stars and galaxies too much. Thus they provide a modest improvement in the visibility of some objects from light-polluted sites. Because of their wide band-pass and high transmission at the Hα line, they are also useful for photography of emission nebulae. However, under dark skies an unfiltered view is preferable to that through a broadband filter.

LIMITING MAGNITUDES
BY DOUGLAS PITCAIRN

Limiting Visual Magnitudes

One of the many difficulties with visual observing from the surface of our planet is the variability of the atmosphere. In any record of observations it is important to note the condition of the sky. Parameters such as brightness and contrast are greatly affected by the transparency of the sky and the presence of light pollution or aurorae.

One of the simplest ways to quantify local sky conditions is to note the magnitude of the faintest star visible with the unaided eye—the *limiting visual magnitude* (LVM). Although individuals differ in their ability to detect faint stars, these differences are generally small, and for any one observer such observations provide a consistent measure of sky quality.

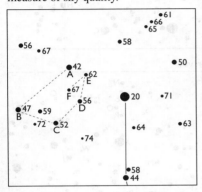

The chart at the left shows a 9°-wide field in the vicinity of Polaris (the brightest star on the chart) and is useful for observers at latitude 20°N or higher. For orientation, the solid lines mark the beginning of the handle of the Little Dipper, as in the ALL-SKY MAPS on p. 344. Several stars have their visual magnitudes indicated (with decimal points omitted). Using this field to determine your LVM has several advantages: it is always above the horizon in midnorthern latitudes; its altitude does not change with the time of night or year, so the variation of atmospheric extinction with altitude is not a consideration; there are no bright stars or planets in the field to dazzle the eye; the faint stars are quite well spaced and therefore easy to identify; and being a simple field, it can be memorized. Especially note the dashed spiral of descending magnitudes labelled "A" through "F."

Limiting Telescopic Magnitudes

Aperture, telescope design, eyepiece design, magnification, and the quality of optical surfaces are a few of the many variables that will determine the faintest stars visible through a given telescope and eyepiece. By determining an instrument's limiting magnitude—the *limiting telescopic magnitude* (LTM)—you can effectively assess the effect of these variables. The quality of the night sky will also affect the LTM. Therefore, changes in the LVM should be taken into account when determining the LTM. (The relationship between LTM and LVM is complex; readers may explore it using the excellent Web-based calculator at **http://www.bogan.ca/astro/optics/maglimit.html**.) The LTM is a useful guide when attempting faint targets (Pluto in a 150-mm scope?), comparing the performance of different instruments ("Can my scope see as faint as yours?"), or determining whether a mirror or lens needs cleaning (many people clean their optics too often, assuming that dust degrades optical performance more than it actually does).

To help determine the LTM of your instrument, use the charts on the next page, which show an 8′-wide section of the northwest quadrant of M67 centred at RA 8h 50.1m and Dec +11°53′. This old open cluster lies 8° south-southeast of M44, Cancer's famous Beehive Cluster. The accompanying table lists the visual magnitudes and the *B* – *V* colour indices of the labelled stars. The diagram was constructed from

STAR	VISUAL	B – V
A	10.60	1.10
B	11.19	0.43
C	11.59	0.42
D	12.01	0.57
E	12.26	0.68
F	12.57	0.59
G	13.04	0.85
H	13.35	0.59
I	13.61	0.59
J	13.96	0.62
K	14.34	0.56
L	14.66	0.67
M	14.96	0.69
N	15.30	0.79
O	15.58	0.84
P	16.06	0.74
Q	16.31	0.99
R	16.62	0.81
S	17.05	1.26
T	17.38	1.17
U	17.64	1.31
V	18.04	1.27
W	18.38	0.76
X	18.69	1.17
Y	19.07	1.56
Z	19.29	0.61
a	19.42	1.34
b	20.10	0.00
c	20.35	0.83
d	20.61	1.55
e	21.03	0.32

"Left-Right Correct" View

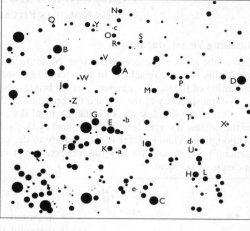

"Mirror Reversed" View

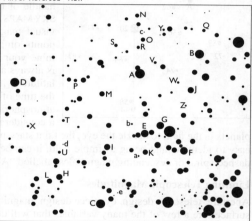

The "left-right correct" chart is for telescopes with an even number of reflecting surfaces (e.g. Newtonian reflectors) and the "mirror-reversed" chart is for telescopes with an odd number of reflecting surfaces (e.g. a refractor with a diagonal). North is at top in both of these charts.

a photograph taken by René Racine of the Université de Montréal, who exposed a 103a-D plate at the f/3.67 focus of the Hale Reflector. The magnitudes are based on work by Racine and Ronald Gilliland of the Space Telescope Science Institute.

Correction for Atmospheric Extinction

Atmospheric extinction varies with altitude above the horizon. To normalize observations to the zenith (altitude 90°), the following values should be added to estimates of faintest visible magnitude obtained using the charts (format: altitude range/**correction**):

18° – 20°/**0.5**; 20° – 24°/**0.4**; 24° – 29°/**0.3**; 29° – 36°/**0.2**; 36° – 52°/**0.1**; 52° – 90°/**0.0**

These corrections are for near sea level and would be reduced at higher elevations. Also, excellent sky conditions are assumed; under less than ideal conditions the corrections are generally larger and can be quite uncertain, especially when the target area is closer to the horizon.

FREQUENCY OF NIGHTTIME CLOUD COVER
BY JAY ANDERSON

APRIL–MAY MEAN NIGHTTIME CLOUD COVER IN PERCENT

The maps on this and the following page are constructed from observations taken from 19 years of satellite observations beginning in 1981. Computer algorithms are used to determine the amount of cloud within a one-degree longitude by one-degree latitude bin for nighttime satellite passages using observations in several infrared wavelengths. The observations suffer from small biases over snow and ice fields and lose some of their reliability at high latitudes in spring. The chart above is an average of April and May observations; that on the following page is for July and August.

In spring, the clearest skies can be found in a band stretching from central Mexico north-westward through Arizona and into southern California. In Canada, best observing prospects are found over southeast Alberta and southwest Saskatchewan, but the cloud amounts are considerably larger than along the Mexico border. Cloud cover is relatively uniform at Canadian latitudes, a result of the many storm systems that travel along and near the border as warmer weather arrives.

JULY–AUGUST MEAN NIGHTTIME CLOUD COVER IN PERCENT

High cloud frequencies are found along the Atlantic coast, the California shoreline (mostly low cloud and fog), over the higher parts of the Rocky Mountain chain (where cirrus cloudiness is endemic), and, to a lesser extent, over the Appalachians. Resolution of the cloud cover within the narrow valleys of the western mountains is not possible at the scale of the observations, although in April the heavy cloudiness of winter is mostly over.

In July and August, the clear springtime skies of the southwestern deserts of the United States give way to an increased cloudiness as the "monsoon season" brings moisture and frequent thunderstorms into Arizona, New Mexico, and Colorado. California's interior retains its reputation as the sunniest location, but clearer skies return to the midwestern plains, extending northward into the Prairie provinces. Almost all regions are clearer than in the April–May chart, although the Appalachians and the Atlantic provinces continue to be among the cloudiest locations. As in the spring, the Cypress Hills area of Alberta and Saskatchewan experiences the most reliable nighttime skies in Canada.

The maps may be used for planning travel to star parties and sunnier climates and to special astronomical events. During April and May, cloud cover is changing rapidly across the centre of the continent, and the average cloudiness shown in the chart at the left is likely too optimistic for April and too pessimistic for May.

STAR-PARTY WEATHER
By Jay Anderson

Have you got a favourite star party? Or do you like to travel from one to another? Here is a set of climatological tables that will let you know how the weather shapes up.

These data are extracted from 20 years of observational data provided by the National Climate Data Center. At each star-party site, the closest location for which cloud-cover data are available was selected, with due regard for similar topographical positioning and climate influences. The tables are a little unfair to some mountain star parties (both on the east and west coast) where the nearest climate station (usually airports) is not particularly close to the star-party site. Some star-party sites and dates also change from year to year, but the most recent information available is included in the tables.

Cloud amounts are observed in eighths of sky cover, known as oktas. "Clear" means no cloud whatsoever. Even the slightest amount will push the observed sky condition to "scattered," defined as 1–4 oktas of cloudiness. "Broken" runs from 5–7 oktas and "overcast" is just that — even the slightest opening in the clouds will turn this category to "broken."

After the month, the first four numbers from left to right, indicate the midnight percentage frequency of the sky being clear, scattered, broken, and overcast. The fifth number (in **bold**) indicates the average cloud cover and is calculated by averaging the frequency of each okta with its corresponding cloud cover.

CANADIAN STAR PARTIES

Name	Location	Month	Clear	Scattered	Broken	Overcast	Average
Tuktoyaktuk Star Party	Tuktoyaktuk, N.W.T.	Jan.	34.5	17.8	15.9	31.8	**49**
Frozen Banana Star Party	Munro Park near Powassan, Ontario	May	29.5	19.4	16.6	34.4	**51**
Rendez-vous des Observateurs du Ciel	Mansonville, Québec	May–Jun.	35.0	19.4	13.0	32.6	**47**
Concours Annuel de Fabricants de Télescopes d'Amateurs	Valleyfield, Québec	Jul.	36.9	25.9	17.7	19.4	**41**
Gateway to the Universe Star Party	Restoule Provincial Park, Ontario	Jul.	24.7	33.1	19.9	22.3	**45**
StarBQ	Eccles Ranch, Caroline, Alberta	Jul.	11.8	44.1	30.0	14.1	**47**
Stargazing Manitoulin	Gordon's Park, Manitoulin Island, Ontario	Jul.	27.8	32.2	17.5	22.5	**43**
Astro Atlantik	Mt. Carleton Prov. Park, New Brunswick	Aug.	24.6	24.6	15.0	35.8	**51**
Butterpot Star Party	Butterpot Prov. Park (near St. John's, Nfld.)	Aug.	11.6	22.5	18.8	47.3	**67**
Huronia Star Party	Highlands Nordic Centre, Duntroon, Ontario	Aug.	12.4	23.3	38.8	25.6	**60**
Manitoulin Star Party	Manitoulin Island, Ontario	Aug.	33.6	27.2	14.3	24.8	**42**
Mt. Kobau Star Party	Mount Kobau, British Columbia	Aug.	37.7	33.4	17.3	11.5	**32**
Nova East	Smileys Prov. Park, Brooklyn, Nova Scotia	Aug.	24.1	21.5	14.5	40.0	**56**
RASCALS Star Party	Malahat, British Columbia	Aug.	31.1	33.5	22.2	13.2	**37**
Saskatchewan Summer Star Party	Cypress Hills, Saskatchewan	Aug.	25.7	44.1	14.3	15.8	**37**
Starfest	River Place Campground, Mount Forest, Ont.	Aug.	12.4	23.3	38.8	25.6	**60**

CANADIAN STAR PARTIES (continued)

Name	Location	Month	Midnight percent frequency of...				
			Clear	Scattered	Broken	Overcast	Average
Alberta Star Party	Drumheller, Alberta	Sep.	29.5	25.9	20.0	24.6	46
Annual Algonquin Adventure	Algonquin Park, Ontario	Sep.	25.7	27.6	14.5	32.2	50
Fall 'n' Stars	North of Belleville, Ontario	Sep.	27.8	27.0	18.7	26.4	46
Merritt Star Quest (Fall)	Loon Lake Gravel Pit, Merritt, British Columbia	Sep.	36.6	23.2	23.6	16.7	40
Northern Prairie Starfest	Black Nugget Lake, Alberta	Sep.	15.8	33.5	28.0	22.8	52
Spruce Woods Star Party	Spruce Woods Provincial Park, Manitoba	Sep.	42.4	22.6	13.1	21.9	37

AMERICAN STAR PARTIES

Name	Location	Month	Midnight percent frequency of...				
			Clear	Scattered	Broken	Overcast	Average
Cedar Key Winter Star Party	Cedar Key, Florida	Feb.	41.9	9.4	11.9	36.8	47
Death Valley Star Party	Death Valley National Park, California	Feb.	36.8	22.3	19.7	21.1	41
Orange Blossom Special Star Party	Alafia River State Park southeast of Tampa, Florida	Feb.	56.0	20.0	12.0	12.0	27
Wagman Winterfest	Deer Lakes Regional Park near Russellton, Pennsylvania	Feb.	22.7	11.2	12.4	53.8	66
Winter Star Party	Girl Scout Camp Wesumkee, Florida Keys, Florida	Feb.	49.1	26.1	12.4	12.4	29
All Arizona Messier Marathon	Farnsworth Ranch near Arizona City, Arizona	Mar.	79.5	7.2	9.2	4.0	13
CFAS Astrofest	Kissimmee Prairie Preserve, Florida	Mar.	70.0	9.4	7.9	12.7	21
Hodges Gardens Star Party	Hodges Gardens State Park, Louisiana	Mar.	54.8	7.6	7.6	30.0	38
Kentuckiana Star Gaze and Messier Marathon	Taylorsville Lake State Park, Kentucky	Mar.	37.6	12.0	12.7	37.6	51
Smoky Mountain Stargaze	near Cherokee, North Carolina	Mar.	43.1	12.3	10.1	34.5	46
Antietam Battlefield Star Party	Antietam battlefield near Sharpsburg, Maryland	Apr.	38.7	15.0	13.1	33.3	47
Delmarva Stargaze	Tuckahoe State Park, Maryland	Apr.	54.3	0.0	2.9	42.9	45
Georgia Sky View Party	Indian Springs State Park south of Jackson, Georgia	Apr.	32.5	28.1	17.5	21.9	43
Mid-South Star Gaze	French Camp, Mississippi	Apr.	63.3	9.4	8.0	19.3	28
South Jersey Spring Star Party	Belleplain State Forest, New Jersey	Apr.	43.5	12.9	10.0	33.7	44
Southern Star Astronomy Convention	Wildacres near Little Switzerland, North Carolina	Apr.	41.5	15.1	11.7	31.7	45
Tennessee Spring Star Party	Fall Creek Falls State Park near Spencer, Tennessee	Apr.	44.1	11.7	10	34.3	44
Texas Star Party	Prude Ranch near Fort Davis, Texas	Apr.	88.1	2.6	5.7	3.8	9
WKAA Spring Star Party	Pennyrile Forest State Park, Kentucky	Apr.	30.6	23.9	19.0	26.5	49
Astro Acres Spring Star Party	south of Morocco, Indiana	May	22.0	21.5	22.9	33.7	55
Prineville Reservoir Star Party	Prineville, Oregon	May	50.9	12.3	13.7	23.1	37
Riverside Telescope Makers Conference	YMCalif. Camp Oakes near Big Bear City, California	May	48.5	12.2	21.2	18.2	38
Southern New Mexico Star Party	City of Rocks State Park, New Mexico	May	90.2	3.0	3.8	3.0	7
North Dakota Star Party	Cross Ranch State Park, North Dakota	May-Jun.	54.4	13.7	7.6	24.4	34
AOS Starfest	Stone Tavern Farm, New York	Jun.	58.0	8.0	11.5	22.5	33

AMERICAN STAR PARTIES (continued)

Name	Location	Month	Clear	Scattered	Broken	Overcast	Average
			Midnight percent frequency of....				
Apollo Rendezvous and Telescope Fair	John Bryan State Park near Yellow Springs, Ohio	Jun.	29.5	31.1	20.5	18.9	44
Bryce Canyon Astronomy Festival	Bryce Canyon National Park, Utah	Jun.	77.2	9.9	7.4	5.4	14
Cherry Springs Star Party	Cherry Springs State Park near Coudersport, Pennsylvania	Jun.	44.7	12.6	10.8	31.9	44
Craters of the Moon Star Party - Jun.	Craters of the Moon National Monument, Idaho	Jun.	80.7	4.0	6.7	8.7	16
Golden State Star Party	Frosty Acres Ranch, Adin, California	Jun.	77.7	3.0	6.3	13.0	19
Grand Canyon Star Party	South Rim, Arizona	Jun.	88.4	5.5	3.5	2.6	7
Green Bank Star Quest	Green Bank, West Virginia	Jun.	39.9	12.8	13.8	33.5	48
Rocky Mountain Star Stare	Pike's National Forest, Colorado	Jun.	70.1	9.9	7.8	12.2	21
Sky Tour	Monroeville, Ohio	Jun.	63.1	12.1	8.9	15.9	26
Starconn	Middletown, Connecticut	Jun.	50.7	12.3	7.6	29.3	39
Wisconsin Observers Weekend (WOW)	Hartman Creek State Park, Wisconsin	Jun.	62.1	12.3	7.3	18.3	29
Connecticut River Valley Astronomers' Conjunction	Northfield Mountain, Massachusetts	Jul.	50.8	14.0	7.2	28.0	37
Indiana Family Star Party	Camp Cullom near Frankfort, Indiana	Jul.	71.4	10.9	10.2	7.5	18
Mason-Dixon Star Party	Shreveport Airport/Footlight Ranch, Pennsylvania	Jul.	39.8	19.8	14.5	26.0	43
Montana Starwatch	Lewis & Clark National Forest, Montana	Jul.	65.9	15.0	10.6	8.5	20
Mount Bachelor Star Party	Mount Bachelor Ski Area, Bend, Oregon	Jul.	83.3	9.0	4.1	3.6	9
Nebraska Star Party	Merritt Reservoir, Nebraska	Jul.	72.6	10.3	4.0	13.0	19
Sola Fide Star Party	Austin, Minnesota	Jul.	60.5	13.2	7.8	18.5	29
Table Mountain Star Party	Table Mountain, near Ellensburg, Washington	Jul.	85.5	6.3	5.9	2.4	8
Almost Heaven Star Party	near Franklin, West Virginia	Aug.	47.5	13.6	13.1	25.9	40
Deception Pass Star Party	Deception Pass State Park, Washington	Aug.	17.6	34.5	27.9	20.0	51
North Dakota Badlands Star Party	North Unit, Theodore Roosevelt Nat. Park, North Dakota	Aug.	71.9	11.4	6.3	10.3	18
Shingletown Star Party	Shingletown, California	Aug.	88.3	8.0	2.0	1.6	5
Sierra Summer Star Party	Alpine County Airport near Markleeville, California	Aug.	95.4	2.4	1.6	0.5	2
Weekend Under the Stars	Foxpark, Wyoming (west of Laramie)	Aug.	92.9	4.5	0.8	1.9	4
Iowa Star Party	Coon Rapids, Iowa	Aug.	43.0	22.0	10.0	25.0	39
Northwoods Starfest	Beaver Creek Reserve near Eau Claire, Wisconsin	Aug.	48.8	18.0	11.5	21.5	35
Oregon Star Party	Ochoco National Forest, Oregon	Aug.	82.3	8.0	4.9	4.9	10
South Dakota Star Party	near Beresford, South Dakota	Aug.	64.8	10.8	10.2	14.2	24
Stellafane	Breezy Hill, Springfield, Vermont	Aug.	47.5	8.5	13.8	30.3	43
Ark-La-Tex Star Party	west of Nashville, Arizona	Sep.	62.1	6.8	10.3	20.6	31
Arunah Hill Days	Arunah Hill near near Pittsfield, Massachusetts	Sep.	49.8	11.0	12.2	27.1	40
Astroblast	Two Mile Run County Park, Franklin, Pennsylvania	Sep.	46.0	13.5	16.3	24.2	40
Astrofest	Kankakee, Illinois	Sep.	55.9	19.6	11.8	12.7	27
Big Meadows Star Gaze	Shenandoa National Park, Virginia	Sep.	47.9	12.3	10.3	29.5	42
Black Forest Star Party	Cherry Springs State Park, Pennsylvania	Sep.	44.2	10.4	9.6	35.9	46

AMERICAN STAR PARTIES (continued)

Name	Location	Month	Midnight percent frequency of...				
			Clear	Scattered	Broken	Overcast	Average
California Star Party (CalStar)	Lake San Antonio, California	Sep.	39.0	5.5	6.4	49.2	56
Connecticut Star Party	Ashford, Connecticut	Sep.	48.4	10.0	7.4	34.2	43
Craters of the Moon Star Party - Sep..	Craters of the Moon National Monument, Idaho	Sep.	79.9	6.2	3.5	10.4	16
Delmarva No Frills Star Party	Tukahoe State Park, Maryland	Sep.	75.0	5.0	5.0	15.0	21
Eagles Park Star Party (Fall)	near Montauk State Park, Missouri	Sep.	61.8	3.6	9.1	25.5	34
Great Lakes Star Gaze	River Valley RV Park, Gladwin, Michigan	Sep.	45.9	8.8	6.8	38.6	48
Hidden Hollow Star Party	Warren Rupp Observatory near Mansfield, Ohio	Sep.	66.9	8.7	5.7	18.7	25
Idaho Star Party	Bruneau Dunes State Park, Idaho	Sep.	38.1	28.3	20.5	13.1	38
Illinois Dark Skies Star Party	Jim Edgar Panther Creek State Fish and Wildlife Area near Springfield, Ill.	Sep.	66.0	7.5	7.0	19.6	27
Okie-Tex Star Party	Kenton, Oklahoma	Sep.	73.1	7.8	4.5	14.7	20
Prairie Skies Star Party	Camp Shaw-Waw-Nas-See near Bourbonnais, Illinois	Sep.	55.9	19.6	11.8	12.7	27
Sola Fide Observatory Star Party	Austin, Minnesota	Sep.	60.3	9.6	5.8	24.3	32
South Jersey Fall Star Party	Belle Plain State Forest, New Jersey	Sep.	49.1	16.9	10.4	23.6	34
Tennessee Star Party	Camp Nakanawa, Crossville, Tennessee	Sep.	63.2	12.0	8.0	16.8	26
White Sands Star Party	White Sands, New Mexico	Sep.	85.2	7.9	3.7	3.2	10
All Arizona Star Party	Farnsworth Ranch, south of Arizona City, Arizona	Oct.	90.1	6.8	2.6	0.6	4
Blackwater Falls Astro Weekend	Blackwater Falls State Park, West Virginia	Oct.	44.4	7.5	8.1	40.0	50
Central Texas Star Party	Canyon of the Eagles Lodge, near Burnet, Texas	Oct.	60.6	7.1	7.4	25.0	33
Eastern Iowa Star Party	Wapsi River Env. Education Center, near Dixon, Iowa	Oct.	62.0	6.5	6.5	25.1	32
Eldorado Star Party	northwest of Sonora, Texas	Oct.	70.8	6.1	4.9	18.2	24
Enchanted Skies Star Party	48 km S of Socorro, New Mexico	Oct.	91.0	1.9	1.9	5.3	7
Heart of America Star Party	24 km SW of Butler, Missouri	Oct.	60.9	9.1	6.1	23.9	31
ICSTARS Star Party	ICSTARS Ranch near Warrensburg, Missouri	Oct.	40.3	20.8	14.5	24.4	43
Jersey Starquest	Hope, New Jersey	Oct.	23.5	34.3	5.6	36.7	49
Mason-Dixon Star Party	Shreveport Airport/Footlight Ranch, Pennsylvania	Oct.	42.6	12.9	13.6	30.9	44
Mid-Atlantic Star Party (MASP)	near Robbins, North Carolina	Oct.	55.2	8.0	5.7	31.0	39
NOVAC Star Gaze	Crockett Park south of Manassas, Virginia	Oct.	50.6	5.6	7.2	36.6	45
Peach State Star Gaze	Deerlick Astronomy Village, Sharon, Georgia	Oct.	54.5	10.9	9.6	24.9	35
Starry Nights Festival	Yucca Valley, California	Oct.	63.4	26.0	9.1	1.6	15
Stella-Della-Valley Star Party	Camp Onas, near Ottsville, Pennsylvania	Oct.	47.6	12.5	8.5	31.3	41
Tennessee Fall Star Gaze	Fall Creek Falls State Park near Spencer, Tennessee	Oct.	57.1	8.5	7.2	27.3	35
Twin Lakes Star Party	Pennyrile Forest State Park, Kentucky	Oct.	62.5	6.2	6.8	24.6	31
Chiefland Astronomy Village Star Party	Chiefland, Florida	Nov.	51.4	14.1	13.8	20.6	34
Deep South Regional Star Gaze	Camp Ruth Lee, north of Baton Rouge, Louisiana	Nov.	46.3	13.9	9.2	30.6	41
RTMC Nightfall	Palm Canyon Resort, Borrego Springs, California	Nov.	62.2	4.1	5.6	28.0	33

WEATHER RESOURCES ON THE INTERNET
BY ALLAN RAHILL

Despite public skepticism, weather forecasts are in fact quite accurate, provided they are from informed sources. Specialized weather services—usually involving a fee—are available for aviation, agriculture, forestry, and marine applications. Until recently there was no such service for astronomy, likely because there was no directly related economy. However, the Canada-France-Hawaii Observatory at Mauna Kea has been using a seeing and transparency forecast for more than six years to "queue schedule" observing activities. This marks a new era in which professional observatories are making the best use of weather conditions and changing planned observing activities accordingly.

Similar information has been freely available to amateur and professional astronomers worldwide on the Internet for several years. With light pollution becoming more and more pervasive, amateur astronomers must drive long distances to get to dark skies. They can avoid frustration by using the information and URLs below to plan their observing sessions.

Satellite Images

Many astronomers rely on satellite images to predict nighttime cloud cover. Real-time images are available from GOES satellites for eastern and western America; other satellites such as Meteosat give the same service for Europe and Africa. These satellites give three main types of images: visible, infrared (IR), and water vapour. Visible images are easy to interpret, but they are available only during the day; for nighttime tracking of clouds, IR images are available. Water vapour images do not track clouds; they indicate the total moisture in the air mass. Usually the darkest areas in those images have good correlation with the best sky transparency.

Particularly useful for short-term forecasting are IR satellite loops, which are available at many Web sites. IR images show the radiance emission from Earth and indicate the temperature of the ground and/or clouds. During cold seasons, the ground can be as cold as, if not colder than, the air mass, and single IR satellite images are not very helpful in identifying low-level clouds such as stratocumulus. One way to separate clouds from the ground in these situations is to use a time-lapse loop and look for motion: the ground doesn't move but clouds do. People in northern latitudes from late fall to early spring should keep this trick in mind.

There are many IR image enhancements available at various Web sites, and you should be aware that many of them do not display *any* low clouds, even with the trick mentioned above. One way to familiarize yourself with low-cloud detection is to compare visible GOES images to IR enhancements in the early morning, when the ground is still cold. In some situations, you may be surprised by the amount of low cloud not displayed in the IR satellite images. By comparing IR and visible images, you can select a Web site that you feel gives accurate images and one that you are comfortable with. I recommend the following Web site for IR satellite images because it provides the ability to zoom into your region, to choose different satellite image enhancements, and to do animation easily and is at **weather.unisys.com/satellite/sat_ir_hem.html.**

To make the best use of weather satellite images, you also should be aware of the behaviour of certain types of cloud. Low-level clouds such as stratus usually develop locally and generally move much more slowly than high clouds. These clouds appear during the night and usually get burned off by the Sun during the day. Coastal regions will usually see the low clouds moving inland in the evening and out to sea in the morning.

In addition, cumulus, towering cumulus, and cumulonimbus clouds arise with daytime convective heating if the air mass is unstable. The depth or height of the

cloud structure is related to the level of instability and can reach up to 20 000 m for severe thunderstorms. On satellite loops, these clouds appear as clear areas that are gradually filled with clouds during the day and that slowly vanish in the evening. In the summer, some of the most unstable cumulonimbus clouds will survive at night. Even though thunderstorms, associated with cumulonimbus clouds, can be far from your location, cirrus blowoff from these cells may reach you quite quickly, depending on the upper wind direction, and thus ruin your observing session. Satellite and radar loops are good ways to keep track of these thunderstorm lines.

Radar

Remote-controlled observatories, where the operator is not physically present, and star parties, where telescopes are often left set up and exposed, are becoming more popular. When the sky conditions are variable, there is one common worry: is there a fast-moving precipitation band approaching the observing site? The best way to track precipitation in the short term is with radar. The radar network is extensive across the United States; it also covers populated regions of Canada.

Radar images require careful interpretation. During the night, the air cools near the ground and creates a temperature inversion. On some nights with strong inversions, radar signals are refracted, or bent, toward the ground and scattered back to the radar, thus appearing as precipitation on the graphical displays. Similar situations occur in mountainous areas, where higher terrain interrupts the radar signal. A radar loop will help you distinguish these areas: sometimes they are nearly motionless; at other times they shift around in a chaotic jumble. Precipitation moves in a smoother fashion, at times linearly. The best Web sites for access to radar loops for Canada and the United States, respectively, are **www.weatheroffice.ec.gc.ca/radar/index_e.html** and **www.intellicast.com** (click on "radar").

Weather Forecasts for Astronomy

Cloud Forecasts: Local media and television "experts" cannot always be relied upon when conditions are uncertain. Usually their forecasts cover a large area, and the weather can be quite different within the region. Also, for most people, including many local weather forecasters, skies are considered clear despite thin, high cloudiness that may interfere with observing.

The best forecasts for clouds are from the direct output of numerical models. Weather models are not perfect, but they are surprisingly good at capturing local effects and predicting cloud formation and dissipation. The biggest problem with numerical forecasting is convection (thunderstorms): it is like trying to predict the next bubble in boiling water. Complex thunderstorm cells can be forecast much farther away than they actually appear, leading to poor cloud progression forecasts for regions hundreds of kilometres ahead.

Some weather channels and Web sites use animated forecasts to show cloud progression for the next day, but these animations generally have low resolution and are not very useful for astronomy. The only North American high-resolution cloud forecast I still know of is produced at the Canadian Meteorological Centre (CMC) and is at **www.weatheroffice.ec.gc.ca/astro/clds_vis_e.html**.

Occasionally, especially in the fall when low clouds (stratocumulus) are omnipresent, a weather balloon can be launched into a cloud hole, and the resulting cloud forecast may be too optimistic for the surrounding regions. To avoid a bad forecast, always compare the cloud cover forecast with the latest satellite picture. In these situations, an old forecast may be a better choice. This is why the most recent old forecast, in addition to the current forecast, is available at this Web site; hourly forecasts are now available.

Sky Transparency Forecasts: For deep-sky observing, sky transparency is critical because it largely determines how dark the sky will be. Aerosols—particles suspended in the atmosphere—and moisture reduce sky transparency and brighten the sky by diffusing the light in the sky. Aerosols include volcanic ash, pollen, sea salts, and smoke from forest fires. Spectacular examples of events that introduced aerosols into the atmosphere are the Mount St. Helens volcanic eruption, which spread roughly 540 million tonnes of ash into the atmosphere in 1980, and the more recent large forest fires: in summer 2003 over British Columbia, which spread smoke over large areas, and in 2002 in northern Québec, which spread smoke over all of northeastern North America. Specialized weather numerical models handle aerosol phenomena; Web sites that track aerosol envelopes with up to five-day forecasts across the world are jwocky.gsfc.nasa.gov and www.nrlmry.navy.mil/aerosol/#currentaerosolmodeling.

Moisture is the only weather element affecting sky transparency that can be forecast with confidence. For many northern-latitude residents, moisture is the most important contributor to reduced sky transparency; despite clear skies, very often high-level ice crystals (extremely thin clouds) are present and can be seen only at sunset and sunrise. In addition, moisture from open waters, vegetation (evapo-transpiration), or moist soil can keep the low-level atmosphere humid.

Over the years, I have compared water-vapour satellite images to various observers' estimates of background sky brightness. The resulting hourly sky transparency forecasts can be found at www.weatheroffice.ec.gc.ca/astro/transparence_e.html.

There is a good correlation between the darkest areas in water-vapour images and the darkest observed sky conditions. There are some cases where the sky background is brighter than expected due to moisture trapped by a temperature inversion. Based on this observation and others, the forecasts in the above Web site emphasize humidity near the surface and also near the tropopause (cirrus heights).

Seeing Forecasts: Seeing conditions determine the steadiness of images through a telescope and are relevant for planetary as well as deep-sky observing. When highest resolution is necessary for planetary imaging or visual observing, seeing should be at its best.

Conditions are favourable when the atmosphere is turbulence-free all across the path of the light. The best weather pattern is weak wind circulation at all levels. These conditions occur more frequently over the southeastern United States than any other region of North America, with Atlantic Canada generally having the worst conditions among populated North American regions. Canadian and U.S. central prairies often experience blocking weather systems that give weak upper wind circulation and excellent seeing conditions.

Another pattern for excellent seeing takes place when moderate winds blow from the same direction at all levels, that is, when horizontal and vertical wind shear are weak at all levels. In other words, no jet stream (strong winds reaching 200 km/h–400 km/h at an altitude of 10 km–12 km) or sudden shifts or increase in wind speed with height are present.

At locations downwind from mountains when winds are moderate, it is best to be far away from the mountains, since "gravity waves"—vertical air-mass oscillations caused by the mountains—can downgrade seeing. In general, topography is quite important because rough terrain increases the wind shear in the low-level atmosphere, due to friction and gravity waves.

Temperature variation at the surface also plays a role in seeing conditions. Nights of excellent wind conditions as described above may nevertheless have marginal seeing. On such nights, temperatures quickly and steadily fall, and large telescopes have trouble cooling at the same rate as the surrounding air. This creates what is called "local seeing": thermal heat released from the optics (despite good ventilation) ruins the seeing despite the excellent weather pattern. The opposite is also true: the best

planetary observations with a large telescope often take place just before thick clouds roll in or when looking through thin cirrostratus cloud. Under these conditions the temperature usually rises a few degrees before the clouds appear. Thin cirrostratus clouds usually keep the temperature steady, eliminating any negative local seeing effects. Thin clouds also play the role of a neutral-density filter, increasing fine detail and contrast on bright planets. Ground fog can also be associated with excellent seeing conditions (until the fog thickens) if you can keep your optics dry.

Predicting favourable seeing conditions requires the ability to interpret weather charts, something that is difficult for most observers to do. The Canadian weather service now has a seeing forecast, available at their astro-weather Web site, which attempts to simulate wind shears, topography, and temperature effects and is at www.weatheroffice.ec.gc.ca/astro/seeing_e.html.

Some Tips to Get the Most Out of Your Telescope: "Local seeing" is the term used to describe the effects of heat radiating from the components of a telescope (e.g. its optics) or from the immediate surroundings (e.g. observatory walls and floor, trees, flowing water, neighbouring houses). If the local seeing is bad, the telescopic viewing will be significantly deteriorated. However, in contrast to atmospheric seeing, the effects of local seeing can be controlled.

Tube currents in particular will dramatically deteriorate telescopic images. Mirror-type instruments are more sensitive to such currents than refractors. Large mirrors can take hours to cool down during the night and in fact may never reach full thermal equilibrium. However, the amateur astronomer can accelerate the cooling of the primary mirror by installing one or more battery-type fans behind it. Their use will cool down the mirror to near the ambient temperature in one or two hours. Another approach is to use a high-quality but thin primary mirror. Many manufacturers offer 1-inch-thick mirror blanks for mirror diameters up to 16-in., in addition to the traditional 2-3-inch-thick mirrors. The thinner mirrors will reach thermal equilibrium 2-3 times faster* than the thicker ones. Many amateurs also ventilate the front of their primary mirror with two fans placed on either side of the mirror, separated by 180°. One fan pulls air into the tube while the other pushes it out. Such ventilation has two benefits: it breaks up the thermal boundary layer near the mirror surface (and therefore reduces convective-type turbulence) and it cools the mirror up to 50 percent more quickly than without the fans*.

The popular Schmidt-Cassegrain telescopes do not come with cooling fans and they are known to suffer from internal turbulence, especially at large apertures. Only a few advanced amateur astronomers will have the courage to add fans to those telescopes. Any telescope, and particularly the Schmidt-Cassegrain type, should always be brought outside to cool it down at least two hours before the observing session. Better yet is to keep a telescope permanently outside in a backyard observatory.

To minimize the occurrence of poor local seeing, one must avoid all potential sources of heat in the surroundings. For example, concrete structures and buildings or houses have the capacity to retain daytime heat and then release it during the night. Even trees during the growing season can release heat at night, and so deteriorate the local seeing for astronomical objects found just above their canopy. Ideally, the amateur should choose an environment free from all these elements. If you are lucky enough to have an observatory, then remember that all the outside walls must be white, since even pale colours will allow the walls to heat up during the day and then create local seeing problems when they release the heat at night.

The local geography can also be used to one's advantage: observing can be better at the top of a hill than at its base. It appears that the local seeing is improved at the top

---

Sky & Telescope, June 2004, page 124 (Improving the Thermal Properties of Newtonian Reflectors - Part 2)

of a hill, due to nighttime katabatic winds that drain air down the slope of the hill to its base. This means that air above the hill must also move downward to replace the air that moved away. This descent creates a dry subsidence inversion which, combined with the cool surface temperature at the top of the hill, stabilizes the air locally. This results in good seeing. Many of my best planetary observations took place on hill tops.

One final tip: near dusk and dawn, if you can spot planets, then there will often be a 20-60-min window during which the seeing will be one or two notches better than during the night. This seems to be related to large-scale tidal motions in the atmosphere that create more stable conditions at those times, but the effect is not well understood. Give it a try in the early morning and the early evening.

The Clear Sky Chart

The Canadian Meteorological Centre's numerical weather forecasts, given in the URLs above, are unique because they are specifically designed for astronomers. In June 2005, these forecasts became official; they can be found in the weather map section of the Environment Canada Web site at www.weatheroffice.gc.ca/astro/index_e.html. We took this opportunity to add a few more products for the astronomy community. We added hourly humidity, temperature, and wind forecast images. However, they include 842 forecast images per day, covering all of North America, so it can be a chore to find the one you want. All the above weather forecasts for astronomy can be viewed at a glance for any particular observing site in North America using Attilla Danko's excellent Clear Sky Chart at www.cleardarksky.com/csk.

Editor's Note: Attilla Danko, a member of the Ottawa Centre of The Royal Astronomical Society of Canada, received the Ken Chilton Prize from the Society in 2005 for his creation of the Clear Sky Chart, which uses the Canadian Meteorological Centre's forecasts for astronomers created by Allan Rahill. Most popular observing locations in North America now have an associated Chart, and many amateur astronomers rely on these forecasts to plan their observing sessions. Several World Wide Web sites give useful information similar to the Clear Sky Chart. The spatial resolution of these sites is quite low compared to the Canadian Meteorological Centre's products.

For the UK: www.metoffice.gov.uk/weather/uk/uk_forecast_irsat.html
For Australia: www.philhart.com/content/cloud-forecasts-astronomers
Worldwide: astroforecast.org:8080/

POLAR ALIGNMENT
By Rajiv Gupta

The charts for the north and south celestial poles on the next pages can be used to align an equatorial mount in either the Northern or Southern Hemisphere. To polar align a mount, that is, to point the polar axis of the mount at the corresponding celestial pole, select a telescope/eyepiece combination for which you know, or have carefully measured, the diameter of the field of view. Depending on the accuracy required (see below), you can use the finderscope, guidescope, or main telescope. Point the chosen telescope in the same direction as the mount's polar axis. Simply adjusting the mount's declination until the setting circle reads 90° is not sufficient; instead, rotate the mount 180° in RA, and check whether the field rotates in the eyepiece without shifting. If not, make adjustments in declination until the amount of shift is minimal. To reduce the shift to an acceptable level, you may have to make further, one-time transverse adjustments, leaving the declination fixed. For example, on a German equatorial mount, shims can be inserted between a mounting ring and the mounting plate.

Next, using one of the charts, adjust the mount's altitude and azimuth so that the starfield seen in the eyepiece is centred at the pole. Circles corresponding to various field diameters are indicated on both charts; you can draw a circle corresponding to your own exact field size using a compass if you prefer.

Precise polar alignment is necessary for long-exposure photography; otherwise, the stars will be elongated as a result of "field rotation." With good guiding on a system that is free of mechanical flexure, the guidestar will remain stationary on the film or imaging CCD chip. However, because of polar misalignment, all other stars will trace tiny arcs about the guidestar. The length of a particular star's arc a depends upon the amount of polar misalignment p (in arcminutes), the length of the exposure t (in hours), the distance d (in millimetres) in the imaging plane between the star and the guidestar, the declination of the guidestar δ (in degrees), and the geometrical circumstances of the exposure. An approximate formula for a (in μm (microns)), assuming the worst possible geometry, is

$$a \approx ptd/(14 \cos \delta).$$

For example, with $p = 5'$, $t = 1$ h, $d = 20$ mm, and $\delta = 20°$, we have $a \approx 7.6$ μm. You can use this formula to determine the value of p needed to keep a within a specified tolerance (such as 10 μm, a good target for high-resolution imaging), and then achieve the required polar-alignment accuracy using the above method. For example, to keep a under 5 μm with $t = 30$ min (0.5 h), $d = 20$ mm, and $\delta = 60°$, the required accuracy is $p \approx (5)(14)(\cos 60°)/(0.5)(20) = 3.5'$. If you need very high polar-alignment accuracy, you may want to shift the mount down by the amount of atmospheric refraction at the altitude of the pole (see p. 30 for some values of atmospheric refraction), so that the mount is aligned on the true pole instead of the refracted pole.

An alternative method for precise polar alignment is the *star drift method*, which involves alternately detecting the drift in declination of two stars near the celestial equator, one near transit and the other rising in the east, and making azimuth and altitude adjustments accordingly. In the Northern Hemisphere, if the first star drifts north, the mount's axis is pointing west of the true pole; if it drifts south, the axis is east of the pole. Also, if the second star drifts north, the axis is pointing too high; if it drifts south, the axis is too low. For the Southern Hemisphere, interchange "north" and "south" in the previous two sentences. The amount of misalignment p (in arcminutes) in terms of the amount of drift d (in arcseconds) and the length of time t the star is observed (in minutes) is given by

$$p \approx 3.8d/t.$$

For example, if a star drifts 10″ in 5 min, the misalignment is $\approx 7.6'$; a rate of drift of 1″/min corresponds to a misalignment of $\approx 3.8'$.

CHARTS FOR THE NORTH CELESTIAL POLE

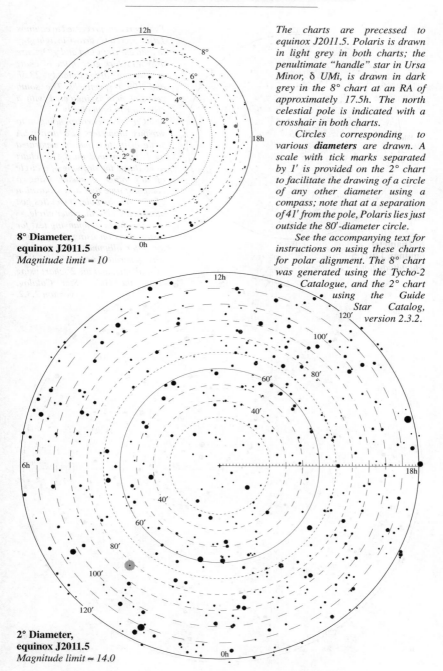

The charts are precessed to equinox J2011.5. Polaris is drawn in light grey in both charts; the penultimate "handle" star in Ursa Minor, δ UMi, is drawn in dark grey in the 8° chart at an RA of approximately 17.5h. The north celestial pole is indicated with a crosshair in both charts.

Circles corresponding to various **diameters** are drawn. A scale with tick marks separated by 1' is provided on the 2° chart to facilitate the drawing of a circle of any other diameter using a compass; note that at a separation of 41' from the pole, Polaris lies just outside the 80'-diameter circle.

See the accompanying text for instructions on using these charts for polar alignment. The 8° chart was generated using the Tycho-2 Catalogue, and the 2° chart using the Guide Star Catalog, version 2.3.2.

8° Diameter,
equinox J2011.5
Magnitude limit = 10

2° Diameter,
equinox J2011.5
Magnitude limit ≈ 14.0

CHARTS FOR THE SOUTH CELESTIAL POLE

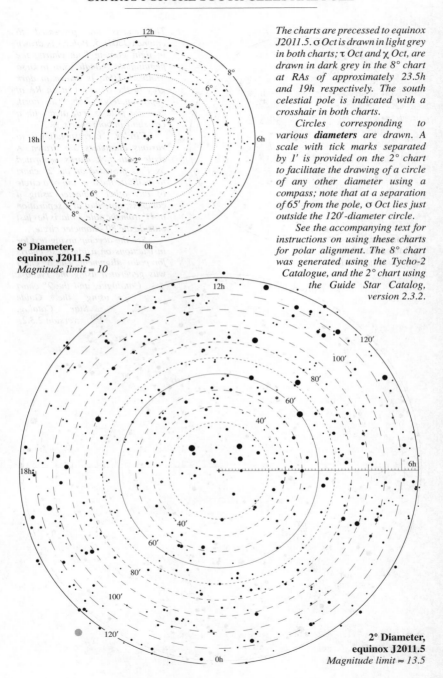

The charts are precessed to equinox J2011.5. σ Oct is drawn in light grey in both charts; τ Oct and χ Oct, are drawn in dark grey in the 8° chart at RAs of approximately 23.5h and 19h respectively. The south celestial pole is indicated with a crosshair in both charts.

*Circles corresponding to various **diameters** are drawn. A scale with tick marks separated by 1' is provided on the 2° chart to facilitate the drawing of a circle of any other diameter using a compass; note that at a separation of 65' from the pole, σ Oct lies just outside the 120'-diameter circle.*

See the accompanying text for instructions on using these charts for polar alignment. The 8° chart was generated using the Tycho-2 Catalogue, and the 2° chart using the Guide Star Catalog, version 2.3.2.

**8° Diameter,
equinox J2011.5**
Magnitude limit = 10

**2° Diameter,
equinox J2011.5**
Magnitude limit ≈ 13.5

LIGHT POLLUTION
By David L. Crawford

A Lost Heritage: During recent decades, most people have lost the spectacular view of the universe that our ancestors enjoyed on clear, dark nights. The development of electrical lighting in the last century and the increase in urban population have caused a rapid increase in sky glow above towns and cities. As a result, fewer and fewer members of the general public have ever seen a prime dark sky; our children and grandchildren may never. For urban dwellers, star-studded nights are limited to planetaria. Even in rural areas, poorly designed yard lights often obscure the splendour of the night sky. As Leslie Peltier, one of the most famous amateur astronomers of the 20th century, stated eloquently in his autobiography *Starlight Nights:*

> *The moon and the stars no longer come to the farm. The farmer has exchanged his birthright in them for the wattage of his all-night sun. His children will never know the blessed dark of night.*

The increased sky glow that adversely affects the environment is called *light pollution*; it originates from excess light that does nothing to increase useful nighttime illumination. It is light that sprays horizontally and upward into the sky from poorly designed lighting fixtures. It is light that glares into the eyes of motorists and homeowners, compromising visibility, safety, and security. It is light that depresses property values by reducing the aesthetic quality

A nighttime satellite view of central North America

of a neighbourhood. It is light that can seriously affect the circadian rhythm of all living things, including humans, as well as creating other hazards for many species (birds, sea turtles, etc.). In the United States and Canada, billions of dollars (plus large amounts of energy) are lost annually in generating this wasted light. It makes for increased air pollution and CO_2 emissions.

A Threat to Astronomy: Light pollution poses special perils to astronomy. Many observations, including most of those of cosmological interest, can be made only from prime observing sites, far removed from centres of population. Some older observatories, such as the David Dunlap in Ontario and Mount Wilson in California, are severely affected by light pollution from nearby urban centres. New observatories usually are located at remote sites, and amateur astronomers routinely drive long distances to escape the glare of towns and cities. The argument that all astronomy can be done from space is incorrect because it does not make sense to do in space, at much higher costs, what can be done from the ground. There are observations that can only be done from space, but more than three decades of space astronomy have greatly increased the need for ground-based observatories.

Solutions: There are solutions to the problem of light pollution: Outdoor lighting ordinances have been instituted in a number of communities, particularly near large observatories, such as Tucson, Arizona, San Diego, California, and Hawaii. *The main solution is the use of fully-shielded (no direct uplight) lighting fixtures that direct all their light below the horizontal, such that the light source itself is not directly visible from the side—an almost universal fault with street and yard lights. Since this puts the light where it is needed, less total light, and thus less electrical energy, is required.*

Inefficient street lighting

The light source makes a difference too; it should be an energy-efficient lamp. Quite a few cities worldwide are realizing substantial savings each year through extensive use of low-pressure sodium (LPS) street lighting. For example, replacing a 175-W mercury-vapour lighting fixture with a fully-shielded, 35-W LPS fixture can get the same amount of useful light, and with none of the glare and light trespass. The energy saving is remarkable, as is the better visibility. In addition to providing light at the lowest cost, LPS lights are nearly monochromatic, with the result that most of their light can be filtered out by astronomers. Low-pressure-sodium lights are especially good for street lighting, parking-lot lighting, security lighting, and any application where colour rendering is not important.

Common Types of Outdoor Lights
(in increasing order of efficiency)

Type	Power (W/klm)
incandescent (ordinary bulbs)	60
mercury vapour (violet-white light)	24
metal halide (white)	17
high-pressure sodium (orange-gold)	12
low-pressure sodium (yellow)	8

A full-cutoff, efficient light fixture

Even less light pollution and more savings can be realized by using *no more light than is required, and ordinances usually regulate the maximum amount of light that can be used for different tasks*. Too much light and/or poorly shielded lights can ruin adaptation to night lighting, blinding us just when we need to see. When we go from too bright to too dark or vice versa, "transient adaptation" is impaired, and we have poor visibility for a while. Do not exceed Illuminating Engineering Society of North America (IESNA) recommended lighting levels. See www.iesna.org. Overkill never helps; it usually just adds glare, and it always wastes energy. In addition, lights should be used only when necessary (timers are useful for controlling lights). Curfews are usually also included in lighting ordinances. IDA, with the help of IESNA and others, has produced a Model Lighting Ordinance as a help for communities wanting more effective and efficient night lighting.

Another common inclusion in lighting ordinances is the use of lighting zones. Different areas have different requirements for lighting; downtown Toronto is not the same as rural Ontario. In addition, some locales have officially declared themselves to be a Dark-Sky Preserve, a region where lighting is strictly controlled or prohibited. A number of these are located in Canada, and the RASC has been instrumental in helping establish these.

Increased lighting generally gives a perception of greater security, yet there is no statistically significant evidence that more lighting results in less crime. Criminals need light. "Security lights" provide this. Furthermore, security lights may draw attention to a house or business that would otherwise not be noticed and mask any additional light that criminals may need to do their work. Our cities and towns are far more brightly lit than ever, yet there has been little or no reduction in the crime rate. We just see more and more bright and glary lights. Security can best be provided by shielded, motion-activated lights that come on only when triggered by movement

nearby. These serve to frighten criminals, alert others that there is a potential problem, and provide glare-free visibility (when properly installed so they are glare-free); they also use insignificant amounts of energy.

Lack of Awareness: The biggest problem in controlling light pollution is lack of awareness rather than resistance. After all, it costs money to light pollute! Unlike the case with many other forms of pollution, simple solutions are available; moreover, *everyone benefits* in applying these solutions. Most people are not yet aware of the expense, the waste, and the harm associated with excess lighting. They put up with distant lights that shine directly into their eyes, not realizing that not only does this do *nothing* to illuminate the area near the light but that it also produces a veiling glare. The pollution usually involves not only the light itself but also other forms of environmental pollution associated with the production of the wasted light: the extraction, transportation, and burning of coal and oil. This general lack of awareness has been summarized nicely by Doug Pitcairn, an astronomy teacher in Nova Scotia:

> *It surprises me how someone who would never think of leaving a plastic bottle on the ground at a picnic site will pay extra money each month to illuminate half the neighbourhood with unnecessary, distracting light.*

Education: Educating the public, government officials, lighting professionals, and astronomers is a major thrust of current programs. These efforts have helped. Most committees in the IESNA and the International Commission on Illumination (CIE) have been addressing these issues, and Recommended Practices and other documents reflect these concerns. As they are issued, one will see them implemented, albeit on a slow time schedule. Astronomers and environmentalists should do all they can to both learn from these documents and to help publicize them and thereby get them into existing practices in our communities.

The International Dark-Sky Association (IDA) has many information sheets available to assist you in educating others—in several languages in addition to English and French—and can provide examples of lighting policies that have been enacted in many communities to enforce high-quality, effective nighttime lighting. For up-to-date information, stay tuned to the IDA Web site and newsletter.

About the International Dark-Sky Association: The IDA is a tax-exempt, nonprofit membership organization dedicated to overcoming this awareness problem. Its goal is to preserve dark skies while at the same time maximizing the quality and efficiency of nighttime outdoor lighting. The IDA needs your help. Membership begins at $30 U.S. per year. To join this effort or to obtain further information on any aspect of the issue, contact the International Dark-Sky Association, 3225 N First Ave, Tucson AZ 85719, USA (phone: (520) 293-3198; fax: (520) 293-3192; email: ida@darksky.org; Web site: www.darksky.org). Plenty of useful information is on the Web site, including images, and content is added regularly.

Within Canada: The Royal Astronomical Society of Canada has an active Light-Pollution Abatement Committee. See www.rasc.ca/committees/lpa.shtml to learn about the committee or to contact the chair of the committee. You may also contact the RASC directly (see p. 10). Also, some Centres of the RASC have light-pollution abatement committees and have taken action to address poor lighting practices in their areas.

Editor's Note: The IDA has members in over 70 countries, and its total membership is over 11 000 (with about 250 from Canada). Of these, about 600 are organizational members and about 200 are individual lifetime members. This is still well less than 10 percent of the community of amateur and professional astronomers. As Daniel Green of the Smithsonian Astrophysical Observatory has put it (see *Sky & Telescope*, May 1998, p. 10): "Where are all the astronomers?" Anyone who values the night sky should support this unique and deserving organization. *You* can help make a difference. Please do!

LIGHT-POLLUTION ABATEMENT IN CANADA
By Robert Dick

Governments rarely act on the needs of an individual. The RASC, however, with over 4000 members, can wield considerable clout, but we must use this clout carefully. The combined experience within the RASC can be used to help members and other groups create an efficient light-pollution abatement (LPA) campaign.

Background

In order to reduce light pollution, we must understand the problem, and the three components to light pollution.

Observers in rural sites are aware of the light domes that arch over urban areas. This is artificial sky glow, the first component. The light that scatters back down to the ground increases the apparent brightness of the sky and can overwhelm the brightness of faint stars and the Milky Way.

The cause of this apparent glow is artificial light that scatters off particles in the atmosphere – primarily below a few thousand metres. These particles are dust, pollen and large molecules of air pollution, raised into the air by the bustle of urban traffic. At high elevations, there is less air to support these particles so that is why towns at high elevations do not produce as much sky glow as those closer to sea level.

Glare is the second component to light pollution, and it severely affects astronomy. Glare is caused by concentrated light in our field of view. The extent of the light is generally restricted by buildings, but it will prevent our eyes from becoming dark adapted. It also prevents us from seeing hazards along a street by producing what appear to be dark shadows.

The third component, light trespass, was once only considered a nuisance, but is now being recognized as a contributor to poor human and environmental health. Artificial outdoor lighting has been recognized by the American Medical Association as a health risk.

Safety comes with visibility not bright lights. Visibility is improved and energy is saved with well-shielded lights that are controlled with a switch (old technology) or a motion detector to ensure the light is on only when needed.

Human and Environmental Health

The design life of our bodies is about 40 years. After that the warranty expires! As the average age of our population grows older, there are problems we can no longer ignore. Changes to our eyes are just one form of change we experience. Our lenses begin to develop incipient cataracts. For most of us, they will not affect our daytime seeing, but at night it is a different story. With glare, our iris (pupil) closes down, allowing light to enter the eye only through the central foggy incipient cataract. This reduces our ability to see beyond the brightly illuminated regions in our field of view. Senior citizens become somewhat blind at night. Without glare, more light will enter through the periphery of the lenses, allowing us to see better.

Our bodies have evolved to repair damage and flush toxins at night when it is dark and we are asleep. Hormones that help repair our bodies after a busy day ebb and flow and are controlled by our internal body clock (the circadian rhythm). To keep the clock in phase with our activity requires a significant day/night contrast. Nocturnal lighting reduces this contrast and confuses the timing of our body clock. So, our body's repair may be delayed or cut short by this unwanted light. We don't get a good night sleep and this results in eroded health, irritability, and all the problems they produce.

It is not just our muscles that need to be serviced. Think of your desk at work after a busy day. It is covered with papers and notes. Our minds are the same. Our memories must be compressed and filed if we are to recall these memories and work

effectively the following day. This clean-up is done in deep sleep that can be reduced by nighttime lighting.

Wildlife has similar body chemistry to humans and experience the same needs for darkness. There are also many nocturnal animals that forage for food under the safety of a dark night. They have adapted their behaviour to accommodate the bright moon, but with light pollution there is no "dark time" during which they can recover. A single outdoor light can contaminate their habitat.

We may not always like insects (such as black flies and mosquitoes) but they are vital to the health of our environment. An outdoor "security" light can attract insects from over 100 m away. The light distracts them from their normal behaviour (feeding, mating, and migrating), resulting in fewer animals that depend on them such as songbirds.

Speaking to Your City

One house light will not make much of a difference in a city's sky glow, and it is very difficult for one person to convince 100 000 homeowners to turn down their lights. There is a more effective way to reduce urban light pollution. We must speak to our city officials. That is a long-term solution but our children will benefit from our efforts.

City managers really do want to do the right thing. Every day city employees work hard and spend a lot of money to provide the services that citizens demand. They want our cities to develop into what we want. So we have to tell them what we think is important, that we want less glare and less light trespass. Otherwise, they will continue to install fixtures that increase light pollution.

How do we begin? We must find out how our city "works." It is far more effective if we work *with* the city instead of *against* it. Your city councillor is a great source of information. If your city has an Environment Committee, contact the chair and ask to be invited to a meeting where you can present your concerns over light pollution. Volunteer to be a member of the committee to ensure it works in our favour. Arm yourself with a list of department-head names provided by a councillor (Engineering Department, Planning and Approvals Department, and others), and schedule meetings with them or their designated representative. The first meeting should be to gather information on what each department does that might be involved with lighting. Gather information through the RASC on what other cities do to reduce light pollution, and present this information to city officials.Initiatives in other cities are more credible than an individual's suggestions regardless of credentials.

The Message

Regrettably, astronomers make up less than 0.1 percent of the population, but 30 to 50 percent of citizens are concerned about the environment, lighting can be adopted as an environmental issue. Naïve ideas about safety and security are used against the reduction of light pollution. Promoting real safety and security are critical to the acceptance of better lighting policies. Glare-free lighting improves visibility, and it increases the aesthetic value of a neighbourhood. Minimizing glare allows lower illumination levels for the same visibility, which in turn reduces electricity consumption. This also translates into an environmental issue, and cutting glare reduces the amount of upward-directed light, which in turn reduces sky glow.

Policies or By-laws?

By-laws correct specific problems using the adversarial legal system. As a legal document, the wording of a by-law tends to be specific and binding and therefore requires careful crafting. We would rather prevent the problem from occurring in the first place. This can be done with a much more constructive document: a lighting policy. A policy is proactive which reduces confrontation. It will guide the development of entire subdivisions.

A policy is more of a political document than a legal one, so it is based on compromise, however, compromise means that LPA measures *will* be included and enforced long before the ground is broken in a new development project.

Dark-Sky Sites

The RASC recognizes dark-sky sites across Canada. As of 2010, there are seven DSPs across Canada, and the list is growing:

Name	Lat. / Long.	Recogition*	Area (ha)
Kejimkujik, N.S.	44.4/–65.2	2010, NP	40 400
Grasslands, Sask.	49.1/–107.4	2009, NP	52 700
Mt.Carleton. N.B.	47.4/ –66.9	2009, Prov.	17 200
Bruce Peninsula, Ont.	45.2/ –81.4	2009, NP	16 700
Kouchibougauc,N.B.	46.8/ –65.0	2009, NP	23 900
Gordon's Park, Ont.	45.7/ –82.0	2008, Comm.	108
Mont–Mégantic, Qué.	45.5/–71.2	2007, NP	5 800
Beaver Hills, Alta.	53.6/–112.8	2006, NP	29 300
Point Pelee, Ont,	41.9/–82.5	2006, NP	2 000
Cypress Hills, Alta.–Sask.	49. 7/–110.2	2005, NP, Prov	39 600
McDonald Park, B.C.	49.1/–122.	2003, Munc.	2 200
Torrance Barrens, Ont.	44.9/ –79.5	1999, Prov.	2 000

* NP – National Park; Prov. – Provincial Park; Comm. – Commercial Park

The RASC has developed two designations for dark-sky sites. The first is the dark-sky preserve (DSP) for sites with good dark skies. A DSP would be in a rural area and somewhat remote from the sky glow of urban areas. The second is the Urban Star Park (USP) with not-so-good skies, but very good access for astronomers and the general public. A USP may be near an urban area or even within a city.

The common requirements are lighting guidelines to restrict artificial lighting in order to protect the natural environment and to allow observing within the park. It also requires outreach activities to promote the reduction of light pollution, and outreach for the public.

A glare-free urban site can be better for stargazing than a dark sky with offending lights. The lighting guidelines recommend full-cutoff lighting and low illumination levels. Instead of asking for illumination levels a notch lower than urban areas, one should first justify the need for any light. Artificial lighting is recommended only in high-traffic areas. Retro-reflective signage and phosphorescent materials can provide navigation around the site, precluding the need to bury electrical wires and install overhead fixtures. Generally, the incentive is to reduce the cost of lighting.

A Simple Home Project

Do you have neighbours with offending lights? You could ask them to turn the lights off when you are observing. You could also suggest a simple light shade. A cardboard shade painted with outdoor paint will cut the glare and light trespass, and it will increase safety by deflecting the light down onto a porch or steps. It is surprising how effective a small, 5-W bulb can be without glare. And you can be a good neighbour by not letting your lights shine across the adjacent property. Turn them off when you go to bed to protect wildlife and to save energy.

Reducing light pollution is not just a matter for astronomers. It has been proven to impact the health of humans and the environment. We have the technology to use light effectively and to reduce light pollution. Let's encourage our municipal officials, businesses, and our neighbours to take advantage of these improvements.

Reference

www.starlight-theatre.ca/LT-POLLUTION.HTM

DEEP-SKY OBSERVING HINTS
BY ALAN DYER

In the 1960s and 1970s, few observers owned telescopes larger than 200-mm aperture. Today, 250-mm to 600-mm Dobsonian-mounted reflectors are commonplace. Using computerized telescopes, observers can now find thousands of objects at the push of a button. As a result, deep-sky observing has soared in popularity.

However, owners of less-sophisticated, small-aperture instruments shouldn't think they are shut out of deep-sky viewing. In a dark sky, an 80-mm to 100-mm telescope will show all the Messier objects and reveal hundreds of brighter NGC (New General Catalogue) objects. In fact, many large objects are best seen in fast (f/4 to f/6), small-aperture telescopes or in giant 70-mm and 80-mm binoculars. Contrary to popular belief, even slow f-ratio instruments (f/11 to f/16) are useful; their only disadvantage is the difficulty of achieving a low-power wide field. No matter what telescope you use, follow these techniques to get the most out of a night's deep-sky viewing:

- Always plan each night's observing: Prepare a list of a dozen or so objects for the night. Hunt them down on star charts or with computer programs first during the day to become familiar with their location.
- Seek out dark skies; a black sky improves contrast and makes up for lack of aperture.
- To preserve night vision, always use a dim red flashlight for reading charts.
- Avoid prolonged exposure to bright sunlight earlier in the day (such as a day at the beach); it will reduce your ability to dark adapt and make for tired eyes at night.
- Use averted vision; looking to one side of an object places it on a more sensitive part of the retina.
- Another technique for picking out faint objects is to jiggle the telescope (and the image) slightly.
- Don't be afraid to use high power; it often brings out small, faint objects such as planetary nebulae and galaxies and resolves detail in globulars, in small, rich open clusters, and in bright galaxies.
- Use a nebular filter on emission and planetary nebulae (see FILTERS on p. 67); even in a dark sky, filters can dramatically enhance the view of these kinds of objects, often making obvious an otherwise elusive nebula.
- Be comfortable; sit down while at the eyepiece and be sure to dress warmly.
- Collimate and clean your optics; a poorly maintained telescope will produce distorted star images, reduce image contrast, and make it more difficult to see faint stars and other threshold objects.
- Don't expect to use analogue setting circles; in a portable telescope "dial-type" circles will rarely be accurate.
- Digital setting circles and Go To telescopes can find objects precisely. While they are wonderful observing aids, they can overwhelm observers with thousands of targets, often supplying scant information about each one. When making a list for a night's viewing, books such as the three-volume *Burnham's Celestial Handbook* and the two-volume *Night Sky Observer's Guide* by Kepple and Sanner are still the best guides.
- Don't be in a rush to check off targets; take time to examine each object, and take notes or make drawings. Both will help train your eye to see subtle detail; you'll learn to see the most through your telescope.
- Consider keeping a logbook or journal of your nightly tours of the sky; including eyepiece impressions and drawings provides a record of your improving observing skills that is fun to look back upon in future years. See the section THE OBSERVING LOGBOOK (immediately following) for suggestions on organizing a journal.

THE OBSERVING LOGBOOK
BY PAUL MARKOV

There are many good reasons for maintaining an observing logbook: A logbook is useful for recalling the details of previous observations and comparing past observations with current ones; maintaining one will make your observing organized and methodical; and having to describe an object forces you to *look* for more details, thus sharpening your observing skills. Finally, if you are planning to apply for an observing certificate (e.g. the RASC's Explore the Universe, Messier, or Finest NGC Certificate; see p. 319), then a logbook with your observations may be required when submitting your application.

Logbooks can be chronological or sectional. In a chronological logbook all observations are listed sequentially by date, regardless of object type. In a sectional logbook observations are grouped by object type, such as open clusters and galaxies. With either format, you may want to keep a master index of objects for cross referencing to the correct page in your logbook.

What about the book itself? Typical choices are the simple three-ring binder with standard lined paper, spiral-bound notebooks, and hardcover record/accounting books. In my opinion, the most practical is the three-ring binder because it allows you to insert auxiliary materials into your logbook with the help of a three-hole punch. With this choice, entering observations out of sequence is never an issue because you can easily rearrange the sheets. Also, should you wish to make a "soft" copy of your logbook using a photocopier that outputs Adobe Acrobat PDF files, it is much easier with loose sheets.

For recording observations, using a preprinted observing form offers these advantages: the fill-in-the-blank fields remind you to record the relevant data; many of these forms have a space for making a drawing of the observed object; and they give your book a neat and organized look. An example of an observing form can be found at www.rasc.ca/handbook/obsform.pdf; you may prefer to design your own observing form by using the fields suggested below. However, I prefer to use plain lined paper as there is less repetition when writing observing session details, and I do not have to worry about using different forms for different objects or running out of forms.

There are two choices for recording your observations: using full sentences and using acronyms and abbreviations. Using full sentences is the preferred method if you enjoy re-reading your observations from past years, or if you want others to be able to easily read your logbook. But if your intent is to keep a data book for reference purposes only, then acronyms and abbreviations are the recommended choices.

It is useful to record the following information for each observing session: date; time of arrival and departure (if you have travelled somewhere to observe); location; names of other people at the observing site; sky transparency (i.e. clarity of the atmosphere, which is generally noted by faintest visible stellar magnitude; see LIMITING MAGNITUDES p. 73); seeing (i.e. the steadiness of the atmosphere: if stars and planets appear to shimmer, that indicates poor seeing; if they appear sharp and steady, that indicates good seeing), and environmental conditions (e.g. temperature, dew, wind, sources of light pollution, snow cover, and mosquitoes). You can also number each observing session sequentially for easy referencing within your logbook.

Be sure to standardize your time/date format. For recording time, choose either the military time or a.m./p.m. format. In addition, use alpha characters to specify the month rather than numbers. For example, use 2011 Aug. 5 instead of 8/5/11; this will avoid ambiguity in reading the date.

For each object observed, record the following information as a minimum: date and time of observation, object name or designation, type of object, constellation, telescope and magnification used, type of filter (if any), and visual description. Making drawings is highly recommended and adds substantially to the value of your logbook. It is also

important to record failed observations because these entries will remind you to try again in your next observing session. Remember to update the observing notes if the sky conditions change, if you have equipment trouble, if you take extended "coffee breaks," or if you see something unusual like a fireball or aurora.

If you are able to write neatly while observing, it is best to enter observations directly into your logbook. However, if this proves too difficult given the environmental circumstances, you can record your observations in a temporary notebook and transcribe them into your logbook the next day. An audio recorder can also be used if you are careful to ensure its mechanical integrity while in the field and if you are diligent enough to transcribe the recorded observations into your observing logbook regularly. Below are some suggestions on what to look for when observing deep-sky objects.

All Object Types: What is the shape of the object? What is its size (based on the field of view of your eyepiece)? Is averted vision required to see the object? Does averted vision allow you to see more detail? (If yes, describe the extra detail.) Is the object near (or in the same field of view as) other deep-sky objects or bright stars? What magnification gives the best view of the object? Does a filter improve the view? (See the section FILTERS on p. 69.)

Open Cluster: Is there a greater concentration of stars in a specific part of the cluster? Is it fully resolved into its component stars, or are there any unresolved stars causing the cluster to appear nebulous? How many stars can you see (only if reasonable to count them)? Are there any bright stars within the cluster? Are there any coloured stars? (If so, describe their tints and locations within the cluster.) Does the cluster stand out from the background star field?

Globular Cluster: What is the degree of star concentration (high, medium, low)? How much can be resolved to component stars (none, outer edges, middle, to the core)?

Galaxy: Is it uniform in brightness, or does it have a brighter nucleus? Is it diffuse or stellar? Can any detail or mottling be seen in the arms? Are any stars visible within the arms?

Emission or Reflection Nebula: Is the brightness even, or are there brighter/darker areas? Are the edges of the nebula well defined? Are there any stars within the nebula? Is there a hint of any colour?

Planetary Nebula: Is it stellar in appearance, or can a disk be seen? Are the edges well defined or diffuse? Are there any brighter/darker areas? Can a central star be seen? Is there a hint of any colour? Can it be "blinked" with a filter or averted vision?

Dark Nebula: Is it easy or difficult to discern the dark nebula from the background sky? Are there any stars within the nebula?

Logbooks and Databases

If you enjoy using computers, an electronic database can be a helpful complement to an observing logbook. You can obtain commercially available deep-sky databases that allow you to enter your own observations for any object. These databases are also useful for creating observing lists and planning observing sessions. A highly recommended database, which also happens to be freeware, is the Saguaro Astronomy Club (SAC) deep-sky database, available at **www.saguaroastro.org**. With minimal tweaking, the SAC database can be formatted to accept your own observations.

You can transcribe complete observations from your logbook into the database or simply enter four valuable pieces of information for each observed object: seen (Y/N), date, telescope used, and location. With these fields filled in, in a matter of seconds you can determine which and how many objects you have observed, and the date field for any object will direct you to the correct page in your observing logbook. You can also determine interesting facts such as from which observing location you observed the most objects or which telescope produced the most observations.

THE SKY MONTH BY MONTH

LEFT-HAND PAGES BY
DAVE LANE (TABLES) AND ROY BISHOP (TEXT)

INTRODUCTION

In the descriptions on the left-hand monthly pages (pp. 102–124), the right ascension (**RA**), declination (**Dec**) (both for equinox J2000.0), distance from Earth's centre in astronomical units (**Dist**), visual magnitude (**Mag**), and equatorial angular diameter (**Size**) are tabulated for seven planets for 0h UT on the 1st, 11th, and 21st day of each month. The RA, Dec, distance, and diameter of the Sun are also given. **With an error of no more than a minute or two, on the left-hand pages the UT for meridian transit at Greenwich may be read as Standard Time at an observer's standard meridian. If the observer is west (east) of the standard meridian, the Standard Time of transit will be later (earlier) by 4 min per degree of longitude difference from the standard meridian.**

Sun

Data concerning the position, transit, orientation, rotation, and activity of the Sun plus times of sunrise and sunset appear on pp. 187–188, 192–196, and 208–210. For detailed information on this year's solar eclipses, see ECLIPSES IN 2011 on p. 130.

Moon

Conjunctions of the Moon with the naked-eye planets and the bright Messier objects that lie near the ecliptic—the Beehive Cluster (M44), M35, and the Pleiades Cluster (M45)—are given in the right-hand monthly tables (pp. 103–125). Only events for which the elongation of the Moon is at least 14° are included, and only selected such events involving the Messier objects are listed. See p. 20 for the definition of conjunction and elongation.

The Moon's phases and perigees and apogees (distances from *Astronomical Tables of the Sun, Moon, and Planets*, by Jean Meeus, 2nd ed., Willmann-Bell, 1995) are also given in the right-hand tables. The phases new Moon, first quarter, full Moon, and last quarter correspond, respectively, to the Moon having a longitude 0°, 90°, 180°, and 270° east of that of the Sun. The age of the Moon is the time since the new phase; first-quarter, full, and last-quarter phases correspond approximately to 7.4, 14.8, and 22.1 days, respectively. For times of moonrise and moonset, see pp. 154–161.

The Sun's selenographic colongitude (SSC), given on the left-hand monthly pages, indicates the position of the sunrise terminator as it moves across the face of the Moon and provides a method of ascertaining the angle of illumination of features on the Moon's surface. The SSC is the angle of the sunrise terminator measured toward the observer's east (i.e. westward on the Moon) starting from the lunar meridian that passes through the mean centre of the apparent disk. Its value increases by nearly 12.2° per day, or about 0.5° per hour, and is approximately 0°, 90°, 180°, and 270° at the first-quarter, full, last-quarter, and new phases, respectively. Values of the SSC are given on pp. 102–124 for the 0th day of each month.

Selenographic longitude (λ) is measured toward the observer's west (i.e. eastward on the Moon) from the mean central lunar meridian. Thus sunrise will occur at a given point on the Moon when SSC = 360° − λ; values of 360° − λ for several lunar features are listed in the MAP OF MOON on p. 152. The longitude of the sunset terminator differs by 180° from that of the sunrise terminator.

Libration, also given on the left-hand pages, is the apparent rocking motion of the Moon as it orbits Earth. As a consequence, over time, about 59 percent of the lunar surface can be viewed from Earth (see *Sky & Telescope*, July 1987, p. 60). Libration in longitude (±8°) results from the nearly uniform axial rotation of the Moon combined with its varying orbital speed along its elliptical orbit, while libration in latitude (±7°) is caused by the tilt of the Moon's equator to its orbital plane. A smaller contribution (up to ±1°), called *diurnal libration*, is associated with the shifting of the observer due to Earth's rotation.

When the libration in longitude is positive, more of the Moon's east limb, the limb near Mare Crisium, is exposed to view (in reference to the lunar limbs, *east* and *west* are used in this lunar sense; see also the "E" and "W" labels on the MAP OF MOON, p. 152). When the libration in latitude is positive, more of the Moon's north limb is exposed to view. The monthly dates of the greatest positive and negative values of the libration in longitude and latitude and the dates of greatest northern and southern declination are given on the left-hand pages.

The lunar graphics on the right-hand pages give the geocentric appearance of the Moon at 0h UT on odd-numbered days of the month. They depict the Moon's phase, size, and libration. A small dot of size proportional to the amount of libration appears near the limb that is exposed. The graphics were prepared by Rajiv Gupta from images provided by Roger Fell using the *Lunar Calculator* computer program written by Alister Ling (see **www3.telus.net/public/aling/lunarcal/lunarcal.htm**). Lunar libration, phase, and distance data provided by Dave Lane is generated by custom-made software.

The Moon's orbit is inclined 5°09′ to the ecliptic. The gravitational influences of Earth and the Sun cause (i) the orbital plane to wobble, and (ii) the major axis of the orbit to precess. (i) The wobble shifts the line of nodes (see below) westward (retrograde) along the ecliptic with a period of 18.60 years. During 2011, the ascending node regresses from longitude 272.3° to 253.0°, moving from Sagittarius into Ophiuchus over the course of the year. The monthly range of the Moon's declination continues to decrease from its 2006 maximum of ±29° (Jan. 17 for extreme northern declination of +24.2°, and Jan. 2 for the extreme southern declination of −24.1°). (ii) The precession shifts the perigee point eastward (prograde) with a period of 8.85 years, although the positions of successive perigees fluctuate considerably from the mean motion. The Moon's mean equatorial plane, its mean orbital plane, and the plane of the ecliptic intersect along a common line of nodes, the equator being inclined at 1°32′ to the ecliptic and at 1°32′ + 5°09′ = 6°41′ to the orbit (i.e. the ascending node of the equator on the ecliptic coincides with the descending node of the orbit).

Jupiter's Satellites

The configurations of Jupiter's Galilean satellites, provided by Larry Bogan, are given on the right-hand monthly pages. In these diagrams the vertical double line represents the equatorial diameter of the disk of Jupiter. Time is shown on the vertical scale, successive horizontal lines indicating 0h UT on the various days of the month. The relative east–west positions of the four satellites with respect to the disk of Jupiter are given by the four curves, where I = Io, II = Europa (dashed curve), III = Ganymede, and IV = Callisto. Note the "West–East" orientation given at the top of each diagram; these directions are those of the observer's sky, not Jupiter's limbs, and correspond to the view in an inverting telescope.

Double-shadow transits of Jupiter's Galilean satellites that are not within 1.5 months of Jupiter's conjunction with the Sun are listed. Double-satellite transits that are not accompanied by a double-shadow event are generally also listed. For more information about the various transits, occultations, and eclipses of Jupiter's Galilean satellites, see PHENOMENA OF THE GALILEAN SATELLITES (p. 239).

Occultations Involving the Moon, Stars, Planets, and Asteroids

Occultations by the Moon of the bright stars that lie near the ecliptic—Aldebaran, Antares, Regulus, and Spica—and of the planets and bright asteroids—Ceres, Pallas, Juno, and Vesta—are given in the right-hand tables. If the elongation of the Moon is less than 14°, the event is not listed. Footnotes give areas of visibility; for more details on occultations visible in North America, including several involving members of the Pleiades (M45), see OCCULTATIONS BY THE MOON (p.166) and PLANETARY AND ASTEROIDAL OCCULTATIONS (p. 253).

Minima of Algol

Predicted times of mid-eclipse are based on the formula heliocentric minimum = 245 2253.567 + 2.867 321E and are expressed as geocentric times for comparison with observations. The first number is the Julian Date for the minimum of 2001 Dec. 10.067, and the second is the period of Algol in days; E is an integer.

Planets

Conjunctions of the planets with each other and the bright ecliptic stars and Messier objects are listed in the right-hand tables, with the elongation of the inner planet indicated in parentheses. Only events for which the elongation of the inner planet is greater than 11° are included, and not all events involving the Messier objects are listed. Also included are oppositions, conjunctions with the Sun, greatest elongations, and stationary times. See pp. 20–21 for definitions of these terms, and TABLE OF CONTENTS or the INDEX for the location of more information on each of the planets. The diagrams below give an overview of the circumstances of the planets in 2011.

Miscellaneous Entries

The lunation number is the number of times the Moon has circled the Earth since January 1923, based on a series described by Ernest W. Brown in *Planetary Theory*, 1933. Peaks of major meteor showers (see also p. 260), equinoxes and solstices, heliocentric phenomena of the planets, phenomena of the bright asteroids, and a few other events and occasional notes are given in the right-hand tables.

MAGNITUDES OF NAKED-EYE PLANETS IN 2011

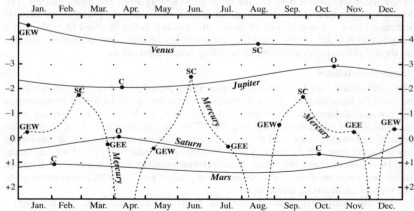

The visual magnitudes of the five classical (naked-eye) planets during 2011 are given. Oppositions (O), conjunctions (C), inferior and superior conjunctions (IC, SC), and greatest elongations east and west (GEE, GEW) are indicated. A diagram explaining these terms is on p. 21. Greatest illuminated extent, (GIE), if shown, occurs when the illuminated area of Venus, as viewed from Earth, covers the most square degrees.

RIGHT ASCENSIONS OF THE SUN, PLANETS, AND PLUTO IN 2011

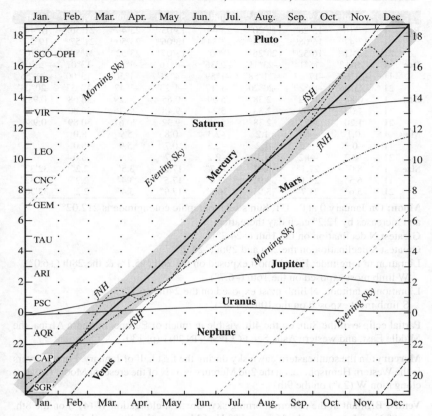

This diagram shows the variation during the year in the right ascension (vertical axis) of the Sun, the planets, and Pluto. The slightly curved, heavy diagonal line represents the Sun; the shaded regions approximately indicate parts of the night sky affected by twilight. The two thin, dashed diagonal lines at the upper left and lower right represent the boundary between the evening sky and the morning sky.

The diagram may be used to determine in what part of the sky a planet may be found (including in which constellation—note the abbreviations along the vertical axis), when a superior planet is in conjunction with the Sun or at opposition (opposition is approximately where its curve intersects the dashed diagonal lines, and note that, due to retrograde motion, this point is also where the planet's curve has its maximum negative slope), when Mercury and Venus have their various greatest elongations and conjunctions, and when there are conjunctions of planets—that is, when the curves for two planets intersect. For example, note the opposition of Saturn in early April, Mercury, Venus, and Mars coming together in the morning in late May. Neptune, Uranus, and Jupiter reach opposition later in the year at roughly monthly intervals.

For observers in mid-latitudes, at certain times of the year the ecliptic stands steeply to the horizon in the western evening sky or the eastern morning sky, making apparitions of planets in these parts of the sky favourable from the Northern Hemisphere ("fNH" on the diagram) or favourable from the Southern Hemisphere ("fSH").

For more information on all these events, see the following 24 monthly pages and THE PLANETS FOR 2011 *(p. 214).*

THE SKY FOR JANUARY

		Mercury	Venus	Mars	Jupiter	Saturn	Uranus	Neptune	Sun
RA	1	17ʰ16ᵐ	15ʰ28ᵐ	19ʰ20ᵐ	23ʰ49ᵐ	13ʰ05ᵐ	23ʰ49ᵐ	21ʰ56ᵐ	18ʰ44ᵐ
	11	17ʰ47ᵐ	16ʰ08ᵐ	19ʰ53ᵐ	23ʰ54ᵐ	13ʰ06ᵐ	23ʰ50ᵐ	21ʰ57ᵐ	19ʰ28ᵐ
	21	18ʰ41ᵐ	16ʰ52ᵐ	20ʰ26ᵐ	0ʰ00ᵐ	13ʰ07ᵐ	23ʰ52ᵐ	21ʰ58ᵐ	20ʰ10ᵐ
Dec	1	−20°12′	−15°14′	−23°11′	−2°36′	−4°16′	−1°57′	−13°07′	−23°03′
	11	−21°56′	−17°27′	−21°58′	−1°59′	−4°21′	−1°50′	−13°00′	−21°55′
	21	−23°06′	−19°20′	−20°20′	−1°17′	−4°23′	−1°42′	−12°53′	−20°04′
Dist	1	0.84	0.62	2.38	5.09	9.65	20.29	30.68	0.983
	11	1.04	0.69	2.38	5.24	9.48	20.46	30.80	0.983
	21	1.20	0.77	2.38	5.38	9.32	20.61	30.89	0.984
Mag	1	0.1	−4.4	1.2	−2.3	0.8	5.9	8.0	
	11	−0.3	−4.3	1.2	−2.3	0.7	5.9	8.0	
	21	−0.2	−4.2	1.1	−2.2	0.7	5.9	8.0	
Size	1	8.0″	27.1″	3.9″	38.7″	17.2″	3.5″	2.2″	32′32″
	11	6.5″	24.1″	3.9″	37.6″	17.5″	3.4″	2.2″	32′32″
	21	5.6″	21.7″	3.9″	36.6″	17.9″	3.4″	2.2″	32′30″

Moon: On January 0 at 0h UT, Sun's selenographic colongitude is 212.02° and increases by 12.2° each day thereafter.
Greatest N declination on the 16th (+24.2°).
Greatest S declination on the 2nd and 29th (−24.2°).
Libration in longitude: E limb most exposed on the 2nd (+5.1°) & the 28th (+6.0°),
    W limb most exposed on the 16th (−6.7°).
Libration in latitude: N limb most exposed on the 24th (+6.7°),
    S limb most exposed on the 10th (−6.8°)

Partial eclipse of the Sun, on the 4th, visible in much of Europe, northern Africa, the Middle East, and western Asia. See ECLIPSES IN 2011 (p. 130).

Mercury: In the southeastern dawn sky during the first half of January. For observers in the Western Hemisphere, on the 2nd Mercury is 5° N of the crescent Moon. Greatest elongation W (23°) on the 9th.

Venus: Brilliant in the eastern morning sky. Greatest elongation W (47°) on the 8th. Lies 8° N of Antares on the 15th, and 3° N of Moon on the 30th at 4h UT.

Mars: Not visible. Approaching conjunction with the Sun (Feb. 4)

Jupiter: In the early evening sky in Pisces. Sets in late evening. Meridian transit at Greenwich on the 1st and 16th at 17:05 and 16:14 UT*. Uranus lies 0.6° N of Jupiter on the 2nd, the last of the recent triplet of Jupiter-Uranus geocentric conjunctions (see Jun. 6 and Sep. 22 of last year's Handbook), and the last conjunction of these two planets until 2024

Saturn: Morning sky in Virgo, 4° S of the celestial equator, rising near midnight. Begins retrograde motion on the 27th. Meridian transit at Greenwich on the 1st and 16th at 06:22 and 05:25 UT*. The N side of Saturn's rings is visible during 2011, their tilt varying from 10.1° early in January to a minimum of 7.3° in early June, and opening to 14.8° by year-end.

Uranus: In the western evening sky in Pisces, and sets late evening (see Jupiter above).

Neptune: Low in the western early evening sky on the Aquarius-Capricornus border. Vanishes into the evening twilight by month-end, approaching conjunction.

*See the last two sentences of the first paragraph on p. 98.

Time (UT) d h m	JANUARY EVENTS	Jupiter's Satellites West East

Sat.	1		
Sun.	2	13	**Jupiter 0.6° S of Uranus**
		15	Mercury 4° N of Moon
Mon.	3	19	Earth at perihelion (147 105 721 km)
		19 40	Algol at minimum
		19 11	**Double shadow transit on Jupiter**
Tue.	4	1	**Quadrantid meteors peak**
		9 03	**New Moon** (lunation 1089)
			Partial Solar Eclipse (p. 130)
Wed.	5		
Thu.	6	16 30	Algol at minimum
Fri.	7		
Sat.	8	16	**Venus greatest elongation W (47°)**
Sun.	9	13 19	Algol at minimum
		15	**Mercury greatest elongation W (23°)**
Mon.	10	3 50	**Double satellite transit on Jupiter**
		6	Moon at apogee (404 977 km)
		17	Jupiter 7° S of Moon
		21 07	**Double shadow transit on Jupiter**
Tue.	11		
Wed.	12	10 08	Algol at minimum
		11 31	**First Quarter**
Thu.	13		
Fri.	14	8	Mercury 1.9° N of Lagoon (M8)
Sat.	15	6 57	Algol at minimum
		13	**Moon 1.3° S of Pleiades (M45)**
		21	Venus 8° N of Antares
Sun.	16		
Mon.	17	21 52	**Double satellite transit on Jupiter**
		23	**Moon 0.9° S of M35**
Tue.	18	0 43	**Double shadow transit on Jupiter**
			Venus at greatest heliocentric lat. N
		3 47	Algol at minimum
Wed.	19	21 21	**Full Moon**
Thu.	20		
Fri.	21		Mercury at descending node
		0 36	Algol at minimum
Sat.	22	0	Moon at perigee (362 792 km)
		23	Juno stationary
Sun.	23	21 25	Algol at minimum
Mon.	24		
Tue.	25	0 05	**Double satellite transit on Jupiter**
		10	Saturn 8° N of Moon
Wed.	26	12 57	**Last Quarter**
		18 14	Algol at minimum
Thu.	27	8	Saturn stationary
Fri.	28		
Sat.	29	15 04	Algol at minimum
Sun.	30	4	Venus 3° N of Moon
Mon.	31		Mercury at aphelion

Jupiter's Satellites scale: 1.0 – 31.0 with satellites I, II, III, IV

THE SKY FOR FEBRUARY

		Mercury	Venus	Mars	Jupiter	Saturn	Uranus	Neptune	Sun
RA	1	19^h50^m	17^h44^m	21^h01^m	0^h08^m	13^h07^m	23^h53^m	22^h00^m	20^h56^m
	11	20^h57^m	18^h32^m	21^h32^m	0^h15^m	13^h06^m	23^h55^m	22^h01^m	21^h36^m
	21	22^h05^m	19^h22^m	22^h03^m	0^h23^m	13^h05^m	23^h57^m	22^h03^m	22^h15^m
Dec	1	−22°19′	−20°43′	−18°06′	−0°26′	−4°20′	−1°31′	−12°45′	−17°18′
	11	−19°19′	−21°09′	−15°44′	+0°24′	−4°13′	−1°20′	−12°38′	−14°15′
	21	−14°00′	−20°39′	−13°06′	+1°16′	−4°03′	−1°08′	−12°30′	−10°49′
Dist	1	1.32	0.85	2.38	5.52	9.14	20.76	30.96	0.985
	11	1.38	0.92	2.37	5.64	9.00	20.87	30.99	0.987
	21	1.39	1.00	2.37	5.74	8.87	20.96	31.00	0.989
Mag	1	−0.3	−4.1	1.1	−2.2	0.6	5.9	8.0	
	11	−0.6	−4.1	1.1	−2.1	0.6	5.9	8.0	
	21	−1.3	−4.0	1.1	−2.1	0.5	5.9	8.0	
Size	1	5.1″	19.6″	3.9″	35.7″	18.2″	3.4″	2.2″	32′28″
	11	4.9″	18.0″	3.9″	34.9″	18.5″	3.4″	2.2″	32′25″
	21	4.8″	16.7″	4.0″	34.3″	18.7″	3.3″	2.2″	32′21″

Moon: On February 0 at 0 UT, Sun's selenographic colongitude is 228.97° and increases by 12.2° each day thereafter.

Greatest N declination on the 13th (+24.1°).

Greatest S declination on the 25th (−24.0°).

Libration in longitude: E limb most exposed on the 25th (+7.4°),
    W limb most exposed on the 13th (−7.6°).

Libration in latitude: N limb most exposed on the 20th (+6.6°),
    S limb most exposed on the 7th (−6.7°).

Large tides on the 18th, 19th, 20th, and 21st.

Mercury: Vanishes into the dawn twilight early in the month. Superior conjunction on the 25th.

Venus: Brilliant in the eastern morning sky. Angle of the ecliptic favours observers in Southern Hemisphere.

Mars: Not visible. In conjunction with Sun on the 4th.

Jupiter: In the early evening western sky. Sets in mid-evening. Jupiter crosses to the north side of the celestial equator on the 5th, where it will remain until 2016 Sep. 21.

Saturn: Morning sky, retrograding in Virgo. Rises in mid-evening. Meridian transit at Greenwich on the 1st and 16th at 04:22 and 03:22 UT*.

Uranus: Vanishes into the evening twilight by month-end, approaching conjunction.

Neptune: Not visible. In conjunction with Sun on the 17th.

*See the last two sentences of the first paragraph on p. 98.

Time (UT) d h m	FEBRUARY EVENTS	Jupiter's Satellites West East
Tue. 1	Jupiter at greatest heliocentric lat. S	
11 53	Algol at minimum	
18	Mercury 4° S of Moon	
Wed. 2		
Thu. 3 2 31	**New Moon** (lunation 1090)	
Fri. 4 8 42	Algol at minimum	
16	Mars in conjunction with the Sun	
Sat. 5 4	Venus 3° N of Lagoon (M8)	
Sun. 6 23	Moon at apogee (405 924 km)	
Mon. 7 5 32	Algol at minimum	
10	Jupiter 7° S of Moon	
Tue. 8		
Wed. 9		
Thu. 10 2 21	Algol at minimum	
Fri. 11	Mars at greatest heliocentric lat. S	
7 18	**First Quarter**	
22	**Moon 1.4° S of Pleiades (M45)**	
Sat. 12 23 10	Algol at minimum	
Sun. 13		
Mon. 14 10	**Moon 1.0° S of M35**	
Tue. 15 20 00	Algol at minimum	
Wed. 16		
Thu. 17 10	Neptune in conjunction with the Sun	
Fri. 18 8 36	**Full Moon**	
16 49	Algol at minimum	
Sat. 19 7	Moon at perigee (358247 km) **Large tides**	
Sun. 20	Mercury at greatest heliocentric lat. S	
	Zodiacal Light vis. in N lat. in W	
	after evening twilight for next two weeks	
Mon. 21 13 38	Algol at minimum	
17	Saturn 8° N of Moon	
Tue. 22		
Wed. 23		
Thu. 24 10 27	Algol at minimum	
23 26	**Last Quarter**	
Fri. 25 9	Mercury in superior conjunction	
Sun. 27 7 17	Algol at minimum	
Mon. 28 0	**Vesta 0.9° N of Moon, occultation†**	

† Antarctica, S Pacific Ocean

THE SKY FOR MARCH

		Mercury	Venus	Mars	Jupiter	Saturn	Uranus	Neptune	Sun
RA	1	23ʰ00ᵐ	20ʰ02ᵐ	22ʰ27ᵐ	0ʰ30ᵐ	13ʰ03ᵐ	23ʰ58ᵐ	22ʰ04ᵐ	22ʰ46ᵐ
	11	0ʰ08ᵐ	20ʰ51ᵐ	22ʰ57ᵐ	0ʰ38ᵐ	13ʰ01ᵐ	0ʰ00ᵐ	22ʰ05ᵐ	23ʰ23ᵐ
	21	1ʰ04ᵐ	21ʰ39ᵐ	23ʰ26ᵐ	0ʰ47ᵐ	12ʰ59ᵐ	0ʰ02ᵐ	22ʰ07ᵐ	23ʰ59ᵐ
Dec	1	–8°07'	–19°34'	–10°50'	+2°00'	–3°52'	–0°57'	–12°24'	–7°52'
	11	+0°45'	–17°23'	–7°51'	+2°55'	–3°36'	–0°44'	–12°16'	–4°00'
	21	+8°55'	–14°23'	–4°45'	+3°51'	–3°19'	–0°30'	–12°09'	–0°03'
Dist	1	1.35	1.05	2.36	5.80	8.79	21.02	30.98	0.991
	11	1.21	1.12	2.36	5.87	8.70	21.07	30.94	0.993
	21	0.96	1.19	2.35	5.92	8.64	21.08	30.87	0.996
Mag	1	–1.7	–4.0	1.1	–2.1	0.5	5.9	8.0	
	11	–1.2	–3.9	1.1	–2.1	0.4	5.9	8.0	
	21	–0.5	–3.9	1.2	–2.1	0.4	5.9	8.0	
Size	1	5.0"	15.8"	4.0"	34.0"	18.9"	3.3"	2.2"	32'17"
	11	5.6"	14.9"	4.0"	33.6"	19.1"	3.3"	2.2"	32'12"
	21	7.0"	14.0"	4.0"	33.3"	19.2"	3.3"	2.2"	32'07"

Moon: On March 0 at 0 UT, Sun's selenographic colongitude is 209.59° and increases by 12.2° each day thereafter.
Greatest N declination on the 12th (+23.8°).
Greatest S declination on the 25th (–23.7°).
Libration in longitude: E limb most exposed on the 25th (+7.6°),
 W limb most exposed on the 13th (–8.0°).
Libration in latitude: N limb most exposed on the 19th (+6.5°),
 S limb most exposed on the 6th (–6.6°).

Large tides on the 19th, 20th, 21st, and 22nd.

Mercury: Western evening sky during the last half of March. Passes 2° N of Jupiter on the 16th. The tilt of the ecliptic plus Mercury's northern heliocentric latitude in late March favours observers in the Northern Hemisphere. At greatest elongation E (19°) on the 23rd and dims rapidly during the last week of March.

Venus: Brilliant in the eastern morning sky. Angle of the ecliptic favours observers in Southern Hemisphere. Lies 1.6° S of Moon on the 1st at 4h UT, and 6° S of Moon on the 31st at 13h UT.

Mars: Not visible. Was in conjunction with Sun last month.

Jupiter: Vanishes into the evening twilight during March. Reaches perihelion on the 17th, the first time since 1999 and, by a small amount, its smallest perihelion distance in over half a century. Also, see Mercury above.

Saturn: Rises early evening. Retrograding in Virgo. Meridian transit at Greenwich on the 1st and 16th at 02:29 and 01:26 UT*.

Uranus: Not visible. In conjunction with Sun on the 21st. Passes 0.8°S of the vernal equinox on the 6th.

Neptune: Reappears in the morning sky this month, near the Aquarius-Capricornus border. Angle of ecliptic favors observers in Southern Hemisphere.

*See the last two sentences of the first paragraph on p. 98.

Time (UT) d h m	MARCH EVENTS	Jupiter's Satellites West East
Tue. 1 4	**Venus 1.6° S of Moon**	
Wed. 2 4 06	Algol at minimum	1.0
Thu. 3		2.0
Fri. 4 20 46	**New Moon** (lunation 1091)	I
Sat. 5 0 55	Algol at minimum	3.0
Sun. 6 8	Moon at apogee (406 583 km)	4.0 II
Mon. 7 5	Jupiter 7° S of Moon	5.0
21 44	Algol at minimum	IV
Tue. 8		6.0
Wed. 9	Mars at perihelion	7.0 III
Thu. 10 18 34	Algol at minimum	
Fri. 11	Mercury at ascending node	8.0
5	**Moon 1.7° S of Pleiades (M45)**	9.0
Sat. 12 10	**Juno at opposition**	
23 45	**First Quarter**	10.0
Sun. 13	**Daylight Saving Time begins**	11.0
15 23	Algol at minimum	
19	**Moon 1.2° S of M35**	12.0
Mon. 14		13.0
Tue. 15	Venus at descending node	14.0
Wed. 16	Mercury at perihelion	
12 12	Algol at minimum	15.0
17	**Mercury 2° N of Jupiter**	16.0
Thu. 17	Jupiter at perihelion	
Fri. 18		17.0
Sat. 19 9 01	Algol at minimum	18.0
18 10	**Full Moon** (largest in 2011)	
19	Moon at perigee (356575 km) **Large tides**	19.0
Sun. 20 23 21	**Equinox**	20.0
Mon. 21	**Zodiacal Light vis. in N lat. in W after evening twilight for next two weeks**	21.0
0	Saturn 8° N of Moon	22.0
12	Uranus in conjunction with the Sun	
Tue. 22 5 51	Algol at minimum	23.0
Wed. 23 1	**Mercury greatest elongation E (19°)**	24.0
Thu. 24		
Fri. 25 2 40	Algol at minimum	25.0
Sat. 26 12 07	**Last Quarter**	26.0
Sun. 27	Mercury at greatest heliocentric lat. N	
0	**Venus 0.1° S of Neptune**	27.0
23 29	Algol at minimum	28.0
Mon. 28 7	**Vesta 1.2° S of Moon, occultation†**	29.0
Tue. 29		
Wed. 30 17	Mercury stationary	30.0
20 18	Algol at minimum	31.0
Thu. 31 13	Venus 6° S of Moon	

† Iceland

THE SKY FOR APRIL

		Mercury	Venus	Mars	Jupiter	Saturn	Uranus	Neptune	Sun
RA	1	1ʰ24ᵐ	22ʰ31ᵐ	23ʰ57ᵐ	0ʰ57ᵐ	12ʰ56ᵐ	0ʰ05ᵐ	22ʰ08ᵐ	0ʰ40ᵐ
	11	1ʰ05ᵐ	23ʰ16ᵐ	0ʰ26ᵐ	1ʰ06ᵐ	12ʰ53ᵐ	0ʰ07ᵐ	22ʰ09ᵐ	1ʰ16ᵐ
	21	0ʰ49ᵐ	0ʰ01ᵐ	0ʰ54ᵐ	1ʰ15ᵐ	12ʰ50ᵐ	0ʰ09ᵐ	22ʰ10ᵐ	1ʰ53ᵐ
Dec	1	+12°27′	−10°18′	−1°18′	+4°53′	−2°59′	−0°15′	−12°02′	+4°16′
	11	+9°14′	−6°05′	+1°51′	+5°49′	−2°41′	−0°02′	−11°56′	+8°03′
	21	+4°38′	−1°33′	+4°56′	+6°44′	−2°24′	+0°10′	−11°51′	+11°37′
Dist	1	0.69	1.26	2.35	5.94	8.62	21.07	30.76	0.999
	11	0.58	1.32	2.34	5.95	8.62	21.03	30.64	1.002
	21	0.61	1.38	2.33	5.93	8.66	20.96	30.50	1.005
Mag	1	2.1	−3.8	1.2	−2.1	0.4	5.9	8.0	
	11	5.9	−3.8	1.2	−2.1	0.4	5.9	7.9	
	21	2.3	−3.8	1.2	−2.1	0.4	5.9	7.9	
Size	1	9.7″	13.2″	4.0″	33.2″	19.3″	3.3″	2.2″	32′01″
	11	11.5″	12.6″	4.0″	33.1″	19.3″	3.3″	2.2″	31′56″
	21	10.9″	12.1″	4.0″	33.2″	19.2″	3.3″	2.2″	31′50″

Moon: On April 0 at 0 UT, Sun's selenographic colongitude is 227.19° and increases by 12.2° each day thereafter.

Greatest N declination on the 8th (+23.6°).

Greatest S declination on the 21st (−23.4°).

Libration in longitude: E limb most exposed on the 22nd (+7.2°),
   W limb most exposed on the 11th (−7.6°).

Libration in latitude: N limb most exposed on the 16th (+6.6°),
   S limb most exposed on the 2nd (−6.6°) & the 29th (−6.7°).

Large tides on the 17th, 18th, 19th, and 20th.

Mercury: At inferior conjunction on the 9th and reappears in the dawn sky during the last half of the month. Passes 0.8° N of Mars on the 19th. In order of increasing elongation from the Sun and spanning less than 20°, Jupiter, Mars, Mercury, and Venus decorate the dawn twilight during the last ten days of April. Angle of ecliptic favours observers in the Southern Hemisphere.

Venus: Brilliant in the eastern morning sky. Angle of the ecliptic favours observers in Southern Hemisphere. Lies 7° S of Moon on the 30th at 23h UT (and see Uranus below).

Mars: Becomes visible in the dawn sky in Pisces early in the month for southern observers, by month-end for northern observers (see Mercury above).

Jupiter: In conjunction with Sun on the 6th. Reappears in the dawn twilight by mid-month for southern observers, by month-end for northern observers.

Saturn: Visible most of the night. At opposition on the 4th, 72 light-minutes from Earth. At opposition, the north side of the ring plane is tilted 8.7° toward Earth, and the rings span 44″. Meridian transit at Greenwich on the 1st and 16th at 00:19 and 23:12 UT*.

Uranus: Reappears in the dawn sky in Pisces by mid-month for southern observers, by month-end for northern observers. Venus is 0.9° S of Uranus on the 22nd. On the 9th Uranus crosses to the north side of the celestial equator for the first time since 1969.

Neptune: In the eastern morning sky in Aquarius. Angle of ecliptic favors observers in Southern Hemisphere.

*See the last two sentences of the first paragraph on p. 98.

Time (UT) d h m	APRIL EVENTS	Jupiter's Satellites West East
Fri. 1		
Sat. 2 9	Moon at apogee (406 656 km)	
17 07	Algol at minimum	
Sun. 3 14 32	**New Moon** (lunation 1092)	
Mon. 4 0	**Saturn at opposition**	
Tue. 5 13 56	Algol at minimum	
Wed. 6 15	Jupiter in conjunction with the Sun	
Thu. 7 11	**Moon 1.9° S of Pleiades (M45)**	
Fri. 8 10 46	Algol at minimum	
Sat. 9 7	Pluto stationary	
20	Mercury in inferior conjunction	
Sun. 10 1	**Moon 1.5° S of M35**	
Mon. 11 7 35	Algol at minimum	
12 05	**First Quarter**	
Tue. 12		
Wed. 13		
Thu. 14 4 24	Algol at minimum	
Fri. 15		
Sat. 16		
Sun. 17 1 13	Algol at minimum	
6	Moon at perigee (358 090 km) **Large tides**	
8	Saturn 8° N of Moon	
Mon. 18	Venus at aphelion	
	Mercury at descending node	
2 44	**Full Moon**	
Tue. 19 8	**Mercury 0.8° N of Mars**	
22 02	Algol at minimum	
Wed. 20		
Thu. 21		
Fri. 22 5	Mercury stationary	
18	**Venus 0.9° S of Uranus**	
18 51	Algol at minimum	
23	Lyrid meteors peak	
Sat. 23		
Sun. 24		
Mon. 25 2 47	**Last Quarter**	
15 40	Algol at minimum	
Tue. 26		
Wed 27		
Thu. 28 12 29	Algol at minimum	
Fri. 29	Mercury at aphelion	
16	Juno stationary	
18	Moon at apogee (406 039 km)	
Sat. 30 23	Venus 7° S of Moon	

THE SKY FOR MAY

		Mercury	Venus	Mars	Jupiter	Saturn	Uranus	Neptune	Sun
RA	1	0h59m	0h46m	1h23m	1h24m	12h47m	0h11m	22h11m	2h31m
	11	1h32m	1h31m	1h51m	1h32m	12h45m	0h12m	22h11m	3h10m
	21	2h22m	2h17m	2h20m	1h41m	12h44m	0h14m	22h12m	3h49m
Dec	1	+3°37'	+3°07'	+7°55'	+7°37'	−2°09'	+0°22'	−11°47'	+14°51'
	11	+6°17'	+7°43'	+10°45'	+8°28'	−1°57'	+0°33'	−11°44'	+17°42'
	21	+11°20'	+12°03'	+13°23'	+9°17'	−1°48'	+0°42'	−11°42'	+20°02'
Dist	1	0.73	1.43	2.32	5.90	8.72	20.87	30.35	1.007
	11	0.88	1.48	2.31	5.84	8.82	20.76	30.18	1.010
	21	1.05	1.53	2.30	5.77	8.93	20.63	30.01	1.012
Mag	1	0.9	−3.8	1.2	−2.1	0.5	5.9	7.9	
	11	0.3	−3.8	1.3	−2.1	0.6	5.9	7.9	
	21	−0.2	−3.8	1.3	−2.1	0.7	5.9	7.9	
Size	1	9.2"	11.6"	4.0"	33.4"	19.1"	3.4"	2.2"	31'45"
	11	7.6"	11.2"	4.0"	33.7"	18.9"	3.4"	2.2"	31'41"
	21	6.4"	10.9"	4.1"	34.2"	18.6"	3.4"	2.2"	31'37"

Moon: On May 0 at 0 UT, Sun's selenographic colongitude is 233.10° and increases by 12.2° each day thereafter.

Greatest N declination on the 6th (+23.4°).

Greatest S declination on the 18th (−23.4°).

Libration in longitude: E limb most exposed on the 21st (+6.4°),
   W limb most exposed on the 8th (−6.6°).

Libration in latitude: N limb most exposed on the 13th (+6.8°),
   S limb most exposed on the 26th (−6.9°).

Mercury: Eastern morning sky. Angle of ecliptic favours observers in Southern Hemisphere. Greatest elongation W (27°) on the 7th, a week past aphelion. Becomes brighter as the days pass. Mercury, Venus, Mars, and Jupiter lie within 10° during the first three weeks of May, with Mercury, Venus, and Jupiter lying within 3° from the 9th to the 13th. Mercury, Venus, and Mars lie within 3° from the 19th to the 23rd (see Venus below).

Venus: Brilliant in the eastern morning sky. Angle of ecliptic favours observers in Southern Hemisphere. Venus remains within 2° of Mercury from the 4th through the 22nd. Venus passes 0.6° S of Jupiter on the 11th, 1.0° S of Mars on the 22nd, and 4° S of Moon on the 31st at 4h UT (see Mercury above).

Mars: Low in the eastern dawn sky. Lies 0.4° N of Jupiter on the 1st (see Mercury and Venus above).

Jupiter: Low in the eastern dawn sky in Pisces. Angle of ecliptic favours observers in Southern Hemisphere. (see Mercury, Venus, and Mars above).

Saturn: Visible most of the night, past opposition and retrograding in Virgo. Meridian transit at Greenwich on the 1st and 16th at 22:09 and 21:07 UT*.

Uranus: In the eastern morning sky in Pisces.

Neptune: Rises after midnight in Aquarius. Meridian transit at Greenwich on the 1st and 16th at 07:35 and 06:37 UT*.

*See the last two sentences of the first paragraph on p. 98.

Time (UT) d h m	MAY EVENTS	Jupiter's Satellites West East
Sun. 1 7	Mercury 8° S of Moon	
9 18	Algol at minimum	
11	**Mars 0.4° N of Jupiter**	
19	Jupiter 6° S of Moon	
20	Mars 6° S of Moon	
Mon. 2		
Tue. 3 6 51	**New Moon** (lunation 1093)	
Wed. 4 6 07	Algol at minimum	
Thu. 5		
Fri. 6 12	η-Aquarid meteors peak	
Sat. 7 2 56	Algol at minimum	
7	**Moon 1.7° S of M35**	
19	**Mercury greatest elongation W (27°)**	
Sun. 8 3	**Mercury and Venus 1.4° apart**	
Mon. 9 23 45	Algol at minimum	
Tue. 10 20 33	**First Quarter**	
22	**Mercury 2° S of Jupiter**	
Wed. 11	Venus at greatest heliocentric lat. S	
9	**Venus 0.6° S of Jupiter**	
Thu. 12 20 34	Algol at minimum	
Fri. 13		
Sat. 14 15	Saturn 8° N of Moon	
18 41	**Double shadow transit on Jupiter**	
Sun. 15 11	Moon at perigee (362 135 km)	
17 23	Algol at minimum	
Mon. 16		
Tue. 17 11 09	**Full Moon**	
Wed. 18 7 39	**Double shadow transit on Jupiter**	
8	**Mercury and Venus 1.4° apart**	
14 12	Algol at minimum	
Thu. 19	Mercury at greatest heliocentric lat. S	
Fri. 20 1	**Mercury 2° S of Mars**	
Sat. 21 11 01	Algol at minimum	
20 36	**Double shadow transit on Jupiter**	
Sun. 22 15	**Venus 1.1° S of Mars**	
Mon. 23		
Tue. 24 7 49	Algol at minimum	
18 52	**Last Quarter**	
Wed. 25 9 33	**Double shadow transit on Jupiter**	
15	Pallas stationary	
Fri. 27 4 38	Algol at minimum	
10	Moon at apogee (404 003 km)	
Sat. 28 22 30	**Double shadow transit on Jupiter**	
Sun. 29 15	Jupiter 6° S of Moon	
Mon. 30 1 27	Algol at minimum	
20	Mars 4° S of Moon	
Tue. 31 4	Venus 4° S of Moon	

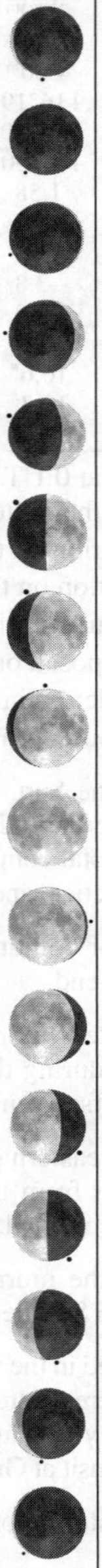

Jupiter's Satellites diagram labels: III, IV, I, II; West/East scale 1.0 through 31.0

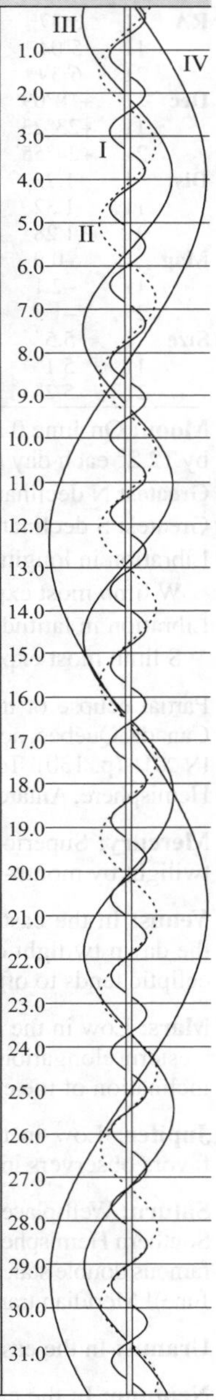

THE SKY FOR JUNE

		Mercury	Venus	Mars	Jupiter	Saturn	Uranus	Neptune	Sun
RA	1	3ʰ37ᵐ	3ʰ09ᵐ	2ʰ52ᵐ	1ʰ50ᵐ	12ʰ42ᵐ	0ʰ15ᵐ	22ʰ12ᵐ	4ʰ34ᵐ
	11	5ʰ04ᵐ	3ʰ59ᵐ	3ʰ21ᵐ	1ʰ58ᵐ	12ʰ42ᵐ	0ʰ16ᵐ	22ʰ12ᵐ	5ʰ15ᵐ
	21	6ʰ39ᵐ	4ʰ50ᵐ	3ʰ50ᵐ	2ʰ05ᵐ	12ʰ42ᵐ	0ʰ17ᵐ	22ʰ12ᵐ	5ʰ56ᵐ
Dec	1	+18°09′	+16°19′	+16°00′	+10°06′	−1°43′	+0°51′	−11°42′	+21°57′
	11	+23°23′	+19°30′	+18°06′	+10°48′	−1°42′	+0°57′	−11°42′	+23°02′
	21	+24°55′	+21°50′	+19°54′	+11°26′	−1°46′	+1°01′	−11°44′	+23°26′
Dist	1	1.23	1.58	2.28	5.67	9.08	20.47	29.83	1.014
	11	1.32	1.62	2.27	5.56	9.23	20.31	29.67	1.015
	21	1.28	1.65	2.25	5.44	9.39	20.15	29.51	1.016
Mag	1	−0.9	−3.8	1.3	−2.1	0.7	5.9	7.9	
	11	−2.1	−3.8	1.3	−2.2	0.8	5.9	7.9	
	21	−1.3	−3.8	1.4	−2.2	0.8	5.9	7.9	
Size	1	5.5″	10.6″	4.1″	34.8″	18.3″	3.4″	2.2″	31′33″
	11	5.1″	10.3″	4.1″	35.4″	18.0″	3.4″	2.3″	31′30″
	21	5.2″	10.1″	4.2″	36.2″	17.7″	3.5″	2.3″	31′29″

Moon: On June 0 at 0 UT, Sun's selenographic colongitude is 251.69° and increases by 12.2° each day thereafter.

Greatest N declination on the 2nd and the 29th (+23.4°).

Greatest S declination on the 15th (−23.4°).

Libration in longitude: E limb most exposed on the 17th (+5.4°),
  W limb most exposed on the 4th (−5.4°) & the 30th (−5.2°).

Libration in latitude: N limb most exposed on the 9th (+6.8°),
  S limb most exposed on the 22nd (−6.9°).

Partial eclipse of the Sun, on the 1st, visible in Iceland, Greenland, much of Atlantic Canada, Québec, northern Canada, northern Alaska, and northeastern Asia. See ECLIPSES IN 2011 (p. 130). Total eclipse of the Moon, on the 15th, visible in most of the Eastern Hemisphere, Antarctica, and much of South America. See ECLIPSES IN 2011 (p. 130).

Mercury: Superior conjunction on the 13th. Reappears low in the western evening twilight by month-end.

Venus: In the eastern morning sky. For southern observers Venus drops lower into the dawn twilight during the month. For northern observers the increasing tilt of the ecliptic tends to offset Venus' decreasing elongation from the Sun.

Mars: Low in the eastern dawn sky. During the summer its visibility improves as its western elongation from the Sun slowly increases and, for northern observers, the inclination of the ecliptic becomes steeper.

Jupiter: Low in the morning sky, near the Aries-Pisces border. Angle of ecliptic favors observers in Southern Hemisphere.

Saturn: Well-placed in the western late-evening sky. Angle of ecliptic favors observers in Southern Hemisphere. Retrograde motion ends on the 14th with Saturn only 16′ from the famous double star, γ Vir (and remains within 20′ of the star during the first three weeks of June)! Meridian transit at Greenwich on the 1st and 16th at 20:02 and 19:03 UT*.

Uranus: In the eastern morning sky in Pisces.

Neptune: In the eastern morning sky in Aquarius. Rises after midnight. Retrograde motion begins on the 3rd. Meridian transit at Greenwich on the 1st and 16th at 05:34 and 04:35 UT*.

*See the last two sentences of the first paragraph on p. 98.

Time (UT) d h m	JUNE EVENTS	Jupiter's Satellites West East
Wed. 1 11 27	**Double shadow transit on Jupiter**	
21 03	**New Moon** (lunation 1094)	
	Partial Solar Eclipse (p. 131)	
22 16	Algol at minimum	
Thu. 2 7	Mercury 5° S of Pleiades (M45)	
Fri. 3 5 55	**Double shadow transit on Jupiter**	
13	**Moon 1.7° S of M35**	
15	Neptune stationary	
Sat. 4 19 05	Algol at minimum	
Sun. 5 0 24	**Double shadow transit on Jupiter**	
Mon. 6		
Tue. 7	Mercury at ascending node	
15 53	Algol at minimum	
Wed. 8 13 30	**Double shadow transit on Jupiter**	
16	Venus 5° S of Pleiades (M45)	
Thu. 9 2 11	**First Quarter**	
Fri. 10 9 26	**Double shadow transit on Jupiter**	
12 42	Algol at minimum	
21	Saturn 8° N of Moon	
Sat. 11		
Sun. 12	Mercury at perihelion	
2	Moon at perigee (367 189 km)	
2 48	**Double shadow transit on Jupiter**	
Mon. 13 0	Mercury in superior conjunction	
9 31	Algol at minimum	
Tue. 14 5	Saturn stationary	
Wed. 15 16 08	**Double shadow transit on Jupiter**	
20 14	**Full Moon**	
	Total Lunar Eclipse (p. 131)	
Thu. 16 6 20	Algol at minimum	
Fri. 17		
Sat. 18 7	Venus 5° N of Aldebaran	
Sun. 19 3 08	Algol at minimum	
5 26	**Double shadow transit on Jupiter**	
20	Mars 4° S of Pleiades (M45)	
Mon. 20		
Tue. 21 17 16	**Solstice**	
23 57	Algol at minimum	
Wed. 22	Mercury at greatest heliocentric lat. N	
18 46	**Double shadow transit on Jupiter**	
Thu. 23 11 48	**Last Quarter**	
Fri. 24 4	Moon at apogee (404 271 km)	
19	Vesta stationary	
20 46	Algol at minimum	
Sat. 25		
Sun. 26 8 04	**Double shadow transit on Jupiter**	
9	Jupiter 5° S of Moon	
Mon. 27 17 34	Algol at minimum	
Tue. 28 6	Pluto at opposition	
7	**Moon 2.0° S of Pleiades (M45)**	
19	**Mars 1.7° S of Moon**	
22	Mercury 5° S of Pollux	
Wed, 29		
Thu. 30 14 23	Algol at minimum	

THE SKY FOR JULY

		Mercury	Venus	Mars	Jupiter	Saturn	Uranus	Neptune	Sun
RA	1	8^{h}01^m	5^{h}42^m	4^{h}20^m	2^{h}12^m	12^{h}43^m	0^{h}17^m	22^{h}11^m	6^{h}38^m
	11	9^{h}03^m	6^{h}36^m	4^{h}50^m	2^{h}18^m	12^{h}44^m	0^{h}17^m	22^{h}11^m	7^{h}19^m
	21	9^{h}46^m	7^{h}29^m	5^{h}20^m	2^{h}23^m	12^{h}46^m	0^{h}17^m	22^{h}10^m	7^{h}59^m
Dec	1	+22°23′	+23°09′	+21°22′	+12°00′	−1°53′	+1°03′	−11°47′	+23°09′
	11	+17°38′	+23°22′	+22°30′	+12°29′	−2°04′	+1°04′	−11°50′	+22°12′
	21	+12°26′	+22°26′	+23°16′	+12°53′	−2°18′	+1°02′	−11°55′	+20°36′
Dist	1	1.15	1.68	2.22	5.31	9.55	19.98	29.37	1.017
	11	1.00	1.70	2.20	5.17	9.72	19.82	29.25	1.017
	21	0.84	1.72	2.17	5.02	9.88	19.66	29.15	1.016
Mag	1	−0.4	−3.8	1.4	−2.2	0.9	5.8	7.9	
	11	0.0	−3.8	1.4	−2.3	0.9	5.8	7.8	
	21	0.5	−3.8	1.4	−2.4	0.9	5.8	7.8	
Size	1	5.8″	9.9″	4.2″	37.1″	17.4″	3.5″	2.3″	31′28″
	11	6.7″	9.8″	4.3″	38.1″	17.1″	3.5″	2.3″	31′28″
	21	8.0″	9.7″	4.3″	39.2″	16.8″	3.6″	2.3″	31′29″

Moon: On July 0 at 0 UT, Sun's selenographic colongitude is 258.33° and increases by 12.2° each day thereafter.

Greatest N declination on the 27th (+23.3°).

Greatest S declination on the 12th (−23.3°).

Libration in longitude: E limb most exposed on the 15th (+4.9°),
 W limb most exposed on the 28th (−5.9°).

Libration in latitude: N limb most exposed on the 6th (+6.8°),
 S limb most exposed on the 20th (−6.8°).

Partial eclipse of the Sun, on the 1st, visible from a small section of the Southern Ocean. It is the first eclipse in a new Saros series, #156. See ECLIPSE PATTERNS (p. 126) and ECLIPSES IN 2011 (p. 130).

Mercury: Western evening sky. Greatest elongation E (27°) on the 20th, six days prior to aphelion. Angle of ecliptic favours observers in Southern Hemisphere.

Venus: Vanishes into the dawn twilight early in the month.

Mars: In the eastern morning sky in Taurus. During the summer its visibility improves as its western elongation from the Sun slowly increases and, for northern observers, the inclination of the ecliptic becomes steeper. On the 27th from parts of South America and the Pacific, Mars is occulted by the waning crescent Moon.

Jupiter: Morning sky in Pisces. Rises well after midnight.

Saturn: In the western evening sky, and sets near midnight. Angle of ecliptic favors observers in Southern Hemisphere.

Uranus: Rises near midnight in Pisces. Retrograde motion begins on the 10th. Meridian transit at Greenwich on the 1st and 16th at 05:41 and 04:42 UT*.

Neptune: In the morning sky in Aquarius. Rises in late evening. Meridian transit at Greenwich on the 1st and 16th at 03:35 and 02:35 UT*.

*See the last two sentences of the first paragraph on p. 98.

Time (UT) d h m	JULY EVENTS	Jupiter's Satellites West East
Fri. 1 8 54	**New Moon** (lunation 1095) **Partial Solar Eclipse** (p. 132) First new Saros in 83 years.	
Sat. 2		
Sun. 3 2	Mercury 5° N of Moon	
11 12	Algol at minimum	
Mon. 4 15	Earth at aphelion (152 102 140 km)	
Tue. 5		
Wed. 6	Venus at ascending node	
6	Mars 5° N of Aldebaran	
8 00	Algol at minimum	
21	**Mercury 0.3° S of Beehive (M44)**	
Thu. 7 14	Moon at perigee (369 570 km)	
Fri. 8	Mars at ascending node	
4	Saturn 8° N of Moon	
6 29	**First Quarter**	
Sat. 9 4 49	Algol at minimum	
Sun. 10 8	Uranus stationary	
Mon. 11		
Tue. 12 1 38	Algol at minimum	
22 27	**Happy Birthday, Neptune!** (p. 9)	
Wed. 13		
Thu. 14 22 26	Algol at minimum	
Fri. 15	Mercury at descending node	
6 40	**Full Moon**	
Sat. 16		
Sun. 17 19 15	Algol at minimum	
Mon. 18		
Tue. 19		
Wed. 20 5	**Mercury greatest elongation E (27°)**	
16 04	Algol at minimum	
Thu. 21 23	Moon at apogee (404 355 km)	
Fri. 22		
Sat. 23 5 02	**Last Quarter**	
12 52	Algol at minimum	
Sun. 24 1	Jupiter 5° S of Moon	
Mon, 25		
Tue. 26	Mercury at aphelion	
9 41	Algol at minimum	
Wed. 27 17	**Mars 0.5° N of Moon, occultation**†	
Thu. 28 5	Moon 1.8° S of M35	
Fri. 29 6 29	Algol at minimum	
14	**Pallas at opposition**	
15	S. δ-Aquarid meteors peak	
Sat. 30 18 40	**New Moon** (lunation 1096)	
Sun. 31		

† Samoa, Kiribati, French Polynesia, S half of South America except southernmost tip

THE SKY FOR AUGUST

		Mercury	Venus	Mars	Jupiter	Saturn	Uranus	Neptune	Sun
RA	1	10^h07^m	8^h26^m	5^h52^m	2^h27^m	12^h49^m	0^h17^m	22^h09^m	8^h43^m
	11	9^h56^m	9^h17^m	6^h21^m	2^h30^m	12^h51^m	0^h16^m	22^h08^m	9^h21^m
	21	9^h27^m	10^h05^m	6^h50^m	2^h32^m	12^h55^m	0^h15^m	22^h07^m	9^h59^m
Dec	1	+8°05′	+20°10′	+23°43′	+13°13′	−2°38′	+0°59′	−12°01′	+18°12′
	11	+7°32′	+17°05′	+23°46′	+13°26′	−2°58′	+0°53′	−12°06′	+15°29′
	21	+10°56′	+13°12′	+23°30′	+13°33′	−3°21′	+0°47′	−12°12′	+12°21′
Dist	1	0.69	1.73	2.13	4.86	10.05	19.50	29.06	1.015
	11	0.61	1.73	2.09	4.71	10.19	19.37	29.01	1.014
	21	0.65	1.73	2.05	4.56	10.32	19.26	29.00	1.012
Mag	1	1.3	−3.8	1.4	−2.4	0.9	5.8	7.8	
	11	3.4	−3.8	1.4	−2.5	0.9	5.8	7.8	
	21	4.0	−3.8	1.4	−2.6	0.9	5.8	7.8	
Size	1	9.7″	9.7″	4.4″	40.6″	16.5″	3.6″	2.3″	31′31″
	11	11.0″	9.6″	4.5″	41.9″	16.3″	3.6″	2.3″	31′33″
	21	10.4″	9.6″	4.6″	43.2″	16.1″	3.6″	2.3″	31′37″

Moon: On August 0 at 0 UT, Sun's selenographic colongitude is 277.26° and increases by 12.2° each day thereafter.

Greatest N declination on the 23rd (+23.2°).

Greatest S declination on the 8th (−23.3°).

Libration in longitude: E limb most exposed on the 10th (+5.4°),
    W limb most exposed on the 25th (−6.8°).

Libration in latitude: N limb most exposed on the 2nd (+6.6°) & the 30th (+6.5°),
    S limb most exposed on the 16th (−6.7°).

Mercury: Dims and vanishes into the evening twilight early in the month. Inferior conjunction on the 17th. Reappears in the dawn sky by month-end.

Venus: Not visible this month. Superior conjunction on the 16th.

Mars: In the eastern morning sky in Gemini. During the summer its visibility improves as its western elongation from the Sun slowly increases and, for northern observers, the inclination of the ecliptic becomes steeper.

Jupiter: Rises north of east near midnight in Aries. Retrograde motion begins on the 30th. Meridian transit at Greenwich on the 1st and 16th at 05:49 and 04:54 UT*.

Saturn: Low in the western mid-evening sky. Sets in late evening.

Uranus: Rises in late evening, in Pisces. Meridian transit at Greenwich on the 1st and 16th at 03:38 and 02:38 UT*.

Neptune: Visible all night. At opposition on the 22nd, 4.0 light-hours from Earth, 2.3″ in diameter, and 12° S of the celestial equator. Meridian transit at Greenwich on the 1st and 16th at 01:31 and 00:31 UT*.

*See the last two sentences of the first paragraph on p. 98.

Time (UT)			AUGUST EVENTS	Jupiter's Satellites
d	h	m		West East

Mon. 1	0		Ceres stationary	
	3	18	Algol at minimum	
	11		**Mercury 1.5° N of Moon**	
Tue. 2	7		Mercury stationary	
	21		Moon at perigee (365 761 km)	
Wed. 3				
Thu. 4	0	07	Algol at minimum	
	12		Saturn 8° N of Moon	
Fri. 5	10		**Vesta at opposition**	
Sat. 6	11	08	**First Quarter**	
	16		**Mars 0.5° S of M35**	
	20	55	Algol at minimum	
Sun. 7				
Mon. 8				
Tue. 9			Venus at perihelion	
	17	44	Algol at minimum	
Wed. 10				
Thu. 11				
Fri. 12	14	32	Algol at minimum	
Sat. 13	6		**Perseid meteors peak**	
	18	57	**Full Moon**	
Sun. 14				
Mon. 15			Mercury at greatest heliocentric lat. S	
	11	21	Algol at minimum	
Tue. 16	13		Venus in superior conjunction	
Wed. 17	1		Mercury in inferior conjunction	
Thu. 18	8	09	Algol at minimum	
	16		Moon at apogee (405 161 km)	
Fri. 19				
Sat. 20	12		Jupiter 5° S of Moon	
Sun. 21	4	58	Algol at minimum	
	21	54	**Last Quarter**	
Mon. 22	23		**Neptune at opposition**	
Tue. 23				
Wed. 24	1	47	Algol at minimum	
	15		Moon 1.9° S of M35	
Thu. 25	14		Mars 3° N of Moon	
Fri. 26	4		Mercury stationary	
	22	35	Algol at minimum	
Sat. 27				
Sun. 28	1		Mercury 3° N of Moon	
Mon. 29	3	04	**New Moon** (lunation 1097)	
	19	24	Algol at minimum	
Tue. 30			Venus at greatest heliocentric lat. N	
	17		Jupiter stationary	
	18		Moon at perigee (360 858 km)	
Wed. 31	23		Saturn 7° N of Moon	

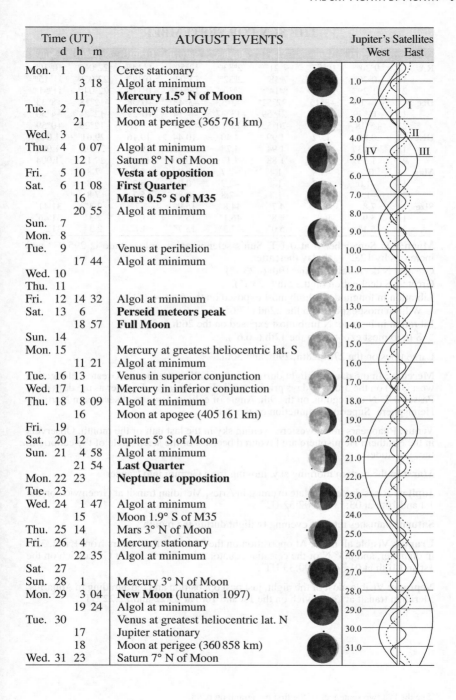

THE SKY FOR SEPTEMBER

		Mercury	Venus	Mars	Jupiter	Saturn	Uranus	Neptune	Sun
RA	1	9^{h}30^m	10^{h}57^m	7^{h}21^m	2^{h}33^m	12^{h}59^m	0^{h}14^m	22^{h}06^m	10^{h}39^m
	11	10^{h}20^m	11^{h}43^m	7^{h}48^m	2^{h}32^m	13^{h}03^m	0^{h}12^m	22^{h}05^m	11^{h}15^m
	21	11^{h}29^m	12^{h}28^m	8^{h}14^m	2^{h}30^m	13^{h}07^m	0^{h}11^m	22^{h}04^m	11^{h}51^m
Dec	1	+14°04'	+8°15'	+22°51'	+13°33'	–3°48'	+0°38'	–12°18'	+8°33'
	11	+11°49'	+3°21'	+21°59'	+13°27'	–4°14'	+0°29'	–12°24'	+4°50'
	21	+5°18'	–1°44'	+20°53'	+13°15'	–4°41'	+0°20'	–12°29'	+0°59'
Dist	1	0.86	1.72	1.99	4.40	10.44	19.16	29.01	1.009
	11	1.13	1.71	1.94	4.28	10.53	19.11	29.05	1.007
	21	1.33	1.69	1.88	4.17	10.60	19.08	29.12	1.004
Mag	1	0.2	–3.8	1.4	–2.7	0.9	5.7	7.8	
	11	–1.0	–3.8	1.4	–2.7	0.9	5.7	7.8	
	21	–1.4	–3.8	1.3	–2.8	0.8	5.7	7.8	
Size	1	7.8"	9.7"	4.7"	44.8"	15.9"	3.7"	2.3"	31'41"
	11	5.9"	9.8"	4.8"	46.1"	15.8"	3.7"	2.3"	31'46"
	21	5.1"	9.9"	5.0"	47.3"	15.7"	3.7"	2.3"	31'51"

Moon: On September 0 at 0 UT, Sun's selenographic colongitude is 295.97° and increases by 12.2° each day thereafter.

Greatest N declination on the 19th (+23.1°).

Greatest S declination on the 5th (–23.1°).

Libration in longitude: E limb most exposed on the 6th (+6.6°), W limb most exposed on the 22nd (–7.6°).

Libration in latitude: N limb most exposed on the 26th (+6.6°), S limb most exposed on the 12th (–6.6°).

Large tides on the 27th, 28th, 29th, and 30th.

Mercury: In the dawn twilight during the first half of the month. Greatest elongation west (18°) on the 3rd, five days prior to perihelion. Becomes brighter as the days pass. Passes 0.7° N of Regulus on the 9th. Angle of ecliptic favours observers in Northern Hemisphere. Superior conjunction on the 28th.

Venus: Reappears in the western evening sky in the last half of the month. Observers in the Southern Hemisphere are favoured because of the steep angle of the ecliptic in those latitudes.

Mars: In the eastern morning sky, moving from Gemini into Cancer.

Jupiter: Rises due east in late evening in Aries. Meridian transit at Greenwich on the 1st and 16th at 03:53 and 02:52 UT*.

Saturn: Vanishes into the evening twilight during the month.

Uranus: Visible all night. At opposition on the 26th, 2.6 light-hours from Earth, 3.7" in diameter, and 0.3° N of the celestial equator. Meridian transit at Greenwich on the 1st and 16th at 01:34 and 00:33 UT*.

Neptune: Visible most of the night, just past opposition and retrograding in Aquarius. Meridian transit at Greenwich on the 1st and 16th at 23:22 and 22:22 UT*.

*See the last two sentences of the first paragraph on p. 98.

Time (UT)			SEPTEMBER EVENTS	Jupiter's Satellites	
	d	h m		West	East
Thu.	1	16 12	Algol at minimum		
Fri.	2				
Sat.	3		Mercury at ascending node		
		6	**Mercury greatest elongation W (18°)**		
Sun.	4	13 01	Algol at minimum		
		17 39	**First Quarter**		
Mon.	5				
Tue.	6				
Wed.	7	9 50	Algol at minimum		
Thu.	8		Mercury at perihelion		
Fri.	9	2	**Mercury 0.7° N of Regulus**		
Sat.	10	2	Mars 6° S of Pollux		
		6 38	Algol at minimum		
Sun.	11				
Mon.	12	9 27	**Full Moon**		
Tue.	13	3 27	Algol at minimum		
Wed.	14				
Thu.	15	6	Moon at apogee (406 065 km)		
Fri.	16	0 16	Algol at minimum		
		12	Pluto stationary		
		17	**Ceres at opposition**		
		18	Jupiter 5° S of Moon		
		22	Pallas stationary		
Sat.	17				
Sun.	18		Mercury at greatest heliocentric lat. N		
		2	Vesta stationary		
		21 04	Algol at minimum		
Mon.	19				
Tue.	20	13 39	**Last Quarter**		
Wed.	21	17 53	Algol at minimum		
Thu.	22				
Fri.	23	8	Mars 5° N of Moon		
		9 05	**Equinox**		
Sat.	24	14 42	Algol at minimum		
Sun.	25		**Zodiacal Light vis. in N lat. in E before morning twilight for next two weeks**		
Mon.	26	0	**Uranus at opposition**		
Tue.	27	11 09	**New Moon** (lunation 1098)		
		11 30	Algol at minimum		
Wed.	28	1	Moon at perigee (357 557 km) **Large tides**		
		10	Venus 6° N of Moon		
		14	Saturn 7° N of Moon		
		20	Mercury in superior conjunction		
Thu.	29	23	**Venus and Saturn 1.3° apart**		
Fri.	30	8 19	Algol at minimum		

THE SKY FOR OCTOBER

		Mercury	Venus	Mars	Jupiter	Saturn	Uranus	Neptune	Sun
RA	1	12^{h}35^m	13^{h}14^m	8^{h}39^m	2^{h}27^m	13^{h}12^m	0^{h}09^m	22^{h}03^m	12^{h}27^m
	11	13^{h}36^m	14^{h}00^m	9^{h}03^m	2^{h}22^m	13^{h}16^m	0^{h}08^m	22^{h}02^m	13^{h}03^m
	21	14^{h}35^m	14^{h}48^m	9^{h}26^m	2^{h}18^m	13^{h}21^m	0^{h}07^m	22^{h}02^m	13^{h}41^m
Dec	1	−2°30′	−6°47′	+19°36′	+12°58′	−5°09′	+0°10′	−12°33′	−2°54′
	11	−9°54′	−11°36′	+18°10′	+12°36′	−5°37′	+0°01′	−12°37′	−6°45′
	21	−16°17′	−15°58′	+16°37′	+12°11′	−6°04′	−0°08′	−12°40′	−10°26′
Dist	1	1.41	1.67	1.81	4.08	10.65	19.08	29.22	1.001
	11	1.41	1.64	1.74	4.01	10.67	19.12	29.34	0.998
	21	1.36	1.61	1.67	3.98	10.66	19.18	29.48	0.996
Mag	1	−1.5	−3.8	1.3	−2.8	0.8	5.7	7.8	
	11	−0.7	−3.8	1.2	−2.9	0.7	5.7	7.9	
	21	−0.4	−3.8	1.2	−2.9	0.7	5.7	7.9	
Size	1	4.8″	10.0″	5.2″	48.3″	15.6″	3.7″	2.3″	31′57″
	11	4.8″	10.2″	5.4″	49.1″	15.6″	3.7″	2.3″	32′02″
	21	4.9″	10.3″	5.6″	49.6″	15.6″	3.7″	2.3″	32′08″

Moon: On October 0 at 0 UT, Sun's selenographic colongitude is 302.04° and increases by 12.2° each day thereafter.

Greatest N declination on the 17th (+22.7°).

Greatest S declination on the 2nd and the 29th (−22.7°).

Libration in longitude: E limb most exposed on the 4th (+7.6°),
   W limb most exposed on the 20th (−7.6°).

Libration in latitude: N limb most exposed on the 23rd (+6.7°),
   S limb most exposed on the 9th (−6.7°).

Large tides on the 26th, 27th, 28th, and 29th.

Mercury: In the evening twilight during the last half of the month. The crescent Moon is nearby on the 27th, with an occultation visible from the southwestern Pacific on the 28th. Mercury lies 2° from Venus at month-end. Angle of ecliptic favours observers in Southern Hemisphere.

Venus: Low in the southwestern evening twilight. Passes 3° N of Spica on the 3rd. Waxing crescent Moon passes 2° S of Venus on the 28th at 5h UT (see Mercury above). Angle of ecliptic favours observers in Southern Hemisphere.

Mars: In the eastern morning sky moving from Cancer into Leo.

Jupiter: Rises early evening and is visible all night. At opposition on the 29th, 33 light-minutes from Earth, and 12° N of the celestial equator. Jupiter attains nearly a 12-year-maximum diameter of 49.6″ at this opposition because it was at perihelion last March (it reached 49.8″ at its September 2010 opposition). Meridian transit at Greenwich on the 1st and 16th at 01:48 and 00:43 UT*.

Saturn: In conjunction with the Sun on the 13th, and reappears in the dawn twilight late in the month. Angle of ecliptic favors observers in Northern Hemisphere.

Uranus: Visible most of the night, just past opposition and retrograding in western Pisces. On the 16th Uranus crosses back to the south side of the celestial equator (see April) but remains there only until 2012 Jan. 28. Meridian transit at Greenwich on the 1st and 16th at 23:27 and 22:26 UT*.

Neptune: Well-placed in the evening sky, in Aquarius. Meridian transit at Greenwich on the 1st and 16th at 21:21 and 20:21 UT*.

*See the last two sentences of the first paragraph on p. 98.

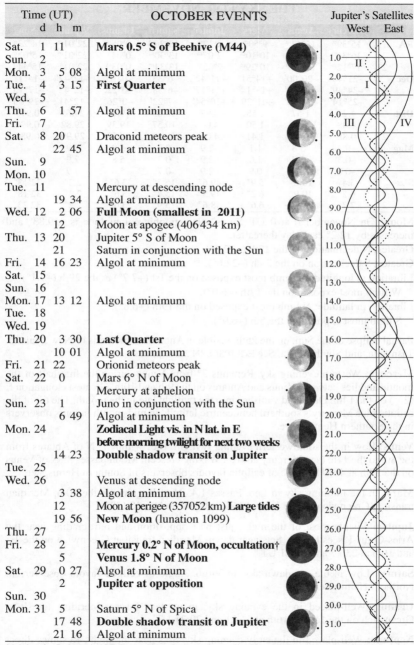

Time (UT) d h m	OCTOBER EVENTS	Jupiter's Satellites West East
Sat. 1 11	**Mars 0.5° S of Beehive (M44)**	
Sun. 2		
Mon. 3 5 08	Algol at minimum	
Tue. 4 3 15	**First Quarter**	
Wed. 5		
Thu. 6 1 57	Algol at minimum	
Fri. 7		
Sat. 8 20	Draconid meteors peak	
22 45	Algol at minimum	
Sun. 9		
Mon. 10		
Tue. 11	Mercury at descending node	
19 34	Algol at minimum	
Wed. 12 2 06	**Full Moon (smallest in 2011)**	
12	Moon at apogee (406 434 km)	
Thu. 13 20	Jupiter 5° S of Moon	
21	Saturn in conjunction with the Sun	
Fri. 14 16 23	Algol at minimum	
Sat. 15		
Sun. 16		
Mon. 17 13 12	Algol at minimum	
Tue. 18		
Wed. 19		
Thu. 20 3 30	**Last Quarter**	
10 01	Algol at minimum	
Fri. 21 22	Orionid meteors peak	
Sat. 22 0	Mars 6° N of Moon	
	Mercury at aphelion	
Sun. 23 1	Juno in conjunction with the Sun	
6 49	Algol at minimum	
Mon. 24	**Zodiacal Light vis. in N lat. in E**	
	before morning twilight for next two weeks	
14 23	**Double shadow transit on Jupiter**	
Tue. 25		
Wed. 26	Venus at descending node	
3 38	Algol at minimum	
12	Moon at perigee (357052 km) **Large tides**	
19 56	**New Moon** (lunation 1099)	
Thu. 27		
Fri. 28 2	**Mercury 0.2° N of Moon, occultation†**	
5	**Venus 1.8° N of Moon**	
Sat. 29 0 27	Algol at minimum	
2	**Jupiter at opposition**	
Sun. 30		
Mon. 31 5	Saturn 5° N of Spica	
17 48	**Double shadow transit on Jupiter**	
21 16	Algol at minimum	

† Malaysia, Indonesia, SE Papua New Guinea, Australia, New Zealand, New Caledonia, French Polynesia

THE SKY FOR NOVEMBER

		Mercury	Venus	Mars	Jupiter	Saturn	Uranus	Neptune	Sun
RA	1	15^h39^m	15^h43^m	9^h50^m	2^h12^m	13^h26^m	0^h05^m	22^h01^m	14^h23^m
	11	16^h33^m	16^h35^m	10^h10^m	2^h07^m	13^h30^m	0^h04^m	22^h01^m	15^h02^m
	21	17^h12^m	17^h29^m	10^h29^m	2^h02^m	13^h34^m	0^h03^m	22^h01^m	15^h44^m
Dec	1	$-21°40'$	$-20°00'$	$+14°51'$	$+11°42'$	$-6°33'$	$-0°16'$	$-12°42'$	$-14°11'$
	11	$-24°39'$	$-22°43'$	$+13°14'$	$+11°17'$	$-6°58'$	$-0°22'$	$-12°42'$	$-17°13'$
	21	$-25°14'$	$-24°20'$	$+11°39'$	$+10°54'$	$-7°22'$	$-0°26'$	$-12°41'$	$-19°45'$
Dist	1	1.24	1.57	1.58	3.97	10.63	19.28	29.65	0.993
	11	1.08	1.54	1.50	4.00	10.57	19.39	29.82	0.990
	21	0.88	1.49	1.41	4.06	10.49	19.53	29.99	0.988
Mag	1	−0.2	−3.8	1.1	−2.9	0.7	5.8	7.9	
	11	−0.3	−3.8	1.0	−2.9	0.7	5.8	7.9	
	21	−0.0	−3.8	0.9	−2.9	0.7	5.8	7.9	
Size	1	5.4″	10.6″	5.9″	49.6″	15.7″	3.6″	2.3″	32′13″
	11	6.2″	10.9″	6.2″	49.3″	15.7″	3.6″	2.2″	32′18″
	21	7.7″	11.2″	6.6″	48.6″	15.9″	3.6″	2.2″	32′23″

Moon: On November 0 at 0 UT, Sun's selenographic colongitude is 319.83° and increases by 12.2° each day thereafter.

Greatest N declination on the 13th (+22.6°).

Greatest S declination on the 26th (−22.6°).

Libration in longitude: E limb most exposed on the 1st (+7.7°) & the 29th (+7.1°),
 W limb most exposed on the 17th (−6.9°).

Libration in latitude: N limb most exposed on the 19th (+6.8°),
 S limb most exposed on the 5th (−6.9°).

Partial eclipse of the Sun, on the 25th, visible in Antarctica and parts of New Zealand, Tasmania, and South Africa. See ECLIPSES IN 2011 (p. 130)

Mercury: Western evening sky. Remains 2° from Venus during the first half of the month, and lies between Venus and Antares on the 9th and 10th. Greatest elongation E (23°) on the 14th. Dims and vanishes into the twilight late in the month. The tilt of the ecliptic plus Mercury's southern heliocentric latitude in mid-month favours observers in the Southern Hemisphere.

Venus: Low in the southwestern evening twilight. Lies within 5° N of Antares from the 8th to the 11th (see Mercury above). Waxing crescent Moon passes 3° N of Venus on the 27th at 4h UT. Angle of ecliptic favours observers in Southern Hemisphere

Mars: In the morning sky in Leo. Passes 1.4° N of Regulus on the 10th. Meridian transit at Greenwich on the 1st and 16th at 07:09 and 06:40 UT*.

Jupiter: Visible most of the night, just past opposition and retrograding near the Aries-Cetus-Pisces border. Sets near dawn. Meridian transit at Greenwich on the 1st and 16th at 23:27 and 22:21 UT*.

Saturn: Low in the pre-dawn sky, in Virgo. Angle of ecliptic favors observers in Northern Hemisphere.

Uranus: Well-placed in the evening sky, in western Pisces. Meridian transit at Greenwich on the 1st and 16th at 21:21 and 20:21 UT*.

Neptune: Well-placed in the early evening sky. Sets near midnight. Resumes direct eastward motion against the stars on the 9th. Meridian transit at Greenwich on the 1st and 16th at 19:18 and 18:19 UT*.

*See the last two sentences of the first paragraph on p. 98.

Time (UT)			NOVEMBER EVENTS	Jupiter's Satellites	
d	h	m		West	East
Tue. 1					
Wed. 2	0		**Mercury and Venus 2.0° apart**		
	16	38	**First Quarter**		
Thu. 3	18	05	Algol at minimum		
Fri. 4					
Sat. 5	23		S. Taurid meteors peak		
Sun. 6			**Daylight Saving Time ends**		
	14	54	Algol at minimum		
Mon. 7					
Tue. 8	13		Moon at apogee (406 177 km)		
Wed. 9	11	43	Algol at minimum		
	19		Jupiter 5° S of Moon		
	20		Venus 4° N of Antares		
	21		Neptune stationary		
Thu. 10	4		**Mars 1.4° N of Regulus**		
	5		**Mercury 1.9° N of Antares**		
	20	16	**Full Moon**		
Fri. 11			Mercury at greatest heliocentric lat. S		
Sat. 12	6		Ceres stationary		
	8	32	Algol at minimum		
	22		N. Taurid meteors peak		
Sun. 13	5		**Mercury and Venus 2.0° apart**		
Mon. 14	9		**Mercury greatest elongation E (23°)**		
Tue. 15	5	21	Algol at minimum		
Wed. 16					
Thu. 17					
Fri. 18	2	10	Algol at minimum		
	4		**Leonid meteors peak**		
	15	09	**Last Quarter**		
Sat. 19	10		Mars 8° N of Moon		
Sun. 20	22	59	Algol at minimum		
Mon. 21					
Tue. 22	22		Saturn 7° N of Moon		
Wed. 23	19	48	Algol at minimum		
	23		Moon at perigee (359 691 km)		
Thu. 24	10		Mercury stationary		
Fri. 25	6	10	**New Moon** (lunation 1100)		
			Partial Solar Eclipse (p. 132)		
Sat. 26	10		**Mercury 1.7° S of Moon**		
	16	37	Algol at minimum		
Sun. 27	4		Venus 3° S of Moon		
Mon. 28					
Tue. 29			Venus at aphelion		
	13	26	Algol at minimum		
Wed. 30			Mercury at ascending node		

IV
I
III
II

THE SKY FOR DECEMBER

		Mercury	Venus	Mars	Jupiter	Saturn	Uranus	Neptune	Sun
RA	1	17^{h}00^m	18^{h}24^m	10^{h}46^m	1^{h}58^m	13^{h}38^m	0^{h}03^m	22^{h}02^m	16^{h}26^m
	11	16^{h}12^m	19^{h}18^m	11^{h}02^m	1^{h}56^m	13^{h}42^m	0^{h}03^m	22^{h}02^m	17^{h}10^m
	21	16^{h}22^m	20^{h}11^m	11^{h}16^m	1^{h}54^m	13^{h}45^m	0^{h}03^m	22^{h}03^m	17^{h}54^m
Dec	1	−22°34′	−24°45′	+10°10′	+10°37′	−7°43′	−0°29′	−12°39′	−21°41′
	11	−18°24′	−23°56′	+8°48′	+10°25′	−8°02′	−0°29′	−12°36′	−22°56′
	21	−19°09′	−21°54′	+7°39′	+10°21′	−8°18′	−0°28′	−12°32′	−23°26′
Dist	1	0.69	1.45	1.32	4.14	10.38	19.68	30.16	0.986
	11	0.75	1.40	1.23	4.25	10.26	19.85	30.33	0.985
	21	0.97	1.35	1.14	4.38	10.12	20.02	30.48	0.984
Mag	1	3.3	−3.8	0.7	−2.8	0.7	5.8	7.9	
	11	1.3	−3.8	0.6	−2.7	0.7	5.8	7.9	
	21	−0.3	−3.8	0.4	−2.7	0.7	5.8	7.9	
Size	1	9.7″	11.5″	7.1″	47.5″	16.0″	3.6″	2.2″	32′26″
	11	9.0″	11.9″	7.6″	46.3″	16.2″	3.5″	2.2″	32′29″
	21	6.9″	12.3″	8.2″	45.0″	16.4″	3.5″	2.2″	32′31″

Moon: On December 0 at 0 UT, Sun's selenographic colongitude is 324.94° and increases by 12.2° each day thereafter.

Greatest N declination on the 10th (+22.5°).

Greatest S declination on the 23rd (−22.5°).

Libration in longitude: E limb most exposed on the 27th (+5.9°),
    W limb most exposed on the 14th (−5.7°).

Libration in latitude: N limb most exposed on the 17th (+6.8°),
    S limb most exposed on the 2nd (−6.9°) & the 30th (−6.8°).

Total eclipse of the Moon, on the 10th, visible from much of North America (except the east), most of the Pacific and the Eastern Hemisphere, and Arctic regions. See ECLIPSES IN 2011 (p. 130).

Mercury: Inferior conjunction on the 4th. Visible in the eastern dawn sky during the last half of the month. Greatest elongation W (22°) on the 23rd.

Venus: In the southwestern evening twilight. Waxing crescent Moon passes 6° N of Venus on the 27th at 11h UT (in North America the best configuration is on the evening of the 26th).

Mars: In the morning sky in Leo. Meridian transit at Greenwich on the 1st and 16th at 06:07 and 05:31 UT*.

Jupiter: Well-placed in the evening sky, on the Aries-Pisces border. Resumes direct eastward motion against the stars on the 26th. Meridian transit at Greenwich on the 1st and 16th at 21:16 and 20:14 UT*.

Saturn: Well-placed in the dawn sky. Meridian transit at Greenwich on the 1st and 16th at 08:58 and 08:05 UT*.

Uranus: Well-placed in the early evening sky. Sets after midnight. Resumes direct eastward motion against the stars on the 10th. Meridian transit at Greenwich on the 1st and 16th at 19:21 and 18:22 UT*.

Neptune: In the western early evening sky near the Aquarius-Capricornus border. Meridian transit at Greenwich on the 1st and 16th at 17:20 and 16:22 UT*.

*See the last two sentences of the first paragraph on p. 98.

Time (UT) d h m	DECEMBER EVENTS	Jupiter's Satellites West East

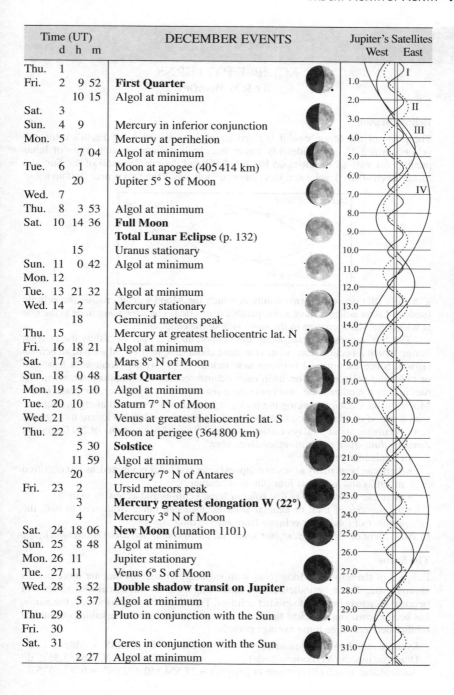

Thu. 1		
Fri. 2 9 52	**First Quarter**	
10 15	Algol at minimum	
Sat. 3		
Sun. 4 9	Mercury in inferior conjunction	
Mon. 5	Mercury at perihelion	
7 04	Algol at minimum	
Tue. 6 1	Moon at apogee (405 414 km)	
20	Jupiter 5° S of Moon	
Wed. 7		
Thu. 8 3 53	Algol at minimum	
Sat. 10 14 36	**Full Moon**	
	Total Lunar Eclipse (p. 132)	
15	Uranus stationary	
Sun. 11 0 42	Algol at minimum	
Mon. 12		
Tue. 13 21 32	Algol at minimum	
Wed. 14 2	Mercury stationary	
18	Geminid meteors peak	
Thu. 15	Mercury at greatest heliocentric lat. N	
Fri. 16 18 21	Algol at minimum	
Sat. 17 13	Mars 8° N of Moon	
Sun. 18 0 48	**Last Quarter**	
Mon. 19 15 10	Algol at minimum	
Tue. 20 10	Saturn 7° N of Moon	
Wed. 21	Venus at greatest heliocentric lat. S	
Thu. 22 3	Moon at perigee (364 800 km)	
5 30	**Solstice**	
11 59	Algol at minimum	
20	Mercury 7° N of Antares	
Fri. 23 2	Ursid meteors peak	
3	**Mercury greatest elongation W (22°)**	
4	Mercury 3° N of Moon	
Sat. 24 18 06	**New Moon** (lunation 1101)	
Sun. 25 8 48	Algol at minimum	
Mon. 26 11	Jupiter stationary	
Tue. 27 11	Venus 6° S of Moon	
Wed. 28 3 52	**Double shadow transit on Jupiter**	
5 37	Algol at minimum	
Thu. 29 8	Pluto in conjunction with the Sun	
Fri. 30		
Sat. 31	Ceres in conjunction with the Sun	
2 27	Algol at minimum	

ECLIPSES
ECLIPSE PATTERNS
BY ROY BISHOP

Eclipse Seasons

The plane of the Moon's orbit is tilted about 5° to the plane of Earth's orbit, the ecliptic. Since 5° is considerably larger than both the north–south range of lunar parallax for various localities on Earth (≈1.9°) and the angular radii of the Sun and Moon (each ≈0.25°), solar eclipses can occur only when the Sun is near (within about

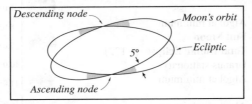

±15° to ±18°) one of the two points at which the Moon's orbit crosses the ecliptic (nodes). Lunar eclipses have a comparable restriction. The *ascending* node is the one at which the Moon crosses to the *north* side of the ecliptic.

The Sun moves eastward along the ecliptic about 1° per day; thus the interval during which an eclipse can occur is at most about (2 × 18°) ÷ 1°/d = 36 d, an *eclipse season*. Since the interval between new moons (29.5 days) is somewhat less, one or two solar eclipses will occur in each eclipse season. Six months later, when the Sun is near the other node, another eclipse season occurs. However, the plane of the Moon's orbit wobbles, making the nodes regress slowly westward along the ecliptic with a period of 18.60 years; thus the two eclipse seasons drift backward through the year, occurring about 19 days earlier each year. *The eclipse seasons of 2011 occur in January, June-July, and November-December.*

In a calendar year,
- there can be as many as seven eclipses (solar and lunar combined, as last occurred in 1982) and as few as four (the usual number);
- there can be as many as five solar or lunar eclipses and as few as two;
- the number of total or annular solar eclipses can range from zero to two, the number of total lunar eclipses from zero to three.

In 2011, there are six eclipses: four solar (all partial) and two lunar (both total).

The Saros

Eclipses of the Sun and Moon recur with various periodicities that are more or less approximate. These periodicities are interesting both as numerical curiosities and because they may be used to predict eclipses. The most famous periodicity, the *Saros*, has been known since ancient times. It is a consequence of a remarkable commensurability between three lunar average periods:

Synodic month *(S)* (new to new)   = 29.530 589 d, 223S = 6585.3213 d
Draconic month *(N)* (node to node)   = 27.212 221 d, 242N = 6585.3575 d
Anomalistic month *(P)* (perigee to perigee) = 27.554 550 d, 239P = 6585.5375 d

Several aspects of this arithmetic are relevant to the pattern of eclipses (for brevity, the following comments are restricted primarily to the case of solar eclipses):

(1) An integer number of Ss (223) ensures a new Moon and hence the possibility of a second solar eclipse.

(2) $242N \approx 223S$ means that the new Moon will be at almost the same position relative to a node, ensuring that an eclipse *will* occur again and that it will occur on Earth's globe about the same distance north or south of the ecliptic plane as did the first eclipse.

(3) The Saros $(223S) = 6585.3213$ d $= 18$ years $+$ *only* 10.3213 d or 11.3213 d (depending on the number of intervening leap years). Thus one Saros later Earth will be at almost the same point in its elliptical orbit and hence at nearly the same distance from the Sun. Moreover, the inclination of Earth toward the Sun (season) will be nearly the same; thus the same latitude region of Earth will be exposed to the eclipse.

(text continues on next page)

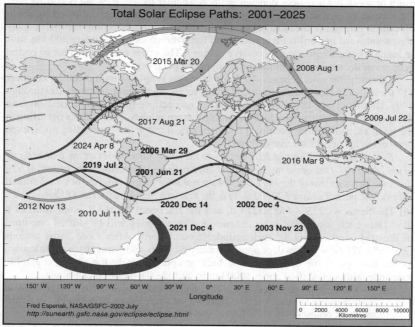

The figure shows the paths of all total solar eclipses, excluding hybrid annular/ total eclipses, occurring during the years 2001–2025. There are 15 eclipses, one in each of the years 2001, 2002, 2003, 2006, 2008, 2009, 2010, 2012, 2015, 2016, 2017, 2019, 2020, 2021, and 2024. Because the 25-year period covered by the figure is somewhat longer than the 18-year Saros interval, the first four and last four eclipses, drawn with heavy shading and with labels in bold type, make up four Saros pairs, with Saros numbers 127, 142, 152, and 139, respectively. Note that the members of each pair are both total eclipses, are separated in time by one Saros, have similar path shapes, and occur at similar latitudes; note also that the later member is shifted 120° westward in longitude (see items (2) through (6) of the text explaining these features). The figure was produced by Fred Espenak and is presented here with his permission. For figures showing total solar eclipses, annular eclipses, and hybrid annular/total eclipses for the period –1999 to +3000 (2000 BC to AD 3000), see eclipse.gsfc.nasa.gov/SEatlas/SEatlas.html.

(4) $239P \approx 223S$ means that one Saros later the new Moon will be at almost the same point in its elliptical orbit and thus at the same distance from Earth. With the same lunar and solar distances, the type of eclipse (total or annular) will be the same. Since the eclipse will occur near the same geographic latitude (see (2) and (3)), the duration of totality or annularity, or the magnitude of partial eclipse if the eclipse is not central, will be almost the same as it was one Saros earlier.

(5) $242N - 223S = 0.0361$ d $= 0.87$ h. This, together with the 0.55°/h eastward speed of the Moon in its orbit, means that after one Saros the Moon will be about 0.5° west of its former position relative to its node. Thus a Saros series does not last forever; there will be about $36°/0.5° \approx 72$ eclipses in a Saros series (the number ranges from 69 to 87). Furthermore, any one Saros series will last for about $72 \times 18 \approx 1300$ years (the range is 1226 to 1551 years).

A Saros series begins with about 10 partial eclipses of increasing magnitude in the north or south polar region, depending upon whether the eclipses are occurring near the ascending or descending lunar node, respectively. These are followed by about 50 central eclipses (either total or annular), which over many centuries progressively shift southward or northward across Earth (on average an approximate 300-km shift in latitude occurs with each successive eclipse). The series ends with 10 or so partial eclipses of decreasing magnitude in the opposite polar region.

Currently, for solar eclipses, 40 Saros series are running simultaneously, numbers 117 through 156 (for lunar eclipses, 41 Saros series are running, numbers 109 through 149). That is, in any 18-year 11-day interval, one eclipse from each of these 40 (and 41) series takes place, after which the whole pattern repeats. Those series occurring at the lunar ascending node are given odd numbers; those at the descending node, even numbers (vice versa for lunar eclipses).

Four of the six eclipses of 2011 belong to the same Saros series as the four eclipses of the year 1993. One of the two additional 2011 eclipses (the partial solar of Jan. 4) is of the same Saros as that of the 1992 Dec. 24 partial solar eclipse, and the other additional eclipse (the partial solar of 2011 Jul. 1) is the first of a new Saros series (#156).

(6) The Saros $= 223S = 6585.3213$ d, and the fractional 0.3213 d $\approx$ one-third of a day. Thus each successive solar eclipse in a Saros series will be shifted one-third of the way westward (120° in longitude) around Earth. After three Saros periods $(3 \times 6585.3213$ d $\approx 19\,756$ d, or approximately 54 years and 1 month), a cycle known as the *Exeligmos*, the eclipse will be back at approximately the same geographic longitude, although shifted about 1000 km in latitude. Two examples follow.

  (a) The Middle East total lunar eclipse of 2011 Jun. 15 (#34 of Saros 130) will not be visible in North America, however, one Saros later (#35 of Saros 130, on 2029 Jun. 26) is a similar total lunar eclipse centred 120° further west and visible from much of the Americas.

  (b) The total solar eclipse of 2024 Apr. 8 (no. 30 of Saros 139), which sweeps northeastward across eastern North America, will be geographically similar to that of 1970 Mar. 7 (no. 27 of Saros 139), which followed the eastern seaboard of North America one Exeligmos earlier. Also, one Saros earlier we had the similar total solar eclipse of 2006 Mar. 29 (no. 29 of Saros 139), which occurred about 120° to the east, across Africa and the Mediterranean (see the figure on the previous page). You, the reader, should now be able to figure out the date, the shape of the path of totality, and the geographic location of solar eclipse no. 28 of Saros 139!

The Metonic Cycle

The sequence of lunar phases and the year repeat their relative pattern at 19-year intervals, a cycle known to astronomers in ancient Babylon and that was discovered independently around 430 BC by Meton, a Greek astronomer. We have

  $235S = 235 \times 29.530\,589 = 6939.6884$ d;
  19 years $= 6939$ d or 6940 d (depending on leap years).

Moreover, $255N$ is also very close to 19 years:

$255N = 255 \times 27.212\,221 = 6939.1164$ d.

Thus solar and lunar eclipses also repeat on a 19-year "Metonic" cycle. Since $255N$ is less than $235S$, the Moon does not reach the same phase (new or full for an eclipse) until it has moved eastward relative to the node by

$(235S - 255N) \times 24$ h $\times\ 0.55°$/h = $7.5°$.

Thus a Metonic eclipse series will have only

eclipse season width on the ecliptic $(36°) \div 7.5° \approx 4$ or 5 eclipses;

and the geographic latitude of successive solar eclipses in a series will change substantially (north or south, depending upon whether the Moon is at its ascending node or descending node, respectively).

What about the Moon's position in its orbit relative to its perigee? Using the anomalistic month P (the Moon returns to perigee on average every 27.554 550 d),

$235S \div P = 251.85$, which is *not* near an integer.

Thus in a Metonic series the Moon's distance is not the same from one eclipse to another. Hence the type of solar eclipse (total or annular) will vary within the series.

With only about four eclipses in a series, a mix of eclipse types, and scattered geographic occurrence, a Metonic eclipse series is not as elegant or useful as a Saros series. The main feature of a Metonic eclipse series is that, like lunar phases, the successive eclipses occur on (almost) the *same day* of the year.

Examples of the Metonic cycle for a lunar phase, lunar eclipses, and two recent Western Hemisphere total solar eclipses are given below. The numbers in parentheses are Saros numbers.

Last-Q Moon	Lunar Eclipses	Solar Eclipses
1954 Jul. 23	1954 Jun. 15 (no eclipse)	1960 Feb. 26 (no eclipse)
1973 Jul. 23	1973 Jun. 15 Penumbral (110)	**1979** Feb. 26 Total (120)
1992 Jul. 22	1992 Jun. 15 Partial (120)	**1998** Feb. 26 Total (130)
2011 Jul. 23	**2011** Jun. 15 Total (130)	2017 Feb. 26 Annular (140)
2030 Jul. 22	2030 Jun. 15 Partial (140)	2036 Feb. 27 Partial (150)
2049 Jul. 21	2049 Jun. 15 Penumbral (150)	2055 Feb. 27 (no eclipse)
	2068 Jun. 15 (no eclipse)	

Canons of Eclipses

Anyone with an interest in eclipses will be blown away by the *Five Millennium Canon of Solar Eclipses* (2006) and the *Five Millennium Canon of Lunar Eclipses* (2009) and their accompanying catalogues (four books in all), by Fred Espenak and Jean Meeus, and published by NASA. These monumental works give maps and tabular data for all 23 962 eclipses (11 898 solar and 12 064 lunar) occurring during the 5000-year period from –1999 to +3000 (2000 BC to AD 3000). The books are available from: NASA Center for AeroSpace Information, 7115 Standard Drive, Hanover MD 21076-1320, USA.

Over two decades ago NASA published Fred Espenak's *Fifty Year Canon of Solar Eclipses* and *Fifty Year Canon of Lunar Eclipses*. Included are maps and data for all eclipses during the two centuries, 1901–2100, plus diagrams and maps (larger scale than in the *Five Millennium* canons) for eclipses during the 50-year period 1986–2035.

ECLIPSES IN 2011
By Fred Espenak

Four partial solar and two total lunar eclipses take place in 2011. This 4:2 combination of solar and lunar eclipses in a single year is rather rare with only six cases during the 21st century (2011, 2029, 2047, 2065, 2076, and 2094). The first and last eclipses always occur in January and December.

The dates and types of eclipses during 2011 are as follows:

Jan. 4:	Partial solar eclipse
Jun. 1:	Partial solar eclipse
Jun. 15:	Total lunar eclipse
Jul. 1:	Partial solar eclipse
Nov. 25:	Partial solar eclipse
Dec. 10:	Total lunar eclipse

Predictions for the eclipses are summarized in Figures 1 through 6 (pp. 145–150). World maps show the regions of visibility for each eclipse. The lunar-eclipse diagrams also include the path of the Moon through Earth's shadows. Contact times for each principal phase are tabulated along with the magnitudes and geocentric coordinates of the Sun and Moon at greatest eclipse.

Partial Solar Eclipse of January 4

The first solar eclipse of 2011 occurs at the Moon's ascending node in eastern Sagittarius. A partial eclipse will be visible from much of Europe, North Africa, and central Asia (Figure 1, p. 145).

The penumbral shadow first touches Earth's surface in northern Algeria at 6:40:11 UT. As the shadow travels east, Western Europe will be treated to a partial eclipse at sunrise. The eclipse magnitude[1] from European cities like Madrid (0.576), Paris (0.732), London (0.747), and Copenhagen (0.826) will give early morning risers an excellent opportunity to photograph the sunrise eclipse with interesting foreground scenery.

Greatest eclipse[2] occurs at 08:50:35 UT in northern Sweden where the eclipse in the horizon will have a magnitude of 0.858. At that time, the axis of the Moon's shadow will pass a mere 510 km above Earth's surface. Most of northern Africa, the Middle East, and Central Asia also lie in the penumbra's path. The citizens of Cairo (0.551), Jerusalem (0.574), Istanbul (0.713), and Tehran (0.507) all witness a large magnitude partial eclipse.

A sunset eclipse will be visible from central Russia, Kazakhstan, Mongolia, and northwest China. The partial eclipse ends when the penumbra leaves Earth at 11:00:54 UT.

Local circumstances and eclipse times for a number of cities in the penumbral path are listed in Table 2. All times are in Universal Time. The Sun's altitude and azimuth, the eclipse magnitude, and eclipse obscuration[3] are all given at the instant of maximum eclipse. When the eclipse is in progress at sunrise or sunset, this information is indicated by a '–'.

The NASA JavaScript Solar Eclipse Explorer is an interactive web page that can quickly calculate the local circumstances of the eclipse from any geographic location not included in Table 1 and is at **eclipse.gsfc.nasa.gov/JSEX/JSEX-index.html**.

This is the 14th eclipse of Saros[4] 151 (Espenak and Meeus, 2006). The family begins with a series of 18 partial eclipses from 1776 to 2083. Complete details for

---

[1] Eclipse magnitude for solar eclipses is defined as the fraction of the Sun's *diameter* occulted by the Moon.
[2] The instant of greatest eclipse occurs when the distance between the Moon's shadow axis and Earth's geocentre reaches a minimum.
[3] Eclipse obscuration is defined as the fraction of the Sun's *area* occulted by the Moon.

the entire series of 72 eclipses (in the order: 18 partial, 6 annular, 1 hybrid, 39 total, and 8 partial) spanning 1280 years can be found at eclipse.gsfc.nasa.gov/SEsaros/SEsaros151.html.

Partial Solar Eclipse of June 1

The next partial solar eclipse occurs at the Moon's descending node in Taurus. The event is visible from high latitudes in the Northern Hemisphere (Figure 2, p. 146).

The eclipse begins at sunrise in Siberia and northern China where the penumbral shadow first touches Earth at 19:25:18 UT. Two hours later, greatest eclipse occurs at 21:16:11 UT. At that time, an eclipse of magnitude 0.601 will be visible from the Arctic coast of western Siberia as the midnight Sun skirts the northern horizon. Although most of Alaska and northern Canada will witness the partial eclipse, the southern limit of the penumbra falls along a curve from south of Fairbanks to central New Brunswick and Nova Scotia.

Reykjavik, Iceland, receives a 0.462 magnitude eclipse just before sunset. Northernmost Norway, Sweden, and Finland also get a midnight solar eclipse with the event hanging above the northern horizon. The partial eclipse ends at 23:06:56 UT when the penumbra leaves Earth just north of Newfoundland in the Atlantic Ocean.

Eclipse times and local circumstances for major cities in North America, Europe, and Asia are given in Table 2. The Sun's altitude, azimuth, the eclipse magnitude, and obscuration are given at the instant of maximum eclipse.

This is the 68th eclipse of Saros 118. The family began with a group of 8 partial eclipses from the years 803 to 929. The Saros ends with a small partial eclipse in 2083. Complete details for the entire series of 72 eclipses (in the order: 8 partial, 40 total, 2 hybrid, 15 annular and 7 partial) spanning 1280 years can be found at: eclipse.gsfc.nasa.gov/SEsaros/SEsaros118.html.

Total Lunar Eclipse of June 15

The first lunar eclipse of 2011 occurs at the Moon's ascending node in southern Ophiuchus about 7° west of the Lagoon Nebula (M8). The Moon passes deeply through Earth's umbral shadow during this rather long event. The total phase itself lasts 100 minutes. The last eclipse to exceed this duration was in July 2000. The Moon's contact times with Earth's umbral and penumbral shadows are listed below.

Penumbral Eclipse Begins:	17:24:34 UT
Partial Eclipse Begins:	18:22:56 UT
Total Eclipse Begins:	19:22:30 UT
Greatest Eclipse:	20:12:37 UT
Total Eclipse Ends:	21:02:42 UT
Partial Eclipse Ends:	22:02:15 UT
Penumbral Eclipse Ends:	23:00:45 UT

At the instant of greatest eclipse[5] the umbral eclipse magnitude[6] will reach 1.6998 as the Moon's centre passes within 5.3 arc-minutes of the shadow axis. The Moon's southern limb will lay 54.2′ from the edge of the umbra while the northern limb will lay 22.3′ from the umbra's edge. Thus, the northern regions of the Moon will probably appear brighter than the southern regions that lie deeper in the shadow. Since the Moon

---

(4) The Saros is a period of 6,585.3 days (18 years, 11 days, 8 hours) in which eclipses (both solar and lunar) repeat. The geometry is not exact but close enough for a Saros series to last 12 or more centuries.

(5) The instant of greatest eclipse for lunar eclipses occurs when the distance between the Moon's shadow axis and Earth's geocentre reaches a minimum.

(6) Umbral eclipse magnitude is defined as the fraction of the Moon's diameter occulted by the umbral shadow.

samples a large range of umbral depths during totality, its appearance will change dramatically with time. It is difficult to predict the exact brightness distribution in the umbra so observers are encouraged to estimate the Danjon value at different times during totality (see Danjon Scale of Lunar Eclipse Brightness). Note that it may also be necessary to assign different Danjon values to different portions of the Moon (i.e. north vs. south).

Nearly 30 years ago (1982 Jul. 06), the author watched another total lunar eclipse with the Moon in the same part of the sky. I was amazed at how brilliantly the summer Milky Way glowed since it was all but invisible during the partial phases. Observers will have a similar opportunity during June's eclipse. In this case, the totally eclipsed Moon will lie in southern Ophiuchus just 8° northwest of the brightest Sagittarian star clouds. The summer constellations are well placed for viewing so a number of bright stars can be used for magnitude comparisons with the totally eclipsed Moon.

Antares ($m_v = +0.92$v) is 15° to the west, Shaula ($m_v = +1.63$) is 14° south, Epsilon Sgr ($m_v = +1.85$) is 15° southeast, Arcturus ($m_v = -0.05$) stands 55° to the northwest, and Altair ($m_v = +0.77$) is 46° northeast of the Moon.

Figure 3 (p. 147) shows the path of the Moon through the penumbra and umbra as well as a map of Earth showing the regions of eclipse visibility. The entire event will be seen from the eastern half of Africa, the Middle East, central Asia, and western Australia. Observers throughout Europe will miss the early stages of the eclipse because they occur before moonrise. Fortunately, totality will be seen throughout the continent except for northern Scotland and northern Scandinavia. Eastern Asia, eastern Australia, and New Zealand will miss the last stages of eclipse because they occur after moonset. Again, the total phase will be seen from most of these regions. Even observers in eastern Brazil, Uruguay, and Argentina will witness totality. None of the eclipse will be visible from North America. At mid-eclipse, the Moon is near the zenith for observers from Reunion and Mauritius.

Table 3 (p. 142) lists predicted umbral immersion and emersion times for 20 well-defined lunar craters. The timing of craters is useful in determining the atmospheric enlargement of Earth's shadow (see Crater Timings During Lunar Eclipses).

The June 15 total lunar eclipse is the 34th member of Saros 130, a series of 71 eclipses occurring in the following order: 8 penumbral, 20 partial, 14 total, 22 partial, and 7 penumbral lunar eclipses (Espenak and Meeus, 2009a) spanning 1262 years. Complete details for Saros 130 can be found at eclipse.gsfc.nasa.gov/LEsaros/LEsaros130.html.

Partial Solar Eclipse of July 1

Just one lunation after the previous one, the third solar eclipse of the year takes place at the Moon's descending node in western Gemini. This Southern Hemisphere event is visible from a D-shaped region in the Antarctic Ocean south of Africa (Figure 4, p. 148). Such a remote and isolated path means that it may very well turn out to be the solar eclipse that nobody sees. At greatest eclipse (08:38:23 UT), the magnitude is just 0.097.

This event is the first eclipse of Saros 156. The family will produce 8 partial eclipses, followed by 52 annular eclipses and ending with 9 more partials. Complete details for the entire series of 69 eclipses spanning the years 2011 through 3237 can be found at eclipse.gsfc.nasa.gov/SEsaros/SEsaros156.html.

Partial Solar Eclipse of November 25

The fourth and final solar eclipse of the year occurs at the Moon's ascending node in western Scorpius. The event is visible from high latitudes in the Southern Hemisphere and includes southern South Africa, Antarctica, Tasmania, and most of New Zealand (Figure 5, p. 149).

At the instant of greatest eclipse (6:20:17 UT) the eclipse magnitude is 0.905, making it the largest partial eclipse of the year. At that time, the lunar shadow axis will pass just 330 km above Earth's surface near the coast of Antarctica.

This is the 53rd eclipse of Saros 123. The family began with 6 partial eclipses from the years 1074 to 1164. By the time the series ends in 2318, it will have produced 70 eclipses in the following order: 6 partial, 27 annular, 3 hybrid, 14 total, and 20 partial eclipses. Complete details for Saros 123 can be found at eclipse.gsfc.nasa.gov/SEsaros/SEsaros123.html.

Total Lunar Eclipse of December 10

The last eclipse of 2011 is a total lunar eclipse that takes place at the Moon's descending node in eastern Taurus, four days after apogee.

The Moon's orbital trajectory takes it through the southern half of Earth's umbral shadow. Although the eclipse is not central, the total phase still lasts 51 minutes. The Moon's path through Earth's shadows as well as a map illustrating worldwide visibility of the event are shown in Figure 6 (p. 150). The timings of the major eclipse phases are listed below.

Penumbral Eclipse Begins:	11:33:32 UT
Partial Eclipse Begins:	12:45:42 UT
Total Eclipse Begins:	14:06:16 UT
Greatest Eclipse:	14:31:49 UT
Total Eclipse Ends:	14:57:24 UT
Partial Eclipse Ends:	16:17:58 UT
Penumbral Eclipse Ends:	17:30:00 UT

At the instant of greatest eclipse (14:32 UT) the Moon lies at the zenith in the Pacific Ocean near Guam and the Northern Mariana Islands. The umbral eclipse magnitude peaks at 1.1061 as the Moon's centre passes 21.4′ south of the shadow axis. The Moon's northern limb is then 6.4′ south of the shadows axis and 33.3′ from the umbra's edge. In contrast, the Moon's southern limb lays 36.5′ from the shadow centre and 3.2′ from the southern edge of the umbra. Thus, the northern half of the Moon will appear much darker than the southern half because it lies deeper in the umbra.

Since the Moon samples a large range of umbral depths during totality, its appearance will change dramatically with time. It is difficult to predict the brightness distribution in the umbra, so observers are encouraged to estimate the Danjon value at different times during totality (see Danjon Scale of Lunar Eclipse Brightness). Note that it may also be necessary to assign different Danjon values to different portions of the Moon (i.e. north vs. south).

During totality, the winter constellations are well placed for viewing so a number of bright stars can be used for magnitude comparisons. Aldebaran (m_v = +0.87) is 9° to the southwest of the eclipsed Moon, while Betelgeuse (m_v = +0.45) is 19° to the southeast, Pollux (m_v = +1.16) is 37° east, and Capella (m_v = +0.08) is 24° north.

The entire event is visible from Asia and Australia. For North Americans, the eclipse is in progress as the Moon sets with western observers favored by a larger fraction of the eclipse before moonset. Observers throughout Europe and Africa will miss the early eclipse phases because they occur before moonrise. None of the eclipse can be seen from South America or Antarctica.

The NASA JavaScript Lunar Eclipse Explorer is an interactive web page that can quickly calculate the altitude of the Moon during each phase of the eclipse from any geographic location and is at eclipse.gsfc.nasa.gov/JLEX/JLEX-index.html.

Table 5 (p. 144) lists predicted umbral immersion and emersion times for 20 well-defined lunar craters. The timing of craters is useful in determining the atmospheric enlargement of Earth's shadow (see Crater Timings During Lunar Eclipses).

The December 10 total lunar eclipse is the 23rd member of Saros 135, a series of 71 eclipses occurring in the following order: 9 penumbral, 10 partial, 23 total, 7 partial, and 22 penumbral lunar eclipses. Complete details for Saros 135 can be found at eclipse.gsfc.nasa.gov/LEsaros/LEsaros135.html.

Solar-Eclipse Figures

For each solar eclipse, an orthographic projection map of Earth shows the path of penumbral (partial), umbral (total), or antumbral (annular) eclipse. North is to the top in all cases, and the daylight terminator is plotted for the instant of greatest eclipse. An asterisk (*) indicates the subsolar point[7] on Earth.

The limits of the Moon's penumbral shadow delineate the region of visibility of the partial solar eclipse. This irregular or saddle-shaped region often covers more than half of the daylight hemisphere of Earth, and consists of several distinct zones, or limits. At the northern and/or southern boundaries lie the limits of the penumbra's path. Partial eclipses have only one of these limits, as do central eclipses when the Moon's shadow axis falls no closer than about 0.45 radii from Earth's centre. Great loops at the western and eastern extremes of the penumbra's path identify the areas where the eclipse begins/ends at sunrise and sunset, respectively. If the penumbra has both a northern and southern limit, the rising and setting curves form two separate closed loops. Otherwise, the curves are connected in a distorted figure 8. Bisecting the "eclipse begins/ends" loops is the curve of maximum eclipse at sunrise (western loop) and sunset (eastern loop). The points P1 and P4 mark the coordinates where the penumbral shadow first contacts (partial eclipse begins) and last contacts (partial eclipse ends) Earth's surface. If the penumbral path has both a northern and southern limit, then points P2 and P3 are also plotted. These correspond to the coordinates where the penumbral shadow cone becomes internally tangent to Earth's disk.

A curve of maximum eclipse is the locus of all points where the eclipse is at maximum at a given time, and is plotted at each half-hour Universal Time. The points generally run between the penumbral limits in the north/south direction, or from the "maximum eclipse at sunrise and sunset" curves to one of the limits. If the eclipse is central (i.e. total or annular), the curves of maximum eclipse run through the outlines of the umbral shadow, plotted at 10-min intervals. The curves of constant eclipse magnitude delineate the locus of all points where the magnitude at maximum eclipse is constant. These curves run exclusively between the curves of maximum eclipse at sunrise and sunset. Furthermore, they are parallel to the northern/southern penumbral limits and the umbral paths of central eclipses. In fact, the northern and southern limits of the penumbra can be thought of as curves of constant magnitude of 0.0. The adjacent curves are for magnitudes of 0.2, 0.4, 0.6, and 0.8. For total eclipses, the northern and southern limits of the umbra are curves of constant magnitude of 1.0. Umbral path limits for annular eclipses are curves of maximum eclipse magnitude.

Greatest eclipse is defined as the instant when the axis of the Moon's shadow passes closest to Earth's centre. Although greatest eclipse differs slightly from the instants of greatest magnitude and greatest duration (for total eclipses), the differences are negligible. The point on Earth's surface intersected by the axis at greatest eclipse is marked by an asterisk. For partial eclipses, the shadow axis misses Earth entirely, so the point of greatest eclipse lies on the day/night terminator and the Sun appears on the horizon.

Data pertinent to the eclipse appear with each map. At the top are listed the instant of ecliptic conjunction of the Sun and Moon (i.e. new Moon) and the instant of greatest eclipse, expressed in Terrestrial Dynamical Time and Universal Time. The eclipse magnitude is defined as the fraction of the Sun's diameter obscured by the Moon at

---

[7] The subsolar point is the geographic location where the Sun appears directly overhead (zenith).

greatest eclipse. For central eclipses (total or annular), the magnitude is replaced by the geocentric ratio of diameters of the Moon and the Sun. Gamma is the minimum distance of the Moon's shadow axis from Earth's centre in Earth radii at greatest eclipse. The Saros series of the eclipse is listed, followed by the member position. The first member number identifies the sequence position of the eclipse in the Saros, while the second is the total number of eclipses in the series.

In the upper left and right corners are the geocentric coordinates of the Sun and the Moon, respectively, at the instant of greatest eclipse. They are:

R.A.   Right ascension
Dec.   Declination
S.D.   Apparent semi-diameter
H.P.   Horizontal parallax

To the lower left in the figures are exterior/interior contact times of the Moon's penumbral shadow with Earth, which are defined as follows:

P1   Instant of first exterior tangency of penumbra with Earth's limb
     (partial eclipse begins)
P2   Instant of first interior tangency of penumbra with Earth's limb
P3   Instant of last interior tangency of penumbra with Earth's limb
P4   Instant of last exterior tangency of penumbra with Earth's limb
     (partial eclipse ends)

Not all eclipses have P2 and P3 penumbral contacts. They are only present in cases where the penumbral shadow falls completely within Earth's disk. For central eclipses, the lower right corner lists exterior/interior contact times of the Moon's umbral shadow with Earth's limb, which are defined as follows:

U1   Instant of first exterior tangency of umbra with Earth's limb
     (umbral [total/annular] eclipse begins)
U2   Instant of first interior tangency of umbra with Earth's limb
U3   Instant of last interior tangency of umbra with Earth's limb
U4   Instant of last exterior tangency of umbra with Earth's limb
     (umbral [total/annular] eclipse ends)

At bottom centre are the geographic coordinates of the position of greatest eclipse, along with the local circumstances at that location (i.e. Sun altitude, Sun azimuth, path width, and duration of totality/annularity). At bottom left is a list of parameters used in the eclipse predictions, while bottom right gives the Moon's geocentric libration (optical + physical) at greatest eclipse.

The solar-eclipse figures are updates of versions originally published in *Fifty Year Canon of Solar Eclipses: 1986–2035* (Espenak, 1988).

Lunar-Eclipse Figures

Each lunar eclipse has two diagrams associated with it along with data pertinent to the eclipse. The top figure shows the path of the Moon through Earth's penumbral and umbral shadows. Above this figure are listed the instant of ecliptic conjunction of the Moon with the point 180° from the Sun (i.e. full Moon) and the instant of greatest eclipse, expressed in Terrestrial Dynamical Time and Universal Time. The penumbral and umbral magnitudes are defined as the fraction of the Moon's diameter immersed in the two shadows at greatest eclipse. The radii of the penumbral and umbral shadows, P. Radius and U. Radius, are also listed. Gamma is the minimum distance in Earth radii of the Moon's centre from Earth's shadow axis at greatest eclipse, and Axis is the same parameter expressed in degrees. The Saros series of the eclipse is listed, followed by a pair of numbers. The first number identifies the sequence position of the eclipse in the Saros; the second is the total number of eclipses in the series.

In the upper left and right corners are the geocentric coordinates of the Sun and the Moon, respectively, at the instant of greatest eclipse, defined as in the solar-eclipse diagrams.

To the lower left are the semi, or half, durations of the penumbral and partial (umbral) eclipses. Below them are the Sun/Moon ephemerides used in the predictions, followed by the extrapolated value of ΔT (the difference between Terrestrial Dynamical Time and Universal Time). To the lower right are the contact times of the Moon with Earth's penumbral and umbral shadows, defined as follows:

P1   Instant of first exterior tangency of Moon with penumbra
        (penumbral eclipse begins)

U1   Instant of first exterior tangency of Moon with umbra
        (partial umbral eclipse begins)

U4   Instant of last exterior tangency of Moon with umbra
        (partial umbral eclipse ends)

P4   Instant of last exterior tangency of Moon with penumbra
        (penumbral eclipse ends)

The bottom figure is a cylindrical equidistant projection map of Earth that shows the regions of visibility for each stage of the eclipse. In particular, the moonrise/moonset terminator is plotted for each contact and is labelled accordingly. The point where the Moon is in the zenith at greatest eclipse is indicated by an asterisk. Observers in the region that is completely unshaded will observe the entire eclipse, while those in the darkly shaded area will witness no eclipse. Observers in the remaining lightly shaded areas will experience moonrise or moonset while the eclipse is in progress. Those in the shaded zones east of the asterisk will witness moonset before the eclipse ends, and those in the shaded zones west will witness moonrise after the eclipse has begun.

The lunar-eclipse figures are updates of versions originally published in *Fifty Year Canon of Lunar Eclipses: 1986–2035* (Espenak, 1989).

Danjon Scale of Lunar-Eclipse Brightness

The Moon's appearance during a total lunar eclipse can vary enormously from one eclipse to the next. Obviously, the geometry of the Moon's path through the umbra plays an important role. Not as apparent is the effect that Earth's atmosphere has on total eclipses. Although the physical mass of Earth blocks all direct sunlight from the umbra, the planet's atmosphere refracts some of the Sun's rays into the shadow. Earth's atmosphere contains varying amounts of water (clouds, mist, precipitation) and solid particles (meteoric dust, organic debris, volcanic ash). This material significantly filters and attenuates the sunlight before it is refracted into the umbra. For instance, very dark, red eclipses often follow large or frequent volcanic eruptions dumping huge quantities of ash into the atmosphere for several years. Extensive cloud cover along Earth's limb also tends to darken the eclipse by blocking sunlight.

The French astronomer André-Louis Danjon proposed a useful five-point scale for evaluating the visual appearance and brightness of the Moon during total lunar eclipses. L values for various luminosities are defined as follows:

L=0   Very dark eclipse.
      (Moon almost invisible, especially at mid-totality)

L=1   Dark eclipse, grey or brownish in colouration.
      (details distinguishable only with difficulty)

L=2   Deep red or rust-coloured eclipse.
      (very dark central shadow, while outer umbra is relatively bright)

L=3   Brick-red eclipse.
      (umbral shadow usually has a bright or yellow rim)

L=4   Very bright copper-red or orange eclipse.
      (umbral shadow has a bluish, very bright rim)

The assignment of an L value to lunar eclipses is best done with the naked eye, binoculars, or a small telescope near the time of mid-totality. It is also useful to examine the Moon's appearance just after the beginning and just before the end of totality. The Moon is then near the edge of the shadow, providing an opportunity to assign an L value to the outer umbra. In making any evaluations, the instrumentation used and the time should both be recorded. Also note any variations in colour and brightness in different parts of the umbra, as well as the apparent sharpness of the shadow's edge. Pay attention to the visibility of lunar features within the umbra. Notes and sketches made during the eclipse are often invaluable in recalling important details, events, and impressions.

Crater Timings During Lunar Eclipses

In 1702, Pierre de La Hire made a curious observation about Earth's umbra. In order to accurately predict the duration of a lunar eclipse, he found it necessary to increase the radius of the shadow about 1 percent more than is warranted by geometric considerations. Although the effect is clearly related to Earth's atmosphere, it is not completely understood, since the shadow enlargement seems to vary from one eclipse to the next. The enlargement can be measured through careful timings of lunar craters as they enter and exit the umbra.

Such observations are best made using a low-power telescope and a clock or watch synchronized with radio time signals. Timings should be made to a precision of about 5 s. Record the instant when the most abrupt gradient at the umbra's edge crosses the apparent centre of the crater. In the case of large craters like Tycho and Copernicus, record the times when the shadow touches the two opposite edges of the crater. The average of these times is equal to the instant of crater bisection.

As a planning guide, Tables 3 and 6 list a number of well-defined craters with predicted umbral immersion and emersion times during the two lunar eclipses of 2011. You should be thoroughly familiar with these features before viewing an eclipse in order to prevent confusion and misidentification. The four umbral contacts with the Moon's limb can also be used in determining the shadow's enlargement. However, these events are less distinct and therefore difficult to time accurately. Observers are encouraged to make crater timings, and to send their results to *Sky & Telescope* (Sky & Telescope, 90 Sherman Street, Cambridge MA 02140-3264, USA) for analysis.

Note that all predictions presented here use Danjon's rule of shadow enlargement (see: Shadow Diameters and Lunar Eclipses). In particular, the diameter of the umbral shadow has been calculated assuming an enlargement of Earth's radius of 1/85 to account for the opacity of the terrestrial atmosphere. The effects of Earth's oblateness have also been included.

Shadow Diameters and Lunar Eclipses

To compensate for Earth's atmosphere when calculating the circumstances for lunar eclipses, Chauvenet [1891] introduced an empirical enlargement of 1/50 to the diameters of the umbral and penumbral shadows. This rule has been employed by many of the national institutes in their official eclipse predictions (including the author's work at NASA). However, the French astonomer André-Louis Danjon [1951] pointed out a flaw in this method because it applies the same relative correction to the umbra and penumbra instead of using the same absolute correction. From eclipse observations, Danjon proposed to enlarge Earth's diameter by 1/85 to compensate for the atmosphere. The umbral and penumbral shadow diameters are then calculated based on this modified geometry. The French almanac *Connaissance des Temps* has used the Danjon rule in its eclipse predictions since 1951. The resulting umbral and penumbral eclipse magnitudes are approximately 0.005 and 0.026 magnitudes smaller, respectively, than predictions using the traditional 1/50 rule.

Beginning in 2007, we use the Danjon rule in calculating lunar-eclipse circumstances.

Eclipse Altitudes and Azimuths

The altitude a and azimuth A of the Sun or Moon during an eclipse depend on the time and the observer's geographic coordinates. They are calculated as follows:

$$h = 15 (GST + UT - \alpha) + \lambda$$
$$a = \arcsin [\sin \delta \sin \phi + \cos \delta \cos h \cos \phi]$$
$$A = \arctan [-(\cos \delta \sin h)/(\sin \delta \cos \phi - \cos \delta \cos h \sin \phi)]$$

where

h	=	hour angle of Sun or Moon
a	=	altitude
A	=	azimuth
GST	=	Greenwich Sidereal Time at 0:00 UT
UT	=	Universal Time
α	=	right ascension of Sun or Moon
δ	=	declination of Sun or Moon
λ	=	observer's longitude (east +, west –)
ϕ	=	observer's latitude (north +, south –)

During the eclipses of 2011, the values for GST and the geocentric RA and Dec of the Sun or the Moon (at greatest eclipse) are as follows:

Eclipse	Date	GST	α	δ
Partial Solar	Jan. 4	6.884	18.987	–22.739
Partial Solar	Jun. 1	16.609	4.631	22.096
Total Lunar	Jun. 15	17.584	17.592	–23.231
Partial Solar	Jul. 1	18.580	6.667	23.118
Partial Solar	Nov. 25	4.239	16.037	–20.682
Total Lunar	Dec. 10	5.265	5.143	22.554

Two Web-based tools can be used to calculate the local circumstances for all solar and lunar eclipses visible from any location. They are the Javascript Solar Eclipse Explorer and the Javascript Lunar Eclipse Explorer. The URLs for these tools are

eclipse.gsfc.nasa.gov/JSEX/JSEX-index.html;
eclipse.gsfc.nasa.gov/JLEX/JLEX-index.html.

Eclipses In 2012

Next year (2012), there will be two solar and two total lunar eclipses:

2012 May 20:	Annular solar eclipse
2012 Jun. 4:	Partial lunar eclipse
2012 Nov. 13:	Total solar eclipse
2012 Nov. 28:	Penumbral lunar eclipse

A full report on these eclipses will be published next year in the *Observer's Handbook 2012*.

Eclipse Web Sites

The URL of the NASA Eclipse home page is eclipse.gsfc.nasa.gov/eclipse.html.

The site features predictions and maps for all solar and lunar eclipses throughout the 21st century. Special pages devoted to the total and annular solar eclipses of 2011 feature detailed path maps, tables, graphs, and meteorological data. A world atlas of solar eclipses provides maps of all central eclipse paths from 2000 BC to AD 3000. The entire *Five Millennium Catalog of Solar Eclipses* [Espenak and Meeus, 2006]

and *Five Millennium Catalog of Lunar Eclipses* [Espenak and Meeus, 2009a] can be downloaded as a PDF file, and all maps are also online as individual GIF images. On-line versions of the entire *Five Millennium Catalog of Solar Eclipses* [Espenak and Meeus, 2009c] and *Five Millennium Catalog of Lunar Eclipses* [Espenak and Meeus, 2009b] list details for every solar and lunar eclipse over the same 5000-year period.

Detailed information on solar- and lunar-eclipse photography and tips on eclipse observing and eye safety may be found at www.MrEclipse.com

Acknowledgments

All eclipse predictions were generated on an Apple G4 PowerMac computer using algorithms developed from the *Explanatory Supplement* (1974) with additional algorithms from Meeus, Grosjean, and Vanderleen (1966). The solar coordinates used in the eclipse predictions are based on the JPL DE200/LE200. The lunar coordinates are based on ELP-2000/85 [M. Chapront-Touzé and J. Chapront, 1983]. For lunar eclipses, the diameters of the umbral and penumbral shadows were calculated using Danjon's rule of enlarging Earth's radius by 1/85 to compensate for the opacity of the terrestrial atmosphere; corrections for the effects of oblateness have also been included.

All calculations, diagrams, tables, and opinions presented in this paper are those of the author, and he assumes full responsibility for their accuracy.

This publication is available electronically through the Internet along with additional information and updates at eclipse.gsfc.nasa.gov/eclipse/OH/OH2011.html

References

Bretagnon P. and Francou G., "Planetary Theories in rectangular and spherical variables: VSOP87 solution," *Astron. and Astrophys., vol. 202, no. 309* (1988).

Chapront-Touzé, M and Chapront, J., "The Lunar Ephemeris ELP 2000," *Astron. and Astrophys., vol. 124, no. 1*, pp 50-62 (1983).

Chauvenet, W., *Manual of Spherical and Practical Astronomy, Vol. 1*, 1891, Dover edition, 1961.

Danjon, A., "Les éclipses de Lune par la pénombre en 1951," *L'Astronomie, 65*, 51–53, Feb. 1951.

Espenak, F., *Fifty Year Canon of Solar Eclipses: 1986–2035*, Sky Publishing, Cambridge, Mass., 1988.

Espenak, F., *Fifty Year Canon of Lunar Eclipses: 1986–2035*, Sky Publishing, Cambridge, Mass., 1989.

Espenak, F. and Meeus, J., *Five Millennium Canon of Solar Eclipses: –1999 to +3000 (2000 BCE to 3000 CE)*, NASA TP–2006-214141, Goddard Space Flight Center, Greenbelt MD, 2006.

Espenak, F. and Meeus, J., *Five Millennium Canon of Lunar Eclipses: –1999 to +3000 (2000 BCE to 3000 CE)*, NASA TP–2009-214172, Goddard Space Flight Center, Greenbelt MD, 2009a.

Espenak, F. and Meeus, J., *Five Millennium Catalog of Lunar Eclipses: –1999 to +3000 (2000 BCE to 3000 CE)*, NASA TP–2009-214173, Goddard Space Flight Center, Greenbelt MD, 2009b.

Espenak, F. and Meeus, J., *Five Millennium Catalog of Solar Eclipses: –1999 to +3000 (2000 BCE to 3000 CE)*, NASA TP–2009-214174, Goddard Space Flight Center, Greenbelt MD, 2009c.

Explanatory Supplement to the Astronomical Ephemeris and the American Ephemeris and Nautical Almanac, Her Majesty's Nautical Almanac Office, London, 1974.

Littmann, M., Willcox, K., and Espenak, F., *Totality—Eclipses of the Sun*, Oxford University Press, London, 2008.

Meeus, J., Grosjean, C.C., and Vanderleen, W., *Canon of Solar Eclipses*, Pergamon Press, New York, 1966.

Meeus, J. and Mucke, H., *Canon of Lunar Eclipses: –2002 to +2526*, Astronomisches Buro, Wien, 1979.

TABLE 1—LOCAL CIRCUMSTANCES FOR THE
PARTIAL SOLAR ECLIPSE OF 2011 JANUARY 4

Geographic Location		Eclipse Begins h:m	Max. Eclipse h:m	Eclipse Ends h:m	Sun Alt. °	Sun Azm. °	Ecl. Mag.	Ecl. Obs.	Umbral Durat.
EUROPE									
AUSTRIA	Vienna	7:03	8:25	9:53	11	144	0.779	0.706	—
BELARUS	Minsk	7:23	8:48	10:16	11	160	0.826	0.762	—
BELGIUM	Brussel	— r	8:15	9:36	3	132	0.762	0.685	—
BULGARIA	Sofija	7:03	8:28	10:02	19	150	0.733	0.651	—
CROATIA	Zagreb	7:00	8:21	9:50	12	143	0.754	0.676	—
CZECH REPUBLIC	Prague	7:05	8:25	9:52	9	143	0.791	0.720	—
DENMARK	København	— r	8:31	9:54	4	143	0.826	0.761	—
FINLAND	Helsinki	7:30	8:50	10:14	5	158	0.852	0.792	—
FRANCE	Paris	— r	8:09	9:30	3	130	0.732	0.649	—
GERMANY	Berlin	— r	8:27	9:52	7	142	0.807	0.739	—
	Frankfurt	— r	8:18	9:42	6	136	0.773	0.698	—
	Hamburg	— r	8:25	9:48	5	139	0.806	0.737	—
	München	— r	8:18	9:45	9	139	0.765	0.688	—
GREECE	Athens	6:57	8:23	9:58	22	148	0.674	0.582	—
HUNGARY	Budapest	7:05	8:28	9:58	13	147	0.778	0.704	—
IRELAND	Dublin	— r	8:42 r	9:26	0	129	0.504	0.388	—
ITALY	Rome	6:52	8:10	9:38	13	137	0.696	0.607	—
LATVIA	Riga	7:24	8:46	10:12	8	156	0.842	0.781	—
LITHUANIA	Vilnius	7:22	8:45	10:13	10	157	0.832	0.769	—
MACEDONIA	Skopje	7:00	8:24	9:57	18	147	0.723	0.639	—
MOLDOVA	Kisin'ov	7:15	8:43	10:16	18	159	0.775	0.701	—
NETHERLANDS	Amsterdam	— r	8:18	9:39	3	133	0.779	0.704	—
NORWAY	Oslo	— r	8:35	9:56	1	142	0.841	0.779	—
POLAND	Warsaw	7:14	8:36	10:05	10	151	0.818	0.752	—
PORTUGAL	Lisbon	— r	7:57 r	8:54	0	119	0.484	0.366	—
ROMANIA	Bucharest	7:08	8:35	10:09	19	155	0.753	0.675	—
RUSSIA	Kujbysev	7:55	9:22	10:45	14	189	0.733	0.650	—
	Moskva	7:38	9:04	10:30	11	173	0.812	0.745	—
	Gorki	7:48	9:13	10:37	11	181	0.789	0.717	—
	Novosibirsk	8:48	9:56	— s	1	226	0.489	0.372	—
	St. Petersburg	7:35	8:56	10:20	6	164	0.846	0.785	—
	Samara	7:55	9:22	10:45	14	189	0.733	0.650	—
SERBIA AND MONTENEGRO	Beograd	7:02	8:26	9:58	16	148	0.754	0.675	—
SPAIN	Barcelona	— r	7:58	9:18	6	127	0.633	0.533	—
	Madrid	— r	7:52	9:06	2	122	0.576	0.468	—
SWEDEN	Stockholm	— r	8:42	10:05	4	150	0.849	0.789	—
SWITZERLAND	Zurich	— r	8:13	9:38	7	135	0.745	0.665	—
UKRAINE	Kiev	7:22	8:49	10:20	15	162	0.800	0.731	—
UNITED KINGDOM	Birmingham	— r	8:20 r	9:30	0	129	0.728	0.644	—
	Glasgow	— r	8:49 r	9:33	0	132	0.504	0.388	—
	London	— r	8:12	9:31	0	128	0.747	0.667	—
	Manchester	— r	8:27 r	9:31	0	130	0.697	0.607	—
AFRICA									
ALGERIA	Algiers	— r	7:52	9:11	8	126	0.564	0.454	—
CHAD	Ndjamena	7:01	7:43	8:29	30	125	0.121	0.049	—
EGYPT	Cairo	7:02	8:31	10:06	33	155	0.551	0.441	—
ETHIOPIA	Addis Abeba	7:43	8:28	9:14	55	155	0.087	0.030	—
LIBYA	Tripoli	6:44	7:59	9:26	18	134	0.560	0.451	—
MOROCCO	Marrakech	— r	7:38	8:39	1	117	0.373	0.253	—
SUDAN	Khartoum	7:09	8:19	9:34	45	148	0.262	0.152	—
TUNISIA	Tunis	6:45	8:00	9:25	14	133	0.610	0.506	—

All times are Universal Time.
"r" indicates eclipse in progress at sunrise; "s" indicates eclipse in progress at sunset.

TABLE 1—LOCAL CIRCUMSTANCES FOR THE
PARTIAL SOLAR ECLIPSE OF 2011 JANUARY 4 (continued)

Geographic Location		Eclipse Begins h:m	Max. Eclipse h:m	Eclipse Ends h:m	Sun Alt. °	Sun Azm. °	Ecl. Mag.	Ecl. Obs.	Umbral Durat.
ASIA									
AFGHANISTAN	Kabul	8:48	9:52	10:51	23	216	0.267	0.156	—
AZERBAIJAN	Baku	7:49	9:20	10:46	26	189	0.593	0.487	—
IRAN	Tehran	7:52	9:21	10:45	31	191	0.507	0.392	—
IRAQ	Baghdad	7:32	9:04	10:35	34	179	0.536	0.424	—
ISRAEL	Tel Aviv-Yafo	7:09	8:41	10:16	33	162	0.574	0.467	—
JORDAN	Amman	7:12	8:43	10:19	34	164	0.568	0.460	—
KAZAKHSTAN	Karaganda	8:38	9:52	11:00	9	217	0.498	0.381	—
KYRGYZSTAN	Bishkek	8:50	9:57	10:59	14	220	0.363	0.243	—
LEBANON	Beirut	7:12	8:44	10:20	32	164	0.600	0.496	—
PAKISTAN	Karachi	9:04	9:46	10:25	33	216	0.093	0.033	—
SYRIA	Damascus	7:13	8:46	10:21	32	165	0.591	0.486	—
TAJIKISTAN	Dusanbe	8:41	9:51	10:56	20	215	0.351	0.233	—
TURKEY	Ankara	7:13	8:44	10:20	25	162	0.692	0.603	—
	Istanbul	7:08	8:37	10:12	23	157	0.713	0.627	—
UZBEKISTAN	Taskent	8:39	9:52	10:58	18	215	0.396	0.276	—

All times are Universal Time.

TABLE 2—LOCAL CIRCUMSTANCES FOR THE
PARTIAL SOLAR ECLIPSE OF 2011 JUNE 1

Geographic Location		Eclipse Begins h:m	Max. Eclipse h:m	Eclipse Ends h:m	Sun Alt. °	Sun Azm. °	Ecl. Mag.	Ecl. Obs.	Umbral Durat.
—	North Pole	20:27	21:21	22:14	22	321	0.469	0.354	
CANADA	Alert, Nun.	20:43	21:36	22:29	23	265	0.434	0.317	—
	Charlottetown, P.E.I.	22:32	22:45	22:59	10	292	0.025	0.005	—
	Chatham, N.B.	22:32	22:44	22:57	12	290	0.020	0.003	—
	Churchill, Man.	22:02	22:17	22:31	34	256	0.021	0.003	—
	Glace Bay, N.S.	22:26	22:44	23:02	8	294	0.049	0.013	—
	Inuvik, N.W.T.	20:51	21:26	22:01	43	191	0.104	0.039	—
	Iqaluit, Nun.	21:31	22:14	22:56	22	276	0.241	0.136	—
	Resolute, Nun.	20:57	21:46	22:34	31	238	0.285	0.174	—
	St. John's, N.L.	22:11	22:39	23:07	5	298	0.124	0.051	—
CHINA	Changchun	— r	20:01 r	20:34	0	58	0.209	0.110	—
	Harbin	— r	20:01	20:37	2	59	0.227	0.124	—
	Shenyang	— r	20:15 r	20:31	0	59	0.132	0.056	—
FAEROE ISLANDS	Torshavn	21:08	21:52 s	— s	0	325	0.501	0.388	—
GREENLAND	Godthåb	21:26	22:12	22:5	15	290	0.331	0.215	—
ICELAND	Reykjavík	21:13	22:01	22:48	5	314	0.462	0.346	—
JAPAN	Sapporo	19:27	19:50	20:14	8	67	0.085	0.029	—
NORWAY	Hammerfest	20:40	21:30	22:20	3	348	0.586	0.483	—
	Tromso	20:43	21:33	22:23	3	344	0.581	0.477	—
	Trondheim	20:54	21:02 s	— s	0	329	0.129	0.054	—
NORTH KOREA	P'yongyang	— r	20:15 r	20:21	0	61	0.050	0.013	—
SVALBARD	Svalbard	20:36	21:28	22:20	11	344	0.561	0.455	—

All times are Universal Time.
"r" indicates eclipse in progress at sunrise; "s" indicates eclipse in progress at sunset.

TABLE 3—CRATER IMMERSION AND EMERSION TIMES
FOR THE TOTAL LUNAR ECLIPSE OF 2011 JUNE 15

Immersion	Crater Name	Emersion	Crater Name
18:24	Grimaldi	21:06	Grimaldi
18:29	Billy	21:08	Aristarchus
18:31	Aristarchus	21:11	Billy
18:32	Kepler	21:13	Kepler
18:40	Campanus	21:18	Pytheas
18:40	Copernicus	21:20	Plato
18:41	Pytheas	21:20	Copernicus
18:45	Timocharis	21:21	Timocharis
18:49	Tycho	21:21	Campanus
18:51	Plato	21:28	Aristoteles
18:55	Manilius	21:29	Eudoxus
18:58	Menelaus	21:29	Tycho
18:59	Dionysius	21:33	Manilius
18:59	Eudoxus	21:36	Menelaus
19:00	Aristoteles	21:39	Dionysius
19:02	Plinius	21:40	Plinius
19:11	Goclenius	21:49	Proclus
19:12	Proclus	21:51	Taruntius
19:12	Taruntius	21:53	Goclenius
19:17	Langrenus	21:58	Langrenus

All times are Universal Time. Predictions include an enlargement of the umbral shadow of appoximately one percent due to Earth's atmosphere.

TABLE 4—LOCAL CIRCUMSTANCES FOR
PARTIAL SOLAR ECLIPSE OF 2011 NOVEMBER 25

Geographic Location		Eclipse Begins h:m	Max. Eclipse h:m	Eclipse Ends h:m	Sun Alt. °	Sun Azm. °	Ecl. Mag.	Ecl. Obs.	Umbral Durat.
ANTARCTICA	Amundsen-Scott	5:35	6:30	7:25	21	300	0.778	0.725	—
	Casey	6:03	6:54	7:45	38	313	0.370	0.257	—
	Davis	5:31	6:26	7:20	42	3	0.416	0.304	—
	McMurdo	5:58	6:52	7:45	20	263	0.705	0.635	—
	Mirny	5:47	6:39	7:31	43	339	0.357	0.244	—
AUSTRALIA	Hobart	7:30	7:49	8:08	15	256	0.056	0.016	—
NEW ZEALAND	Christchurch	7:07	7:42	— s	0	240	0.278	0.170	—
	Dunedin	7:03	7:41	— s	3	242	0.306	0.194	—
	Invercargill	7:03	7:41	— s	4	244	0.299	0.188	—
	Wellington	7:10	7:28 s	— s	0	241	0.192	0.098	—
SOUTH AFRICA	Cape Town	4:28	4:53	5:18	15	105	0.106	0.041	—
	Port Elizabeth	4:38	4:53	5:08	21	101	0.032	0.007	—

All times are Universal Time.
"r" indicates eclipse in progress at sunrise; "s" indicates eclipse in progress at sunset.

TABLE 5—CRATER IMMERSION AND EMERSION TIMES
FOR THE TOTAL LUNAR ECLIPSE OF 2011 DECEMBER 10

Immersion	Crater Name	Emersion	Crater Name
12:52	Grimaldi	15:14	Grimaldi
12:55	Aristarchus	15:16	Billy
13:00	Kepler	15:17	Tycho
13:01	Billy	15:19	Campanus
13:07	Pytheas	15:29	Kepler
13:09	Copernicus	15:32	Aristarchus
13:11	Timocharis	15:38	Copernicus
13:12	Plato	15:42	Pytheas
13:19	Campanus	15:47	Timocharis
13:21	Aristoteles	15:54	Dionysius
13:22	Eudoxus	15:54	Manilius
13:25	Manilius	15:55	Plato
13:28	Menelaus	15:58	Menelaus
13:32	Plinius	15:59	Goclenius
13:32	Dionysius	16:01	Plinius
13:35	Tycho	16:03	Eudoxus
13:42	Proclus	16:03	Aristoteles
13:46	Taruntius	16:04	Langrenus
13:50	Goclenius	16:07	Taruntius
13:55	Langrenus	16:10	Proclus

All times are Universal Time. Predictions include an enlargement of the umbral shadow of appoximately one percent due to Earth's atmosphere.

FIGURE 1 — PARTIAL SOLAR ECLIPSE OF 2011 JANUARY 4

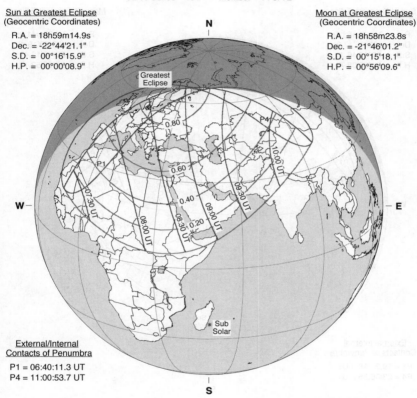

Ecliptic Conjunction = 09:03:42.7 TD (= 09:02:35.6 UT)
Greatest Eclipse = 08:51:42.0 TD (= 08:50:34.9 UT)

Eclipse Magnitude = 0.8576   Gamma = 1.0626

Saros Series = 151   Member = 14 of 72

Sun at Greatest Eclipse
(Geocentric Coordinates)

R.A. = 18h59m14.9s
Dec. = -22°44'21.1"
S.D. = 00°16'15.9"
H.P. = 00°00'08.9"

Moon at Greatest Eclipse
(Geocentric Coordinates)

R.A. = 18h58m23.8s
Dec. = -21°46'01.2"
S.D. = 00°15'18.1"
H.P. = 00°56'09.6"

External/Internal
Contacts of Penumbra

P1 = 06:40:11.3 UT
P4 = 11:00:53.7 UT

Constants & Ephemeris

ΔT =   67.1 s
k1 = 0.2724880
k2 = 0.2722810
Δb = 0.0"   Δl = 0.0"
Eph. = VSOP87/ELP2000-85

0   1000   2000   3000   4000   5000
Kilometres

F. Espenak, NASA's GSFC

eclipse.gsfc.nasa.gov/eclipse.html

Geocentric Libration
(Optical + Physical)

l =   4.63°
b = -1.30°
c = -4.24°

Brown Lun. No. = 1089

See pp. 134–135 for an explanation of this figure.

FIGURE 2—PARTIAL SOLAR ECLIPSE OF 2011 JUNE 1

Ecliptic Conjunction = 21:03:42.8 TD (= 21:02:35.5 UT)
Greatest Eclipse = 21:17:18.4 TD (= 21:16:11.1 UT)

Eclipse Magnitude = 0.6011   Gamma = 1.2130

Saros Series = 118   Member = 68 of 72

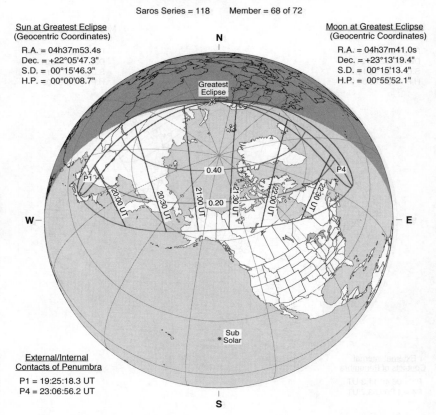

Sun at Greatest Eclipse
(Geocentric Coordinates)

R.A. = 04h37m53.4s
Dec. = +22°05'47.3"
S.D. = 00°15'46.3"
H.P. = 00°00'08.7"

Moon at Greatest Eclipse
(Geocentric Coordinates)

R.A. = 04h37m41.0s
Dec. = +23°13'19.4"
S.D. = 00°15'13.4"
H.P. = 00°55'52.1"

External/Internal
Contacts of Penumbra

P1 = 19:25:18.3 UT
P4 = 23:06:56.2 UT

Constants & Ephemeris

ΔT =   67.3 s
k1 = 0.2724880
k2 = 0.2722810
Δb =   0.0"   Δl =   0.0"
Eph. = VSOP87/ELP2000-85

0   1000   2000   3000   4000   5000
Kilometres

F. Espenak, NASA's GSFC
eclipse.gsfc.nasa.gov/eclipse.html

Geocentric Libration
(Optical + Physical)

l = -4.65°
b = -1.48°
c = -9.54°

Brown Lun. No. = 1094

See pp. 134–135 for an explanation of this figure.

FIGURE 3—TOTAL LUNAR ECLIPSE OF 2011 JUNE 15

Ecliptic Conjunction = 20:14:40.7 TD (= 20:13:33.4 UT)
Greatest Eclipse = 20:13:43.1 TD (= 20:12:35.8 UT)

Penumbral Magnitude = 2.6868   P. Radius = 1.2504°   Gamma = 0.0897
Umbral Magnitude = 1.6998   U. Radius = 0.7256°   Axis = 0.0875°

Saros Series = 130   Member = 34 of 72

Sun at Greatest Eclipse
(Geocentric Coordinates)

R.A. = 05h35m33.6s
Dec. = +23°19'06.1"
S.D. = 00°15'44.7"
H.P. = 00°00'08.7"

Moon at Greatest Eclipse
(Geocentric Coordinates)

R.A. = 17h35m32.3s
Dec. = -23°13'51.6"
S.D. = 00°15'57.2"
H.P. = 00°58'33.0"

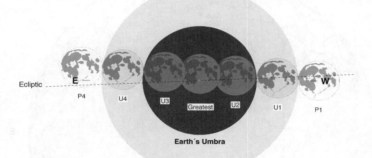

Eclipse Durations

Penumbral = 05h36m12s
Umbral = 03h39m19s
Total = 01h40m13s

ΔT =   67 s
Rule = CdT (Danjon)
Eph. = VSOP87/ELP2000-85

F. Espenak, NASA's GSFC
eclipse.gsfc.nasa.gov/eclipse.html

Eclipse Contacts

P1 = 17:24:33 UT
U1 = 18:22:55 UT
U2 = 19:22:29 UT
U3 = 21:02:41 UT
U4 = 22:02:14 UT
P4 = 23:00:44 UT

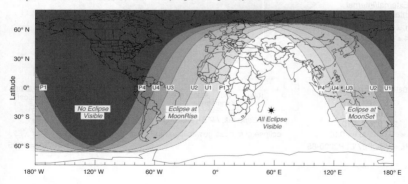

See pp. 135–136 for an explanation of this figure.

FIGURE 4—PARTIAL SOLAR ECLIPSE OF 2011 JULY 1

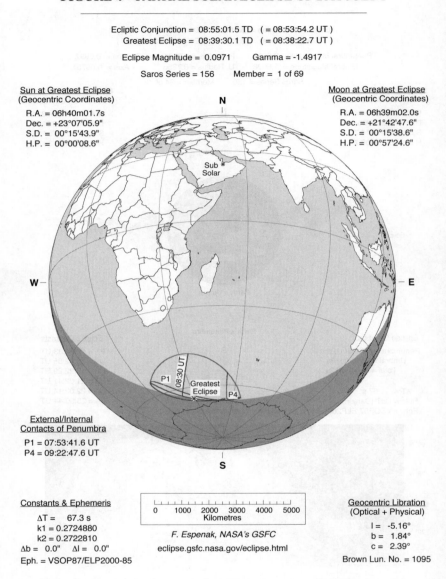

Ecliptic Conjunction = 08:55:01.5 TD (= 08:53:54.2 UT)
Greatest Eclipse = 08:39:30.1 TD (= 08:38:22.7 UT)

Eclipse Magnitude = 0.0971   Gamma = -1.4917

Saros Series = 156   Member = 1 of 69

Sun at Greatest Eclipse
(Geocentric Coordinates)

R.A. = 06h40m01.7s
Dec. = +23°07'05.9"
S.D. = 00°15'43.9"
H.P. = 00°00'08.6"

Moon at Greatest Eclipse
(Geocentric Coordinates)

R.A. = 06h39m02.0s
Dec. = +21°42'47.6"
S.D. = 00°15'38.6"
H.P. = 00°57'24.6"

External/Internal
Contacts of Penumbra

P1 = 07:53:41.6 UT
P4 = 09:22:47.6 UT

Constants & Ephemeris

ΔT = 67.3 s
k1 = 0.2724880
k2 = 0.2722810
Δb = 0.0" Δl = 0.0"
Eph. = VSOP87/ELP2000-85

0 1000 2000 3000 4000 5000
Kilometres

F. Espenak, NASA's GSFC

eclipse.gsfc.nasa.gov/eclipse.html

Geocentric Libration
(Optical + Physical)

l = -5.16°
b = 1.84°
c = 2.39°

Brown Lun. No. = 1095

See pp. 134–135 for an explanation of this figure.

FIGURE 5—PARTIAL SOLAR ECLIPSE OF 2011 NOVEMBER 25

Ecliptic Conjunction = 06:10:47.0 TD (= 06:09:39.5 UT)
Greatest Eclipse = 06:21:24.1 TD (= 06:20:16.6 UT)

Eclipse Magnitude = 0.9046   Gamma = -1.0537

Saros Series = 123   Member = 53 of 70

Sun at Greatest Eclipse
(Geocentric Coordinates)

R.A. = 16h02m13.7s
Dec. = -20°40'56.3"
S.D. = 00°16'12.1"
H.P. = 00°00'08.9"

Moon at Greatest Eclipse
(Geocentric Coordinates)

R.A. = 16h01m46.2s
Dec. = -21°44'25.6"
S.D. = 00°16'32.6"
H.P. = 01°00'42.7"

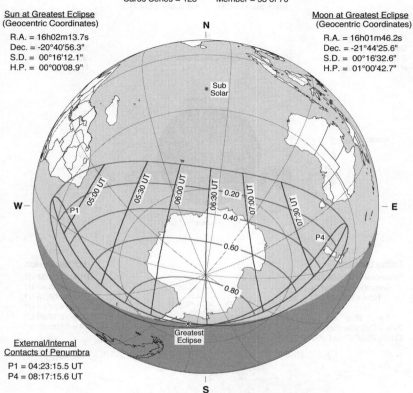

External/Internal
Contacts of Penumbra

P1 = 04:23:15.5 UT
P4 = 08:17:15.6 UT

Constants & Ephemeris

ΔT = 67.5 s
k1 = 0.2724880
k2 = 0.2722810
Δb = 0.0" Δl = 0.0"
Eph. = VSOP87/ELP2000-85

0 1000 2000 3000 4000 5000
Kilometres

F. Espenak, NASA's GSFC

eclipse.gsfc.nasa.gov/eclipse.html

Geocentric Libration
(Optical + Physical)

l = 2.93°
b = 1.38°
c = 12.80°

Brown Lun. No. = 1100

See pp. 134-135 for an explanation of this figure.

FIGURE 6—TOTAL LUNAR ECLIPSE OF 2011 DECEMBER 10

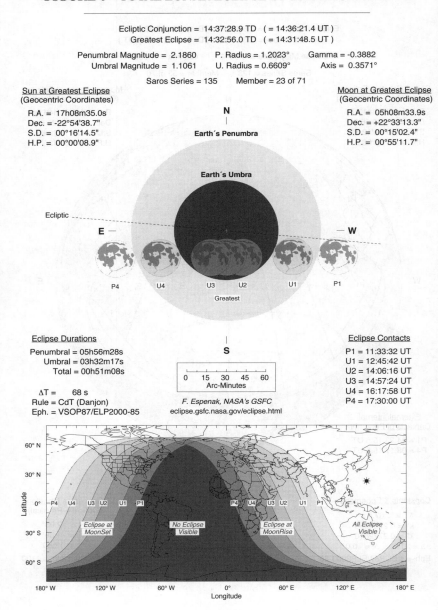

Ecliptic Conjunction = 14:37:28.9 TD (= 14:36:21.4 UT)
Greatest Eclipse = 14:32:56.0 TD (= 14:31:48.5 UT)

Penumbral Magnitude = 2.1860   P. Radius = 1.2023°   Gamma = -0.3882
Umbral Magnitude = 1.1061   U. Radius = 0.6609°   Axis = 0.3571°

Saros Series = 135   Member = 23 of 71

Sun at Greatest Eclipse
(Geocentric Coordinates)

R.A. = 17h08m35.0s
Dec. = -22°54'38.7"
S.D. = 00°16'14.5"
H.P. = 00°00'08.9"

N

Earth's Penumbra

Earth's Umbra

Ecliptic

E —

— **W**

P4   U4   U3   U2   U1   P1

Greatest

Moon at Greatest Eclipse
(Geocentric Coordinates)

R.A. = 05h08m33.9s
Dec. = +22°33'13.3"
S.D. = 00°15'02.4"
H.P. = 00°55'11.7"

S

| 0 | 15 | 30 | 45 | 60 |
Arc-Minutes

Eclipse Durations

Penumbral = 05h56m28s
Umbral = 03h32m17s
Total = 00h51m08s

ΔT =   68 s
Rule = CdT (Danjon)
Eph. = VSOP87/ELP2000-85

F. Espenak, NASA's GSFC
eclipse.gsfc.nasa.gov/eclipse.html

Eclipse Contacts

P1 = 11:33:32 UT
U1 = 12:45:42 UT
U2 = 14:06:16 UT
U3 = 14:57:24 UT
U4 = 16:17:58 UT
P4 = 17:30:00 UT

See pp. 135–136 for an explanation of this figure.

VIEWING A SOLAR ECLIPSE—A WARNING

Solar eclipses are among the most widely publicized and observed celestial events. It is essential to be aware of the visual danger associated with a solar eclipse. The safety rule is simple but not widely appreciated: **Never look at the surface of the Sun, either directly with the unaided eyes or through binoculars or a telescope.** To do so one risks permanent partial blindness, and this can occur almost instantly in the case of telescopic viewing. Viewing our Sun is just as dangerous on any clear day, but at the time of an eclipse people have a reason to want to look at it—and often resort to dangerous methods.

A direct view of the Sun is safe only if a suitable filter is used in a proper manner. In the case of binoculars or a telescope, the filter must be one that attaches *securely* to the *front* end of the instrument, never one that attaches to the eyepiece end (the heat developed near the eyepiece can shatter such a filter).

Filters specifically designed for solar viewing include aluminized Mylar and glass filters plated with a slightly transparent, metallic film. Such filters may be purchased at telescope supply stores. Shade #14 (no other shade) rectangular welder's glass may be used; however, since these filters are of low optical quality, they are useful only for views not involving binoculars or a telescope. All of these are commercial items and cannot be replaced with ordinary household items. For example, layers of photographic colour film, coloured glass, stacked sunglasses, crossed polarizers, smoked glass, or photographic neutral-density filters must never be used. Although one may devise a combination that dims the *visible* sunlight to a comfortable level, the makeshift filter may be quite transparent in the infrared part of the solar spectrum, and this invisible radiation will damage the retina of the observer's eye. For the same reason, one must never rely on clouds or heavy atmospheric haze to dim the solar image when using a telescope. Two layers of fully exposed and developed, silver-based, black and white photographic film provides adequate protection, but many modern films, including all colour films, are based on dyes that do not provide protection in the infrared. Thus it is best to avoid using filters made of photographic film.

One of the simplest, safest, and least known ways to observe the partial phases of a solar eclipse is *pinhole mirror projection*. Take a small pocket mirror and, with masking tape, cover all but a small section of the mirror's surface. The shape and size of the small opening are not critical, but a square about 6 mm on a side works well. Prop the mirror up on a sunny windowsill and orient the mirror so the reflected sunlight shines on the ceiling or a wall of the room—but not directly into anyone's eyes! The spot of light on the viewing surface will be a *pinhole image* of the solar disk. The mirror has a great advantage over the usual "pinhole-in-a-box arrangement" in that the image can be aimed across a substantial distance to a convenient viewing screen. The greater the projection distance, the larger, but dimmer, the Sun's image. The size of the mirror aperture should be adjusted for the best compromise between image brightness and image sharpness. With this simple device the progress of a solar eclipse can be viewed in complete safety by a group of children in a darkened room.

A sharper and brighter image of the solar disk may be projected onto a white viewing screen placed 30 or 40 cm behind the eyepiece of binoculars or a small telescope (the telescope aperture should be stopped down to about 50 mm in order to limit the intensity of sunlight passing through the instrument, and the viewing screen should be shielded from direct sunlight). However, one must *not* look through the instrument when aiming it, and, especially if children are present, a physical barrier should be used to prevent anyone from attempting to look into the eyepiece. If the telescope has a finderscope, it should be either covered or removed.

THE MOON
MAP OF MOON
BY ROY BISHOP

Maria	
LS	Lacus Somniorum (Lake of Dreams) (330°)
MC	Mare Crisium (Sea of Crises) (300°)
MFe	Mare Fecunditatis (Sea of Fertility) (310°)
MFr	Mare Frigoris (Sea of Cold) (0°)
MH	Mare Humorum (Sea of Moisture) (40°)
MI	Mare Imbrium (Sea of Rains) (20°)
MNe	Mare Nectaris (Sea of Nectar) (325°)
MNu	Mare Nubium (Sea of Clouds) (15°)
MS	Mare Serenitatis (Sea of Serenity) (340°)
MT	Mare Tranquillitatis (Sea of Tranquillity) (330°)
MV	Mare Vaporum (Sea of Vapours) (355°)
OP	Oceanus Procellarum (Ocean of Storms) (50°)
SA	Sinus Aestuum (Seething Bay) (8°)
SI	Sinus Iridum (Bay of Rainbows) (32°)
SM	Sinus Medii (Central Bay) (0°)
SR	Sinus Roris (Bay of Dew) (60°)

Lunar Probes

2 *Luna 2*, First to reach Moon (1959–9–13) (0°)
7 *Ranger 7*, First close pictures (1964–7–31) (21°)
9 *Luna 9*, First soft landing (1966–2–3) (64°)
11 *Apollo 11*, First men on Moon (1969–7–20) (337°)
12 *Apollo 12* (1969–11–19) (23°)
14 *Apollo 14* (1971–2–5) (17°)
15 *Apollo 15* (1971–7–30) (356°)
16 *Apollo 16* (1972–4–21) (344°)
17 *Apollo 17* (1972–12–11) (329°)

Angles in parentheses equal 360°– λ, where λ is the selenographic longitude of the centre of the feature. 0° marks the mean centre of the lunar disk and the angles increase toward the observer's east (i.e. westward on the Moon). These angles facilitate locating the feature on the accompanying map, and may be correlated with the Sun's selenographic colongitude (see THE SKY MONTH BY MONTH (p. 98)) to determine the optimum times for viewing the feature.

MAP OF MOON (continued)

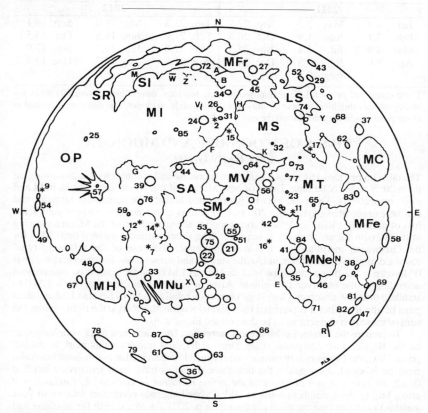

Craters

21 Albategnius (356°)
22 Alphonsus (3°)
23 Arago (338°)
24 Archimedes (4°)
25 Aristarchus (47°)
26 Aristillus (358°)
27 Aristoteles (342°)
28 Arzachel (2°)
29 Atlas (315°)
31 Autolycus (358°)
32 Bessel (342°)
33 Bullialdus (22°)
34 Cassini (355°)
35 Catharina (336°)
36 Clavius (15°)
37 Cleomedes (304°)
38 Cook (311°)
39 Copernicus (20°)
41 Cyrillus (336°)
42 Delambre (342°)

43 Endymion (305°)
44 Eratosthenes (11°)
45 Eudoxus (343°)
46 Fracastorius (326°)
47 Furnerius (299°)
48 Gassendi (40°)
49 Grimaldi (68°)
51 Halley (354°)
52 Hercules (321°)
53 Herschel (2°)
54 Hevelius (66°)
55 Hipparchus (354°)
56 Julius Caesar (345°)
57 Kepler (38°)
58 Langrenus (299°)
59 Lansberg (27°)
61 Longomontanus (21°)
62 Macrobius (314°)
63 Maginus (6°)
64 Manilius (351°)
65 Maskelyne (330°)
66 Maurolycus (345°)

67 Mersenius (49°)
68 Newcomb (316°)
69 Petavius (298°)
71 Piccolomini (327°)
72 Plato (10°)
73 Plinius (336°)
74 Posidonius (330°)
75 Ptolemaeus (2°)
76 Reinhold (23°)
77 Ross (338°)
78 Schickard (55°)
79 Schiller (40°)
81 Snellius (304°)
82 Stevinus (305°)
83 Taruntius (313°)
84 Theophilus (333°)
85 Timocharis (13°)
86 Tycho (11°)
87 Wilhelm (20°)

Mountains

A Alpine Valley (356°)
B Alps Mts. (359°)
E Altai Mts. (336°)
F Apennine Mts. (2°)
G Carpathian Mts. (24°)
H Caucasus Mts. (352°)
K Haemus Mts. (349°)
M Jura Mts. (34°)
N Pyrenees Mts. (319°)
R Rheita Valley (312°)
S Riphaeus Mts. (27°)
V Spitzbergen (5°)
W Straight Range (20°)
X Straight Wall (8°)
Y Taurus Mts. (319°)
Z Teneriffe Mts. (13°)

UNIVERSAL TIME OF NEW-MOON DATES

2011			2012		
Jan. 4.4	May 3.3	Sep. 27.5	Jan. 23.3	May 21.0	Sep. 16.1
Feb. 3.1	Jun. 1.9	Oct. 26.8	Feb. 21.9	Jun. 19.6	Oct. 15.5
Mar. 4.9	Jul. 1.4	Nov. 25.3	Mar. 22.6	Jul. 19.2	Nov. 13.9
Apr. 3.6	Jul. 30.8	Dec. 24.8	Apr. 21.3	Aug. 17.7	Dec. 13.4
	Aug. 29.1				

These dates will be useful for planning observing sessions, determining favourable dates for observing very thin lunar crescents, and setting Moon dials on clocks. The dates are indicated to lower precision in the calendar on the inside back cover.

TIMES OF MOONRISE AND MOONSET
By Rajiv Gupta

The table on pp. 156–161 gives the times of moonrise and moonset for locations ranging from 20°N to 60°N latitude. Dates of new Moon and full Moon are given in **bold** and *italic* respectively. The table may be interpolated linearly for nontabular latitudes and can be extrapolated beyond the 20° and 60° limits a few degrees without significant loss of accuracy. "Rise" and "Set" correspond to the upper limb of the Moon appearing at the horizon for an observer at sea level. The times are local mean time (LMT) for the Greenwich meridian (i.e. UT at 0° longitude). Because of the relatively rapid eastward motion of the Moon, unlike the sunrise and sunset table, for observers not near 0° longitude the times cannot be read directly as LMT; the table must be interpolated according to the observer's longitude. Also, to convert from the observer's LMT to standard time, the observer's longitude correction relative to his or her standard meridian must be applied. After it is prepared for a given location, the chart at the right enables the sum of these two corrections to be determined in one step.

To prepare the **Moonrise/Moonset Correction Diagram,** first mark your longitude on the *West or East Longitude* scale. Draw a diagonal line from this mark to the 0,0 point. Next, the *Correction in minutes* axis (which is subdivided at two-minute intervals) must be labelled. As a guide, the first three divisions have been tentatively labelled 0, ±2, ±4 (*use + if you are west of the prime meridian in Greenwich, England, – if east*); but, to these numbers must be added your longitude correction relative to your standard meridian (see the third paragraph on p. 202). As an aid both for labelling and for reading the chart, the vertical lines at 10-min intervals are wider. **Examples:** For Toronto, which is 4.5° W of its standard meridian of 75°W, the longitude correction is +18 min, so an observer in Toronto would label the Correction axis 18, 20, 22, 24,...; an observer in Boston (longitude correction –16) would label the axis –16, –14, –12,...; an observer in Hong Kong (east longitude, longitude correction +24) would label the axis 24, 22, 20,...; an observer in Vienna (longitude correction –6) would label the axis –6, –8, –10,....

The chart is now ready for use on any day from your position. Interpolating for nontabular latitudes, from the table obtain today's time for the event (moonrise, or moonset) and tomorrow's time if you are west of Greenwich, yesterday's time if east, enter the difference on the *Tabular Delay* axis, and run horizontally across to meet the diagonal line. The correction, to the nearest minute, can then be read directly below off the Correction axis. This correction is applied to the tabular "today's time" and results in the standard time of the event for your position. **Example:** The latitude of Toronto is 44°N. Interpolating the 40°N and 45°N entries, the table gives for 44°N a moonrise time of 22:11 on Jun. 19 and 22:36 on Jun. 20. The Correction corresponding to a 25-min Tabular Delay, when the chart is prepared for Toronto as described above, is +21 min; hence the time of moonrise is 22:11 + 21 min = 21:32 EST Jun. 19 or 20:32 EDT Jun. 19.

Note: Due to a difference in height between the observer and the actual horizon, the observed time may differ by several minutes from the predicted time.

MOONRISE/MOONSET CORRECTION DIAGRAM

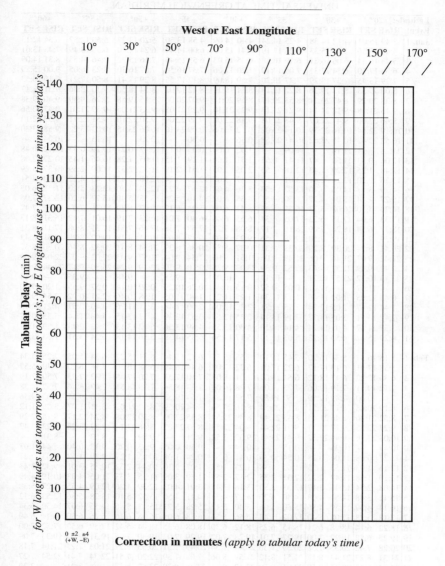

West or East Longitude

Tabular Delay (min)

for W longitudes use tomorrow's time minus today's; for E longitudes use today's time minus yesterday's

0 ±2 ±4
(+W, −E)

Correction in minutes *(apply to tabular today's time)*

MOONRISE AND MOONSET, 2011 JANUARY, FEBRUARY
UNIVERSAL TIME AT GREENWICH MERIDIAN

Latitude:	+20°		+30°		+35°		+40°		+45°		+50°		+55°		+60°	
Event:	RISE	SET	RISE	SET	RISE	SET	RISE	SET	RISE	SET	RISE	SET	RISE	SET	RISE	SET
Jan. 1	3:49	15:01	4:12	14:38	4:25	14:24	4:40	14:09	4:58	13:50	5:20	13:27	5:50	12:57	6:34	12:13
2	4:48	15:56	5:11	15:33	5:25	15:19	5:41	15:03	6:00	14:44	6:24	14:20	6:56	13:49	7:43	13:01
3	5:43	16:54	6:06	16:31	6:19	16:18	6:35	16:03	6:53	15:45	7:16	15:22	7:46	14:53	8:31	14:09
4	6:33	17:50	6:54	17:31	7:06	17:19	7:20	17:06	7:37	16:50	7:57	16:30	8:23	16:05	9:00	15:29
5	7:19	18:45	7:37	18:29	7:47	18:20	7:59	18:09	8:12	17:56	8:29	17:41	8:50	17:21	9:19	16:53
6	8:00	19:38	8:14	19:26	8:22	19:19	8:31	19:11	8:42	19:02	8:54	18:50	9:10	18:36	9:31	18:17
7	8:38	20:29	8:47	20:21	8:53	20:17	8:59	20:11	9:07	20:06	9:15	19:58	9:26	19:49	9:40	19:38
8	9:13	21:18	9:18	21:14	9:21	21:13	9:25	21:10	9:29	21:08	9:33	21:05	9:39	21:01	9:47	20:56
9	9:46	22:06	9:47	22:07	9:48	22:08	9:48	22:08	9:49	22:09	9:50	22:10	9:51	22:11	9:53	22:13
10	10:19	22:54	10:16	22:59	10:14	23:02	10:12	23:06	10:09	23:10	10:06	23:15	10:03	23:22	9:58	23:30
11	10:52	23:42	10:45	23:52	10:41	23:58	10:36	—	10:30	—	10:23	—	10:15	—	10:04	—
12	11:28	—	11:16	—	11:09	—	11:02	0:04	10:53	0:12	10:42	0:21	10:29	0:33	10:12	0:48
13	12:06	0:33	11:50	0:47	11:41	0:55	11:31	1:04	11:19	1:15	11:05	1:28	10:46	1:45	10:22	2:08
14	12:48	1:25	12:29	1:43	12:18	1:53	12:05	2:05	11:51	2:19	11:32	2:37	11:09	2:59	10:37	3:29
15	13:36	2:20	13:14	2:41	13:01	2:53	12:47	3:07	12:29	3:24	12:08	3:45	11:40	4:12	11:00	4:51
16	14:29	3:17	14:05	3:40	13:52	3:53	13:36	4:08	13:17	4:27	12:54	4:50	12:23	5:20	11:38	6:05
17	15:27	4:14	15:04	4:37	14:50	4:51	14:35	5:07	14:16	5:25	13:53	5:49	13:22	6:20	12:37	7:05
18	16:29	5:10	16:08	5:32	15:55	5:45	15:41	6:00	15:24	6:17	15:03	6:39	14:36	7:07	13:57	7:47
19	17:33	6:04	17:15	6:23	17:05	6:34	16:53	6:46	16:40	7:01	16:23	7:19	16:01	7:42	15:31	8:13
20	18:37	6:54	18:24	7:09	18:16	7:17	18:08	7:27	17:58	7:38	17:46	7:51	17:31	8:08	17:11	8:31
21	19:39	7:41	19:32	7:50	19:28	7:56	19:23	8:02	19:17	8:09	19:11	8:18	19:02	8:29	18:51	8:43
22	20:41	8:24	20:39	8:29	20:38	8:31	20:37	8:34	20:36	8:37	20:34	8:41	20:32	8:46	20:30	8:52
23	21:42	9:07	21:46	9:06	21:48	9:05	21:51	9:05	21:54	9:04	21:57	9:03	22:02	9:02	22:07	9:00
24	22:42	9:49	22:52	9:43	22:57	9:39	23:03	9:35	23:10	9:30	23:19	9:24	23:30	9:17	23:44	9:08
25	23:43	10:32	23:57	10:21	—	10:14	—	10:07	—	9:58	—	9:48	—	9:35	—	9:18
26	—	11:17	—	11:01	0:05	10:52	0:15	10:41	0:26	10:29	0:39	10:14	0:57	9:55	1:20	9:30
27	0:43	12:05	1:02	11:46	1:13	11:34	1:25	11:21	1:40	11:05	1:58	10:46	2:21	10:22	2:54	9:48
28	1:44	12:57	2:05	12:34	2:18	12:21	2:32	12:06	2:50	11:48	3:11	11:26	3:40	10:57	4:21	10:15
29	2:42	13:51	3:05	13:27	3:19	13:14	3:35	12:58	3:53	12:39	4:17	12:15	4:48	11:44	5:35	10:57
30	3:37	14:47	4:01	14:24	4:14	14:10	4:30	13:55	4:49	13:36	5:12	13:13	5:43	12:43	6:29	11:57
31	4:29	15:42	4:50	15:22	5:03	15:10	5:17	14:56	5:35	14:39	5:56	14:18	6:24	13:51	7:03	13:12
Feb. 1	5:15	16:37	5:34	16:20	5:45	16:10	5:58	15:58	6:12	15:44	6:31	15:27	6:54	15:05	7:25	14:34
2	5:58	17:31	6:13	17:17	6:22	17:09	6:32	17:00	6:44	16:49	6:58	16:36	7:16	16:20	7:40	15:57
3	6:36	18:22	6:47	18:12	6:54	18:07	7:01	18:01	7:10	17:53	7:20	17:45	7:33	17:33	7:50	17:19
4	7:12	19:11	7:19	19:06	7:23	19:03	7:28	19:00	7:33	18:56	7:39	18:51	7:47	18:46	7:57	18:38
5	7:46	20:00	7:49	19:59	7:50	19:59	7:52	19:58	7:54	19:58	7:57	19:57	8:00	19:57	8:03	19:56
6	8:19	20:48	8:17	20:51	8:17	20:54	8:16	20:56	8:14	20:59	8:13	21:02	8:11	21:07	8:09	21:12
7	8:52	21:36	8:46	21:44	8:43	21:49	8:39	21:54	8:35	22:00	8:30	22:08	8:24	22:17	8:15	22:29
8	9:27	22:25	9:17	22:37	9:11	22:44	9:04	22:53	8:57	23:02	8:48	23:14	8:37	23:28	8:22	23:47
9	10:03	23:16	9:49	23:32	9:41	23:41	9:32	23:52	9:21	—	9:09	—	8:53	—	8:31	—
10	10:43	—	10:25	—	10:15	—	10:04	—	9:50	0:05	9:33	0:20	9:12	0:40	8:44	1:07
11	11:27	0:08	11:06	0:28	10:54	0:39	10:41	0:52	10:24	1:08	10:05	1:27	9:39	1:52	9:03	2:27
12	12:16	1:03	11:53	1:25	11:40	1:38	11:25	1:52	11:07	2:10	10:44	2:32	10:15	3:01	9:32	3:43
13	13:10	1:58	12:47	2:22	12:33	2:35	12:17	2:51	11:59	3:09	11:35	3:33	11:05	4:03	10:19	4:49
14	14:08	2:54	13:46	3:17	13:33	3:30	13:18	3:45	13:01	4:03	12:39	4:26	12:09	4:55	11:27	5:38
15	15:11	3:48	14:51	4:08	14:40	4:20	14:27	4:34	14:11	4:50	13:52	5:10	13:28	5:36	12:53	6:12
16	16:14	4:39	15:59	4:56	15:50	5:06	15:40	5:17	15:28	5:31	15:13	5:46	14:55	6:07	14:30	6:34
17	17:18	5:28	17:08	5:40	17:02	5:48	16:56	5:56	16:48	6:05	16:38	6:16	16:26	6:30	16:11	6:49
18	18:22	6:14	18:18	6:21	18:15	6:25	18:12	6:30	18:08	6:35	18:04	6:42	17:59	6:50	17:52	7:00
19	19:25	6:58	19:27	7:00	19:27	7:01	19:28	7:02	19:29	7:03	19:30	7:05	19:31	7:07	19:33	7:09
20	20:28	7:42	20:35	7:38	20:39	7:36	20:44	7:34	20:49	7:31	20:55	7:27	21:03	7:23	21:14	7:18
21	21:31	8:27	21:44	8:17	21:51	8:12	21:59	8:06	22:08	7:59	22:20	7:51	22:34	7:41	22:54	7:27
22	22:34	9:13	22:51	8:59	23:01	8:50	23:12	8:41	23:26	8:30	23:42	8:17	—	8:01	—	7:39
23	23:36	10:02	23:57	9:43	—	9:32	—	9:20	—	9:06	—	8:48	0:03	8:26	0:32	7:56
24	—	10:53	—	10:32	0:09	10:19	0:23	10:05	0:39	9:48	0:59	9:26	1:26	8:59	2:04	8:20
25	0:36	11:47	0:59	11:24	1:12	11:11	1:28	10:55	1:46	10:36	2:09	10:13	2:39	9:43	3:24	8:58
26	1:33	12:43	1:56	12:20	2:10	12:06	2:26	11:51	2:45	11:32	3:08	11:09	3:39	10:38	4:25	9:53
27	2:26	13:38	2:48	13:17	3:01	13:04	3:16	12:50	3:33	12:33	3:55	12:12	4:24	11:44	5:05	11:03
28	3:14	14:33	3:33	14:15	3:45	14:04	3:58	13:51	4:13	13:37	4:32	13:18	4:57	12:55	5:31	12:22

MOONRISE AND MOONSET, 2011 MARCH, APRIL
UNIVERSAL TIME AT GREENWICH MERIDIAN

Latitude:	+20°		+30°		+35°		+40°		+45°		+50°		+55°		+60°	
Event:	RISE	SET	RISE	SET	RISE	SET	RISE	SET	RISE	SET	RISE	SET	RISE	SET	RISE	SET
Mar. 1	3:57	15:26	4:13	15:11	4:23	15:03	4:34	14:53	4:46	14:41	5:02	14:27	5:21	14:09	5:47	13:44
2	4:36	16:18	4:49	16:07	4:56	16:00	5:04	15:53	5:14	15:45	5:25	15:35	5:40	15:22	5:59	15:05
3	5:13	17:07	5:21	17:01	5:26	16:57	5:32	16:52	5:38	16:47	5:46	16:41	5:55	16:34	6:07	16:24
4	5:47	17:56	5:51	17:53	5:54	17:52	5:56	17:51	6:00	17:49	6:04	17:47	6:08	17:45	6:14	17:41
5	6:20	18:44	6:20	18:46	6:20	18:47	6:20	18:49	6:20	18:50	6:20	18:52	6:20	18:55	6:20	18:58
6	6:54	19:32	6:49	19:38	6:47	19:42	6:44	19:46	6:41	19:51	6:37	19:57	6:33	20:05	6:27	20:14
7	7:28	20:21	7:19	20:31	7:14	20:37	7:09	20:45	7:03	20:53	6:55	21:03	6:46	21:15	6:34	21:32
8	8:03	21:11	7:51	21:25	7:44	21:34	7:36	21:43	7:26	21:55	7:15	22:09	7:01	22:27	6:42	22:50
9	8:42	22:02	8:26	22:20	8:16	22:31	8:06	22:43	7:53	22:57	7:38	23:15	7:19	23:38	6:54	—
10	9:24	22:55	9:04	23:16	8:53	23:28	8:40	23:42	8:25	23:59	8:07	—	7:43	—	7:10	0:09
11	10:10	23:49	9:48	—	9:35	—	9:21	—	9:04	—	8:42	0:19	8:15	0:47	7:35	1:25
12	11:00	—	10:37	0:11	10:24	0:24	10:09	0:40	9:50	0:58	9:28	1:20	8:58	1:50	8:14	2:34
13	11:55	0:43	11:33	1:05	11:19	1:19	11:04	1:34	10:46	1:52	10:24	2:15	9:54	2:45	9:10	3:29
14	12:54	1:35	12:33	1:57	12:21	2:09	12:07	2:24	11:51	2:41	11:30	3:02	11:04	3:29	10:26	4:08
15	13:54	2:26	13:37	2:45	13:27	2:56	13:16	3:08	13:02	3:23	12:45	3:40	12:24	4:03	11:54	4:34
16	14:57	3:15	14:44	3:30	14:36	3:38	14:28	3:48	14:18	3:59	14:06	4:12	13:51	4:29	13:30	4:52
17	15:59	4:01	15:52	4:11	15:47	4:17	15:42	4:23	15:37	4:31	15:30	4:40	15:21	4:51	15:09	5:05
18	17:03	4:46	17:01	4:51	16:59	4:53	16:58	4:56	16:57	5:00	16:55	5:04	16:53	5:09	16:50	5:15
19	18:06	5:30	18:10	5:29	18:12	5:29	18:15	5:28	18:18	5:28	18:21	5:27	18:26	5:26	18:31	5:25
20	19:11	6:15	19:20	6:09	19:26	6:05	19:32	6:01	19:39	5:56	19:48	5:51	19:59	5:44	20:14	5:35
21	20:16	7:02	20:31	6:50	20:39	6:43	20:49	6:36	21:00	6:27	21:14	6:16	21:32	6:03	21:56	5:46
22	21:21	7:51	21:40	7:35	21:51	7:25	22:04	7:14	22:19	7:02	22:37	6:46	23:01	6:27	23:35	6:01
23	22:25	8:44	22:46	8:23	22:59	8:12	23:14	7:58	23:31	7:42	23:53	7:23	—	6:58	—	6:23
24	23:25	9:39	23:48	9:16	—	9:03	—	8:48	—	8:30	—	8:08	0:22	7:39	1:03	6:57
25	—	10:36	—	10:13	0:01	9:59	0:17	9:44	0:35	9:25	0:58	9:02	1:29	8:32	2:14	7:47
26	0:20	11:33	0:43	11:11	0:56	10:58	1:11	10:43	1:29	10:26	1:51	10:04	2:20	9:35	3:02	8:54
27	1:11	12:29	1:31	12:09	1:43	11:58	1:56	11:45	2:12	11:30	2:32	11:11	2:58	10:46	3:33	10:11
28	1:56	13:22	2:13	13:07	2:23	12:57	2:34	12:47	2:48	12:34	3:04	12:19	3:25	11:59	3:53	11:33
29	2:36	14:14	2:50	14:02	2:58	13:55	3:07	13:47	3:17	13:38	3:30	13:27	3:46	13:12	4:06	12:53
30	3:14	15:04	3:23	14:56	3:29	14:52	3:35	14:47	3:42	14:41	3:51	14:33	4:02	14:24	4:16	14:12
31	3:48	15:53	3:54	15:49	3:57	15:47	4:01	15:45	4:05	15:42	4:10	15:39	4:16	15:35	4:24	15:30
Apr. 1	4:22	16:41	4:23	16:41	4:24	16:42	4:25	16:42	4:26	16:43	4:27	16:44	4:29	16:45	4:31	16:46
2	4:55	17:29	4:52	17:34	4:51	17:37	4:49	17:40	4:47	17:44	4:44	17:49	4:41	17:54	4:37	18:02
3	5:29	18:17	5:22	18:26	5:18	18:32	5:13	18:38	5:08	18:45	5:02	18:54	4:54	19:05	4:44	19:19
4	6:04	19:07	5:53	19:20	5:47	19:28	5:40	19:37	5:31	19:47	5:21	20:00	5:09	20:16	4:53	20:37
5	6:42	19:58	6:27	20:15	6:19	20:25	6:09	20:36	5:58	20:50	5:44	21:06	5:27	21:27	5:04	21:55
6	7:23	20:51	7:05	21:10	6:54	21:22	6:42	21:35	6:28	21:51	6:11	22:11	5:49	22:36	5:19	23:12
7	8:08	21:44	7:47	22:06	7:35	22:18	7:21	22:33	7:05	22:51	6:44	23:13	6:18	23:41	5:41	—
8	8:56	22:37	8:34	23:00	8:21	23:13	8:06	23:28	7:48	23:46	7:26	—	6:57	—	6:15	0:23
9	9:49	23:29	9:27	23:51	9:13	—	8:58	—	8:40	—	8:18	0:09	7:48	0:38	7:05	1:22
10	10:45	—	10:24	—	10:11	0:04	9:57	0:18	9:40	0:36	9:19	0:57	8:52	1:25	8:12	2:05
11	11:43	0:19	11:25	0:39	11:14	0:50	11:02	1:03	10:47	1:19	10:29	1:37	10:06	2:02	9:34	2:35
12	12:42	1:07	12:28	1:23	12:19	1:33	12:10	1:43	11:58	1:56	11:44	2:11	11:27	2:30	11:03	2:55
13	13:43	1:52	13:33	2:04	13:27	2:11	13:20	2:19	13:13	2:28	13:04	2:39	12:52	2:52	12:37	3:10
14	14:43	2:36	14:39	2:43	14:36	2:47	14:33	2:52	14:29	2:57	14:25	3:04	14:20	3:11	14:13	3:21
15	15:45	3:19	15:46	3:21	15:46	3:22	15:47	3:23	15:47	3:25	15:48	3:26	15:49	3:28	15:51	3:31
16	16:48	4:03	16:54	3:59	16:58	3:57	17:02	3:55	17:07	3:52	17:13	3:49	17:21	3:45	17:31	3:41
17	17:53	4:48	18:04	4:39	18:11	4:34	18:19	4:28	18:28	4:22	18:40	4:14	18:54	4:04	19:13	3:51
18	18:59	5:36	19:15	5:22	19:25	5:14	19:36	5:05	19:49	4:55	20:05	4:42	20:26	4:26	20:54	4:05
19	20:04	6:28	20:25	6:10	20:37	5:59	20:50	5:47	21:07	5:33	21:27	5:16	21:53	4:54	22:31	4:24
20	21:08	7:24	21:31	7:02	21:44	6:50	21:59	6:36	22:17	6:19	22:40	5:58	23:09	5:31	23:53	4:52
21	22:08	8:22	22:31	7:59	22:44	7:46	22:59	7:30	23:17	7:12	23:40	6:49	—	6:20	—	5:36
22	23:02	9:21	23:23	8:59	23:36	8:46	23:50	8:31	—	8:13	—	7:50	0:10	7:21	0:53	6:38
23	23:51	10:19	—	9:59	—	9:47	—	9:34	0:07	9:17	0:27	8:57	0:54	8:31	1:32	7:54
24	—	11:15	0:09	10:58	0:20	10:48	0:32	10:37	0:46	10:23	1:04	10:07	1:26	9:46	1:56	9:17
25	0:34	12:09	0:49	11:56	0:57	11:48	1:07	11:39	1:18	11:29	1:32	11:16	1:49	11:00	2:12	10:39
26	1:13	13:00	1:24	12:51	1:30	12:45	1:37	12:39	1:45	12:32	1:55	12:24	2:08	12:13	2:24	11:59
27	1:49	13:49	1:56	13:44	1:59	13:41	2:04	13:38	2:09	13:34	2:15	13:30	2:23	13:24	2:32	13:17
28	2:23	14:37	2:25	14:37	2:27	14:36	2:29	14:36	2:31	14:35	2:33	14:35	2:36	14:34	2:40	14:33
29	2:56	15:25	2:55	15:29	2:54	15:31	2:53	15:33	2:52	15:36	2:50	15:39	2:48	15:44	2:46	15:49
30	3:30	16:13	3:24	16:21	3:21	16:26	3:17	16:31	3:13	16:37	3:08	16:44	3:01	16:54	2:53	17:06

MOONRISE AND MOONSET, 2011 MAY, JUNE
UNIVERSAL TIME AT GREENWICH MERIDIAN

Latitude: Event	+20° RISE SET	+30° RISE SET	+35° RISE SET	+40° RISE SET	+45° RISE SET	+50° RISE SET	+55° RISE SET	+60° RISE SET
May 1	4:05 17:03	3:55 17:15	3:49 17:22	3:43 17:30	3:36 17:39	3:27 17:50	3:16 18:04	3:02 18:23
2	4:42 17:54	4:28 18:09	4:20 18:18	4:11 18:29	4:01 18:41	3:48 18:56	3:33 19:16	3:12 19:42
3	5:22 18:46	5:05 19:05	4:55 19:16	4:44 19:29	4:30 19:44	4:14 20:02	3:54 20:26	3:26 21:00
4	6:06 19:39	5:46 20:01	5:34 20:13	5:21 20:28	5:05 20:45	4:46 21:06	4:21 21:33	3:47 22:13
5	6:54 20:33	6:32 20:56	6:19 21:09	6:05 21:24	5:47 21:42	5:26 22:04	4:57 22:33	4:17 23:16
6	7:46 21:26	7:23 21:48	7:10 22:01	6:55 22:15	6:37 22:33	6:15 22:55	5:45 23:23	5:03 —
7	8:41 22:16	8:19 22:37	8:07 22:48	7:52 23:02	7:35 23:18	7:13 23:37	6:45 —	6:05 0:04
8	9:38 23:04	9:18 23:21	9:07 23:31	8:54 23:43	8:39 23:56	8:20 —	7:56 0:02	7:22 0:38
9	10:36 23:49	10:20 —	10:11 —	10:00 —	9:48 —	9:33 0:12	9:14 0:33	8:48 1:00
10	11:34 —	11:23 0:03	11:16 0:10	11:09 0:19	11:00 0:29	10:49 0:41	10:36 0:56	10:18 1:16
11	12:33 0:32	12:26 0:41	12:22 0:46	12:18 0:52	12:13 0:58	12:07 1:06	12:00 1:16	11:50 1:28
12	13:32 1:14	13:30 1:18	13:29 1:20	13:29 1:23	13:29 1:25	13:26 1:29	13:25 1:33	13:23 1:38
13	14:32 1:56	14:36 1:55	14:38 1:54	14:41 1:53	14:44 1:52	14:48 1:51	14:52 1:49	14:58 1:48
14	15:34 2:39	15:43 2:32	15:48 2:28	15:54 2:24	16:02 2:19	16:10 2:14	16:21 2:06	16:36 1:57
15	16:37 3:24	16:52 3:13	17:00 3:06	17:10 2:58	17:21 2:50	17:35 2:39	17:52 2:26	18:16 2:09
16	17:43 4:13	18:01 3:57	18:12 3:48	18:24 3:37	18:39 3:24	18:58 3:09	19:21 2:50	19:54 2:25
17	18:48 5:06	19:09 4:47	19:22 4:35	19:36 4:22	19:54 4:06	20:15 3:47	20:43 3:22	21:24 2:48
18	19:50 6:04	20:13 5:42	20:26 5:29	20:42 5:14	21:00 4:56	21:22 4:34	21:52 4:05	22:36 3:24
19	20:49 7:04	21:10 6:41	21:23 6:28	21:38 6:13	21:55 5:54	22:17 5:32	22:45 5:02	23:26 4:18
20	21:41 8:04	22:01 7:43	22:12 7:30	22:25 7:16	22:40 6:59	22:59 6:38	23:23 6:10	23:57 5:30
21	22:28 9:03	22:44 8:44	22:53 8:33	23:04 8:21	23:17 8:06	23:32 7:48	23:51 7:25	— 6:53
22	23:09 9:59	23:22 9:44	23:29 9:35	23:37 9:26	23:46 9:14	23:58 9:00	— 8:42	0:17 8:18
23	23:47 10:52	23:55 10:41	— 10:35	— 10:28	— 10:20	— 10:10	0:12 9:57	0:30 9:41
24	— 11:43	— 11:36	0:00 11:32	0:05 11:28	0:12 11:23	0:19 11:17	0:28 11:10	0:40 11:01
25	0:22 12:31	0:26 12:29	0:28 12:28	0:31 12:27	0:34 12:25	0:38 12:23	0:42 12:21	0:48 12:18
26	0:56 13:20	0:56 13:22	0:56 13:23	0:56 13:25	0:55 13:26	0:55 13:28	0:55 13:31	0:55 13:34
27	1:29 14:08	1:25 14:14	1:23 14:18	1:20 14:22	1:17 14:27	1:13 14:33	1:08 14:41	1:02 14:50
28	2:04 14:57	1:55 15:07	1:51 15:13	1:45 15:20	1:39 15:29	1:31 15:38	1:22 15:51	1:10 16:07
29	2:40 15:47	2:28 16:01	2:21 16:10	2:12 16:19	2:03 16:31	1:52 16:45	1:38 17:02	1:20 17:26
30	3:19 16:39	3:03 16:57	2:54 17:07	2:43 17:19	2:31 17:34	2:16 17:51	1:57 18:13	1:32 18:44
31	4:02 17:33	3:43 17:53	3:32 18:05	3:19 18:19	3:04 18:35	2:46 18:56	2:23 19:22	1:50 20:00
Jun. 1	4:49 18:27	4:27 18:49	4:15 19:02	4:01 19:17	3:44 19:35	3:23 19:57	2:56 20:26	2:17 21:08
2	5:40 19:21	5:18 19:43	5:05 19:56	4:50 20:11	4:32 20:29	4:09 20:51	3:40 21:20	2:58 22:02
3	6:35 20:13	6:13 20:34	6:00 20:46	5:45 21:00	5:28 21:16	5:06 21:37	4:37 22:03	3:56 22:40
4	7:32 21:02	7:12 21:20	7:01 21:31	6:47 21:43	6:31 21:57	6:12 22:14	5:46 22:36	5:10 23:06
5	8:31 21:49	8:14 22:03	8:04 22:11	7:53 22:21	7:40 22:32	7:24 22:45	7:03 23:02	6:34 23:24
6	9:29 22:32	9:17 22:42	9:09 22:48	9:01 22:55	8:51 23:02	8:39 23:11	8:24 23:22	8:04 23:37
7	10:27 23:14	10:19 23:19	10:15 23:22	10:10 23:26	10:04 23:29	9:56 23:34	9:47 23:40	9:35 23:47
8	11:25 23:54	11:22 23:55	11:21 23:55	11:19 23:55	11:17 23:55	11:14 23:56	11:11 23:56	11:06 23:56
9	12:24 —	12:26 —	12:27 —	12:29 —	12:30 —	12:33 —	12:35 —	12:39 —
10	13:23 0:36	13:30 0:31	13:35 0:28	13:40 0:25	13:45 0:22	13:52 0:17	14:01 0:12	14:12 0:06
11	14:24 1:19	14:36 1:09	14:44 1:03	14:52 0:57	15:02 0:50	15:13 0:41	15:28 0:30	15:48 0:16
12	15:27 2:05	15:44 1:50	15:53 1:42	16:05 1:32	16:18 1:21	16:35 1:08	16:56 0:52	17:25 0:30
13	16:30 2:55	16:51 2:36	17:03 2:25	17:16 2:13	17:33 1:59	17:53 1:41	18:19 1:19	18:57 0:48
14	17:33 3:49	17:56 3:28	18:09 3:15	18:24 3:01	18:42 2:44	19:04 2:23	19:34 1:56	20:17 1:17
15	18:33 4:47	18:56 4:24	19:09 4:11	19:24 3:56	19:42 3:38	20:04 3:15	20:34 2:45	21:17 2:02
16	19:29 5:47	19:49 5:25	20:01 5:12	20:15 4:57	20:32 4:39	20:52 4:17	21:19 3:48	21:56 3:06
17	20:18 6:47	20:36 6:27	20:47 6:15	20:58 6:02	21:12 5:46	21:29 5:27	21:51 5:01	22:20 4:25
18	21:03 7:45	21:17 7:29	21:25 7:19	21:34 7:08	21:45 6:55	21:58 6:39	22:15 6:19	22:37 5:51
19	21:43 8:40	21:53 8:28	21:59 8:21	22:05 8:12	22:13 8:03	22:22 7:51	22:33 7:36	22:48 7:16
20	22:19 9:33	22:25 9:25	22:29 9:20	22:33 9:15	22:37 9:08	22:42 9:01	22:49 8:51	22:57 8:39
21	22:54 10:23	22:56 10:20	22:57 10:17	22:58 10:15	22:59 10:12	23:00 10:08	23:02 10:04	23:04 9:58
22	23:28 11:12	23:25 11:13	23:24 11:13	23:22 11:14	23:20 11:14	23:18 11:14	23:15 11:15	23:11 11:16
23	— 12:01	23:55 12:05	23:51 12:08	23:47 12:11	23:42 12:15	23:36 12:20	23:28 12:25	23:19 12:32
24	0:02 12:49	— 12:58	— 13:03	— 13:09	— 13:16	23:56 13:25	23:43 13:35	23:28 13:49
25	0:37 13:39	0:27 13:52	0:20 13:59	0:13 14:08	0:05 14:18	— 14:30	— 14:46	23:39 15:06
26	1:15 14:30	1:01 14:47	0:52 14:56	0:43 15:07	0:31 15:20	0:18 15:36	0:01 15:57	23:54 16:25
27	1:56 15:23	1:38 15:42	1:28 15:54	1:16 16:07	1:02 16:23	0:45 16:42	0:24 17:07	— 17:42
28	2:41 16:17	2:21 16:39	2:09 16:51	1:55 17:06	1:39 17:23	1:19 17:45	0:53 18:13	0:17 18:54
29	3:31 17:12	3:09 17:34	2:56 17:47	2:41 18:02	2:23 18:20	2:02 18:42	1:33 19:12	0:52 19:54
30	4:25 18:05	4:03 18:27	3:50 18:39	3:35 18:54	3:17 19:11	2:54 19:32	2:25 20:00	1:43 20:39

MOONRISE AND MOONSET, 2011 JULY, AUGUST
UNIVERSAL TIME AT GREENWICH MERIDIAN

Latitude:	+20°		+30°		+35°		+40°		+45°		+50°		+55°		+60°	
Event:	RISE	SET	RISE	SET	RISE	SET	RISE	SET	RISE	SET	RISE	SET	RISE	SET	RISE	SET
Jul. 1	5:22	18:57	5:01	19:16	4:49	19:27	4:35	19:40	4:18	19:55	3:58	20:14	3:31	20:37	2:52	21:10
2	6:22	19:45	6:04	20:01	5:53	20:10	5:41	20:21	5:27	20:33	5:09	20:47	4:46	21:06	4:15	21:31
3	7:22	20:30	7:07	20:42	6:59	20:49	6:50	20:56	6:39	21:05	6:25	21:16	6:08	21:29	5:45	21:46
4	8:21	21:13	8:12	21:20	8:06	21:24	8:00	21:29	7:52	21:34	7:44	21:40	7:33	21:47	7:18	21:57
5	9:20	21:55	9:16	21:57	9:13	21:58	9:10	21:59	9:07	22:00	9:03	22:02	8:57	22:04	8:51	22:07
6	10:19	22:36	10:19	22:33	10:20	22:31	10:20	22:29	10:21	22:27	10:22	22:24	10:22	22:20	10:23	22:16
7	11:18	23:18	11:24	23:10	11:27	23:05	11:31	23:00	11:35	22:54	11:41	22:46	11:48	22:37	11:57	22:26
8	12:17	—	12:28	23:49	12:35	23:42	12:42	23:34	12:50	23:24	13:01	23:12	13:13	22:57	13:31	22:38
9	13:18	0:02	13:34	—	13:43	—	13:53	—	14:05	23:58	14:20	23:42	14:39	23:22	15:05	22:54
10	14:20	0:50	14:40	0:33	14:51	0:23	15:04	0:11	15:19	—	15:38	—	16:03	23:54	16:37	23:18
11	15:22	1:41	15:44	1:21	15:56	1:09	16:11	0:55	16:29	0:39	16:50	0:19	17:19	—	18:01	23:55
12	16:22	2:36	16:44	2:14	16:58	2:01	17:13	1:46	17:31	1:28	17:54	1:06	18:24	0:37	19:07	—
13	17:18	3:34	17:40	3:12	17:52	2:59	18:07	2:44	18:24	2:26	18:46	2:03	19:14	1:33	19:53	0:50
14	18:10	4:34	18:29	4:13	18:40	4:00	18:53	3:46	19:08	3:29	19:27	3:09	19:50	2:41	20:23	2:02
15	18:56	5:32	19:12	5:14	19:21	5:04	19:32	4:51	19:44	4:37	19:59	4:19	20:18	3:57	20:43	3:25
16	19:38	6:29	19:50	6:14	19:57	6:06	20:05	5:56	20:14	5:45	20:25	5:32	20:38	5:14	20:56	4:51
17	20:16	7:23	20:24	7:13	20:29	7:07	20:34	7:00	20:39	6:52	20:46	6:43	20:55	6:31	21:06	6:15
18	20:52	8:14	20:56	8:09	20:58	8:05	21:00	8:02	21:02	7:57	21:05	7:52	21:09	7:45	21:14	7:37
19	21:27	9:04	21:26	9:03	21:25	9:02	21:25	9:01	21:24	9:00	21:23	8:59	21:23	8:57	21:21	8:55
20	22:01	9:53	21:56	9:56	21:53	9:58	21:49	10:00	21:46	10:02	21:41	10:05	21:36	10:08	21:29	10:13
21	22:35	10:42	22:26	10:49	22:21	10:53	22:15	10:58	22:08	11:03	22:00	11:10	21:50	11:18	21:37	11:29
22	23:12	11:31	22:59	11:42	22:51	11:49	22:43	11:56	22:33	12:05	22:21	12:15	22:06	12:29	21:47	12:46
23	23:51	12:21	23:35	12:36	23:25	12:45	23:14	12:55	23:01	13:06	22:46	13:21	22:27	13:39	22:00	14:04
24	—	13:12	—	13:31	—	13:41	23:50	13:54	23:35	14:08	23:16	14:26	22:52	14:49	22:19	15:21
25	0:34	14:05	0:14	14:26	0:03	14:38	—	14:52	—	15:09	23:54	15:30	23:27	15:57	22:48	16:35
26	1:21	14:59	0:59	15:22	0:47	15:35	0:33	15:49	0:15	16:07	—	16:29	—	16:58	23:31	17:41
27	2:13	15:53	1:50	16:15	1:37	16:28	1:22	16:43	1:04	17:01	0:42	17:23	0:13	17:51	—	18:32
28	3:08	16:46	2:47	17:06	2:34	17:18	2:19	17:32	2:02	17:48	1:41	18:08	1:12	18:34	0:31	19:09
29	4:07	17:36	3:48	17:54	3:36	18:04	3:23	18:15	3:08	18:29	2:49	18:46	2:24	19:06	1:49	19:35
30	5:08	18:24	4:52	18:37	4:43	18:45	4:32	18:54	4:19	19:04	4:04	19:17	3:44	19:32	3:18	19:52
31	6:09	19:09	5:57	19:18	5:51	19:23	5:43	19:29	5:34	19:35	5:23	19:43	5:10	19:53	4:51	20:05
Aug. 1	7:10	19:52	7:03	19:56	6:59	19:58	6:55	20:01	6:50	20:04	6:44	20:07	6:37	20:11	6:27	20:16
2	8:10	20:35	8:09	20:33	8:08	20:33	8:07	20:32	8:06	20:31	8:05	20:29	8:04	20:28	8:02	20:26
3	9:11	21:17	9:15	21:11	9:17	21:07	9:20	21:03	9:23	20:58	9:27	20:52	9:31	20:45	9:37	20:36
4	10:11	22:02	10:21	21:50	10:26	21:44	10:32	21:36	10:39	21:28	10:48	21:17	10:59	21:04	11:13	20:48
5	11:13	22:48	11:27	22:33	11:35	22:23	11:44	22:13	11:55	22:01	12:09	21:46	12:26	21:28	12:48	21:03
6	12:14	23:38	12:32	23:19	12:43	23:08	12:55	22:55	13:10	22:40	13:27	22:21	13:50	21:57	14:22	21:24
7	13:16	—	13:37	—	13:49	23:57	14:03	23:43	14:20	23:26	14:41	23:04	15:08	22:36	15:48	21:56
8	14:15	0:32	14:38	0:10	14:51	—	15:06	—	15:24	—	15:46	23:57	16:16	23:27	16:59	22:44
9	15:12	1:28	15:34	1:06	15:47	0:53	16:02	0:37	16:19	0:19	16:41	—	17:10	—	17:51	23:49
10	16:04	2:26	16:24	2:04	16:36	1:52	16:50	1:37	17:06	1:20	17:25	0:58	17:50	0:30	18:26	—
11	16:52	3:24	17:09	3:04	17:19	2:53	17:30	2:40	17:44	2:25	18:00	2:06	18:20	1:42	18:48	1:07
12	17:35	4:20	17:48	4:04	17:56	3:55	18:05	3:44	18:15	3:32	18:28	3:17	18:43	2:57	19:04	2:31
13	18:14	5:14	18:23	5:02	18:29	4:56	18:35	4:48	18:42	4:39	18:51	4:27	19:01	4:13	19:15	3:55
14	18:51	6:07	18:56	5:59	18:59	5:55	19:02	5:50	19:06	5:44	19:11	5:37	19:17	5:28	19:24	5:17
15	19:26	6:57	19:27	6:54	19:27	6:52	19:28	6:50	19:29	6:48	19:29	6:45	19:30	6:41	19:32	6:36
16	20:00	7:46	19:57	7:47	19:55	7:48	19:53	7:49	19:50	7:50	19:47	7:51	19:44	7:52	19:39	7:54
17	20:35	8:35	20:27	8:40	20:23	8:44	20:18	8:47	20:13	8:51	20:06	8:56	19:58	9:03	19:47	9:11
18	21:10	9:24	20:59	9:33	20:52	9:39	20:45	9:45	20:36	9:53	20:26	10:02	20:13	10:13	19:57	10:27
19	21:48	10:13	21:33	10:27	21:24	10:35	21:15	10:43	21:03	10:54	20:49	11:07	20:32	11:23	20:09	11:44
20	22:29	11:04	22:11	11:21	22:00	11:31	21:48	11:42	21:34	11:55	21:17	12:11	20:55	12:32	20:25	13:01
21	23:13	11:56	22:53	12:15	22:41	12:27	22:27	12:40	22:11	12:56	21:51	13:15	21:25	13:40	20:49	14:15
22	—	12:48	23:40	13:10	23:27	13:22	23:13	13:37	22:55	13:54	22:33	14:15	22:05	14:43	21:24	15:24
23	0:02	13:41	—	14:03	—	14:16	—	14:31	23:48	14:49	23:26	15:11	22:57	15:39	22:16	16:21
24	0:55	14:33	0:33	14:55	0:20	15:07	0:05	15:21	—	15:38	—	15:59	—	16:26	23:24	17:04
25	1:45	15:24	1:31	15:43	1:19	15:54	1:05	16:07	0:49	16:21	0:28	16:40	0:02	17:03	—	17:34
26	2:50	16:13	2:33	16:28	2:22	16:37	2:11	16:47	1:57	16:59	1:39	17:14	1:17	17:32	0:47	17:56
27	3:51	16:59	3:37	17:10	3:29	17:17	3:20	17:24	3:10	17:32	2:56	17:43	2:40	17:55	2:18	18:11
28	4:53	17:44	4:44	17:50	4:38	17:54	4:32	17:58	4:26	18:03	4:17	18:08	4:07	18:15	3:53	18:23
29	5:54	18:28	5:51	18:29	5:48	18:29	5:46	18:30	5:43	18:31	5:40	18:32	5:35	18:33	5:30	18:34
30	6:56	19:12	6:58	19:08	6:59	19:05	7:00	19:02	7:01	18:59	7:03	18:55	7:05	18:51	7:07	18:45
31	7:59	19:57	8:06	19:48	8:10	19:42	8:15	19:36	8:20	19:29	8:27	19:21	8:35	19:10	8:46	18:57

MOONRISE AND MOONSET, 2011 SEPTEMBER, OCTOBER
UNIVERSAL TIME AT GREENWICH MERIDIAN

Latitude:	+20°		+30°		+35°		+40°		+45°		+50°		+55°		+60°	
Event:	RISE	SET	RISE	SET	RISE	SET	RISE	SET	RISE	SET	RISE	SET	RISE	SET	RISE	SET
Sep. 1	9:02	20:44	9:14	20:30	9:21	20:22	9:29	20:13	9:39	20:02	9:50	19:49	10:05	19:33	10:24	19:11
2	10:06	21:35	10:22	21:17	10:32	21:06	10:43	20:54	10:56	20:40	11:12	20:23	11:33	20:01	12:01	19:31
3	11:09	22:28	11:29	22:07	11:40	21:55	11:54	21:41	12:10	21:24	12:30	21:04	12:55	20:38	13:32	20:00
4	12:10	23:24	12:32	23:02	12:45	22:49	12:59	22:34	13:17	22:16	13:39	21:54	14:08	21:25	14:49	20:43
5	13:08	—	13:30	—	13:43	23:47	13:58	23:32	14:15	23:15	14:37	22:53	15:06	22:25	15:48	21:43
6	14:01	0:21	14:22	0:00	14:34	—	14:48	—	15:04	—	15:24	23:59	15:50	23:33	16:27	22:57
7	14:50	1:19	15:08	0:59	15:18	0:47	15:30	0:34	15:44	0:18	16:01	—	16:23	—	16:53	—
8	15:33	2:15	15:48	1:58	15:57	1:48	16:06	1:37	16:17	1:24	16:31	1:08	16:48	0:47	17:11	0:18
9	16:13	3:09	16:24	2:56	16:30	2:49	16:38	2:40	16:46	2:30	16:55	2:17	17:08	2:02	17:23	1:41
10	16:51	4:01	16:57	3:52	17:01	3:47	17:06	3:41	17:11	3:34	17:16	3:26	17:24	3:16	17:33	3:02
11	17:26	4:52	17:28	4:47	17:30	4:45	17:31	4:41	17:33	4:38	17:36	4:34	17:38	4:28	17:42	4:21
12	18:00	5:41	17:59	5:41	17:58	5:41	17:58	5:40	17:55	5:40	17:54	5:40	17:52	5:39	17:50	5:39
13	18:35	6:30	18:29	6:34	18:26	6:36	18:22	6:39	18:18	6:42	18:12	6:45	18:06	6:50	17:58	6:55
14	19:10	7:19	19:00	7:27	18:55	7:31	18:48	7:37	18:41	7:43	18:32	7:50	18:21	8:00	18:07	8:12
15	19:47	8:08	19:34	8:20	19:26	8:27	19:17	8:35	19:07	8:44	18:54	8:55	18:39	9:09	18:18	9:28
16	20:27	8:58	20:10	9:13	20:00	9:22	19:49	9:33	19:36	9:45	19:20	10:00	19:00	10:19	18:33	10:44
17	21:09	9:49	20:50	10:07	20:39	10:18	20:26	10:31	20:10	10:45	19:52	11:03	19:28	11:26	18:54	11:59
18	21:56	10:40	21:35	11:01	21:22	11:13	21:08	11:27	20:51	11:44	20:30	12:04	20:03	12:31	19:25	13:08
19	22:46	11:32	22:24	11:54	22:11	12:07	21:57	12:21	21:39	12:39	21:18	13:00	20:49	13:28	20:09	14:09
20	23:39	12:23	23:18	12:45	23:06	12:57	22:52	13:12	22:35	13:29	22:14	13:50	21:47	14:18	21:08	14:57
21	—	13:13	—	13:33	—	13:45	23:53	13:58	23:38	14:14	23:19	14:33	22:56	14:58	22:22	15:32
22	0:36	14:02	0:17	14:19	0:06	14:29	—	14:40	—	14:53	—	15:09	—	15:29	23:47	15:57
23	1:34	14:48	1:15	15:01	1:09	15:09	0:59	15:17	0:47	15:28	0:32	15:40	0:13	15:55	—	16:14
24	2:34	15:33	2:22	15:41	2:16	15:47	2:08	15:52	1:59	15:59	1:49	16:06	1:35	16:16	1:18	16:28
25	3:34	16:17	3:28	16:20	3:24	16:23	3:20	16:25	3:15	16:28	3:09	16:31	3:02	16:35	2:52	16:40
26	4:36	17:01	4:35	16:59	4:34	16:58	4:33	16:58	4:33	16:56	4:32	16:55	4:30	16:53	4:29	16:51
27	5:39	17:46	5:43	17:39	5:46	17:36	5:49	17:31	5:52	17:26	5:56	17:20	6:01	17:13	6:07	17:03
28	6:43	18:34	6:53	18:22	6:59	18:15	7:05	18:07	7:12	17:59	7:21	17:48	7:33	17:34	7:48	17:17
29	7:49	19:25	8:03	19:08	8:12	18:59	8:22	18:48	8:33	18:36	8:47	18:20	9:05	18:01	9:29	17:35
30	8:54	20:19	9:13	19:59	9:24	19:48	9:36	19:35	9:51	19:19	10:09	19:00	10:33	18:36	11:05	18:02
Oct. 1	9:59	21:16	10:20	20:54	10:32	20:42	10:47	20:27	11:03	20:10	11:24	19:49	11:52	19:21	12:31	18:41
2	11:00	22:15	11:22	21:53	11:35	21:40	11:49	21:25	12:07	21:08	12:29	20:46	12:57	20:18	13:39	19:37
3	11:56	23:13	12:17	22:53	12:29	22:41	12:44	22:27	13:00	22:11	13:21	21:51	13:48	21:25	14:26	20:48
4	12:47	—	13:06	23:53	13:17	23:43	13:29	23:31	13:44	23:17	14:02	23:00	14:25	22:38	14:56	22:07
5	13:32	0:11	13:48	—	13:57	—	14:07	—	14:19	—	14:34	—	14:52	23:52	15:17	23:30
6	14:14	1:05	14:25	0:51	14:32	0:43	14:40	0:34	14:49	0:23	15:00	0:09	15:13	—	15:31	—
7	14:51	1:58	14:59	1:48	15:04	1:42	15:09	1:35	15:15	1:28	15:22	1:18	15:31	1:06	15:42	0:51
8	15:27	2:49	15:31	2:43	15:33	2:39	15:35	2:36	15:38	2:31	15:42	2:25	15:46	2:19	15:51	2:10
9	16:02	3:38	16:01	3:36	16:01	3:35	16:01	3:34	16:00	3:33	16:00	3:31	16:00	3:29	15:59	3:27
10	16:36	4:27	16:31	4:29	16:29	4:29	16:26	4:32	16:23	4:34	16:19	4:36	16:14	4:39	16:07	4:43
11	17:11	5:15	17:02	5:22	16:58	5:26	16:52	5:30	16:46	5:35	16:38	5:41	16:29	5:49	16:17	5:59
12	17:47	6:04	17:35	6:15	17:28	6:21	17:20	6:28	17:11	6:36	17:00	6:46	16:46	6:58	16:28	7:15
13	18:26	6:54	18:11	7:08	18:02	7:16	17:51	7:26	17:39	7:37	17:25	7:51	17:06	8:08	16:42	8:31
14	19:08	7:44	18:49	8:02	18:39	8:12	18:26	8:24	18:12	8:37	17:54	8:54	17:32	9:16	17:01	9:46
15	19:53	8:36	19:32	8:56	19:20	9:07	19:07	9:21	18:51	9:36	18:31	9:56	18:05	10:21	17:28	10:57
16	20:41	9:27	20:20	9:48	20:07	10:01	19:53	10:15	19:36	10:32	19:15	10:53	18:47	11:21	18:07	12:00
17	21:33	10:18	21:12	10:39	20:59	10:52	20:45	11:06	20:28	11:23	20:07	11:45	19:40	12:12	19:01	12:52
18	22:27	11:07	22:07	11:28	21:56	11:40	21:43	11:53	21:27	12:09	21:08	12:29	20:43	12:54	20:08	13:30
19	23:23	11:55	23:06	12:13	22:56	12:23	22:45	12:35	22:32	12:49	22:15	13:06	21:55	13:28	21:26	13:58
20	—	12:40	—	12:55	23:59	13:04	23:50	13:13	23:40	13:25	23:28	13:38	23:12	13:55	22:52	14:18
21	0:20	13:24	0:07	13:35	—	13:41	—	13:48	—	13:56	—	14:06	—	14:17	—	14:33
22	1:18	14:07	1:09	14:13	1:04	14:16	0:58	14:20	0:52	14:25	0:44	14:30	0:34	14:37	0:21	14:45
23	2:17	14:50	2:13	14:51	2:11	14:51	2:09	14:52	2:06	14:53	2:02	14:54	1:58	14:55	1:53	14:56
24	3:18	15:33	3:19	15:29	3:20	15:27	3:21	15:24	3:22	15:21	3:24	15:18	3:25	15:13	3:28	15:08
25	4:20	16:19	4:27	16:10	4:31	16:05	4:36	15:59	4:41	15:52	4:47	15:44	4:55	15:34	5:06	15:21
26	5:25	17:09	5:37	16:55	5:44	16:47	5:52	16:38	6:01	16:27	6:13	16:14	6:27	15:58	6:46	15:37
27	6:32	18:02	6:48	17:44	6:58	17:34	7:09	17:22	7:22	17:08	7:38	16:51	7:59	16:29	8:27	15:59
28	7:39	19:00	7:59	18:39	8:10	18:27	8:24	18:13	8:40	17:57	8:59	17:36	9:25	17:10	10:01	16:33
29	8:44	20:00	9:05	19:39	9:18	19:26	9:32	19:11	9:50	18:54	10:11	18:32	10:39	18:04	11:20	17:23
30	9:44	21:01	10:06	20:41	10:18	20:28	10:33	20:14	10:50	19:57	11:11	19:37	11:38	19:09	12:18	18:31
31	10:39	22:01	10:59	21:43	11:10	21:32	11:23	21:19	11:39	21:05	11:58	20:46	12:22	20:23	12:56	19:50

MOONRISE AND MOONSET, 2011 NOVEMBER, DECEMBER
UNIVERSAL TIME AT GREENWICH MERIDIAN

Latitude:	+20°		+30°		+35°		+40°		+45°		+50°		+55°		+60°	
Event:	RISE	SET	RISE	SET	RISE	SET	RISE	SET	RISE	SET	RISE	SET	RISE	SET	RISE	SET
Nov. 1	11:28	22:59	11:45	22:43	11:54	22:35	12:05	22:24	12:18	22:12	12:34	21:58	12:54	21:39	13:20	21:14
2	12:12	23:53	12:25	23:42	12:32	23:35	12:41	23:28	12:51	23:19	13:03	23:08	13:17	22:55	13:37	22:37
3	12:51	—	13:00	—	13:05	—	13:11	—	13:18	—	13:26	—	13:36	—	13:49	23:57
4	13:28	0:45	13:33	0:38	13:36	0:34	13:39	0:29	13:42	0:23	13:47	0:17	13:52	0:08	13:59	—
5	14:03	1:35	14:03	1:32	14:04	1:30	14:04	1:28	14:05	1:26	14:06	1:23	14:07	1:20	14:08	1:15
6	14:37	2:23	14:34	2:25	14:32	2:25	14:30	2:26	14:27	2:27	14:24	2:28	14:21	2:30	14:16	2:31
7	15:12	3:12	15:04	3:17	15:00	3:20	14:55	3:24	14:50	3:28	14:44	3:33	14:36	3:39	14:25	3:47
8	15:48	4:00	15:36	4:10	15:30	4:15	15:23	4:21	15:14	4:29	15:04	4:37	14:52	4:48	14:36	5:02
9	16:26	4:50	16:11	5:03	16:03	5:10	15:53	5:19	15:42	5:29	15:28	5:42	15:12	5:57	14:49	6:18
10	17:07	5:40	16:49	5:57	16:39	6:06	16:27	6:17	16:13	6:30	15:57	6:46	15:36	7:06	15:07	7:34
11	17:51	6:32	17:31	6:51	17:19	7:02	17:06	7:15	16:50	7:30	16:31	7:49	16:06	8:13	15:32	8:47
12	18:39	7:23	18:17	7:44	18:05	7:56	17:51	8:10	17:34	8:27	17:13	8:48	16:46	9:15	16:07	9:53
13	19:29	8:15	19:08	8:36	18:56	8:49	18:41	9:03	18:24	9:20	18:03	9:41	17:36	10:09	16:56	10:48
14	20:23	9:05	20:03	9:25	19:51	9:37	19:37	9:51	19:21	10:08	19:02	10:28	18:36	10:54	18:00	11:31
15	21:17	9:52	21:00	10:11	20:49	10:22	20:38	10:34	20:24	10:49	20:07	11:07	19:45	11:30	19:14	12:01
16	22:13	10:38	21:59	10:54	21:50	11:03	21:41	11:13	21:30	11:25	21:16	11:40	20:59	11:58	20:36	12:23
17	23:09	11:21	22:59	11:33	22:53	11:40	22:46	11:48	22:38	11:57	22:29	12:08	22:17	12:21	22:01	12:39
18	—	12:03	—	12:11	23:57	12:15	23:53	12:20	23:49	12:26	23:44	12:33	23:37	12:41	23:29	12:52
19	0:06	12:44	0:00	12:47	—	12:49	—	12:51	—	12:53	—	12:56	—	12:59	—	13:03
20	1:03	13:25	1:02	13:23	1:02	13:22	1:02	13:21	1:01	13:20	1:01	13:18	1:00	13:16	0:59	13:14
21	2:02	14:08	2:07	14:02	2:09	13:58	2:12	13:53	2:16	13:48	2:20	13:42	2:25	13:35	2:31	13:25
22	3:04	14:55	3:13	14:43	3:19	14:36	3:25	14:29	3:33	14:20	3:41	14:09	3:53	13:56	4:07	13:39
23	4:08	15:45	4:22	15:29	4:31	15:20	4:40	15:09	4:51	14:57	5:05	14:42	5:22	14:23	5:46	13:58
24	5:14	16:40	5:32	16:21	5:43	16:09	5:55	15:56	6:10	15:41	6:28	15:22	6:51	14:58	7:23	14:25
25	6:21	17:40	6:41	17:18	6:54	17:06	7:08	16:51	7:25	16:34	7:45	16:13	8:12	15:45	8:51	15:06
26	7:25	18:42	7:46	18:20	7:59	18:08	8:14	17:53	8:31	17:36	8:53	17:14	9:21	16:46	10:01	16:06
27	8:24	19:44	8:45	19:24	8:57	19:13	9:10	18:59	9:27	18:44	9:47	18:24	10:13	17:59	10:50	17:23
28	9:17	20:45	9:35	20:28	9:46	20:18	9:58	20:07	10:12	19:54	10:29	19:37	10:51	19:17	11:21	18:48
29	10:05	21:42	10:19	21:29	10:28	21:22	10:37	21:13	10:49	21:03	11:02	20:51	11:19	20:35	11:42	20:15
30	10:47	22:37	10:58	22:28	11:04	22:23	11:11	22:17	11:19	22:10	11:29	22:02	11:41	21:52	11:56	21:38
Dec. 1	11:26	23:28	11:32	23:24	11:36	23:21	11:40	23:18	11:45	23:15	11:51	23:11	11:58	23:06	12:07	22:59
2	12:02	—	12:04	—	12:06	—	12:07	—	12:09	—	12:11	—	12:13	—	12:16	—
3	12:37	0:18	12:35	0:18	12:34	0:18	12:33	0:18	12:31	0:17	12:30	0:17	12:28	0:17	12:25	0:17
4	13:11	1:07	13:05	1:11	13:02	1:13	12:58	1:16	12:54	1:19	12:49	1:22	12:42	1:27	12:34	1:33
5	13:47	1:55	13:37	2:03	13:31	2:08	13:25	2:13	13:18	2:19	13:09	2:27	12:58	2:36	12:44	2:48
6	14:24	2:44	14:11	2:56	14:03	3:03	13:54	3:11	13:44	3:20	13:32	3:31	13:16	3:45	12:56	4:04
7	15:04	3:34	14:47	3:50	14:38	3:59	14:27	4:09	14:14	4:21	13:58	4:36	13:38	4:54	13:12	5:19
8	15:47	4:26	15:28	4:44	15:17	4:54	15:04	5:07	14:49	5:21	14:30	5:39	14:07	6:02	13:34	6:34
9	16:34	5:18	16:13	5:38	16:01	5:50	15:47	6:04	15:30	6:20	15:10	6:40	14:43	7:06	14:06	7:43
10	17:24	6:10	17:03	6:31	16:50	6:43	16:36	6:58	16:19	7:15	15:58	7:36	15:30	8:04	14:51	8:43
11	18:18	7:01	17:57	7:22	17:45	7:34	17:31	7:48	17:15	8:05	16:54	8:26	16:28	8:52	15:50	9:30
12	19:13	7:50	18:54	8:09	18:43	8:21	18:31	8:34	18:16	8:49	17:58	9:08	17:35	9:32	17:03	10:05
13	20:09	8:37	19:53	8:53	19:44	9:03	19:34	9:14	19:22	9:27	19:07	9:43	18:49	10:03	18:23	10:29
14	21:05	9:21	20:53	9:34	20:47	9:42	20:39	9:50	20:30	10:00	20:19	10:12	20:06	10:27	19:48	10:47
15	22:01	10:03	21:54	10:12	21:50	10:17	21:45	10:23	21:40	10:30	21:33	10:38	21:25	10:48	21:15	11:01
16	22:57	10:43	22:55	10:48	22:53	10:51	22:52	10:54	22:50	10:57	22:48	11:01	22:45	11:06	22:42	11:12
17	23:54	11:24	23:57	11:24	23:58	11:24	—	11:23	—	11:23	—	11:23	—	11:23	—	11:23
18	—	12:05	—	12:00	—	11:57	0:00	11:54	0:02	11:50	0:04	11:46	0:07	11:40	0:11	11:33
19	0:52	12:48	1:00	12:38	1:04	12:33	1:09	12:26	1:15	12:19	1:22	12:10	1:31	12:00	1:42	11:46
20	1:53	13:35	2:05	13:20	2:12	13:12	2:21	13:03	2:30	12:52	2:42	12:39	2:57	12:23	3:16	12:01
21	2:56	14:26	3:12	14:08	3:22	13:57	3:33	13:45	3:46	13:31	4:02	13:14	4:23	12:53	4:51	12:23
22	4:00	15:21	4:20	15:01	4:32	14:49	4:45	14:35	5:01	14:18	5:20	13:58	5:46	13:32	6:21	12:56
23	5:04	16:21	5:26	16:00	5:38	15:47	5:53	15:32	6:10	15:15	6:32	14:53	7:00	14:25	7:40	13:45
24	6:06	17:23	6:27	17:03	6:39	16:50	6:54	16:36	7:11	16:19	7:32	15:59	8:00	15:32	8:39	14:53
25	7:02	18:26	7:22	18:07	7:33	17:56	7:46	17:44	8:02	17:29	8:21	17:11	8:45	16:48	9:19	16:15
26	7:53	19:26	8:10	19:11	8:19	19:02	8:30	18:52	8:43	18:40	8:59	18:26	9:18	18:08	9:44	17:43
27	8:39	20:23	8:52	20:12	8:59	20:06	9:07	19:59	9:17	19:50	9:29	19:40	9:43	19:27	10:02	19:10
28	9:20	21:17	9:29	21:11	9:34	21:07	9:39	21:03	9:46	20:58	9:53	20:52	10:03	20:44	10:15	20:35
29	9:59	22:09	10:03	22:07	10:05	22:06	10:08	22:04	10:11	22:03	10:15	22:01	10:19	21:58	10:25	21:55
30	10:35	22:59	10:34	23:01	10:34	23:02	10:34	23:04	10:34	23:06	10:34	23:08	10:34	23:10	10:34	23:13
31	11:10	23:48	11:05	23:54	11:03	23:58	11:00	—	10:57	—	10:53	—	10:49	—	10:43	—

LUNAR OBSERVING
By Bruce McCurdy

> *I feel quite sure that I first viewed the moon in my small scope
> with just as much incredible delight as Galileo did in his. It is true
> that I had seen photographs of the moon and therefore had some
> vague idea of what its appearance would be like, but I was still
> wholly unprepared for all the wonders which I found on that first
> night as I explored the lunar surface. No photograph has yet been
> made which is not cold and flat and dead when compared with
> the scenes that meet one's eyes when the moon is viewed through
> even a small telescope.*
>
> Leslie Peltier, *Starlight Nights*

The Moon is the first astronomical object to grab anyone's eye in the night sky, and has provided "first light" for countless telescopes in the four centuries from Galileo's time to the present. Galileo himself was beaten to the punch by the underappreciated Englishman, Thomas Harriot, who was likely the first telescopic visual observer of Earth's satellite, and certainly the first to sketch an eyepiece view, on 1609 Jul. 26. This was some four months before Galileo did the same.

While the invention of the telescope may be considered the birth of modern astronomy, the Moon has been an object of fascination and mystique since the earliest annals of history, and presumably long before that. Early scientists in ancient observatories carefully tracked lunar cycles and recorded the extremes of its rising and setting points along the horizon. Some 23 centuries ago, the enterprising Aristarchus of Samos carefully observed a total lunar eclipse and derived impressively accurate measurements of the Moon's diameter (1/3 that of Earth; the actual percentage is 27.2) and distance (30 Earth diameters, similar to the modern accepted mean value).

One hardly needs a telescope to enjoy the Moon. If observed even briefly on a regular basis, Earth's only natural satellite has much to offer the modern-day naked-eye observer. Noteworthy phenomena include its wandering path through the constellations of the zodiac, the inexorable progression of phases, frequent conjunctions with planets and bright stars, occasional eclipses, libration, earthshine, and atmospheric effects.

Many of the cycles that fascinated the ancients can be observed directly. Understanding these cycles is interesting in its own right. It is also of value to telescopic lunar observers who can benefit when the Moon is favourably placed in the sky, as well as to dark-sky enthusiasts who may be more interested in knowing when it is below the horizon.

Every child learns that the Moon, like the Sun, rises in the east and sets in the west. Relative to a terrestrial landmark (or when viewed through an unpowered telescope!) the Moon appears to move its own diameter (~0.5°) westward in about 2 min. When measured against the background stars, however, it moves about its own diameter *eastward* in an hour, the same direction that Earth rotates. The 30:1 ratio between these rates nicely squares with the time periods involved: one day for Earth to rotate, one sidereal month (about 27.3 d) for the Moon to complete an orbit.

If one observes the Moon at about the same time from night to night, its eastward motion against the background stars becomes apparent. The Moon transits the meridian about 50 min later from one day to the next, a period that rules the tides (see TIDES AND THE EARTH–MOON SYSTEM, p. 182). However, rise and set times vary much more as the Moon's eastward motion also contains a significant northward or southward component, causing moonrise times to bunch together for part of each month, and moonset times to similarly cluster a fortnight later. This is famously

manifest in the Harvest Moon, an observation of interest to almost everyone. Each fortnight, a rise or set event occurs after midnight, explaining why one day has no moonrise and another no moonset; over the course of a synodic month (new Moon to new Moon), Luna transits the meridian one fewer time than does the Sun. See TIMES OF MOONRISE AND MOONSET, p. 154.

Note the Moon's phase during a conjunction with a bright star, and again the following month when it returns: the phase is 2 d less (see the Table). The extra couple of days it needs to get back to the same phase means travelling almost an additional 30°. This is due to the Sun's own apparent motion across the sky, also about 30° per month. If one tracks its position among the stars from, for example, one full Moon to the next, it is easy to see that the full Moon appears to be shifted eastward by about one zodiacal constellation each lunar month.

No two months are the same: the lunar orbit is significantly out of round (e = 0.0549) and its path ever changing. While mean distances and periods are known to high accuracy, the Moon's distance from Earth is not

2011 passages of the Moon through 6h RA (highest declination, in Taurus)		
Date	**Age (d)**	**Phase**
Jan. 17	13	Fat waxing gibbous
Feb. 14	11	Waxing gibbous
Mar. 13	8	First quarter
Apr. 9	6	Thick waxing crescent
May 7	4	Medium waxing crescent
Jun. 3	2	Thin waxing crescent
Jun. 30	29	New Moon
Jul. 28	27	Thin waning crescent
Aug. 24	25	Thick waning crescent
Sep. 20	23	Third quarther
Oct. 18	21	Waning gibbous
Nov. 14	19	Fat waning gibbous
Dec. 10	15	Full Moon

constant, rather it is constrained between 356 000 and 407 000 km. Depending on the orientation of the apsides of the lunar orbit relative to the Sun, each month the Moon's perigee (closest approach to Earth) ranges from 35 000 to 50 000 km closer than its apogee. Thus the Moon varies in size from about 30–34′. Nor is its speed constant; the Moon near perigee and apogee can be travelling as much as 5 percent faster and slower respectively than its mean orbital speed of 1.023 km/s. Our perception of the Moon's ever-changing path is further enhanced through the effects of parallax.

Among the major satellites of the solar system, only the Moon and Neptune's Triton do not orbit in the plane of the equator of its planet. The Moon roughly orbits in the plane of the ecliptic, causing it to ride high or low at different points in the month, and at different phases throughout the calendar year. For example, a first-quarter Moon always cruises high in the sky around the time of the spring equinox but low around the autumn equinox; a full Moon is high around the time of the winter solstice but low around the summer solstice. The same statements apply to both Northern and Southern Hemispheres; however, the seasons themselves are six months out of phase.

Moreover, the Moon's orbit is tilted some 5°09′ to the ecliptic, with the nodes (crossing points) of its orbit regressing rapidly, completing a full cycle (the regression of the nodes) in just 18.61 years. The combination of these two tilts can be constructive or destructive, exaggerating or muting the seasonal effects noted above. The extremes of azimuth for rise and set points, and of altitude for meridian transits, are likewise modulated. In 2011, this effect is largely neutral, with the Moon's declination ranging from –24.2° to +24.2° in January and moderating to ±22.5° in December (see THE SKY MONTH BY MONTH, p. 100). These values are less than the extremes of ±28°43′ during the last Lunar Standstill in 2006 and roughly equal to the ecliptic's tilt of 23°27′ as the Moon's ascending note passes through 90° in 2011. Occultation series for stars near the ecliptic, the brightest of which are listed in the Zodiacal Catalogue, also follow the 18.61-year cycle. See OCCULTATIONS BY THE MOON p. 166.

A period quite similar to the 18.61 year period of "lunar nodes regression" is the 6585 1/3 day (or 18.03 year) period of the Saros. Used for many centuries to explain and predict solar and lunar eclipses, the Saros also explains near-repetitions of the lunar librations and such phenomena as extreme perigees and apogees. Remarkably, the major lunar and solar cycles (draconic, sidereal, anomalistic, and synodic month, eclipse year, and calendar year) all have near-integer values during this important cycle, with the result that all three bodies return to very nearly their starting positions (see: ECLIPSE PATTERNS, p. 126 and SOME ASTRONOMICAL AND PHYSICAL DATA, p. 33).

At the eyepiece, the closest astronomical target offers the greatest wealth of detail available to any given telescope, binocular, or camera, regardless of its size or quality. Of the countless recognizable features on the lunar nearside, over 1000—virtually all of them within reach of a moderate amateur telescope—have been formally named by the International Astronomical Union. Many of the greatest names in astronomy, exploration, and discovery are so commemorated. Observation of the Moon can be a lesson in the history of science. Seven Canadians have been immortalized by having lunar craters named after them: Ostwald Avery (1877–1955), Frederick Banting (1891–1941), Carlyle Beals (1899–1979), Reginald Daly (1871–1957), Simon Newcomb (1835–1909), John S. Plaskett (1865–1941), and Joshua Slocum (1844–1909). Remarkably, four of the seven—Avery, Beals, Newcomb, and Slocum—were born in Nova Scotia. Both Newcomb and Plaskett have been commemorated with RASC awards.

The face of the Moon is itself a history lesson of the early bombardment period of the inner solar system. On a world devoid of erosion processes like wind, water, weather, glaciation, volcanism, plate tectonics, sedimentation, and life itself that have modified Earth, most of the Moon's features were sculpted billions of years ago. The largest of the ancient impact basins were subsequently filled with lava flows from its then-molten interior that hardened into basaltic rock and formed the distinctively dark, primarily circular regions wrongly but permanently identified as lunar maria, or seas. The brighter white areas, highlands that surround the maria and dominate the southern portion of the Earth-facing hemisphere, feature innumerable smaller but similarly ancient impact craters. With bombardment slowed to a relative trickle and the Moon remaining geologically inert since those ancient lava flows, Luna's appearance has changed but little over the past three billion years. Today, only the cosmic sandblasting of micrometeorites serves to gradually soften her features.

Observation of the Moon is nonetheless a very dynamic activity, due to the ever-changing angles of illumination. The terminator (the sunrise/sunset line) shifts westward across lunar features at ~0.5° per hour, a consequence of its 360° rotation in one month, about 12° per 24 hours. (Note that lunar east and west are reversed to celestial east and west, having been changed to the terrestrial standard during the early days of lunar exploration so as not to confuse the astronauts.) This slow but inexorable progression is particularly dramatic near the lunar terminator, where oblique sunlight reveals "in-depth" details of lunar features.

During the Moon's waxing phases (from new Moon to full), the sunrise terminator advances across new ground, exposing the most elevated features first and the lowest last. It can be a fascinating experience to look a little beyond the terminator for little points of light that might be mountain peaks or raised crater rims, and over the course of a single observing session, watch these features gradually expand under the oblique illumination of the rising Sun. It may take a few hours or even days before all the features on the crater floors are completely lighted. It is well worth revisiting an area of interest night after night to observe its changing appearance, even as the advancing Sun is revealing new wonders by the hour. Or, as the eloquent Peltier put it, "the geography of a whole new world...turning page by nightly page."

Under magnification, the darker areas, including the maria and the floors of large craters called "walled plains," are primarily flat and smooth. Occasional shift features such as scarps, wrinkle ridges, rilles, and rounded domes catch the eye, especially under low angles of illumination. Relatively few craters dot the landscape, proof

positive of the greatly reduced rate of bombardment since those lava plains were formed. Frequently they are surrounded by circular mountain ranges that represent the vestiges of the outer rings of the ancient impact structures. At low Sun angles, these cast long and impressive shadows, whose jagged forms give a false impression of the rounded mountain tops. Long shadows yield interesting information about the topography under careful measurement, yet they often obscure features of interest in the lower terrain beyond. Hadley Rille of *Apollo 15* fame, is theoretically well placed near the terminator at first quarter, but is lost in the shadows of towering Mount Hadley and the Apennine Mountains, which take days to recede. A return to this area just before third quarter will reveal the same scene lit from the opposite direction, the western faces of the mountains bathed in sunlight and the rille nicely illuminated.

At times of high angles of illumination, especially around full Moon, a different aspect of the Moon is revealed. The three-dimensional context created in the brain from the pattern of light and dark is lost when the shadows are cast directly behind the features. Depth perception is problematic except right along the terminator, which now effectively encircles the Moon. Although the surface looks flat, a huge range of tonality is gained. Relatively young craters and their splash effects, such as ray systems and ejecta blankets, appear especially bright. Many small and otherwise unremarkable features stand out as brilliant points of light.

Full Moon is also the best time to observe the lunar libration zones. For line-of-sight reasons described on p. 99, the Moon displays a gentle rocking motion, revealing, over time, about 59 percent of its total surface area to the earthbound observer. Librations of longitude are zero when the Moon is at perigee or apogee; librations of latitude are zero when the Moon crosses the ecliptic at its ascending or descending node. Therefore, these librations follow the anomalistic month and draconic month, respectively, and thus gradually change with respect to each other, to bring different quadrants into favourable position. Libration has a more general effect on every lunar observing session, as even accessible nearside features can become more or less favourably situated to the line of sight, offering a more vertical or horizontal aspect from one viewing to the next. Details on current librations can be found in THE SKY MONTH BY MONTH, p. 98.

In 2006, the RASC's Observing Committee introduced the Isabel K. Williamson Lunar Observing Certificate, a detailed program guide containing key information about the lunar surface and how to observe it. The program's booklet begins with an overview of the program guidelines, which outline the observations that are required to obtain the certificate, and additional optional activities such as challenge features, lunar surface drawings, imaging, and more. It then provides a detailed overview of the history of the Moon and the various geological eras that have shaped its surface, explaining each type of lunar feature and providing tips for observing each of them. The entire certificate program can be located at www.rasc.ca/williamson/index.shtml.

From Galileo's earliest observations to the "Galileo Moments" of IYA2009, the Moon has remained among the most reliable and rewarding celestial targets for observers of all experience levels.

Recommended Reading:

Brunier, S. and Legault, T., *New Atlas of the Moon,* Firefly Books Ltd., 2006.
Enright, L., *The Beginner's Observing Guide, 5th Ed.,* RASC,
Peltier, L., *Starlight Nights: The Adventures of a Sky-Gazer,* Sky Publishing, 2007.
Rükl, A., *Atlas of the Moon,* Sky Publishing, 2004.
Sheehan, W. and Dobbins, T., *Epic Moon: A History of Lunar Exploration in the Age of the Telescope,* Willmann-Bell Inc., 2001.
Westfall, J., *Atlas of the Lunar Terminator,* Cambridge University Press, 2000.
Wood, C., *The Modern Moon: A Personal View,* Sky Publishing, 2003.
Lunar Picture of the Day: lpod.wikispaces.com

OCCULTATIONS BY THE MOON
BY DAVID W. DUNHAM

The Moon often passes between Earth and a star, an event called an *occultation*. During an occultation, a star suddenly disappears as the east limb of the Moon crosses the line between the star and the observer. The star reappears from behind the west limb some time later. Because the Moon moves through an angle about equal to its own diameter every hour, the longest time for an occultation is about an hour. The time is shorter if the occultation is not central. Solar eclipses are actually occultations: the star being occulted by the Moon is the Sun.

Since observing occultations is rather easy, amateur astronomers should try this activity. The slow, majestic drift of the Moon in its orbit is an interesting part of such observations, and the disappearance or reappearance of a star at the Moon's limb is a remarkable sight, particularly when it occurs as a *graze* near the Moon's northern or southern limb. During a graze, a star may disappear and reappear several times in succession as mountains and valleys in the Moon's polar regions drift by it. On rarer occasions the Moon occults a planet, but no such events occur visible from North America in 2011. The brightest stars occulted during 2011 are 2.5-magnitude δ Scorpii, 3.0-magnitude π Sagittarii, and the 3.2-magnitude red giant μ Geminorum.

Lunar occultation and graze observations refine our knowledge of the shape of the lunar profile and the fundamental star coordinate system. These observations complement those made by other techniques, such as *Kaguya* laser ranging and photographs. Improved knowledge of the lunar profile is useful in determinations of the Sun's diameter from solar eclipse records. Occultation observations are also useful for detecting double stars and measuring their separations. Binaries with separations as small as 0.02″ have been discovered visually during grazes. Doubles with separations in this range are useful for filling the gap between doubles that can be directly resolved and those whose duplicity has been discovered spectroscopically.

Observations

The **International Occultation Timing Association (IOTA)** analyzes lunar occultation observations and is now the world clearinghouse for such observations, having taken over this role from the **International Lunar Occultation Centre (ILOC)**, which closed in March 2009. Anyone interested in pursuing a systematic program of lunar occultation observations should consult the lunar and grazing occultation sections of *Chasing the Shadow: The IOTA Occultation Observer's Manual*, available as a free PDF file at www.poyntsource.com/IOTAmanual/Preview.htm. If you do not have Web access you can write to IOTA's North American coordinator of lunar occultation observations. Derek Breit, 17370 B Hawkins Lane, Morgan Hill CA 95037, USA, email: breit_ideas@poyntsource.com. For general information, including how to join IOTA, write to IOTA, 2505 Jeannes Trail, Edmond OK 73012, USA; email: business@occultations.org. IOTA provides predictions and coordination services for occultation observers. Detailed predictions for any grazing occultation are available ($1.50 U.S. each; free by email); instructions explaining the use of predictions are also available ($5 U.S. or in IOTA's manual as described above). Annual membership in IOTA is $30 U.S. in North America, $35 U.S. overseas. Less expensive online rates are available. Membership includes free graze predictions, descriptive materials, and a subscription to *Occultation Newsletter* (available separately for $20 U.S. in North America, $25 overseas). IOTA's administrative Web site is www.occultations.org, and its site for predictions, updates, observations, and other technical information is www.lunar-occultations.com/iota, which includes more predictions than can be given here.

For observers in the southwestern Pacific (New Zealand, Australia, Papua New Guinea, and nearby areas), the Royal Astronomical Society of New Zealand (RASNZ) provides occultation data (total lunar, lunar grazing, planetary, and Jupiter's satellites), plus comprehensive instructions for new observers. See the RASNZ Web page: occsec.wellington.net.nz/sitemap.htm.

The main information required in a lunar occultation observation is the time of the event and the observer's location. Supplementary data include the seeing conditions, telescope size, timing method, estimate of the observer's reaction time and the accuracy of the timing, and whether or not the reaction-time correction has been applied. The timing should be accurate to 0.5 s or better (a shortwave radio time signal and audio recorder provide a simple, permanent time record, but a video record provides higher accuracy). The observer's longitude, latitude, and altitude should be reported to the nearest tenth of an arcsecond and 10 m, respectively, and should be accurate to at least 0.5″ or 16 m. These can be determined from either GPS measurements (10 min of position averaging and an unobstructed view of the sky above 15° altitude are needed) or a suitable topographical map. For Canada, the maps are available from Regional Distributors, who are listed at maps.nrcan.gc.ca/distrib_centres_e.php. Email topo.maps@NRCan.gc.ca or call (800) 465–6277 for more information. For the United States (except Alaska), write to USGS Information Services (Product Sales), PO Box 25286, Denver CO 80225, USA, asking for an index to topographical maps in the desired state, or call (303) 202-4200. For Alaska, write to US Geological Survey, Map Sales, 4210 University Dr, Room 101, Anchorage AK 99508-4664, USA, or phone (907) 786-7011. Parts of USGS maps can be viewed and printed at certain Web sites such as msrmaps.com/Default.aspx — enter a location or click on the USA map and click on the "Topo Map" tab. Detailed imagery and maps are also available using Google Earth. IOTA is exploiting these resources for predictions, but they are not accurate enough for reporting lunar occultation observations.

Observers are encouraged to learn how to videotape occultations in order to obtain reliable and accurate timings. Inexpensive yet sensitive video cameras are now available. Visual timings must be accurate to ±0.2 s to be good enough for further improvement of the lunar profile and other parameters, except for grazes, where ±0.5 s is adequate. Information about videotaping occultations is on IOTA's technical Web

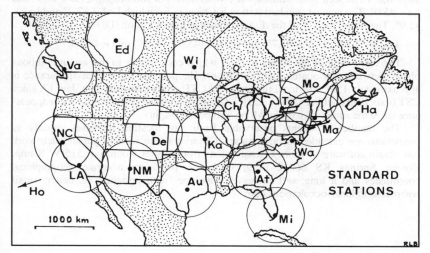

site and in its manual as described above. Check IOTA's technical Web site for report forms and reporting procedures. If you have questions, correspond with the North American coordinator specified on the previous page.

Pages 169–176 give tables of occultation predictions and a table and maps of northern or southern limits for grazing occultations.

1. TOTAL OCCULTATION PREDICTIONS

PREDICTIONS BY THE INTERNATIONAL LUNAR OCCULTATION CENTRE, JAPAN

The total occultation predictions, as given in the tables on pp. 173–175, are for the 18 standard stations identified on the map on the previous page; the longitudes and latitudes of these stations are given in the table headings. Although ILOC ceased operations in 2009, they have kindly provided predictions for 2009, 2010, and 2011.

The predictions are limited to stars of magnitude 5.0 and brighter. The first five columns give for each occultation the date, the Zodiacal Catalogue (ZC) number of the star, its magnitude, the phenomenon, and the elongation of the Moon from the Sun in degrees. Under each station are given the Universal Time of the event, factors A and B (see below), and the position angle P (from the north point, eastward around the Moon's limb to the point of occurrence of the phenomenon). If no data are given for an occultation for a given station, the reason is specified. If A and B give an unrealistic representation, as in the case of near grazes, they are omitted.

The terms A and B are for determining corrections to the times of the events for stations within 300 km of the standard stations. If Lo* and La* represent the longitude and latitude of the standard station, and Lo and La those of the observer, then for the observer,

$$\text{UT of event} = \text{UT of event at the standard station} + A(\text{Lo} - \text{Lo*}) + B(\text{La} - \text{La*}),$$

where Lo, etc., are expressed in degrees, and A and B are in minutes of time per degree. Longitude measured *west* of Greenwich is assumed to be *positive* (which is opposite to the IAU convention and that used by IOTA's *Occult* software). Due regard must be paid to the algebraic signs of the terms. To convert UT to the standard time of the observer, see the section STANDARD TIME ZONES on p 51.

As an example, consider the occultation of ZC 976 (μ Geminorum or Tejat) on 2011 Jan. 18 as seen from Minneapolis, Minnesota. For Minneapolis, Lo = 93.3° and La = 45.0°. The nearest standard station is Chicago, for which Lo* = 87.7° and La* = 41.9°. Therefore, the UT of the disappearance at the dark limb (DD) is:

$$4{:}52.1 - 1.2 \times (93.3° - 87.7°) \text{ min} - 3.9 \times (45.0° - 41.9°) \text{ min} = 4{:}33.4.$$

The elongation of the Moon is 156°, which corresponds to the waxing gibbous phase (between first quarter and full Moon). The position angle of disappearance is approximately 158°. The local time is 22:33 CST, of the **previous** date, Jan. 17, since CST is six hours behind UT (i.e. CST = UT–6 h). Data are not given for the reappearance since the sunlit edge of the Moon will be too bright.

The number of events observable from any location increases *rapidly* as predictions are extended to fainter stars. Observers who wish to pursue such work can obtain software or more extensive lists from Walter Robinson, 515 W Kump, Bonner Springs KS 66012–1439, USA, by providing accurate geographical coordinates and a long, self-addressed envelope (with postage); or, better, email webmaster@lunar-occultations.com.

2. GRAZE PREDICTIONS AND DATA ON OCCULTED STARS

BY EBERHARD RIEDEL AND DAVID W. DUNHAM

(A) GRAZE PREDICTIONS

The table on pp. 176–177 lists lunar grazing occultation predictions for much of North America for 2011. The events are limited to stars of magnitude 6.5 or brighter (paths for stars down to magnitude 7.5 are shown when the Moon is 30 percent or less sunlit) that will graze the limb of the Moon when it is at a favourable elongation from the Sun and at least as high above a land horizon in degrees as the star's magnitude (e.g. a third-magnitude star is included only if its altitude is at least 3°). The star's USNO reference number is the ZC number, unless the number is prefixed with an X. In the latter case, the star is not in the ZC and its number is from the XZ catalogue, a more extensive catalogue of zodiacal stars prepared originally at the U.S. Naval Observatory but now updated by D. Herald in Australia.

The maps on pp. 178–181 show the predicted graze tracks. The maps are "false" projections, since the latitude and longitude scales are both linear. This makes it much easier for measuring coordinates or plotting locations with known coordinates than is possible with any other type of projection. The longitude scale is compressed by a factor of cos 50°. The maps are not detailed enough for locating oneself in the 2- or 3-km-wide zone where multiple disappearances of the star may occur. To obtain detailed predictions of any graze for plotting on larger-scale maps of your region, write to (or email) IOTA (see p. 166). For many grazes, IOTA overlays the predicted limit line on the very detailed maps and imagery of maps.google.com, available at www.timerson.net/IOTA, but further corrections are needed based on the predicted lunar profile and the observer's height above sea level.

Each track is keyed to the sequential number in the table. The computer-drawn number appears at the east and west ends of the track and is aligned parallel to it. Some overlapping numbers have been omitted for legibility; in these cases, check the other end of the track for the number. Conditions are represented by three different types of lines:

solid line = dark limb, night
dashed line = bright limb, night
dotted line = dark or bright limb, day

Thicker lines are drawn for first-magnitude stars and planets. Many tracks begin and/or end with the letter A, B, or S: A denotes that the Moon is at a low altitude, B that the bright limb interferes, and S that sunlight or twilight interferes. The tick marks along the tracks indicate multiples of 10 min of every hour. For example, if the time for the west end of the track is 3:16.2, the tick marks proceeding eastward correspond to 3:20, 3:30, etc. Time always increases from west to east along the path. *The time ticks, track numbers, and the* A, B, *and* S *letters are on the side of the limit with an occultation*, that is north of southern limits and south of northern limits. The locations for the North American standard stations for lunar total occultation predictions are indicated by asterisks on the graze maps (see the map on p. 167).

(B) NAMES OF OCCULTED STARS

The stars that are occulted by the Moon are stars that lie along the zodiac; hence they are known by their number in the ZC compiled by James Robertson and published in the *Astronomical Papers Prepared for the Use of the American Ephemeris and Nautical Almanac, Vol. 10*, Part 2 (U.S. Government Printing Office, Washington, 1940). Robertson's ZC has been out of print for several years. In 1986, Isao Sato, a member of the Lunar Occultation Observers Group in Japan, republished the ZC.

This new edition is based on epoch J2000 and includes much new data, particularly on double stars. Since stars are not usually recognized by their ZC numbers, the equivalent Bayer designations or Flamsteed numbers of the stars occulted during the year are given in the table below. The ZC and XZ (now version XZ80Q) catalogues, updated in 2005 by D. Herald using *HIPPARCOS*, Tycho-2, and UCAC-2 data, are available on IOTA's Web site. An XZ number is given for the last non-ZC stars.

ZC	Name	ZC	Name	ZC	Name
51	45 Psc	1047	36 Gem	2051	CS Vir
233	101 Psc	1077	ζ Gem (Mekbuda)	2290	δ Sco (Dschubba)
244	104 Psc	1113	56 Gem	2347	o Sco
432	45 Ari	1127	61 Gem	2443	26 Oph
435	47 Ari	1158	74 Gem	2490	o Oph
465	δ Ari (Botein)	1175	81 Gem	2513	44 Oph
472	ζ Ari	1207	3 Cnc	2577	63 (Oph)/Sgr
486	τ Ari	1210	5 Cnc	2593	5 Sgr
487	63 Ari	1271	29 Cnc	2736	30 Sgr
582	32 Tau	1309	45 Cnc	2739	31 Sgr
584	33 Tau	1341	α Cnc (Acubens)	2746	33 Sgr
599	37 Tau	1397	ω Leo	2747	ν¹ Sgr(Ain al Rami)
601	39 Tau	1410	6 Leo	2779	o Sgr
634	56 Tau	1428	o Leo (Subra)	2797	π Sgr (Al Baldah)
656	κ Tau	1482	14 Sex	2902	57 Sgr
657	67 Tau	1489	16 Sex	3008	13 Cap
660	υ Tau	1495	19 Sex	3015	τ Cap
709	τ Tau	1528	RX Sex	3070	8 Aqr
742	99 Tau	1566	36 Sex	3093	ν Aqr
784	108 Tau	1587	55 Leo	3187	47 Cap
817	114 Tau	1590	57 Leo	3287	51 Aqr
865	V731 Tau	1605	62 Leo	3320	κ Aqr (Situla)
911	141 (Tau)/Ori	1620	66 Leo	3453	κ Psc
916	1 Gem	1670	87 Leo	3455	9 Psc
929	3 Gem	1771	14 Vir	3482	16 Psc
939	TV Gem	1967	83 Vir	3501	19 (TX) Psc
946	η Gem (Propus)	1970	85 Vir	X23327	o Oph companion
976	μ Gem (Tejat)				

(C) OCCULTED STARS KNOWN TO BE DOUBLE

In the table below are data on double stars for which graze predictions are given. This information is from DSFILE, a comprehensive file of zodiacal double-star data compiled by Don Stockbauer, Henk Bulder, Mitsuru Sôma, David Herald, and David Dunham; most of the data for the ZC stars are in the Sato ZC catalogue. The successive columns give the USNO reference number of the star, the number of the graze track, the double-star code (d), the magnitudes of the brighter (A) and dimmer (B) components, the separation in arcseconds, and the position angle (PA) of B from A measured eastward from north. If the star is triple, the third component's magnitude is given under C, and its separation and PA from A are given in the last columns. XZ numbers are given for the last four non-ZC stars.

The parameters are given for the epoch of the occultation, computed from orbital elements when available or from extrapolations from a long series of observations. If there is little change in the available observations, the last-observed separation and PA are used. Components fainter than magnitude 11.5 are not listed, and some very close doubles whose parameters are not known, generally with separations less than 0.2″, are also not listed. The latter include spectroscopic binaries (code J, U, or sometimes V) and visual occultation doubles (most codes K and X, and many Vs).

The codes have the following meanings:

A, C, or G   visual double

B or V....close double, usually discovered by occultation

D ....primary of wide pair; secondary has separate catalogue entry

E............secondary star of wide pair

F............prediction is for the following component of a visual double

H ....triple, with close occultation pair and third visual component; prediction uses a mean position

I.............data for B component computed from orbital elements, but B component is itself a close double, with data for C component referred to B rather than A

K ....possible double from occultation

L............close triple star (only two stars often listed because inner pair is often spectroscopic)

M..........mean position (centre of light) of a close pair is used by the ZC and/or XZ catalogue

N ....northern component of nearly equal double star

O ....orbital elements available and used to calculate the separation and PA

Q ....= O, but A component may be close double (if triple, C-component data are computed from orbital elements)

R............triple; close pair = O and C component also has orbit relative to centre of close pair

S ....southern component of nearly equal double star

T............visual triple star

W..........= A or C, but A component is a spectroscopic binary

X ....probable double from occultation

Y............triple, K or X (B component) and A or C (C component)

Z............triple, O (B component) and V (C component)

Some close pairs have rapid orbital motion so the current PA is unknown.

USNO	Graze #	d	A	B	Sep. "	PA °	C	Sep. "	PA °
411	136	O	7.4	8.2	3.7	306			
485	158	M	7.0	10.8	0.6	338			
486	11,81	H	5.4	7.9	0.2	38	8.2	0.8	227
487	159	M	5.3	8.5	0.5	289			
594	43	A	6.9	7.8	7.3	128	9.3	58.0	241
601	161	X	6.8	6.8	0.1	358			
656	84, 194	V	5.2	5.2	0.1	110			
660	58, 85, 139	V	4.6	6.5	0.02	336			
709	179	L	4.9	6.4	0.0005		5.6	0.1	90
742	44	A	6.0	12.3	6.2	6			
761	104, 164	M	7.0	8.4	0.4	153			
784	141, 197	C	6.3	12.5	1.9	349			
817	198	T	5.6	5.6	0.1	90	10.9	37.8	348
843	183	O	7.2	7.8	4.1	275			
887	45	V	7.1	9.1	0.1	103			
916	46	Q	4.9	6.9	0.1	130	5.1	0.2	
929	13	M	5.9	8.5	0.6	346			
946	14, 86	Q	3.5	6.1	1.6	254			
976	15, 61, 62	G	3.2	9.8	107.9	141	10.7	0.5	264
997	63	A	6.8	12.5	20.7	110			
1077	87, 88, 168	A	3.7	11.7	99.0	348			
1113	64	A	5.2	12.2	13.6	195			
1341	204	A	4.4	11.8	11.3	325			
1397	116, 216	O	5.9	6.5	0.8	105			
1410	16, 70, 108	A	5.3	8.3	38.9	74			
1410	217	A	5.3	8.3	38.9	74			
1428	49	W	4.4	4.6	0.008		9.9	85.0	44
1528	109	D	6.7	9.3	116.6	191			
1587	95, 131	Q	6.3	8.3	1.1	47	8.0	0.8	
1970	247	L	6.5	8.2	0.04	149	8.4	0.1	329
2045	145	M	6.4	10.5	0.7	99			
2134	21	D	6.2	8.5	26.0	314			
2290	173, 206, 250	O	3.0	5.0	0.08	200			
2328	1	M	6.4	10.4	1.7	221			
2490	74, 113, 119	D	5.4	6.9	10.3	355			
2747	29	A	5.0	10.8	2.5	97			
3015	224	I	5.8	6.3	0.2	132	9.3	0.1	264
3287	30, 123, 226	Z	6.6	6.6	0.4	103	10.1	54.4	342
3320	5, 155	T	6.1	6.1	0.1	94	8.8	90.0	156
3326	6, 211	O	6.7	7.8	0.1	122			
3524	35, 228	O	7.4	7.9	0.4	255			
X04387	82	M	7.9	8.6	1.0	98			
X06484	234	M	8.7	8.9	0.2	311			
X12002	169	A	7.9	13.9	2.5	113			
X23327	75, 150	E	(Companion of ZC 2490)						

TABLE OF TOTAL LUNAR OCCULTATION PREDICTIONS

					HALIFAX 63.6°W, 44.6°N				MONTRÉAL 73.6°W, 45.5°N				TORONTO 79.4°W, 43.7°N			
DATE	ZC	MAG	PH	ELG °	TIME (UT)	A m	B m	P °	TIME (UT)	A m	B m	P °	TIME (UT)	A m	B m	P °
Jan. 14	472	5.0	DD	117	21:32.3	−1.5	1.1	89	Before Sunset				Before Sunset			
18	976	3.2	DD	158	5:12.6	−1.0	−1.8	118	4:59.7	−1.2	−2.0	127	4:56.7	−1.2	−2.5	139
Feb. 15	1077	3.7	DD	139	After Moonset				8:50.2	0.2	−1.4	102	8:54.0	0.2	−1.5	110
Mar. 13	976	3.2	DD	102	24:28.0	−2.4	1.5	53	24:06.5	−2.2	1.5	60	23:51.9	−2.1	1.2	71
24	2347	4.8	RD	244	Bright Twilight				Bright Twilight				10:16.1	−1.9	−0.3	266
Apr. 11	1077	3.7	DD	85	No Occultation				1:22.8	−2.2	0.6	53	1:10.4	−2.0	−0.1	71
May 19	2513	4.3	RD	205	Bright Twilight				8:05.5	−1.6	−0.7	273	7:56.7	−1.8	−0.5	274
Jul. 13	2523	4.9	DD	153	2:41.8	−1.7	0.8	44	2:25.1	−1.9	1.3	41	2:11.3	−2.0	1.5	46
20	3453	4.9	RD	236	2:21.2	−0.2	1.6	265	Before Moonrise				Before Moonrise			
26	656	4.4	RD	305	8:10.3	−0.2	2.3	233	8:10.1	−0.2	1.9	247	8:06.3	0.0	1.7	249
Aug. 11	2797	3.0	DD	148	2:35.0	−1.3	0.8	40	2:22.6	−1.3	1.5	28	2:11.3	−1.5	1.9	28
21	465	4.5	RD	263	6:45.4	−0.3	3.3	206	6:43.9	−0.4	2.5	224	6:37.3	−0.3	2.4	227
22	599	4.5	RD	275	7:36.1			319	No Occultation				No Occultation			
Sep. 20	817	4.8	RD	265	No Occultation				3:49.7			200	Before Moonrise			
Oct. 9	3453	4.9	DD	156	22:12.9	−0.1	3.0	10	Before Sunset				Before Sunset			
28	2290	2.5	DD	27	18:43.4	−1.7	−0.4	89	18:25.9	−1.7	0.0	90	18:15.6	−1.7	0.2	96
28	2290	2.5	RB	28	19:57.3	−1.5	−1.1	281	19:41.0	−1.6	−0.8	285	19:32.4	−1.7	−0.5	282
Dec. 22	2290	2.5	DB	332	16:27.8	−1.4	−1.1	99	16:11.8	−1.6	−0.7	95	16:03.1	−1.8	−0.5	98
22	2290	2.5	RD	333	17:37.1	−0.9	−1.1	265	17:25.1	−1.3	−1.1	273	17:18.9	−1.5	−0.9	273

					WINNIPEG 97.2°W, 49.9°N				EDMONTON 113.4°W, 53.6°N				VANCOUVER 123.1°W, 49.2°N			
DATE	ZC	MAG	PH	ELG °	TIME (UT)	A m	B m	P °	TIME (UT)	A m	B m	P °	TIME (UT)	A m	B m	P °
Jan. 18	946	3.2	DD	155	No Occultation				0:21.9	−0.5	0.4	136	Before Sunset			
18	976	3.2	DD	157	4:19.7	−1.5	−1.1	126	3:55.8	−1.2	0.2	112	3:43.4	−1.2	0.0	123
Feb. 11	472	5.0	DD	90	No Occultation				No Occultation				8:11.2	−0.5	0.1	36
15	1077	3.7	DD	139	8:44.4	−0.1	−1.8	117	8:32.9	−0.4	−2.0	127	8:39.6	−0.3	−2.7	149
Mar. 12	709	4.3	DD	81	6:10.0	0.2	−1.6	100	6:03.9	−0.1	−1.9	107	6:12.1	−0.1	−2.5	128
24	2347	4.8	RD	244	9:45.6	−1.6	0.5	268	9:26.5	−1.2	1.2	260	Before Moonrise			
Apr. 8	656	4.4	DD	51	4:47.4	0.8	−2.5	145	4:50.0			158	No Occultation			
8	660	4.4	DD	51	No Occultation				No Occultation				5:16.8			32
22	2589	4.8	RD	238	Bright Twilight				10:53.8	−1.4	0.2	284	10:37.7	−1.5	0.6	278
May 19	2513	4.3	RD	205	7:24.8	−1.5	0.2	285	7:05.8	−1.1	0.8	282	6:51.3	−1.0	1.2	270
19	2523	4.9	RD	206	Bright Twilight				9:17.0			344	9:09.1			332
26	3453	4.9	RD	288	Bright Twilight				Bright Twilight				10:34.4	−0.4	1.9	253
Jun. 17	2779	3.9	RD	200	No Occultation				9:21.5	−0.9	0.7	207	9:07.1	−1.2	1.2	209
Jul. 26	656	4.4	RD	305	8:15.7	0.1	1.3	278	8:21.9	0.2	1.0	297	Before Moonrise			
Aug. 9	2513	4.3	DD	126	No Occultation				After Moonset				7:25.7	−1.5	−2.0	124
16	3453	4.9	RD	211	Bright Twilight				Bright Twilight				11:38.2	−1.1	0.7	223
21	465	4.5	RD	263	6:44.3	−0.2	1.7	258	6:48.0	0.0	1.5	276	6:42.6	0.2	1.3	278
Oct. 17	817	4.8	RD	239	Bright Twilight				11:58.7	−1.7	1.3	235	11:30.0			211
21	1341	4.3	RD	286	9:47.4			221	9:51.3	−0.3	2.6	244	9:36.7	0.2	3.6	227
28	2290	2.5	DD	27	17:53.0	−1.1	0.7	100	Before Moonrise				Before Moonrise			
28	2290	2.5	RB	28	19:03.4	−1.4	0.3	283	18:46.4	−1.0	0.9	275	18:31.2	−1.1	1.5	258
Nov. 6	3453	4.9	DD	130	No Occultation				5:42.0	−1.8	−1.6	104	5:28.4	−2.3	−1.2	104
Dec. 8	465	4.5	DD	156	No Occultation				10:08.6			360	9:45.3	−1.3	0.6	41
22	2290	2.5	DB	332	15:33.5	−1.4	0.3	96	15:15.9	−1.0	0.8	104	15:04.7	−0.7	0.6	120
22	2290	2.5	RD	332	16:47.2	−1.5	−0.3	282	16:24.9	−1.3	0.4	278	16:09.2	−1.3	1.0	265

					MASSACHUSETTS 72.5°W, 42.5°N				WASHINGTON, D.C. 77.0°W, 38.9°N				CHICAGO 87.7°W, 41.9°N			
DATE	ZC	MAG	PH	ELG °	TIME (UT)	A m	B m	P °	TIME (UT)	A m	B m	P °	TIME (UT)	A m	B m	P °
Jan. 18	976	3.2	DD	158	5:07.5	−1.1	−2.4	135	5:14.0	−0.7	−3.8	156	4:52.1	−1.2	−3.9	156
Feb. 15	1077	3.7	DD	139	8:53.9	0.3	−1.3	106	9:00.4	0.3	−1.4	116	8:58.3	0.2	−1.7	120
Mar. 13	976	3.2	DD	102	24:05.5	−2.2	0.8	71	23:53.8	−2.2	0.2	87	Before Sunset			
24	2347	4.8	RD	244	Bright Twilight				10:21.9	−2.0	−0.2	259	10:00.0		0.2	262
Apr. 11	1077	3.7	DD	85	1:24.2	−2.0	0.0	63	1:16.9	−1.8	−0.6	82	0:54.6	−2.0	−0.5	88
May 19	2513	4.3	RD	205	8:09.4	−1.6	−0.6	267	8:03.3	−1.9	−0.4	264	7:41.6	−2.0	−0.2	274
Jul. 13	2523	4.9	DD	153	2:23.4	−2.0	1.3	46	2:09.2	−2.2	1.4	55	1:52.0	−1.9	1.7	55
26	656	4.4	RD	305	8:04.4	−0.1	2.0	239	7:57.4	0.1	1.9	236	8:03.8	0.1	1.5	254
Aug. 11	2797	3.0	DD	148	2:19.9	−1.5	1.4	35	2:06.7	−1.8	1.7	39	1:54.0	−1.7	2.3	28
21	465	4.5	RD	263	6:36.3	−0.3	2.8	215	6:25.4	0.0	2.8	212	6:31.2	−0.2	2.1	234
22	599	4.5	RD	274	7:13.6			335	7:11.0			324	No Occultation			
Sep. 7	2759	3.6	DD	120	4:09.5			356	4:02.4			4	No Occultation			
Oct. 28	2290	2.5	DD	27	18:28.0	−1.8	−0.1	94	18:19.8	−1.9	−0.1	102	18:01.4	−1.6	0.3	105
28	2290	2.5	RB	28	19:45.1	−1.7	−0.8	281	19:39.2	−1.9	−0.5	275	19:18.0	−1.6	−0.1	277

DB/DD = Disappearance at Bright/Dark limb; RB/RD = Reappearance at Bright/Dark limb
See p. 168 for additional explanation of these tables.

TABLE OF TOTAL LUNAR OCCULTATION PREDICTIONS (continued)

DATE	ZC	MAG	PH	ELG °	MASS. TIME (UT)	A m	B m	P °	WASH. TIME (UT)	A m	B m	P °	CHIC. TIME (UT)	A m	B m	P °
					MASSACHUSETTS (cont) 72.5°W, 42.5°N				**WASHINGTON, D.C. (cont) 77.0°W, 38.9°N**				**CHICAGO (cont) 87.7°W, 41.9°N**			
Dec. 8	465	4.5	DD	156	No Occultation				After Moonset				10:14.1	−0.6	0.7	32
22	2290	2.5	DB	332	16:15.8	−1.7	−0.8	99	16:10.4	−1.9	−0.8	105	15:48.7	−1.8	−0.2	102
22	2290	2.5	RD	333	17:29.5	−1.3	−1.0	268	17:26.4	−1.5	−0.7	264	17:06.8	−1.7	−0.6	272

DATE	ZC	MAG	PH	ELG °	MIAMI TIME (UT)	A m	B m	P °	ATLANTA TIME (UT)	A m	B m	P °	AUSTIN TIME (UT)	A m	B m	P °
					MIAMI 80.3°W, 25.8°N				**ATLANTA 84.3°W, 33.8°N**				**AUSTIN 97.8°W, 30.2°N**			
Feb. 15	1077	3.7	DD	139	After Moonset				9:11.0	0.4	−1.7	133	9:25.5	0.7	−2.7	162
Mar. 13	976	3.2	DD	102	23:59.6	−2.4	−2.7	138	Before Sunset				Before Sunset			
24	2347	4.8	RD	244	10:07.6	−2.8	1.7	228	10:05.0	−2.4	0.5	248	9:22.5	−3.3	2.8	225
Apr. 11	1077	3.7	DD	85	1:28.8	−1.3	−2.0	125	1:08.9	−1.8	−1.4	108	Before Sunset			
22	2589	4.8	RD	239	Bright Twilight				Bright Twilight				11:21.1	−2.1	0.6	241
May 19	2513	4.3	RD	205	7:55.2	−2.2	0.8	238	7:49.3	−2.2	0.1	259	7:16.0	−2.4	0.9	252
19	2523	4.9	RD	206	Bright Twilight				Bright Twilight				10:23.5	−2.0	−0.8	273
26	3453	4.9	RD	288	No Occultation				Bright Twilight				10:08.3	−0.6	2.8	205
Jul. 13	2523	4.9	DD	153	1:47.6	−2.3	0.6	86	1:46.6	−2.1	1.3	70	Before Sunset			
26	656	4.4	RD	305	7:28.9	1.1	3.1	200	7:49.6	0.4	1.8	232	Before Moonrise			
26	660	4.4	RD	305	7:59.8			329	No Occultation				No Occultation			
Aug. 11	2797	3.0	DD	148	1:39.2	−2.4	1.3	66	1:43.3	−2.0	1.9	47	Before Sunset			
21	465	4.5	RD	263	No Occultation				6:12.1	0.2	2.7	210	6:07.6	0.4	2.1	220
22	599	4.5	RD	274	7:07.9	−1.1	0.6	279	7:02.5			317	No Occultation			
Sep. 4	2290	2.5	DD	82	2:30.2	−0.7	−0.1	66	2:31.4	−0.1	1.2	33	2:20.3			26
4	2290	2.5	RB	82	After Moonset				3:09.1	−1.7	−3.2	325	2:53.4			335
7	2759	3.6	DD	120	3:42.2	−1.1	0.9	46	3:52.2	0.3	2.8	9	No Occultation			
Oct. 16	656	4.4	RD	226	7:02.0	−3.0	−0.5	285	RB				No Occultation			
28	2290	2.5	DD	27	18:20.8	−1.9	−1.3	134	18:07.2	−1.8	−0.3	118	17:51.2	−0.8	−1.1	145
28	2290	2.5	RB	28	19:32.5	−2.6	0.6	246	19:25.2	−2.3	0.1	264	18:50.1	−2.6	1.4	244
Dec. 8	465	4.5	DD	156	After Moonset				After Moonset				10:13.0	−0.2	−0.8	84
22	2290	2.5	DB	332	16:18.9	−2.4	−1.9	135	15:59.5	−2.1	−0.8	116	15:35.6	−1.7	−1.0	133
22	2290	2.5	RD	333	17:23.1	−1.7	0.7	234	17:16.8	−1.9	−0.3	257	16:46.8	−2.5	0.6	248

DATE	ZC	MAG	PH	ELG °	KANSAS CITY TIME (UT)	A m	B m	P °	DENVER TIME (UT)	A m	B m	P °	N.M./ARIZ. TIME (UT)	A m	B m	P °
					KANSAS CITY 94.5°W, 39.0°N				**DENVER 105.0°W, 39.8°N**				**NEW MEX., ARIZ. 109.0°W, 34.0°N**			
Jan. 1	2347	4.8	RD	326	No Occultation				No Occultation				13:47.1			355
31	2747	5.0	RD	331	Bright Twilight				13:24.0	−1.1	1.6	255	13:09.2	−1.2	2.0	238
Feb. 15	1077	3.7	RD	139	9:04.6	0.2	−1.9	133	9:04.5	0.1	−2.3	146	9:22.5			172
Mar. 12	709	4.3	DD	82	6:26.5	0.5	−1.7	121	6:30.4	0.5	−2.2	132	6:49.7			163
24	2347	4.8	RD	244	9:44.2	−2.2	0.8	253	9:22.1	−2.1	1.5	243	8:56.9			213
Apr. 22	2589	4.8	RD	238	Bright Twilight				11:08.7	−2.1	0.0	265	10:57.4	−2.3	0.5	256
May 19	2513	4.3	RD	205	7:28.8	−2.1	0.2	270	7:07.7	−1.8	0.7	268	6:54.8	−2.0	1.2	254
19	2523	4.9	RD	206	10:20.0	−1.9	−1.4	290	9:56.8	−2.3	−1.4	304	9:54.6	−2.4	−1.0	293
26	3453	4.9	RD	288	Bright Twilight				10:26.4	−0.8	2.1	231	10:11.0	−0.6	2.3	224
Jul. 26	656	4.4	RD	305	8:01.1	0.3	1.4	255	Before Moonrise				Before Moonrise			
Aug. 11	2797	3.0	DD	148	1:35.1	−1.8	2.4	36	Before Sunset				Before Sunset			
21	465	4.5	RD	263	6:24.7	0.0	2.0	236	6:26.7	0.1	1.6	248	6:18.3	0.3	1.6	241
Oct. 28	2290	2.5	DD	27	17:51.2	−1.3	0.1	118	17:40.7	−0.7	0.0	129	17:41.6	−0.1	−1.2	154
28	2290	2.5	RB	28	19:04.6	−2.0	0.4	268	18:45.2	−1.8	1.0	259	18:28.8	−2.3	2.1	237
Dec. 8	465	4.5	DD	156	10:09.9	−0.5	−0.1	52	10:03.6	−0.7	−0.4	61	10:04.6	−0.7	−0.9	83
22	2290	2.5	DB	332	15:36.8	−1.8	−0.2	111	15:19.8	−1.4	0.0	119	15:16.6	−1.1	−0.7	138
22	2290	2.5	RD	332	16:55.3	−2.0	−0.2	267	16:34.0	−2.0	0.3	264	16:21.7	−2.4	1.0	249

DATE	ZC	MAG	PH	ELG °	LOS ANGELES TIME (UT)	A m	B m	P °	N CALIF. TIME (UT)	A m	B m	P °	HONOLULU TIME (UT)	A m	B m	P °
					LOS ANGELES 118.3°W, 34.1°N				**N CALIFORNIA 122.0°W, 38.0°N**				**HONOLULU 157.9°W, 21.3°N**			
Jan. 1	2347	4.8	RD	326	13:50.8	0.0	−1.0	330	13:47.2	0.4	−1.3	338	Before Moonrise			
Feb. 11	472	5.0	DD	90	After Moonset				8:15.3	−0.1	−0.6	70	No Occultation			
14	916	4.3	DD	126	No Occultation				No Occultation				7:51.9	−1.8	−3.4	145
Mar. 24	2359	4.8	RD	244	No Occultation				No Occultation				10:11.6	0.9	−2.6	344
25	2513	4.3	RD	257	No Occultation				No Occultation				11:09.1	−0.9	1.2	255
Apr. 8	660	4.4	DD	51	5:23.2	−0.1	−0.6	74	5:19.9	−0.3	−0.6	68	No Occultation			
10	946	3.2	DD	74	4:36.8			44	4:36.2			28	Before Sunset			
10	946	3.2	RD	74	RB				4:50.9			4	Bright Twilight			
22	2589	4.8	RD	238	10:36.2	−2.2	0.9	256	10:31.7	−2.0	0.8	263	No Occultation			
May 19	2513	4.3	RD	204	6:37.5	−1.8	1.1	256	6:37.8	−1.5	1.6	250	No Occultation			
19	2523	4.9	RD	206	9:31.9	−2.4	−0.8	298	9:20.7	−2.1	−0.7	307	8:07.7	−1.8	2.4	230

DB/DD = Disappearance at Bright/Dark limb; RB/RD = Reappearance at Bright/Dark limb
See p. 168 for additional explanation of these tables.

TABLE OF TOTAL LUNAR OCCULTATION PREDICTIONS (continued)

DATE	ZC	MAG	PH	ELG °	LOS ANGELES (cont) 118.3°W, 34.1°N				N CALIFORNIA (cont) 122.0°W, 38.0°N				HONOLULU (cont) 157.9°W, 21.3°N			
					TIME (UT)	A m	B m	P °	TIME (UT)	A m	B m	P °	TIME (UT)	A m	B m	P °
May 26	3453	4.9	RD	288	10:07.0	−0.3	2.1	229	10:13.7	−0.3	1.9	238	Before Moonrise			
Jun. 17	2779	3.9	RD	199	No Occultation				8:38.5			172	No Occultation			
17	2797	3.0	RD	201	Bright Twilight				Bright Twilight				11:25.8	−2.8	0.4	263
Jul. 26	709	4.3	RD	309	Bright Twilight				Bright Twilight				15:25.4	−1.0	1.6	245
Aug. 8	2359	4.8	DD	114	7:05.7	−0.5	−0.1	56	7:04.6	−0.3	0.4	39	5:51.1	−3.0	1.1	65
16	3453	4.9	RD	211	No Occultation				11:18.6	−0.2	3.6	183	9:57.1	−1.2	2.7	213
Sep. 3	2290	2.5	DD	80	No Occultation				No Occultation				23:50.7	−0.7	−0.1	115
4	2290	2.5	RB	81	No Occultation				No Occultation				1:02.8	−1.7	0.2	280
Oct. 28	2290	2.5	DD	27	17:46.5			180	17:39.0			166	No Occultation			
28	2290	2.5	RB	27	18:04.1			211	18:10.3			224	Occultation			
Nov. 12	656	4.4	RD	199	No Occultation				No Occultation				14:25.9	−1.5	−1.8	294
Dec. 8	465	4.5	DD	155	9:56.8	−1.0	−1.2	90	9:48.7	−1.2	−0.8	80	No Occultation			
22	2290	2.5	DB	331	15:09.7	−0.3	−1.3	153	15:04.6	−0.4	−0.7	147	No Occultation			
22	2290	2.5	RD	332	16:09.9	−2.3	1.4	246	15:57.4	−2.1	1.7	242	No Occultation			

DB/DD = Disappearance at Bright/Dark limb; RB/RD = Reappearance at Bright/Dark limb
See p. 168 for additional explanation of these tables.

TABLE OF GRAZING LUNAR OCCULTATION PREDICTIONS

The table below lists lunar grazing occultation predictions for much of North America for 2011. The eight maps on pp. 178–181 show the graze tracks (see the descriptive text on pp. 169–170).

For each graze is given:

No. .... a chronological sequential number used on the maps
Date .... the date
USNO d... the star's USNO (U.S. Naval Observatory) reference number (see the bottom of p. 170) and its duplicity code (in the **"d"** column—see section (C) on p. 170 concerning double stars)
m .... its visual magnitude
%sl .... the percent of the Moon sunlit (+ for waxing, – for waning, E for lunar eclipses)
L .... whether the track is a northern (N) or southern (S) limit
W.U.T. ..... the Universal Time at the west end of the track
Lo., La. .... the longitude and latitude of the west end of the track

No.	Date	USNO d	m	%sl	L	W.U.T.	Lo.	La.
1	Jan. 1	2328 M	6.4	9–	S	10:46.3	–84	33
2	1	2347	4.5	9–	N	13:32.1	–120	41
3	2	2483	7.1	4–	S	12:58.1	–83	48
4	8	3216	6.8	12+	S	1:22.1	–126	41
5	8	3320 T	5.0	18+	S	22:56.1	–92	42
6	9	3326O	6.4	19+	S	1:03.2	–111	23
7	9	X30908	7.2	19+	S	1:43.1	–122	27
8	10	3453 V	5.0	28+	S	2:09.7	–130	48
9	12	233 X	6.2	54+	S	22:50.9	–78	23
10	14	375 K	6.8	65+	S	3:23.2	–130	30
11	15	486 H	5.3	74+	S	0:33.3	–113	41
12	15	493	6.9	74+	N	3:35.7	–101	38
13	17	929 M	5.8	95+	N	22:33.1	–89	50
14	18	946 Q	3.5	95+	S	0:24.5	–128	40
15	18	976 G	2.9	96+	S	3:54.8	–130	39
16	21	1410 A	5.1	97–	N	11:08.6	–67	55
17	23	1629	6.6	84–	S	6:32.9	–119	39
18	24	1752	6.5	74–	S	8:09.2	–110	55
19	24	1771	6.8	72–	S	12:57.2	–130	52
20	25	1893	6.9	62–	S	11:32.2	–129	55
21	27	2134 D	5.9	41–	S	8:34.7	–96	37
22	27	2157	6.1	40–	S	12:45.6	–130	36
23	28	2270	5.4	31–	S	8:28.7	–72	45
24	28	X21932	7.2	30–	S	11:39.3	–109	48
25	29	2443 K	5.7	20–	S	11:45.1	–116	32
26	29	2442	5.9	20–	S	11:50.3	–111	39
27	30	2577	6.2	13–	S	11:30.2	–72	53
28	30	2593	6.6	12–	N	13:53.0	–102	55
29	31	2747 A	4.9	7–	S	12:28.8	–109	23
30	Feb. 5	3287 Z	5.8	3+	N	0:31.7	–99	25
31	5	3290	7.3	3+	S	1:04.0	–106	27
32	6	3397	7.0	7+	N	0:05.0	–97	43
33	7	X31997	6.8	13+	N	0:25.2	–100	36
34	7	3511	6.8	13+	N	0:34.2	–101	34
35	7	3524O	6.9	14+	S	2:45.9	–130	36
36	10	435	5.8	46+	N	23:43.5	–89	31
37	11	459K	6.4	49+	N	5:47.4	–78	55
38	11	472K	4.9	50+	N	8:22.6	–122	55
39	11	566	6.0	56+	S	22:44.3	–76	39
40	11	563	7.0	56+	N	22:57.4	–77	54
41	12	582	5.6	57+	S	1:47.5	–122	37
42	12	584 J	6.0	57+	N	2:10.4	–124	27
43	12	594 A	6.9	58+	N	4:33.6	–130	35
44	13	742 A	5.8	68+	N	4:33.4	–130	46
45	14	887 V	7.0	77+	N	3:19.0	–66	55
46	14	916 Q	4.3	79+	N	8:43.1	–130	40
47	15	1047 X	5.3	85+	N	2:01.9	–129	49
48	16	1175 V	4.9	92+	S	0:02.1	–96	40
49	17	1428 W	3.5	100+	N	23:09.9	–81	20
50	20	1713 V	5.6	94–	S	8:24.7	–130	37
51	21	1852 V	6.0	86–	N	12:06.3	–130	42
52	21	1858	6.3	85–	N	13:49.8	–130	49
53	22	1967	5.5	78–	N	9:10.5	–88	55
54	24	2227	5.8	57–	S	7:28.0	–93	40
55	24	2235	6.3	57–	S	8:1.9	–103	37
56	Feb. 25	2398	6.1	46–	N	10:22.5	–80	55
57	Mar. 11	566	6.0	33+	N	7:29.1	–130	46
58	11	660 V	4.3	39+	S	22:43.3	–72	46
59	12	693	6.0	41+	N	3:30.3	–122	55
60	13	865	6.2	54+	N	8:54.8	–130	44
61	13	976 G	2.9	60+	S	23:30.3	–104	20
62	13	976 G	2.9	60+	N	23:23.7	–130	49
63	14	997 A	7.0	62+	N	3:17.6	–130	37
64	15	1113 A	5.1	71+	N	0:24.5	–93	31
65	15	1127 V	5.9	71+	N	2:26.5	–123	26
66	15	1135	6.7	72+	N	4:01.0	–130	54
67	15	1151	6.8	74+	N	8:23.0	–124	55
68	16	1258	6.7	81+	N	1:50.7	–114	53
69	17	1381	6.4	89+	N	1:07.7	–103	51
70	17	1410 A	5.1	91+	N	8:48.9	–109	55
71	22	2039	5.5	91–	N	6:56.2	–102	55
72	24	2347	4.5	73–	S	8:34.6	–126	42
73	24	X22292	7.0	73–	N	9:27.0	–90	28
74	25	2490 D	5.2	63–	N	7:56.9	–89	51
75	25	X23327 E	6.7	63–	N	8:03.1	–78	45
76	25	2510	6.2	62–	N	10:57.3	–120	44
77	25	2513 K	4.2	61–	N	11:17.8	–130	38
78	27	2802 V	6.4	42–	S	8:33.0	–93	32
79	31	3290	7.3	9–	N	10:28.5	–90	22
80	Apr. 6	375 K	6.8	5+	N	1:40.8	–107	27
81	7	486 H	5.3	10+	N	0:00.2	–80	41
82	7	X4387 M	7.4	10+	N	0:47.0	–66	55
83	8	X5675	7.0	18+	N	4:22.9	–130	44
84	8	656 V	4.2	18+	S	4:59.2	–123	55
85	8	660 V	4.3	19+	S	5:22.6	–128	55
86	10	946 Q	3.5	36+	N	4:28.9	–130	42
87	11	1077 B	4.0	44+	N	1:16.8	–85	55
88	11	1077 B	4.0	44+	N	1:19.8	–106	24
89	12	1207 X	5.6	55+	N	1:45.3	–84	55
90	13	1344	6.5	67+	N	2:44.5	–121	38
91	13	1364	6.5	70+	N	8:37.3	–123	55
92	14	1454 K	7.0	77+	N	2:30.6	–119	28
93	14	1457	6.8	78+	N	3:28.5	–130	39
94	15	1566 K	6.3	86+	N	1:01.0	–94	39
95	15	1587 Q	5.9	88+	N	7:18.5	–99	55
96	22	2562 K	7.0	78–	S	5:34.7	–81	43
97	22	2584 V	6.5	78–	S	8:13.4	–130	32
98	23	2739	6.6	68–	N	7:41.5	–95	41
99	27	3259	7.4	29–	N	9:42.9	–107	29
100	27	X30505	7.5	28–	N	11:08.8	–123	45
101	30	51 K	6.8	7–	N	10:51.7	–102	29
102	May 5	599	4.4	3+	S	1:55.5	–110	30
103	6	X6335	7.5	7+	N	0:42.1	–86	31
104	6	761 M	6.7	8+	N	4:22.7	–130	48
105	7	X7846	7.2	13+	N	1:31.0	–82	55
106	7	911 K	6.4	14+	N	4:26.9	–128	54
107	9	1175 V	4.9	30+	N	1:35.8	–107	22
108	11	1410 A	5.1	51+	N	0:42.8	–85	37
109	12	1528 D	6.7	63+	N	1:29.8	–82	53
110	13	1655	6.8	75+	N	3:42.7	–126	41

TABLE OF GRAZING LUNAR OCCULTATION PREDICTIONS (continued)

No.	Date	USNO d	m	%sl	L	W.U.T.	Lo.	La.
111	13	1670	4.8	77+	N	7:14.3	−130	37
112	16	2039	5.5	97+	N	4:33.6	−97	55
113	19	2490 D	5.2	96−	S	2:42.4	−83	35
114	21	2829	6.7	83−	S	5:38.7	−106	23
115	29	244	6.7	12−	N	9:14.9	−101	54
116	Jun. 7	1397O	5.5	30+	S	6:12.8	−128	38
117	9	1605	6.0	49+	N	0:53.3	−86	31
118	11	1852 V	6.0	72+	N	2:44.4	−101	47
119	11	1858	6.3	73+	N	4:35.2	−93	55
120	12	1993 X	6.6	83+	S	5:54.8	−89	25
121	17	2797 C	2.9	97−	S	12:13.3	−114	20
122	18	2902 V	5.9	94−	S	4:23.8	−103	35
123	21	3287 Z	5.8	71−	N	8:36.8	−87	20
124	22	3397	7.0	62−	N	7:05.2	−110	20
125	24	89 K	6.5	42−	N	10:15.9	−130	33
126	28	X5079	7.2	9−	N	9:01.0	−92	36
127	29	734	6.5	4−	N	10:47.9	−91	20
128	29	X6335	7.5	4−	N	12:05.1	−116	20
129	Jul. 3	1235	7.3	3+	N	1:46.2	−96	32
130	6	1582	6.4	25+	N	1:44.7	−92	38
131	6	1587 Q	5.9	26+	N	3:20.0	−121	32
132	7	1713 V	5.6	37+	N	4:37.7	−130	41
133	19	3371	6.4	83−	N	12:06.7	−130	49
134	21	51 K	6.8	67−	N	10:40.1	−130	51
135	22	177	6.9	58−	N	11:19.4	−130	36
136	24	411O	7.0	39−	N	10:41.8	−119	20
137	25	X4692 J	7.3	29−	N	11:08.5	−103	20
138	25	X4722	7.2	29−	N	11:52.3	−130	52
139	26	660 V	4.3	21−	N	7:48.3	−90	22
140	26	X5829	7.5	21−	N	10:11.1	−123	27
141	27	784 C	6.3	14−	S	5:36.5	−62	53
142	Aug. 2	1543	6.6	6+	S	0:07.6	−78	25
143	3	1670	4.8	14+	N	1:45.1	−99	38
144	5	1918	6.8	34+	S	3:11.8	−124	27
145	6	2045 M	6.4	45+	S	2:16.6	−110	29
146	6	2051	5.9	45+	S	2:55.4	−119	32
147	8	X22292	7.0	69+	S	5:35.3	−114	20
148	9	2491	6.6	78+	S	4:33.6	−88	20
149	9	2490 D	5.2	78+	S	3:11.0	−123	32
150	9	X23327 E	6.7	78+	S	3:11.8	−123	32
151	9	2510	6.2	79+	S	7:11.6	−130	38
152	9	2513 K	4.2	79+	S	7:55.0	−130	36
153	10	2779	3.8	92+	S	23:37.7	−68	45
154	11	2797 C	2.9	92+	N	2:08.4	−106	55
155	15	3320 T	5.0	98−	S	6:40.6	−130	22
156	16	3453 V	5.0	94−	S	10:45.9	−122	33
157	19	244	6.7	74−	N	8:17.6	−130	32
158	21	485 M	7.0	55−	N	11:08.0	−130	51
159	21	487 M	5.2	55−	N	12:12.3	−130	44
160	22	599	4.4	46−	N	6:37.2	−106	26
161	22	601 X	5.9	46−	N	7:01.3	−113	33
162	22	621 V	6.1	45−	N	10:32.1	−130	30
163	22	625	7.0	45−	N	11:34.5	−130	35
164	23	761 M	6.7	36−	N	9:44.5	−130	22
165	24	X7846	7.2	27−	N	7:12.2	−89	33
166	24	911 K	6.4	26−	N	10:06.5	−130	33
167	25	X10116	7.4	17−	N	9:22.3	−99	20
168	25	1077 B	4.0	17−	N	12:39.4	−130	31
169	26	X12002 A	7.5	9−	S	12:18.7	−130	38
170	31	X18937 V	7.4	11+	N	23:59.7	−82	21
171	Sep. 1	1858	6.3	11+	S	0:08.0	−84	27
172	2	2011	6.3	22+	S	3:27.5	−130	24
173	4	2290 L	2.3	42+	N	1:18.5	−130	32
174	6	2736	6.3	73+	S	23:37.6	−75	46
175	6	2739	6.6	73+	S	23:55.9	−85	24
176	8	2902 V	5.9	82+	S	2:58.5	−124	53
177	16	297 K	6.5	88−	S	2:08.7	−93	41
178	18	586	6.8	71−	N	11:34.4	−119	40
179	19	709 L	4.3	63−	N	7:43.7	−76	20
180	19	X6037 V	7.0	63−	N	7:43.7	−76	20
181	19	X6070 X	6.9	62−	N	8:18.3	−92	20
182	20	828	6.3	53−	N	4:58.0	−93	39
183	20	8430	7.0	53−	N	7:59.1	−79	50
184	20	861	6.3	52−	N	9:53.9	−130	29
185	Sep. 22	1158 K	5.0	30−	S	14:22.4	−130	55
186	25	X15311 X	7.3	6−	S	8:16.7	−62	49
187	Oct. 1	2226	7.0	17+	S	1:15.2	−109	21
188	6	2986	6.4	69+	S	3:09.1	−87	20
189	6	3008	6.8	71+	S	7:44.4	−130	35
190	10	3482 V	5.7	96+	S	3:11.8	−113	20
191	10	3501	5.0	97+	S	11:25.8	−130	31
192	15	534 V	6.1	90−	S	12:38.5	−130	30
193	16	634	5.3	86−	N	3:08.0	−110	41
194	16	656 V	4.2	85−	N	5:32.1	−113	20
195	16	657	5.3	85−	N	5:27.8	−129	20
196	16	665 U	5.7	85−	N	6:46.6	−130	38
197	17	784 C	6.3	78−	N	4:37.0	−119	41
198	17	817 T	4.9	76−	S	10:54.1	−130	46
199	18	939 X	6.9	69−	N	5:38.9	−111	22
200	18	X8620	7.0	69−	N	6:50.3	−128	23
201	20	1198 K	6.0	49−	S	5:47.0	−90	32
202	20	1210 V	6.0	48−	S	7:01.1	−105	24
203	21	1320	6.7	38−	S	5:00.5	−70	53
204	21	1341 Y	4.3	37−	S	9:17.3	−130	45
205	23	1582	6.4	16−	S	12:43.2	−130	39
206	28	2290 L	2.3	5+	S	17:50.5	−130	39
207	31	X25158	7.3	23+	S	2:52.4	−120	20
208	Nov. 3	3070	6.6	52+	S	0:39.3	−78	20
209	3	3187	6.0	62+	S	22:52.8	−87	39
210	4	3199	6.5	63+	S	1:10.4	−129	54
211	5	3326O	6.4	73+	S	4:19.7	−130	32
212	6	3453 V	5.0	81+	S	5:36.9	−130	39
213	12	634	5.3	98−	S	10:32.5	−130	28
214	17	1309 V	5.6	64−	S	10:47.0	−62	55
215	17	1320	6.7	62−	S	12:26.5	−130	43
216	18	1397O	5.5	54−	S	6:11.7	−101	47
217	18	1410 A	5.1	54−	N	7:06.0	−110	23
218	19	1543	6.6	41−	S	12:08.8	−130	47
219	19	1551	6.7	40−	S	14:42.0	−121	55
220	20	1629	6.6	31−	S	7:21.4	−83	31
221	27	2567	7.2	4+	S	1:05.8	−115	25
222	28	2746	5.7	10+	S	1:23.5	−130	45
223	29	3008	6.8	25+	S	21:54.2	−79	43
224	29	3015 I	5.2	25+	S	22:49.4	−91	39
225	30	3027	6.9	26+	S	1:47.4	−118	20
226	Dec. 2	3287Z	5.8	47+	S	3:35.4	−121	20
227	3	3397	7.0	56+	S	2:44.7	−102	20
228	4	3524O	6.9	66+	S	5:12.9	−130	24
229	5	89 K	6.5	75+	N	6:15.0	−91	45
230	6	197 K	7.0	82+	S	1:43.5	−91	20
231	6	297 K	6.5	88+	S	21:23.8	−73	45
232	8	432	5.8	94+	S	0:01.4	−112	43
233	8	465	4.3	95+	N	10:06.9	−120	55
234	10	X6484 M	8.0	100E	S	14:09.2	−130	51
235	13	1158 K	5.0	92−	N	10:35.5	−100	55
236	14	1246	6.4	88−	S	2:18.5	−84	25
237	14	1271 V	5.9	86−	S	7:47.6	−130	40
238	16	1482 K	6.2	69−	S	5:44.4	−89	34
239	16	1489 V	6.6	69−	S	6:15.3	−112	21
240	16	1495	5.8	68−	S	9:23.4	−111	55
241	17	1590 K	6.7	59−	S	5:14.1	−81	42
242	17	1604 K	6.1	58−	S	10:00.4	−67	55
243	17	1620	6.8	56−	S	12:36.6	−117	55
244	18	1713 V	5.6	47−	S	7:00.9	−91	48
245	19	1852 V	6.0	34−	S	11:58.3	−121	55
246	19	1858	6.3	33−	S	13:50.9	−109	55
247	20	1970 L	6.2	24−	S	9:42.8	−90	49
248	21	2115	7.2	14−	S	11:50.7	−100	48
249	21	X20727 X	7.5	14−	S	13:16.8	−129	39
250	22	2290 L	2.3	6−	S	15:20.1	−130	35
251	26	X28160	7.3	6+	S	23:19.7	−87	24
252	28	3093	4.5	12+	N	0:31.0	−91	20
253	29	X30908	7.2	27+	S	20:59.8	−64	44
254	30	3455 V	6.3	36+	S	20:28.3	−61	49
255	31	3482 V	5.7	38+	S	1:25.9	−130	48

GRAZING OCCULTATION MAPS

JANUARY 1–JANUARY 31

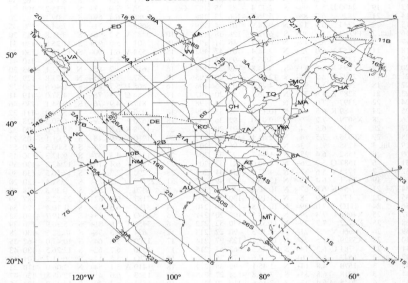

FEBRUARY 1–MARCH 14

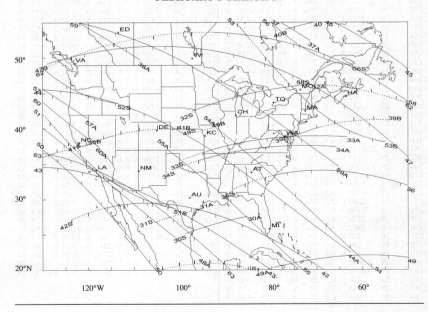

GRAZING OCCULTATION MAPS (continued)

MARCH 15–APRIL 15

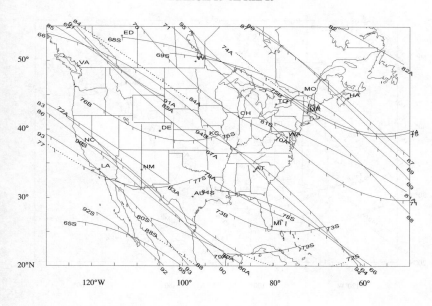

APRIL 16–JUNE 30

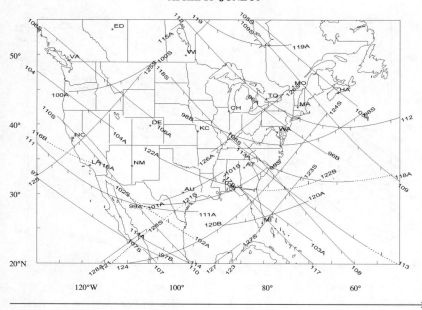

GRAZING OCCULTATION MAPS (continued)

JULY 1–AUGUST 21

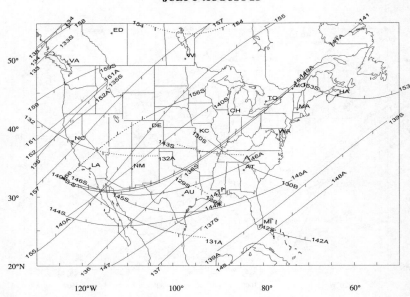

AUGUST 22–OCTOBER 15

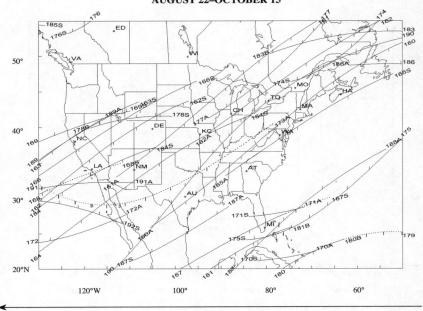

GRAZING OCCULTATION MAPS (continued)

OCTOBER 16–NOVEMBER 30

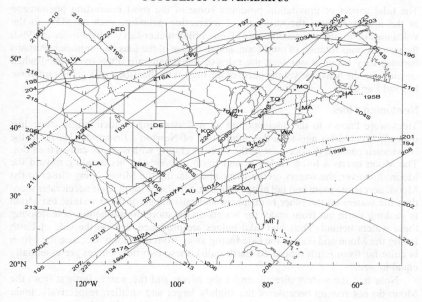

DECEMBER 1–DECEMBER 31

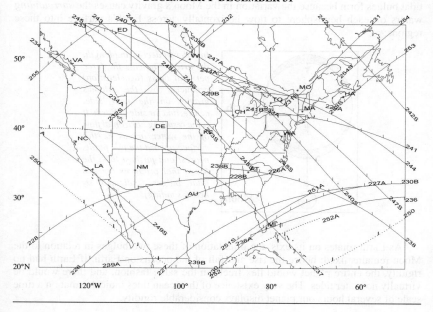

TIDES AND THE EARTH–MOON SYSTEM
By Roy Bishop

The tidal aspect of gravitation produces some of the most interesting phenomena in the universe, from the structure of interacting galaxies, such as M51, to the volcanoes of Io, the fragmentation of Comet Shoemaker-Levy 9 by Jupiter in 1992, the synchronous rotation of our Moon, and the pulse of the seas on our planet. Perhaps because they occur at our feet, the tides of the oceans are often overlooked when considering the heavens; yet the pulse of the tides is the heartbeat of a greater universe beyond Earth.

Newtonian Tides

Tides were known to the ancients, but an understanding of their origin came just over three centuries ago with the publication of Newton's *Principia* (1687). In the Newtonian context, the decrease of the force of gravity with distance causes the tides. The Moon exerts a force on Earth, and Earth responds by accelerating toward the Moon; however, the waters on the hemisphere facing the Moon, being closer to the Moon, accelerate more and fall ahead of Earth. Similarly, Earth itself accelerates more than the waters on the other hemisphere and falls ahead of these waters; the Moon is yanking Earth out from under the waters on the more distant hemisphere, leaving these waters behind. Thus two tidal bulges are produced, one on the side of Earth facing the Moon and one on the side facing away from the Moon. Because the Moon is quite far from Earth (about 60 Earth radii), these two tidal bulges are essentially equal in size.

Note that the waters directly under the Moon and the waters farthest from the Moon do not rise up because of the slightly larger and smaller, respectively, lunar gravity at these two locations; all that results from the Moon's action on the waters at these two points is a slight decrease in the pressure on the floor of the sea. The two tidal bulges form because the variation in the Moon's gravity causes the *surrounding* waters on each hemisphere to flow horizontally across Earth's surface into these regions:

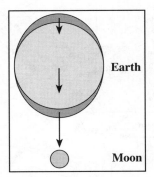

In order of decreasing length, the arrows indicate the force per unit mass (acceleration) produced by the Moon's gravity on the near side, centre, and far side of Earth. It is the resulting horizontal flow of the water across Earth's surface toward the two points nearest and farthest from the Moon that produces the two tidal bulges (indicated by heavy shading).

As Earth rotates on its axis, the orientation of these two bulges in relation to the Moon remains fixed; hence the rise and fall of the oceans on Earth. If Earth had no rigidity, the entire planet would flex freely in the same fashion, and there would be virtually no water tides. The very existence of the ocean tides indicates that on a time scale of several hours our planet displays considerable rigidity.

Because of the Moon's orbital motion, it transits on average 50.47 min later each day. Thus on successive days, high tides recur about 50 min later; or for the many regions experiencing two high tides daily, these tides recur at intervals of 12 h 25 min.

The Sun exerts a gravitational force 180 times stronger than that exerted by the Moon on Earth; however, because the Moon is so much closer, the *variation* in the Moon's force across Earth's diameter is about 2.2 times larger than the variation in the Sun's force. As described above, it is this variation that produces tides; thus the pair of bulges raised by the Moon is considerably larger than the pair raised by the Sun. As the Moon goes through its monthly cycle of phases, the two pairs of tidal bulges get in and out of step, combining in step to produce *spring tides* (no connection with the season) when the Moon is new or full (syzygy) and out of step to produce *neap tides* when the Moon is at first or last quarter (quadrature).

Another factor having a substantial influence on tidal ranges is the elliptical shape of the Moon's orbit. The Moon is only 9 percent to 12 percent closer at perigee than at apogee; however, because the *variation* in its gravitational force varies inversely as the cube of its distance (the force itself varies inversely as the square of the distance), the Moon's tidal influence is 31 percent to 49 percent greater at perigee than at apogee. Because the Sun tidally influences the shape of the Moon's orbit, exceptionally close perigees coincide with full or new Moon, and the resulting extreme tides are known as *perigean spring tides*. If the lunar orbit were fixed in orientation, such tides would recur at half-year intervals, alternately with new and full Moon; however, the major axis of the lunar orbit rotates prograde with a period of 8.85 years, making the average interval between perigean spring tides about 23 days longer than half a year (205.9 days).

The extreme range of a spring tide, or of a perigean spring tide, occurs a day or two after the astronomical influences peak. The variation in the range of the tides at a given locality is determined both by the energy being put into the tides and by the energy being lost through friction with the seabed. As long as the input is greater than the loss, the tide range will increase even though the input may have peaked and already be decreasing. Hence the tide range is greatest not when the astronomical factors are greatest, but a day or two later when the decreasing input equals the increasing loss. At that point the energy in the tides is at a maximum.

Influences on the Tides

Five, basic, astronomical periods impact the tides. In increasing length these are: Earth's mean rotation day, the draconic, sidereal, and anomalistic months, and the sidereal year (see p. 33). The resulting periods that show up in the tides include (in ascending order):

(1) semidiurnal, 12 h 00 min (two solar-induced tidal bulges, as described above);

(2) semidiurnal, 12 h 25 min (two lunar-induced tidal bulges, as described above);

(3) diurnal, 24 h 00 min (the usual nonzero declination of the Sun shifts the pair of solar tidal bulges out of Earth's equatorial plane, resulting in a tidal component with a one-day period);

(4) diurnal, 24 h 50 min (the usual nonzero declination of the Moon shifts the pair of lunar tidal bulges out of Earth's equatorial plane, resulting in a tidal component with a one-day period; this is the dominant tide in some areas, such as parts of the southern coast of Canada's Gulf of St. Lawrence);

(5) semimonthly, 13.66 days (variation in the Moon's declination);

(6) semimonthly, 14.77 days (spring–neap cycle, described above);

(7) monthly, 27.55 days (perigee–apogee cycle, described above);

(8) semiannual, 182.63 days (variation in the Sun's declination);

(9) semiannual, 205.9 days (perigean spring cycle, described above);

(10) annual, 365.26 days (perihelion–aphelion cycle);

(11) 8.85 years (prograde precession of the lunar perigee, described above); and

(12) 18.60 years (retrograde precession of the nodes of the lunar orbit).

In addition to astronomical factors, the tides on Earth are strongly influenced by the sizes, boundaries, and depths of ocean basins and inlets and by Earth's rotation, winds, and barometric pressure fluctuations. Using Newton's gravitation and laws of motion, the French physicist Pierre-Simon Laplace (1749–1827) developed the dynamical theory of the tides on the rotating Earth (*Mécanique Céleste*, 1799), but because of the complexity of the tides the full application of his theory was not possible until the advent of the digital computer in the last third of the 20th century.

Tides typically have ranges (vertical high to low) of a metre or two, but there are regions in the oceans where the various influences conspire to produce virtually no tides at all (called amphidromic points) and others where the tides are greatly amplified. Among the latter regions are the Sea of Okhotsk, the Gulf of Alaska, the northwest coast of Australia, the English Channel, and in Canada, Ungava Bay in northern Québec, and the Bay of Fundy between New Brunswick and Nova Scotia. The tidal ranges in these regions are of the order of 10 m.

Fundy Tides

Only two localities on Earth sometimes have a vertical tide range exceeding 16 m (52 ft.), and both are in Canada: Minas Basin, the eastern extremity of the Bay of Fundy in Nova Scotia, and Leaf Basin, a remote inlet on the southwestern side of Ungava Bay in northern Québec. The current best data give Minas Basin a slight edge; however, several years of tide gauge data continuing through the year 2015 are needed to determine which site, if either (to the precision that measurements can be made), has the greater tide range. (In 2015, the 18.60-year lunar cycle will next have its peak effect on the tides; see below.)

The primary cause of the immense tides of Fundy is a resonance of the Bay of Fundy/Gulf of Maine system. The system is effectively bounded at its outer end by the edge of the continental shelf with its approximately 40:1 increase in depth. The system has a natural period of approximately 13 hours, a Q-value[1] of about 5, and is driven near resonance, not directly by the Moon, but by the dominant semidiurnal tides of the Atlantic Ocean. Like a father pushing his daughter on a swing, the gentle Atlantic tidal pulse pushes the waters of the Bay of Fundy/Gulf of Maine basin at nearly the optimum frequency to cause a large oscillation. The seventh Astronomer Royal, G.B. Airy (1801–1892), first developed the theory of the behaviour of tides in restricted arms of the ocean such as the Fundy system.

Fundy tides are unique in that they respond more to the perigee–apogee influence than they do to the spring–neap influence. That is because the lunar tidal period (12.42 hours) is closer to the system's resonant period than is the solar tidal period (12.00 hours). Although the variation in the Moon's distance is not obvious when viewing the Moon directly, near the head of the Bay of Fundy the 3-m to 6-m *increase* in the vertical tidal range makes it obvious when the Moon is near perigee, clear skies or cloudy!

The most dramatic view of the vertical range of Fundy tides is at the Minas Basin Pulp & Power Company wharf in the town of Hantsport, Nova Scotia. Remarkably,

---

[1] The Q-value, or quality-value, of an oscillator indicates its efficiency. A large Q means low energy loss per cycle and a well-defined resonant frequency. A Q of 5 is relatively small, indicative of considerable damping in the Fundy system, yet it is large enough to make these tides among the highest on Earth.

this site is practically unknown; it is not advertised, and no special provisions have been made to accommodate spectators.

Perhaps the most awesome display of the tides on our planet occurs at Cape Split, Nova Scotia, on the southern side of the entrance to Minas Basin. (Cape Split may be reached by a pleasant two-hour walk along a popular hiking trail from the village of Scots Bay.) Here, at the time of the midpoint of an incoming tide, for a considerable distance the forest on the towering cliffs is filled with a hollow roar produced by the turbulence of the waters surging over the submarine ridges below. The currents exceed 8 knots (4 m/s), and the flow in the deep, 5-km-wide channel on the north side of Cape Split equals the combined flow of all the streams and rivers of Earth ($\approx$4 km^3/h). Three hours later the spectacle pauses and then begins flowing in the opposite direction.

The highest of the high tides in the Bay of Fundy occur when a perigean spring high tide coincides with a low-barometric-pressure storm system sweeping northward across New Brunswick, accompanied by hurricane-force southerly winds over the Gulf of Maine and the Bay of Fundy. The close Moon, the in-phase solar tide, the reduced air pressure above the water, and the wind drag pushing more water into the Bay of Fundy (the last two effects are called a storm surge) all contribute to an especially high tide. An additional favourable influence is if all this occurs near an equinox, for then the axis of the tidal bulges of the spring tide is at a right angle to Earth's rotation axis, optimizing the tidal range (if the axes were parallel there would be no tidal cycle). This right-angle-axes enhancement of the tides is strengthened in those years when the declination range of the Moon ($\pm$18° to $\pm$29°) is near a minimum, a situation that recurs with the 18.60-year period of the retrograde motion of the nodes of its orbit. (The declination range was at its $\pm$18° minimum in 1959, 1978, and 1997 and will be again in 2015. See p. 99 for the shift in the longitude of the ascending node of the Moon's orbit during 2011.) Furthermore, since perihelion occurs in January, the highest tides of all tend to occur just prior to the March equinox or after the September equinox. The infamous Bay of Fundy "Saxby gale" of 1869 Oct. 5 was a time when all seven of these factors approximately coincided (perigee, spring tide, low pressure, south wind, equinox, minimum declination range, and perihelion enhancement). Since weather is unpredictable, so, too, is the next major tidal flood in the Bay of Fundy.

Paradoxically, the large tides of Fundy protect its shores from flooding associated with most storm surges, since the normal variation in its high tide levels is already several metres. Only those rare storm surges that happen to coincide with a perigean spring high tide will be a problem. In contrast, shorelines with small tides are much more susceptible to storm surges.

Sea level is slowly increasing in the Bay of Fundy region. That is bringing the resonant period of the Fundy/Gulf of Maine system closer to the lunar tidal period which, in turn, is causing Fundy tides to gradually become even larger (by a few centimetres per decade).

Tidal Friction

Tidal friction, which occurs primarily in shallow seas around the margins of the oceans, transforms Earth's rotational kinetic energy into heat at a rate of about 3.5 TW, comparable to humankind's total rate of energy use. Approximately 1 percent of this energy transformation occurs in the Bay of Fundy, and, since 1984, a tiny portion of this (20 MW peak) is being turned into commercial electric power at the Annapolis Basin tidal power plant in Nova Scotia. The only other large-scale tidal power installation is in France on the Rance estuary (240 MW peak).

Both the Nova Scotia tidal power plant and the one in France use turbines located in dams. At a few sites, including the Bay of Fundy, studies presently are underway for using isolated turbines located in tidal currents—effectively underwater windmills. The problem with this approach is that the power available in currents of 8 knots or

less is dilute. To generate significant electrical power (100 MW or more), large turbine cross-sections are required, with attendant high capital and maintenance costs.

Tidal friction also transfers angular momentum from Earth to the Moon, lengthening the day and increasing the size of the orbit of the Moon. The day is lengthening by about 1 s every 40 000 years—imperceptible on a human time scale but of profound significance to Earth's rotation over a few billion years. (For example, 900 million years ago, when Earth was already 80 percent of its present age, there were about 480 18-hour days in a year.) The Moon is receding about 3.8 cm per year, with the result that about one billion years from now total solar eclipses will cease. Presently we are well into the transitional phase: Annular eclipses already outnumber total solar eclipses.

General Relativity and Tides

Einstein's theory of gravitation, general relativity, superseded Newton's theory nearly a century ago, yet descriptions of the tides almost invariably ignore Einstein (as has this article to this point). The reasons for using the older, wrong theory are: (1) Newton's theory describes the gentle tides on Earth to high accuracy; (2) the mathematics involved is much simpler than that of general relativity; (3) the Newtonian description of the tides is compatible with cultivated common sense. Because of this last reason, Newton's concepts regarding motion and gravitation form the essential foundation for anyone attempting to understand the tides. One must climb up on Newton's towering shoulders before it is possible to focus clearly on Einstein.

As mentioned in the section ORBITAL MOTION (see p. 31), Newton's Euclidean universe with its force of gravity never did exist. Although Newton's ideas are more than adequate for describing the tides on Earth, for some purposes, such as the Global Positioning System (GPS), Newton's concepts of space, time, and gravitation are inadequate. We inhabit an Einsteinian universe, a universe in which gravitation is a manifestation of the structure of spacetime, the four-dimensional stage of our existence in which space and time are interwoven. The geometry of spacetime is curved by the mass–energy of matter, and the curvature tells matter how to move.

The Moon's mass alters the structure of spacetime at its location, and this distortion propagates outward, becoming more dilute with the volume encompassed according to the inverse cube of the distance. At Earth, the distortion results in the waters of the oceans following slightly different paths through spacetime than does the rigid planet beneath, producing the characteristic egglike shape of the tidal effect. The tidal heartbeat is that of the very fabric of spacetime. The tides at our feet carry a profound message.

References

For more information, see the superb introduction *The Tides* by E.P. Clancy, Anchor Books, Doubleday and Co., 1969 (now, unfortunately, out of print). For a detailed account of the evolution of our understanding of the tides see *Tides, A Scientific History*, by D.E. Cartwright, Cambridge University Press, 1999. (Note, however, that neither Clancy nor Cartwright mentions general relativity.) For a popular account of general relativity, see *A Journey into Gravity and Spacetime*, by J.A. Wheeler, Scientific American Library, 1990. An article dealing specifically with the tides of Fundy and tidal power installations has been written by Christopher Garrett (*Endeavour, 8* (1984), No. 2, pp. 58–64). The major astronomical factors influencing the tides (the phases, perigees, and apogees of the Moon) are tabulated in THE SKY MONTH BY MONTH section (p. 103) of this Handbook. These may be perused to determine days favourable for large tides. For information on tides in Canadian waters see www.lau.chs-shc.gc.ca, a Web site of the Canadian Hydrographic Service.

THE SUN

EPHEMERIS FOR THE SUN

Sundial Correction

The **Greenwich Transit** time in the table opposite may be used to calculate the sundial correction at the observer's position. For example, to find the correction at Halifax on 2011 Aug. 3, determine the following: At Greenwich the Sun transits at 12:06:22 on Aug. 1 and at 12:06:02 on Aug. 5. Thus, to the nearest min, on Aug. 3 at both Greenwich and Halifax the Sun will transit at 12:06 local mean solar time (LMT), or 12:20 Atlantic Standard Time (AST) since Halifax has a longitude correction of +14 min (see the 3rd paragraph on p. 208). Thus a 6-min correction must be added to the reading of a simple sundial to obtain LMT, an additional 14 min must be added to obtain AST, and a further 1 hour for Atlantic Daylight Time (ADT).

A figure accurate to a second or two can be obtained by interpolating for longitude. The interpolated transit time at Greenwich for Aug. 3 is 12:06:12, the daily change in time being –5.0 s. Adjusting this for the longitude of Halifax:

12 h 6 min 12 s – (5.0 s × 4 h 14 min ÷ 24 h) = 12 h 6 min 11 s.

Thus the sundial correction is 6 min 11 s. To find the standard time of the Sun's transit to the nearest second or two, the observer's longitude must be known to 10″ or better. For example, suppose an observer in Halifax is at longitude 63°25′30″W, or 4 h 13 min 42 s W of Greenwich. The time of transit will be 12:06:11 + 13 min 42 s = 12:19:53 AST or 13:19:53 ADT.

Orientation of the Sun

The table on the next page gives three angles that specify the orientation of the Sun.

P is the position angle of the axis of rotation, measured eastward in the observer's sky from the north point on the disk. Note that P varies between +26° (solar north pole tilted eastward) and –26° (tilted westward) during the year. This tilt is associated mainly with the inclination of the ecliptic in the observer's sky, with a smaller contribution from the Sun's 7.2° inclination to the ecliptic (the longitude of the ascending node of the solar equator on the ecliptic is 76°).

B_0 is the heliographic latitude of the centre of the disk, and is the result of the Sun's 7.2° inclination to the ecliptic. Note that positive values of B_0 correspond to the solar equator passing south of the centre of the disk, with the solar north pole being tipped toward the observer.

L_0 is the heliographic longitude of the centre of the disk measured from Carrington's solar prime meridian in the direction of rotation. L_0 decreases about 13° per day. The dates during the year when $L_0 = 0°$ are given in the table below. The rotation period of the Sun depends upon heliographic latitude. The synodic and sidereal periods of rotation at the solar equator are 27.2753 days and 25.38 days, respectively.

Commencement (UT) of Numbered Synodic Solar Rotations

No.*	Commences	No	Commences	No	Commences	No	Commences
2105	'10 Dec. 24.05	2109	Apr. 12.35	2113	Jul. 30.21	2117	Nov. 16.29
2106	'11 Jan. 20.39	2110	May 9.60	2114	Aug. 26.44	2118	Dec. 13.61
2107	Feb. 16.73	2111	Jun. 5.81	2115	Sep. 22.71	2119	'12 Jan. 9.94
2108	Mar. 16.06	2112	Jul. 3.01	2116	Oct. 19.99	2120	Feb. 6.28

*Based on R.C. Carrington's Greenwich photoheliocentric series in which rotation No. 1 commenced 1853 Nov. 9.

EPHEMERIS FOR THE SUN, 2011

Date 0h UT	Apparent RA (2011) h m	Greenwich Dec ° '	Transit UT	Orientation P	B0	L0	Date 0h UT	Apparent RA (2011) h m	Greenwich Dec ° '	Transit UT	Orientation P	B0	L0
Jan. 1	18 44.4	−23 03	12:03:25	+2.2	−3.0	255.3	**Sep.** 2	10 43.2	+8 07	11:59:47	+21.2	+7.2	273.4
5	19 02.0	−22 40	12:05:16	+0.3	−3.4	202.6	6	10 57.6	+6 39	11:58:28	+22.2	+7.2	220.6
9	19 19.5	−22 11	12:07:00	−1.6	−3.9	149.9	10	11 12.0	+5 09	11:57:05	+23.0	+7.2	167.7
13	19 36.9	−21 34	12:08:35	−3.6	−4.3	97.3	14	11 26.4	+3 38	11:55:40	+23.8	+7.2	114.9
17	19 54.1	−20 51	12:10:00	−5.4	−4.7	44.6	18	11 40.7	+2 05	11:54:14	+24.5	+7.2	62.1
21	20 11.1	−20 02	12:11:13	−7.3	−5.1	351.9	22	11 55.0	+0 32	11:52:49	+25.0	+7.1	9.3
25	20 28.0	−19 06	12:12:14	−9.1	−5.4	299.2	26	12 09.4	−1 01	11:51:26	+25.5	+7.0	316.5
29	20 44.6	−18 05	12:13:03	−10.8	−5.8	246.6	30	12 23.8	−2 35	11:50:05	+25.9	+6.8	263.7
Feb. 2	21 01.0	−16 58	12:13:39	−12.4	−6.1	193.9	**Oct.** 4	12 38.3	−4 08	11:48:49	+26.1	+6.6	211.0
6	21 17.2	−15 47	12:14:02	−14.0	−6.3	141.2	8	12 52.9	−5 40	11:47:38	+26.2	+6.4	158.2
10	21 33.1	−14 32	12:14:13	−15.5	−6.6	88.6	12	13 07.6	−7 11	11:46:34	+26.3	+6.1	105.4
14	21 48.9	−13 13	12:14:10	−16.9	−6.8	35.9	16	13 22.4	−8 40	11:45:37	+26.2	+5.8	52.6
18	22 04.4	−11 50	12:13:56	−18.3	−6.9	343.2	20	13 37.4	−10 08	11:44:50	+26.0	+5.5	359.9
22	22 19.8	−10 24	12:13:30	−19.5	−7.1	290.6	24	13 52.5	−11 33	11:44:14	+25.6	+5.2	307.1
26	22 35.0	−8 56	12:12:55	−20.6	−7.2	237.9	28	14 07.8	−12 55	11:43:49	+25.2	+4.8	254.4
Mar. 2	22 50.1	−7 25	12:12:11	−21.7	−7.2	185.2	**Nov.** 1	14 23.4	−14 15	11:43:36	+24.6	+4.4	201.6
6	23 05.0	−5 53	12:11:20	−22.6	−7.2	132.5	5	14 39.1	−15 30	11:43:35	+23.8	+4.0	148.9
10	23 19.8	−4 20	12:10:21	−23.5	−7.2	79.8	9	14 55.0	−16 41	11:43:47	+23.0	+3.6	96.1
14	23 34.5	−2 45	12:09:18	−24.2	−7.2	27.1	13	15 11.2	−17 48	11:44:13	+22.0	+3.1	43.4
18	23 49.2	−1 11	12:08:09	−24.8	−7.1	334.4	17	15 27.6	−18 50	11:44:53	+21.0	+2.7	350.7
22	0 03.7	+0 24	12:06:58	−25.3	−7.0	281.6	21	15 44.3	−19 47	11:45:46	+19.7	+2.2	297.9
26	0 18.3	+1 59	12:05:46	−25.7	−6.8	228.9	25	16 01.1	−20 38	11:46:52	+18.4	+1.7	245.2
30	0 32.9	+3 33	12:04:34	−26.0	−6.7	176.1	29	16 18.2	−21 23	11:48:11	+17.0	+1.2	192.5
Apr. 3	0 47.4	+5 06	12:03:23	−26.2	−6.5	123.4	**Dec.** 3	16 35.4	−22 01	11:49:40	+15.5	+0.7	139.8
7	1 02.1	+6 37	12:02:14	−26.3	−6.2	70.6	7	16 52.8	−22 32	11:51:18	+13.8	+0.2	87.1
11	1 16.7	+8 06	12:01:09	−26.2	−6.0	17.8	11	17 10.3	−22 57	11:53:05	+12.2	−0.3	34.4
15	1 31.5	+9 34	12:00:08	−26.1	−5.6	325.0	15	17 28.0	−23 14	11:54:57	+10.4	−0.8	341.7
19	1 46.3	+10 59	11:59:12	−25.8	−5.3	272.2	19	17 45.7	−23 24	11:56:54	+8.6	−1.4	289.0
23	2 01.3	+12 21	11:58:23	−25.4	−5.0	219.3	23	18 03.4	−23 26	11:58:54	+6.7	−1.9	236.3
27	2 16.3	+13 39	11:57:42	−24.8	−4.6	166.5	27	18 21.2	−23 21	12:00:53	+4.8	−2.4	183.6
May 1	2 31.5	+14 54	11:57:08	−24.2	−4.2	113.6	31	18 38.9	−23 08	12:02:50	+2.8	−2.8	130.9
5	2 46.9	+16 06	11:56:44	−23.4	−3.8	60.8							
9	3 02.4	+17 12	11:56:28	−22.6	−3.4	7.9							
13	3 18.0	+18 15	11:56:21	−21.6	−2.9	315.0							
17	3 33.8	+19 12	11:56:23	−20.5	−2.5	262.1							
21	3 49.7	+20 04	11:56:34	−19.3	−2.0	209.2							
25	4 05.8	+20 51	11:56:54	−18.0	−1.6	156.3							
29	4 22.0	+21 32	11:57:22	−16.7	−1.1	103.3							
Jun. 2	4 38.4	+22 07	11:57:57	−15.2	−0.6	50.4							
6	4 54.8	+22 35	11:58:38	−13.7	−0.1	357.5							
10	5 11.3	+22 58	11:59:24	−12.0	+0.4	304.5							
14	5 27.9	+23 14	12:00:13	−10.4	+0.8	251.6							
18	5 44.5	+23 23	12:01:04	−8.7	+1.3	198.6							
22	6 01.2	+23 26	12:01:56	−6.9	+1.8	145.7							
26	6 17.8	+23 22	12:02:47	−5.1	+2.3	92.7							
30	6 34.4	+23 12	12:03:37	−3.3	+2.7	39.8							
Jul. 4	6 50.9	+22 55	12:04:23	−1.5	+3.2	346.8							
8	7 07.4	+22 32	12:05:03	+0.3	+3.6	293.9							
12	7 23.7	+22 03	12:05:37	+2.1	+4.0	241.0							
16	7 40.0	+21 27	12:06:03	+3.9	+4.4	188.0							
20	7 56.0	+20 46	12:06:21	+5.6	+4.8	135.1							
24	8 12.0	+19 59	12:06:30	+7.4	+5.1	82.2							
28	8 27.8	+19 07	12:06:31	+9.0	+5.5	29.3							
Aug. 1	8 43.4	+18 09	12:06:22	+10.6	+5.8	336.4							
5	8 58.9	+17 07	12:06:03	+12.2	+6.0	283.5							
9	9 14.2	+16 01	12:05:33	+13.7	+6.3	230.6							
13	9 29.4	+14 50	12:04:55	+15.2	+6.5	177.7							
17	9 44.4	+13 36	12:04:08	+16.5	+6.7	124.8							
21	9 59.2	+12 18	12:03:13	+17.8	+6.9	72.0							
25	10 14.0	+10 57	12:02:10	+19.0	+7.0	19.1							
29	10 28.6	+9 33	12:01:01	+20.2	+7.1	326.2							

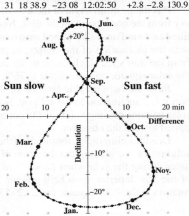

The bowling-pin-shaped analemma depicts the drift of apparent solar time or sundial time relative to LMT (horizontal axis) and the changing declination of the Sun (vertical axis) during 2011. For points to the left of the vertical axis ("Sun slow") the Sun transits after 12:00 LMT. To the right ("Sun fast"), the Sun transits before 12:00 LMT. For each month, a heavy dot marks day 1 with medium dots for days 5, 9, 13, 17, 21, 25, and 29. See pp. 44–45 for further details.

SOLAR OBSERVING
BY KIM HAY

The Sun, our closest star, is a wonderful solar-system object to observe, and any type of telescope can be used. However, the Sun should always be observed **SAFELY**. Never look directly at the Sun, and always use a **solar filter** (Thousand Oaks glass or Baader film). The solar eyepiece filters that screw into the base of an eyepiece should be **thrown out** and **never used**. The telescope's objective will concentrate sunlight on an eyepiece filter, making it very hot and possibly causing it to break. Then the light could flash into your eyes, possibly causing blindness. The only safe filter is the kind that fits at the front of the telescope. This type of filter allows only 1/100000th of the sunlight through the telescope, thus lowering the heating effect on the telescope and allowing you to view the Sun safely. Make sure that the material is specifically certified by the manufacturer as suitable for solar observing.

Generally, the preferred solar filters are the Thousand Oaks glass and Baader film. The Thousand Oaks glass gives the Sun a golden orange colour. The Baader film gives the Sun a white/blue tinge, which can provide good contrast if there is any plage on the Sun (see below). Two more suitable options are lightweight Mylar film and eyepiece projection. Projecting the image from the eyepiece onto white card-stock paper or a wall produces an image that can be shared with others.

The Sun is best observed away from the horizon because the air within the first 100 m is unstable. Try to observe when it is at least 25° above the horizon. Keep in mind that seeing during the daytime is usually very poor, so even a small telescope can be used with no worry of loss of detail.

The finder scope should be covered. You can simply use the cap, or you can create a form-fitting Baader filter for the finder. This will help you align the Sun into the eyepiece. Using the smallest shadow of the telescope on the ground will help you align your telescope on the Sun and is generally the preferred method.

Another tip is to use a dark blue or black hood to cover your head and the eyepiece. This helps to eliminate stray light, giving a better chance to see more details such as plage, pores, sunspots, and solar filaments.

Today's amateur has many opportunities to observe the Sun at different wavelengths. The most common is white light, which requires the use of solar filters as described above. Hydrogen-alpha (Hα) filters (656.3 nm, red in colour) and calcium K-line (CaK) filters (393.4 nm, violet in colour) can be purchased to fit on a telescope. Alternatively, you can purchase a telescope that works at one of these two wavelengths. An Hα filter will show solar prominences. Prominences, which are easiest to observe on the solar limb, are solar plasma ejections. Some fall back to the Sun like teardrops or loops. An intense solar flare can eject protons and electrons from the Sun. These may reach Earth, possibly exciting the upper atmosphere and creating aurorae.

A Herschel wedge, a type of prism used for white-light observing and photography, can be used but with caution. Only 5 percent of the light is reflected to the eyepiece. The remaining 95 percent is directed out the end of the diagonal and is very intense and can burn. Herschel wedges should only be used with refractors or a telescope with an aperture stop to avoid heat buildup, which can damage internal components. The cover should only be taken off after the telescope has been set up. You will also need a neutral-density filter (3.0 ND minimum to 4.0 ND). For increased comfort, a filter (either green or polarizing) may help, depending on the sky conditions. **A Herschel wedge should only be used by an experienced observer.**

Observing the morphology of sunspots and other solar phenomena is a great way to witness how dynamic the Sun is. An area can start with plage (white area) and faculae,

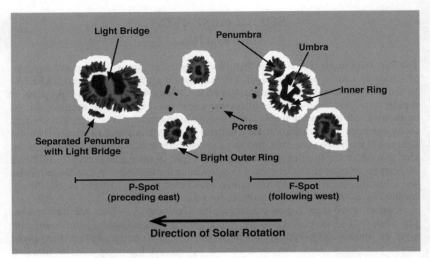

Nomenclature of phenomena related to sunspots. As the morphology of a sunspot changes and it grows into a larger group, it will eventually start to dissipate and have trailing sunspots. Light bridges are formed early and stay with a sunspot over its lifetime. The formation of a light bridge is a slow process and can take several days. The light-bridge material generally appears first on the outside of the umbra-penumbra boundary then extends across the umbra. When the light bridge is seen, it can signify the division or final dissolution of the spot. Light bridges have three general features: classic light bridges, islands, and streamers. Image used with permission from the Solar Astronomy Handbook *and adapted for publication.*

then turn into a pore, and then blossom into a small dark spot. As the sunspot changes, a penumbra, the grey area around the sunspot, forms. The penumbra is cooler than the inner area, or umbra. These solar phenomena result from the strong magnetism within the Sun, which erupts to the surface, producing a sunspot or plage.

Other phenomena to observe (in a turbulent-free atmosphere) are white-light flares. White-light flares are flash-point flares that are produced from sudden discharges of energy. They can last from a few moments to several hours, but they are generally measured in minutes. There are also limb flares, flare kernels/hot cores, two-ribbon/two-strand flares, Hyder/impact flares, homologous flares, and the Moreton wave, which can cause a wave effect from the white-light flare.

Counting sunspots and groups is another interesting activity. If possible, observing should be done at the same time each day for consistency. Start with the edges of the Sun because this is where you will notice plage. Then sweep across the Sun in a grid motion to look for disturbances or sunspots. These can be in either hemisphere and at any latitude, depending on the progression of the sunspot cycle. The relative sunspot number formula is $R = 10g + s$, where R is the relative sunspot number, g is the number of groups, and s is the number of individual spots. The relative sunspot number is based on monthly numbers, and these numbers can be collected and submitted to the AAVSO solar section (**www.aavso.org/solar**). To help you locate the latitude and longitude of the sunspot, visit the AAVSO solar section for instructions and a template called the Stonyhurst disk to place over your sketch or image. See also the chart on p. 188 that lists the orientation of the Sun in four-day increments.

Solar activity can be mapped as an exercise. Use the three elements that determine the orientation of the Sun (p. 187) and the Stonyhurst disk template mentioned above. See more Web sites to visit in the References section.

The solar section of the Association of Lunar & Planetary Observers (ALPO) is the only amateur astronomy group that tracks and uses Carrington rotation numbers[1]. The Sun takes 25 to 29 days to make a full rotation, with an average of 27 days. For an updated Carrington list, visit **www.alpo-astronomy.org/solarblog**. ALPO accepts sketches and photographs (all wavelengths) of the Sun for the study and archiving of solar morphology and prominence activity. Forms are available from their Web site.

A wide range of digital cameras, Webcams, and filters can produce phenomenal images of the Sun. Numerous computer programs allow you to stack several images to give an intense image or animation. Libraries, online chat rooms, and email lists provide a wealth of information of solar photography. The best way to learn is to read and ask questions of experienced solar imagers.

We are now entering Cycle 24 in the 11-year cycle; it is an exciting time for solar observers. If you cannot observe the Sun, you can always go to the Solar and Heliospheric Observatory (SOHO) Web site (see below) and see daily images of the Sun.

The following Handbook sections contain related information: FILTERS (p. 69), SOLAR ACTIVITY (p. 192), and VIEWING A SOLAR ECLIPSE—A WARNING (p. 151).

References

R. Beck, H. Hilbrecht, K. Reinsch, and P. Völker, *Solar Astronomy Handbook*, Willmann-Bell, Inc., Richmond, Virginia, 1995.
R.J. Bray and R.E. Loughhead, *Sunspots*, Dover Publications, 1964.
T. Broxton, *Solar Observer's Handbook*, Authorhouse, 2009.
J.L. Jenkins, *The Sun and How to Observe It*, Springer, 2009.
ALPO Solar Astronomy Handbook, ALPO Solar Section

Web sites

eo.nso.edu/dasl/Lessons/Stony/index.htm
radiojove.gsfc.nasa.gov
sohowww.nascom.nasa.gov/data/realtime-images.html
www.aavso.org/observing/programs/solar/
www.alpineastro.com/Solar_Observation/Solar_Observation.htm
www.alpo-astronomy.org/solar
www.atoptics.co.uk/tiltsun.htm
www.noaa.org
www.petermeadows.com/html/stonyhurst.html
sdo.gsfc.nasa.gov
www.solarcycle24.com

[1] The Carrington rotation number was invented by Richard Carrington. It counts the number of rotations of the Sun with the first rotation on 1895 Nov. 3

SOLAR ACTIVITY
BY KEN TAPPING

In late November or early December 2009, the new activity cycle (Cycle 24) finally started. The extended minimum between Cycles 23 and 24 was the longest in at least 100 years. Now that we are almost a year into the new cycle, it is possible to search for possible changes in solar behaviour. There is evidence that during the early decline of Cycle 23, there was a change in the circulation of plasma and magnetic flux below the photosphere. There have been reports of changes in the relationship between photospheric and coronal activity compared with earlier cycles, and that the average magnetic field strength in the sunspots associated with the new cycle is lower. Predictions are that the peak amplitude of the new cycle will be lower than that of recent cycles.

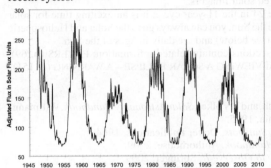

The figure shows solar activity as represented by the adjusted 10.7-cm solar microwave flux activity index (see p. 196) from 1950 to the present. The plotted values are averaged values of the index over each solar (≈27-day) rotation. The ≈11-year activity cycle is clearly evident, as are the dramatic resurgence of activity during 2001 and the resurgences of activity during the cycle's decline. The next cycle, which started late in 2009, should continue to build during 2011.

Solar activity is fundamentally a magnetic phenomenon. Deep below the photosphere, differential rotation and convection cause the solar material to move in a complex manner. The density of this material is high enough for its movement to drag the magnetic fields along with it. This generates electric currents, which in turn produce magnetic fields. The result is a complex system of subphotospheric "magnetic flux ropes." The penetration of sections of these flux ropes through the photosphere and into the chromosphere and corona gives rise to the many observed forms of solar activity. Above the photosphere the situation is strikingly different: the density is much lower, and the magnetic fields trap and confine the ionized gas of the solar atmosphere, supporting loops and filaments and forming the diverse menagerie of photospheric, chromospheric, and coronal structures with which we are familiar, such as sunspots, active regions, complexes of activity, and systems of loops. Changing emissions in the X-ray and ultraviolet wavelengths, and at radio wavelengths, are due to the changing amount of trapped plasma and the strengths of the magnetic fields containing them. The Sun's total energy output is also affected by magnetic activity, fortunately only slightly.

The organization of the subphotospheric magnetic fields gives rise to a consistent pattern in the magnetic configuration of active regions. Each region is magnetically bipolar, with the bipoles arranged east–west on the disk. All bipoles lying in the same hemisphere are arranged with the same magnetic polarity leading (facing in the direction in which the region appears to move as it is carried across the disk by solar rotation—westward in the observer's sky). In the other hemisphere, the leading and following magnetic polarities are reversed.

*The numbering system for solar activity cycles was started by Rudolph Wolf, who arbitrarily designated the activity maximum of 1750 as that of Cycle 1.

Exceptions do occur. Regions are sometimes formed that have a magnetic orientation perpendicular to or even the reverse of the norm for that hemisphere. Such regions usually try to move into the conventional orientation but are impeded by the magnetic linkages formed with their surroundings. These regions tend to produce flares as potential energy builds up in their magnetic structures and is subsequently released catastrophically.

The "conventional" magnetic configurations for active regions reverse on alternate activity cycles. For example, during Cycle 22, active regions in the northern solar hemisphere were oriented with their "negative" (i.e. south-seeking) magnetic polarity ends leading and "positive" (north-seeking) ends following, with the reverse situation in the Southern Hemisphere. In Cycle 23 this arrangement is reversed. Cycle 24 re-establishes the pattern of Cycle 22. A *magnetic* activity cycle, which is probably a more realistic description of the rhythms of solar activity, is equal to two of Wolf's activity cycles and takes about 22 years to complete.

Active regions are not isolated phenomena; they occur in complexes, comprising several active regions at various stages of development, together with the network of elements remaining from decayed regions. This localization of activity gives rise to a rotational modulation of the 10.7-cm flux as active region clusters are carried across the disk and disappear around the west limb. To smooth out this modulation in long-term studies of solar activity, the data are averaged over solar rotations rather than by month. Active regions can persist for one or more solar rotations and the complexes for a dozen or so.

The large-scale organization of solar magnetic activity is also apparent in the spatial distribution of active regions during the solar cycle. The first activity of the new cycle is marked by the formation of active regions at high latitudes. As activity builds toward the maximum of the cycle, the number of active regions increases, and they tend to form at lower latitudes. As the activity wanes toward the next minimum, the number of regions decreases, but the average latitude continues to decrease until the last activity of the cycle is located near the equator. Then, as the new cycle starts, new active regions form at high latitudes.

The formation of a new active region begins with the emergence through the photosphere into the overlying chromosphere and corona of magnetic loops. This is heralded by the appearance of small pores, about 1000 km across, which coalesce and spread into a patch of magnetic flux that may exceed 50 000 km in length. The average magnetic-field strength in such patches is of the order of 0.01 T (100 gauss). The emergence of these magnetic fields modifies the spatial and density structure of the chromosphere, giving rise to enhanced emission in the calcium and magnesium II K spectral lines. These bright patches (called plage), which stand out prominently in filtergrams, are the most conspicuous aspect of active regions. In some areas of the new active region, magnetic field strengths reach or exceed 0.1 T. These magnetic fields are strong enough to impede the transfer of energy from within the Sun, leading to these patches being cooler (3000 K) compared with the surrounding photosphere, which has a temperature of about 6000 K. Although actually quite hot and shining quite brightly, in contrast with their hotter surroundings these flux concentrations appear as dark spots: sunspots. As a region grows, one or more large spots form at the leading end, and a scattering of smaller ones form at the trailing end. Sunspots are a prominent feature of active regions and are the aspect of solar activity that has been longest known.

The growth of the new active region continues through repeated episodes of magnetic flux emergence. In general, the size is directly proportional to the total magnetic flux in the region. Growth stops when the emergence of new magnetic flux ceases. Soon after, the region starts to decay. This proceeds partly by the resubmergence

of magnetic flux and partly by fragmentation. The spots disappear, and eventually, all that remains is a large area of magnetic flux arranged in a network pattern, blending in slowly with the remains of other decayed active regions.

Repeated episodes of magnetic-flux emergence, together with motions of the footpoints, which are the photospheric anchors of magnetic loops, lead to the magnetic field overactive regions becoming complex and tangled and storing enormous amounts of energy. The relaxation of these fields is an important aspect of the evolution and dissipation of active regions. In some cases, this can occur noncatastrophically; otherwise, stresses increase until various plasma instabilities allow rapid relaxation and reconnection of the magnetic fields and a rapid release of the stored energy. These energy releases are known as flares.

The Solar Wind and Aurorae

The solar atmosphere is not stable. It is constantly flowing outward as a stream of particles and magnetic fields—the *solar wind*. The flow is strongest where the magnetic loops are very large and impose the least drag on the outwardly flowing particles. Because of their lower coronal densities, these regions produce a lower flux of X-rays and appear in X-ray images as dark patches, known as "coronal holes." The solar wind is not homogeneous or steady; its speed, density, and direction can change according to the positions of coronal holes and the nature of current solar activity.

The solar wind profoundly changes Earth's magnetic field. The wind pressure pushes the field out of its dipole shape into a long teardrop. The magnetic geometry in the tail of the drop makes it the site of many plasma instabilities. The flow of the solar wind over the boundary of Earth's magnetic field (the magnetopause) excites many types of waves, which move along Earth's magnetic field lines and which can be detected on the ground at high magnetic latitudes. Increases in the density or velocity of the solar wind change the pressure equilibrium between the solar wind and the magnetosphere, producing fluctuations in the strength and direction of the magnetic field lines at ground level. If the fluctuations are strong enough, the events are referred to as magnetic storms and substorms. These can disrupt any human activity that involves connected metal networks covering large geographical areas, especially at high magnetic latitudes.

Complex interactions between the solar wind and Earth's magnetic field lead to an accumulation of trapped particles in the magnetosphere. During magnetic storms, instabilities and waves excited in the magnetosphere by the solar wind accelerate some of the trapped particles downward along Earth's magnetic field into increasingly dense atmosphere, where they collide with the atmospheric constituents, exciting them with sufficient energy to produce light. These displays are called aurorae, or the northern and southern lights: *aurora borealis* and *aurora australis*, respectively. Views from space show that aurorae fall in a rough circle (the auroral oval), centred around the magnetic pole, that is, in a definite band of magnetic latitudes. As activity increases, the auroral oval expands, covering lower and lower magnetic latitudes. It also becomes increasingly distorted. During the period of very high activity in March 1989, auroral displays were seen as far south as the Caribbean.

Aurorae occur in many forms and can be steady, moving, or rapidly pulsating, depending upon the nature of the particle streams causing them. Aurorae can appear green or red, although if they are faint, the eye cannot respond in colour and they appear grey. The greenish colour is due to spectral lines from oxygen (558 nm) and a range of lines from nitrogen covering the band 391 nm to 470 nm. Under highly disturbed conditions, red spectral-line emissions at 630 nm and 636 nm and in a series of bands between 650 nm and 680 nm can also be seen. The green emissions are produced at a height of about 110 km; the red, 630-nm and 636-nm emissions, due

AURORAL FORMS

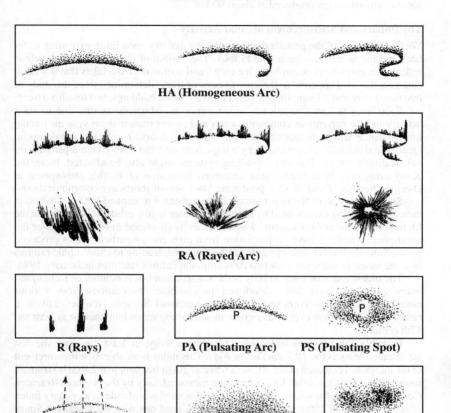

HA (Homogeneous Arc)

RA (Rayed Arc)

R (Rays) PA (Pulsating Arc) PS (Pulsating Spot)

F (Flames) G (Glow) S (Spot or Patch)

The above sketches illustrate standard auroral forms. This simplified classification was devised for visual observers during the International Geophysical Year over five decades ago (1957–58). Although there is great variety in auroral patterns, the sketches emphasize fundamental features and minimize variations that depend on the location of the observer. The light of the aurora is emitted by the upper fringes of Earth's atmosphere (heights of 100 to 400 km) as it is bombarded by electrons of the solar wind (solar wind protons contribute a smaller amount of energy). The modification of the trajectories of these particles by Earth's magnetic field restricts activity to high latitudes, producing the "aurora borealis" in the Northern Hemisphere and the "aurora australis" in the Southern Hemisphere. The wavelengths of four atmospheric molecular and atomic emission lines that can contribute strongly to auroral light are included in the list on p. 39. Whether aurorae appear coloured depends on their luminance—light that is too faint will not activate colour vision and appears white. When the luminance is sufficiently great, the relative contributions of blue, green, and red emission lines can result in a variety of auroral hues.

to atomic oxygen, originate at heights between 200 km and 400 km; the 650-nm to 680-nm emissions are produced at about 90 km.

The Impact and Measurement of Solar Activity

We find evidence of the profound effects of solar activity upon Earth extending as far back in time as we have been able to look. The rhythm of the solar activity cycle is reflected in cores from ocean beds, ice cores, and sediments from lakes that dry up in summer. It is also apparent in the growth rates of trees (determined from the study of tree rings) in recently living timber, wood from medieval buildings, and fossilized trees.

Solar activity can dramatically affect our lives. Magnetic storms due to solar activity induce currents in communications and power transmission systems having long-distance wires, disrupting their operation for hours. The power blackouts in Québec and Scandinavia produced by a large flare on 1989 Mar. 10 are a particularly outstanding example. Railway signalling systems might also be affected. Increased X-ray emissions from flares cause enhanced ionization of Earth's atmosphere at D-region heights (about 90 km), producing blackouts of shortwave communications.

Solar activity heats the upper atmosphere, causing it to expand further into space, increasing the drag experienced by artificial satellites in low orbits. It is ironic that the lifetime of the *Solar Max* satellite was dramatically shortened in this way. Above the atmosphere, satellites have no protection from high-energy particle fluxes produced by the Sun. Their electronic systems can be damaged, leading to catastrophic failures in some cases, as occurred with two *Anik* communications satellites in January 1994.

The oldest index of solar activity is the sunspot number. A number of techniques, many empirical, have been developed to combine observations from various observatories and observers to form the International Sunspot Number. This is a rather poor index; however, it has given us a database extending back to at least the 17th century.

Probably the best available index of solar activity, at least covering the last six decades or so, is the *10.7-cm flux*, or $F_{10.7}$. This index is an objective measurement of the integrated emission at the 10.7-cm wavelength (a frequency of 2.8 GHz) from all sources present on the solar disk. It has been measured daily by the National Research Council of Canada for nearly 60 years and is now used worldwide as a primary index of solar activity. In 2003, the program became a joint one with the Canadian Space Agency. $F_{10.7}$ is expressed in solar-flux units (1 sfu = 10^{-22} W·m^{-2}Hz^{-1}). The 10.7-cm flux has the great advantage that it can be measured in all weather conditions and requires no human involvement or "interpretation." When quiet, the Sun produces a 10.7-cm flux of 64 sfu, due to free-free thermal emission from the quiet solar corona. The 10.7-cm flux can be used as an objective proxy for other activity-related quantities. The strength of the radio emission constituting $F_{10.7}$ is modulated by the annual variation in the distance between Earth and Sun. When considering solar-driven phenomena at the Earth and in near-Earth space, this is not important, so the "Observed" value of the flux may be applicable. On the other hand, when considering solar activity this modulation has to be removed from the data. In such instances, the "Adjusted" flux, which is scaled to an Earth–Sun distance of 1 au, should be used.

We are a long way from understanding the nature and the extent of the effects solar activity has upon Earth. Some correlations, like that between the length of miniskirts and solar activity, are probably spurious; others might not be. As we exploit our environment more fully, we become increasingly sensitive to things that might affect it, even slightly.

(See pages 18, 69, and 151 for safe methods of observing the Sun.)

RAINBOWS AND SOME OTHER
SKY PHENOMENA
BY ROY BISHOP

Sunlight, and more rarely moonlight, interacting with water drops or ice crystals in the sky can result in aerial patterns displaying remarkable symmetry. This brief account is restricted to the more common sky phenomena. For more extensive treatments, including a dozen relatively rare patterns involving ice crystals, see the book by Greenler in the references and the Web sites listed there. For comprehensive accounts of the history and physics of the rainbow, see the books by Boyer, and Lee and Fraser.

The green flash is usually associated with the limb of the Sun. In order of increasing angular distance from the Sun, ice crystals produce coronae, pillars, halos, sundogs, and circumhorizontal arcs. (Other small particles, including water drops, also produce coronae.) In the half of the sky opposite the Sun, water drops produce rainbows and, surrounding the antisolar point, glories. The heiligenschein is not an atmospheric phenomenon, but like the glory is a bright area in the vicinity of the antisolar point.

Because the rainbow is the most famous, most beautiful, and most complex of these apparitions, I begin with rainbows and devote the greater part of this article to them. Also, if you understand the rainbow, it is easy to understand halos, sundogs, circumhorizontal arcs, and pillars.

Rainbows

The rainbow has challenged natural philosophers over the centuries, including Aristotle, Roger Bacon, Theodoric of Freiberg, René Descartes, Sir Isaac Newton, Edmund Halley, Thomas Young, George Airy, and Gustav Mie. It was Descartes (1596–1650) who first understood the basic geometry of the rainbow, and it was Newton (1642–1727) who first understood the origin of the colours of the rainbow. In 1803, 1838, and 1908 Young, Airy, and Mie, respectively, gave successively more accurate treatments of the influence of the wave nature of light on the structure of the rainbow. Recently, Alistair Fraser and Raymond Lee, using the power of the computer, provided additional insights concerning the physics of the rainbow. A few poets, including Keats and Goethe, have derided science for analyzing the rainbow, but understanding only deepens one's admiration for the beauty and subtle nature of this phantom.

The Shape of a Raindrop: The shape of a raindrop is relevant for rainbows. Surface tension arising from molecular attraction shrinks raindrops into the shape with the least surface area per unit volume—a sphere. (Raindrops resemble teardrops only after they have crashed against a surface such as a windowpane.) Aerodynamic forces deform large raindrops into a hamburger-bun shape with the short axis vertical, but an average raindrop is essentially spherical.

The Origin of the Rainbow: Sunlight is refracted and reflected by a raindrop (see Figure 1). The *primary* rainbow involves two refractions (where the light ray enters and leaves the drop) and *one* internal reflection. A portion of a ray that enters a drop head-on is deviated through 180° by the internal reflection, but when the ray is shifted off-centre, the reflection produces a smaller deviation. When the ray is shifted 86 percent of the way toward grazing the drop (as in Figure 1), because of the increasing refraction, a *minimum angle of deviation* of approximately 138° is reached. This *stationary* angle concentrates some of the light leaving a raindrop after one reflection near this direction.

FIGURE 1 *The path of a ray of sunlight interacting with a spherical raindrop is displayed. The ray is shown entering the drop at 86% of the drop radius from head-on entry, causing ray P, exiting after one internal reflection, to be at a minimum angle of deviation of 138° and contributing to the primary rainbow. Ray (S) exiting after two internal reflections is close to but not at the minimum deviation for the secondary rainbow (231°); the ray entering the drop must be shifted closer to grazing incidence (to 95% of the drop radius) before a minimum deviation of 231°*

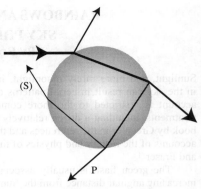

is attained. Rays undergoing three or more reflections within the drop are not shown, and neither is chromatic dispersion in the three rays exiting the drop. The widths of the various rays give an approximate indication of their relative intensities.

FIGURE 2 *Two raindrops are shown, greatly magnified, each with a ray of sunlight striking it such that the exiting ray is at the minimum angle of deviation and heading toward the observer. The drop with one internal reflection is contributing light to the observer's primary rainbow, and the drop with two internal reflections is contributing to the observer's secondary rainbow. Other drops (not shown) located along the rays P and S contribute*

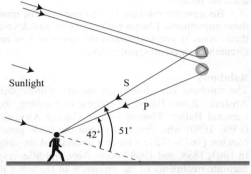

in the same fashion to the two rainbows, and the whole array has rotational symmetry about the dashed line, the extended shadow of the observer's head. The observer, looking from the apices of these conical shells, sees two, circular, coloured bands of light.

Dispersion associated with the two refractions makes the minimum angle vary with wavelength, resulting in a spectrum. This interplay of sunlight with single raindrops in the sky is symmetric about an axis extending from the Sun through the eye of the observer; thus the circular arc of a rainbow is centred on that axis. To look at the primary rainbow, the observer's eyes must be turned toward 138° + 180° = 318° or 42° from the antisolar point, the shadow of the observer's head (see Figure 2).

To Predict Where a Rainbow Might Appear: If the Sun is shining where you are, with the Sun at your back extend your arms together straight out in front of you, splay your fingers and thumbs horizontally, and touch the tips of your thumbs together. Close one eye and align the tip of one little finger with the shadow of your head. As you tilt your hands, the tip of the other little finger will trace out the location of the primary rainbow in the sky. (A double hand-span at arm's length subtends approximately 40°, about the same as the 42° angular radius of the primary rainbow.)

Rainbows: None, Semicircular, and Circular: Don't expect to see a rainbow in the sky at midday in tropical latitudes, or at midday in spring or summer at higher

latitudes. The Sun has to be less than 42° above the horizon for the top of the primary rainbow to be above the horizon (see Figure 2). At sunrise or sunset the antisolar centre of a rainbow is at the horizon, resulting in a semicircular rainbow that meets the horizon at 90°. From an airplane, or by spraying a garden hose, it is possible to see a complete circular rainbow at any time of day, provided there are many water drops and sunlight in the entire region 42° from the antisolar point.

A Rainbow Is Not a Bow: Angle, not distance, determines which raindrops send rainbow light to an observer's eye. Hence, the raindrops contributing to a rainbow lie in a conical shell with its tip at the observer's eye, and its axis coinciding with the extended shadow of the observer's head (see Figure 2). Only those parts of the conical shell having both raindrops and sunlight contribute to the rainbow. Thus, in spatial extent, a rainbow is like an immense, mouse-nibbled, ice-cream cone (sans ice cream). From the perspective of the observer located at the tip of this fragmented conical shell, a rainbow *looks* like a section of a flat circular arc or bow, but the only place a flat bow exists is on the observer's retina. Despite how rainbows are sometimes depicted in art and advertising, a rainbow cannot be viewed obliquely (it always appears circular), and it always has the same immense angular size. (Its 84° diameter spans almost one-quarter of the entire horizon.)

Your Rainbow: A rainbow is located at a particular angle relative to the Sun–observer axis (see Figure 2). When the observer moves, the axis moves, and the rainbow moves. The observer's shadow moves too, but a rainbow is subtler than a shadow; you can see someone else's shadow, but you cannot see their rainbow. Each observer has his or her own private rainbow. Although an observer's eyes image different rainbows, the two rainbows are in the same parallel direction, so when the images fuse, the observer sees one rainbow at infinity. Obviously a rainbow is not an object in the normal sense of the word; it is a pattern of light specific to the observer. Unlike the case of a normal object like a tree, there are as many rainbows as there are observers.

The Secondary Rainbow: If conditions are favourable (lots of rain and sunlight, and a dark sky background), a secondary rainbow will be visible. The *secondary* rainbow involves *two* internal reflections in each raindrop (see Figure 1). A light ray that enters a drop head-on is deviated through 360° by the two internal reflections, but when the ray is shifted off-centre the reflections produce a smaller deviation. When the ray is shifted 95 percent of the way toward grazing the drop, because of the increasing refraction a minimum angle of deviation of approximately 231° is reached. This stationary angle concentrates some of the light leaving a raindrop after two reflections near this direction. Dispersion associated with the two refractions makes the minimum angle vary with wavelength, resulting in a spectrum. To look at the secondary rainbow, the observer's eyes must be turned toward 231° + 180° = 411° or 51° from the antisolar point (see Figure 2). Thus the secondary rainbow lies (51° − 42°) = 9° outside of the primary rainbow (9° is about one fist-width at arm's length).

Width of the Secondary Rainbow: A light ray contributing to the secondary rainbow enters a raindrop closer to the edge of the raindrop than does a light ray contributing to the primary rainbow. Consequently, the amount of refraction and associated spectral dispersion are greater. The additional reflection from the curved inner surface of the raindrop further increases the dispersion, making the spectrum of the secondary bow about 60 percent wider than that of the primary bow (after taking the 0.5° diameter of the Sun into account).

Reversed Spectra: A light ray contributing to the primary rainbow enters the side of a raindrop nearest the convex side of the rainbow, is deviated through 138°, and exits near the opposite side of the drop heading toward the observer (see Figure 2). Long wavelengths are refracted least, emerging at a steeper angle to the rainbow axis, so the convex side of the primary rainbow appears red. A light ray contributing to

the secondary rainbow is deviated through 231°. To reach the observer, the ray must rotate through the raindrop in the *opposite* sense to the path followed by the primary rainbow ray. Long wavelengths are refracted least, emerging at a shallower angle to the rainbow axis, so the concave side of the secondary rainbow appears red. Thus the spectral sequences are reversed, with the red of both bows bordering upon the space that is between the bows.

Alexander's Dark Band: With a raindrop-mandated minimum deviation of 138° for the light of the primary rainbow and 231° in the opposite sense for the light of the secondary rainbow, there is a 138° + 231° − 360° = 9° gap into which the light contributing to the two rainbows cannot enter. Thus the sky between the bows is darker than elsewhere, a feature called *Alexander's Dark Band* after Alexander of Aphrodisias, a Greek philosopher who drew attention to it c. AD 200. The "dark" band is only moderately darker than the region beneath the primary rainbow because of three sources of light between the bows: skylight, external reflections off raindrops (see Figure 1), and diffraction of light waves by the raindrops.

The Tertiary Rainbow: Edmund Halley (1656–1742) first calculated that light rays exiting a raindrop after *three* reflections have a minimum angle of deviation of 318°, placing the *tertiary* rainbow only 42° from the Sun. For at least 2000 years, people had been looking for a tertiary rainbow in the vicinity of the primary and secondary rainbows. They had been looking in the wrong part of the sky! The luminance (surface brightness) of the secondary rainbow is less than that of the primary, and the luminance of the tertiary rainbow is less than that of the secondary because of three effects: (1) Light rays contributing to successively higher-order rainbows strike raindrops closer to grazing incidence, causing a greater fraction of the light to reflect without entering the drops; (2) Some light exits the drops at each internal reflection leaving less for higher-order rainbows; (3) Rainbow width increases as the order increases, spreading the light over a greater area. There is little hope of seeing the faint tertiary rainbow because it is overwhelmed by two sources of white light in that region of the sky (see Figure 1): (1) *Most* of the sunlight entering raindrops passes through without being internally reflected and illuminates the sunward half of the sky. (The lack of a stationary angle in the deviation of these bright, unreflected rays is why there is no "zero-order" rainbow.); (2) Sunlight externally reflected from raindrops. The quaternary rainbow, fainter again than the tertiary, also occurs in the bright sunward half of the sky, about 44° from the Sun. Higher-order rainbows also occur, but only the primary and secondary bows are visible in the sky.

Banding Beneath: The concave side of a primary rainbow may display two or three narrow bands, called *supernumerary bows* or *supernumerary arcs*. They are caused by the interference of two emerging parallel light rays that have entered a raindrop slightly nearer to and farther from grazing incidence than a ray that undergoes minimum deviation. The two paths have different lengths causing interference. Similar pairs of rays emerging at various angles produce the supernumerary bow pattern. British physicist Thomas Young (1773–1829) was the first to present this explanation, although more accurate descriptions involving diffraction were later provided by British astronomer George Airy (1801–1892), German physicist Gustav Mie (1868–1957), and Canadian meteorologist Alistair Fraser (in 1983).

Hamburger Buns and a Pot of Gold: The hamburger-bun distortion of raindrops with increasing drop size has the greatest effect on the top part of a rainbow because light rays in that region traverse a vertical cross section of a raindrop. The distortion has two consequences for the rainbow:

First, the distortion substantially increases the minimum deviation angle such that light from large raindrops of various diameters is spread into a white haze beneath the primary rainbow. Only spherical drops (diameters of about 0.5 mm and smaller)

contribute to the upper part of a rainbow, often causing it to be less bright and its colours less vivid than in the lower part of the bow (assuming the Sun is low in the sky so the lower part of the rainbow is at a steep angle to the horizon). In the lower part, drops of all sizes present circular cross sections to light rays that are redirected toward the observer. Thus *all* drops contribute to the lower part of the rainbow, making it the brightest part when there is a heavy rainfall with a wide range of drop sizes. As Lee and Fraser surmise in their book *The Rainbow Bridge*, the bright glow of vivid colours near the end of the rainbow may be the origin of the pot of gold myth.

Second, the distortion-induced modification in the shift of the position of supernumerary bows with drop size causes distinct supernumerary bows to occur only for raindrops having diameters in the range of about 0.4 to 0.8 mm, and only in the upper part of a rainbow. The contributions of larger and smaller drops are blurred due to overlap. A bright rainbow *without* supernumerary bows typically involves a heavy rain shower during which there is a wide range of drop diameters. Drops in the 0.4 to 0.8 mm range are present, but the bright area beneath the primary rainbow caused by larger raindrops obscures their otherwise distinct supernumerary bows.

Beware of Sunglasses: The reflection that rainbow light undergoes inside a raindrop occurs very near *Brewster's angle* at which light reflected from a nonmetallic surface becomes 100 percent polarized (named in honour of Scottish physicist Sir David Brewster (1781–1868), who discovered this phenomenon). Thus the light of a rainbow is almost 100 percent polarized. The direction of polarization (the direction of the electric field) is tangent to the bow, which for the upper part of a rainbow has the same orientation as that of partially polarized light reflecting from the dash of a car, a highway, or a body of water. Polarizing sunglasses are designed to block polarized light from the latter three sources and will obliterate a rainbow!

Rainbows at Night: Observations of lunar rainbows are rare. The Moon is bright enough to produce a noticeable rainbow only when it is near its full phase. Also, people are usually indoors at night, and when they do step outside it is often into a light-polluted environment, which rules out any chance of seeing a lunar rainbow. Even when conditions are favourable, few people would notice a lunar rainbow because it is usually too dim to activate colour vision and therefore appears white.

Not a Good Spectrum: The rainbow is often cited as the paragon of a white light spectrum. However, five factors make the rainbow spectrum inferior to that produced by a laboratory spectroscope: (1) The minimum property of the stationary angle that produces a rainbow means that light of each wavelength is spread over larger angles, resulting in some overlap of the spectral colours; (2) The Sun is not a point source of light. The 0.5° spread of its rays smears the rainbow spectrum; (3) Sunlight reflected from the front of the raindrops and skylight from behind dilutes the colours making them less saturated; (4) The increase in the minimum angle of deviation associated with aerodynamic drop distortion (significant for drop diameters of 0.5 mm and larger) causes additional spectral smearing in the upper part of a rainbow; (5) Diffraction broadening results in further overlap of the spectral colours, particularly for small raindrops. In the case of fog or cloud (drop diameters in the range 0.01 to 0.1 mm), diffraction broadening causes the various colours to overlap sufficiently to produce a white rainbow, called a *fogbow*. Also known as a *cloudbow*, it may sometimes be seen from an airplane, a large white arc moving along on a cloud layer below the airplane.

Fog and Flashlight: A dark, foggy night provides an opportunity to see the stationary angle that is the key to a primary rainbow. Place a bright, well-collimated flashlight on the ground with its beam directed vertically upward into the fog. Step back a short distance and examine the vertical shaft of light. Look for a bright patch about 40° from the zenith. Fog droplets at that position preferentially redirect the light downward toward your eyes. Diffraction causes the stationary angle to deviate

somewhat from the nominal 42° produced by larger drops. Diffraction broadening may make the faint patch of light from the secondary bow undetectable. It will be located about 54° from the zenith, below the fragment of the primary bow.

Rainbow Light on the Moon: The greater part of Earth's albedo is due to clouds. An observer on the Moon would see Earth brighten noticeably for several hours when the Sun–Earth–Moon angle is near 40° and the cloud droplets provide a 2°-diameter fragment of a cloudbow. At this point, the Moon is in its crescent phase, about three days from new, and earthshine will be enhanced. At Sinus Iridum, the Bay of Rainbows, twice each lunar night the plains and surrounding mountains are bathed in the light of a tattered fragment of a white primary rainbow enveloping Earth.

We Are Part of the Rainbow: Although rain and sunlight have been part of Earth's environment for four billion years, coloured rainbows occurred quite recently with the appearance of animals possessing colour vision. Our visual world with its brightness and colours occurs within our skull. Nevertheless, by some feat of mental projection we think that our visual world coincides spatially with the external world. Thus we confuse the neural rainbow with the external rainbow, and naively attribute the indescribable colours of the former to the latter. Three centuries ago, Sir Isaac Newton, aware of this overpowering illusion, wrote: "The rays to speak properly are not coloured. In them there is nothing else than a certain power and disposition to stir up a sensation of this or that colour." Yet, even today, most people regard the cone cells of the retina as "colour receptors," as if colours existed in the external world. They speak of "the true colours of moonbows and nebulae revealed by time-exposure photographs," unaware that they are attributing a unique property of the neural photograph in their brain to the external photograph in their hands, and subsequently to moonbows and nebulae in the sky. The eye does not detect the colours of the rainbow; the brain creates them. *We* are part of the rainbow, its most beautiful part.

Halos

Under normal conditions of temperature and pressure, the wave and statistical properties of electrons impose hexagonal crystalline structure on water ice. When sunlight interacts with ice crystals in the frosty sky, it translates the atomic architecture into macroscopic aerial patterns of striking symmetry.

Small ice crystals suspended in the air can have a variety of shapes, including multi-crystalline fragments in which the sixfold symmetry is not obvious, rods that resemble pieces of a hexagonal pencil (unsharpened), flat six-sided plates, and snowflakes with their elegant symmetry.

Alternate sides of a hexagonal ice crystal form a 60° prism (see Figure 3). Light passing through this prism is deviated by the two refractions, the angle of deviation being a minimum (about 22°) when the passage is symmetric, with equal refractions at the two surfaces. As in the case of minimum deviation in a water drop, a significant fraction of the light passing through randomly oriented 60° ice prisms is deviated by approximately 22°, enhancing the brightness at that angle.

Adjacent sides of a hexagonal crystal form a 120° prism, but light cannot pass through such a prism; the light undergoes total internal reflection at the second surface. Opposite sides of a hexagonal crystal are parallel and, like a windowpane, provide no net deviation. End faces of the crystal form 90° prisms with the sides; light passing through a 90° ice prism undergoes a minimum deviation of about 46° when the passage is symmetric.

Crystals having lengths about equal to their widths (called "blocks"; see Figure 3) assume random orientations as they fall. Consequently, the refraction of light rays toward an observer by blocks has symmetry about the Sun–observer axis, and the observer sees a *halo* of light in the sky, centred on the Sun and having an angular

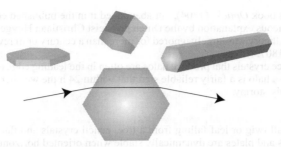

FIGURE 3 *The bottom diagram shows a light ray undergoing a net minimum deviation of 22° when it refracts symmetrically through alternate sides of a hexagonal ice crystal (in effect, a 60° ice prism). The top three diagrams show hexagonal ice crystals having, from left-to-right, increasing length-to-width ratios: a plate, a block, and a pencil. When falling, aerodynamic forces cause the plate and the pencil to orient horizontally, as shown. The block can have any orientation. Plates produce sundogs (refraction) and pillars (reflection). Blocks produce halos (refraction). Pencils produce pillars (reflection) and tangent arcs (refraction).*

FIGURE 4 *A schematic diagram of a 22° halo with sundogs, and a corona and pillar adjacent to the Sun low near the horizon in the centre. Hexagonal ice crystals are in the sky: plates (refraction/sundogs, reflection/pillar); blocks (refraction/halo); and both types of crystal (diffraction/corona). The absence of an upward-curving tangent arc at the top of the halo indicates that pencil crystals are not present.*

radius of 22° (about one hand-span from the Sun at arm's length. See Figure 4.) More rarely, refraction in 90° block prisms results in an immense but fainter 46° halo, concentric with the 22° halo. Like the rainbow, a halo is not a circular hoop but a fragmented conical structure seen from its apex. Moonlight can also produce halos, particularly if the Moon is bright, near its full phase.

Because the 22° stationary angle of deviation is a minimum, the halo has a relatively sharp inner edge and a diffuse outer edge, the sky being brighter on the convex side of the halo. Because the deviation is least at the red end of the spectrum, the inner edge of a halo may appear reddish; however, ice crystals are not as optically perfect as raindrops, so the spectral colours of halos are not as pronounced as in rainbows.

The first person to understand the geometry of the 22° halo (i.e. minimum deviation in 60° ice prisms) was the French scientist Edme Mariotte (1620–1684). Sir Isaac Newton, apparently independently, arrived at the same explanation when

writing his book *Opticks* (1704), but abandoned it in the published editions in favour of an erroneous explanation by the Dutch physicist Christiaan Huygens (1629–1695). Mariotte's theory was largely ignored for more than a century until revived by Thomas Young in 1807.

The ice crystals that produce halos are often in the leading edge of a low-pressure system, so a halo is a fairly reliable sign that within 24 h the weather will be overcast and possibly stormy.

Sundogs

Like a small twig or leaf falling from a tree, pencil crystals and flat crystals such as snowflakes and plates are dynamically stable when oriented horizontally as they fall, maximizing air resistance (see Figure 3). If ice crystals in the air are predominately plates, only those crystals at the same altitude as the Sun can refract light to the observer (provided the Sun is low in the sky), resulting in two bright spots 22° on either side of the Sun (see Figure 4). Called *sundogs* or *parhelia*, under favourable conditions these spots can be almost too bright to look at. Although sundogs appear as spots in the sky, the contributing 60° ice prisms lie along the arms of a 44° "V" with the observer's eye at its vertex.

Rays passing nonsymmetrically through 60° plate prisms are deviated more than 22°, resulting in tails or smearing of the sundogs away from the Sun (see Figure 4). Also, like the 22° halo, sundogs often display a hazy spectrum with red on their sunward side.

Sundogs (or *moondogs*, if the Moon is the light source) may appear singly or in pairs (plate crystals) and may be accompanied by a 22° halo (blocks in addition to plates). Or only a 22° halo may be present (only blocks, or if plates are also present the Sun is too high in the sky for its rays to access the 60° prisms of these horizontally oriented crystals). If the Sun is moderately high in the sky (altitude ~30°), thick plates can still result in sundogs, but the skew rays involved displace the sundogs somewhat farther than 22° from the Sun.

Circumhorizontal Arc

Closely related to the rare 46° halo is the uncommon circumhorizontal arc which can appear as a bright, rainbow-hued band 46° below the Sun. Unlike a rainbow it is not concentric with the observer's shadow, is in the same half of the sky as the Sun, and is parallel to and about 22° above the horizon. The upper side of the arc is red, the lower side, violet.

The circumhorizontal arc is formed by refraction through the lower 90° prism of horizontally-oriented plate crystals. To achieve the symmetric 46° minimum angle of deviation necessary for a bright, well-defined arc, the Sun must be near an altitude of 68°. If the Sun is much higher or lower, the arc is diffuse and dim, and cannot exist at all if the altitude of the Sun is much less than 60°. Thus the circumhorizontal arc cannot be seen at latitudes more than about 50° from the equator, and at that latitude only at solar noon near the summer solstice. Skew rays account for the extent of the arc perpendicular to the vertical plane containing the Sun and observer. Of course, the arc can exist only in those regions of the sky where both sunlight and oriented plate crystals occur.

Pillars

In cold weather when the Sun or Moon is near or just below the horizon, a vertical column or *pillar* of light sometimes is seen, extending upward from the Sun or Moon (see Figure 4). On winter nights, tall narrow pillars sometimes extend into the sky, the light sources being unshielded streetlights, often not in direct line of sight. Pillars (also known as *snow pillars*) are caused by plate crystals and/or snowflakes with

their mirror-like faces oriented horizontally in the air. Reflections from pencil crystals can also produce pillars. *All* these miniature mirrors throughout the sky reflect light, but only those lying near the vertical plane passing through the light source and an observer reflect light toward the observer; hence the observer sees a vertical pillar. The crystals producing the pillar are located between the light source and the observer.

When sundogs accompany a Sun pillar, plate crystals provide at least some of the mirrors causing the pillar. When a short, upward-curving arc tangent to the top of a 22° halo accompanies a Sun pillar, reflections off the sides of pencil crystals contribute to the pillar, the *tangent arc* being due to refraction in the 60° prisms of the horizontally oriented pencils.

Coronae

In the presence of thin, high cloud, hazy bright rings may closely surround the Sun or Moon, a pattern called a *corona* (not to be confused with the solar corona, the hot outer atmosphere of the Sun itself). Lying within several diameters of the Sun or Moon (see Figure 4), a corona often displays pale colours, including a reddish outer border—the reverse of the refraction-based reddish *inner* border of halos and sundogs. The red-reversal indicates that the corona is caused not by refraction but by diffraction scattering of light waves.

The scattering bodies are usually cloud droplets but can be small ice crystals or even pollen grains. The smaller the scattering bodies, the larger the corona; the more uniform their size, the more obvious the ring structure. Thin clouds passing near the Sun or Moon may display a colourful iridescence associated with evaporation-induced variations in drop size, although in the case of the Sun the display may be too bright to view. Very small particles, such as are injected high into the atmosphere by volcanic eruptions, result in a large corona called a *Bishop's Ring.*

When cloud droplets are involved, a corona is caused by light rays that graze the sides of the water drops without entering the drops, and by rays that pass directly through the drops. The theory describing diffraction scattering is complex, and it is not possible to give a simple explanation of the structure and size of the corona. Note that the corona involves scattering of each light ray by only one drop; scattering by multiple drops eliminates the iridescence and structure of the corona.

Glories

The *glory* resembles the corona and is also caused by diffraction scattering of light waves by fog or cloud droplets; however, the glory occurs on the opposite side of the sky, surrounding the antisolar point. Like the corona, the angular size of the glory (seldom more than a few degrees) varies inversely with the size of the scattering drops. Despite the similarity of the corona and the glory, it is easy to remember which is which: the corona is in the same part of the sky as the solar corona (assuming the Sun, not the Moon, to be the light source of the corona).

Usually seen from an airplane on a cloud layer below, the glory appears as a ring-like pattern of hazy colours centred on the observer's position in the shadow of the airplane. If the cloud layer is sufficiently far from the plane, the plane's shadow (then penumbral only) will not be visible. Mountain climbers sometimes see a glory in a cloud (fog) layer below them. If the fog is close, the climber's shadow, distorted by perspective, will appear to the climber as a dark cavity in the fog with its head centred in the glory, a strange apparition called *the spectre of the Brocken* after a mountain in Germany where the phenomenon has often been observed.

In religious art, the rings or disks of light surrounding the heads of saintly figures were likely inspired by observations of the glory, and possibly the heiligenschein (see below). Certainly it flatters an observer to see an aureole surrounding the shadow of one's own head and not those of others!

The glory involves scattering of a light ray by one drop, whereas a white cloud involves scattering of a light ray by more than one drop—which is why clouds are otherwise white. As in the case of the corona, the theory describing the glory is complex, and it is not possible to give a simple explanation of the structure and size of the glory. Light waves moving along the surface of small water drops and reflections within the drops are both involved.

Heiligenschein

Heiligenschein (German for "holy light") refers to a diffuse colourless glow surrounding the shadow of the observer's head when that shadow is projected on a rough surface or on vegetation covered in dewdrops. Unlike the patterns described above, the heiligenschein is not an atmospheric phenomenon; however, like the glory it surrounds the antisolar point so it should be mentioned.

A rough surface appears brightest when viewed in the antisolar direction because the shadows associated with the roughness are hidden behind the objects casting the shadows. For example, on a sunny day a person walking past shrubbery or a field of grass will see a glowing aura surrounding the shadow of his or her head. A forest viewed from an airplane displays a bright patch surrounding the shadow of the airplane. In the case of vegetation covered in dewdrops, the spherical drops redirect the incident light back from whence it came, enhancing the brightness associated with hidden shadows. Tiny glass spheres imbedded in highway-marker paint or on automobile license plates do the same. If the Moon had a perfectly diffuse matte surface, at full phase it would provide π times more light than at quarter phase when it is half illuminated; however, because of heiligenschein, at full phase the Moon provides more than ten times as much light—the multitude of shadows on the lunar surface are hidden, and impact-produced glass beads littering the lunar surface redirect sunlight toward Earth.

The Green Flash

The light from any astronomical object not at the zenith is refracted downward a small amount by Earth's atmosphere making the object appear higher in the sky. The refraction increases rapidly near the horizon (see p. 34, lines 6 and 7) which is why the Moon or Sun appear squashed when near the horizon. For white light the amount of refraction also varies with frequency, being least for low frequencies (red) and greatest for high frequencies (violet), a phenomenon called dispersion. As a consequence the image of an object, be it a star in the night sky, a planet, the Moon, or the Sun, is chromatically smeared in a vertical direction, the top of the image being fringed in blue-violet and the bottom of the image fringed in red.

The effect is usually not large enough to notice, unless a telescope is used and the object is near the horizon. At very low altitudes the light has traversed much atmosphere, and atmospheric scattering, which increases strongly at higher frequencies, will have removed most of the violet and blue light (which is why the sky is blue and sunsets red). Thus at sunset, as the top part of the Sun dips below the horizon, the red and orange parts of the chromatically smeared top edge of the Sun set first, followed a second or two later by the green part (I am using the colour adjectives in the common sense). The blue-violet light has been removed, so the last tip of the Sun to be seen appears — for about one second — as a *green flash*.

Whether or not a green flash is visible depends upon several variables, including the clarity of the atmosphere (transparent air is best), the nature of the horizon (a sea horizon is best), the altitude of the observer (the observer should not be exactly at sea level), and whether or not there are temperature variations in the layers of air near the horizon (resulting in various mirage effects which may either obscure or enhance the green flash).

The green flash is usually associated with the setting Sun, although it also may be seen at sunrise, provided one is looking at the right location on the horizon at the instant of sunrise. With optical aid and favorable conditions, a green flash may be seen at moonset, or when a bright planet or star dips below the horizon.

Special Warning: Except within a few seconds of a possible green flash, do not look directly at the solar disc with binoculars or a telescope (at least, not without a proper, securely-mounted solar filter). The retina has no pain receptors and can be damaged within a second or less, resulting in permanent partial loss of vision. A dull-red Sun near the horizon is particularly dangerous when using binoculars or a telescope— there may still be sufficient invisible infrared radiation to thermally cook the retina.

With the exception of the green flash, none of these apparitions—rainbows, halos, sundogs, circumhorizontal arcs, pillars, coronae, glories, and heiligenschein—are objects in the normal sense of the word They are patterns of light specific to the individual observer. Anyone who understands them will find the world to be a more interesting place.

References

Benn, C.R., "Rainbows, Haloes, and Earthshine," *The Observatory 114*, No. 1120 (1994), p. 115.

Boyer, C.B., *The Rainbow: From Myth to Mathematics*, Princeton University Press, 1987.

Fraser, A.B., "Why Can the Supernumerary Bows Be Seen in a Rain Shower?" *J. Opt. Soc. Am. 73* (1983), p. 1626.

Greenler, R., *Rainbows, Halos, and Glories*, Cambridge University Press, 1980.

Lee, R.L., Jr., "Mie Theory, Airy Theory, and the natural rainbow," *Appl. Opt. 37* (1998), p. 1506.

Lee, R.L., Jr. and Fraser, A.B., *The Rainbow Bridge*, Pennsylvania State University Press, 2001.

Minnaert, M., *Light and Colour in the open air*, Bell and Sons, 1940.

Newton, I., *Opticks* (4th ed. 1730), Dover Publications, 1952.

Nussenzveig, H.M., "The Theory of the Rainbow," *Sci. Am. 236* (4) (1977), p. 116.

Shapiro, A.E., "Newton and Huygens' Explanation of the 22° Halo," *Centaurus 24* (1980), p. 273.

Walker, J., "Rainbows in a Water Drop," *Sci. Am.*, July 1977, p. 138.

Walker, J., "Mysteries of Rainbows," *Sci. Am.*, June 1980, p. 174.

Wright, W.D., *The Rays are not Coloured*, Adam Hilger Ltd., London, 1967.

Web sites:
www.atoptics.co.uk
www.meteoros.de/haloe.htm
www.philiplaven.com/index1.html

TIMES OF SUNRISE AND SUNSET
By Rajiv Gupta

The table on the following two pages gives the times of sunrise and sunset at four-day intervals for locations ranging from 20° to 60° north latitude. "Rise" and "set" correspond to the upper limb of the Sun appearing at the horizon for an observer at sea level. The times are local mean time (LMT) for the Greenwich meridian (i.e. UT at 0° longitude), although for North American observers the stated values may be read directly as LMT at the observer's position with an error less than 1 min. The table may be interpolated linearly for both nontabular latitudes and dates, and can be extrapolated beyond the 20° and 60° latitude limits a few degrees without significant loss of accuracy.

It is a common misconception that extreme values for sunrise and sunset times occur on the shortest and the longest days of the year. This is not the case and is due to the tilt of Earth's spin axis to the axis of its orbit and to Earth's varying speed along its elliptical orbit (as Kepler described in his second law). At midnorthern latitudes, the earliest sunset occurs early in December and the latest sunrise in early January whereas the shortest day (in the sense of hours of daylight) is Dec. 21 or 22. For more information see *Sky & Telescope*, December 1988, p. 674 and July 1972, p. 20, and an article by Terence Hicks in *JRASC, 88*, p. 86, February 1994.

The standard time of an event at a particular location must take account of the observer's longitude relative to his or her standard meridian (see STANDARD TIME ZONES on p. 51). The table below lists the latitude and the longitude correction (in minutes of time) for a number of cities in Canada and the United States. For example, to find the time of sunrise at Boston on 2011 May 18: the latitude is 42°, and from the table the time of sunrise at 0° longitude is 4:37 UT (after interpolating for latitude). Thus, at Boston, the time of sunrise will be approximately 4:37 LMT. Boston is in the Eastern time zone (E) and is 16 minutes of time east of the standard meridian for this zone (75°W). Thus, sunrise in Boston will occur at 5:21 EDT (Eastern Daylight Time). The longitude correction for any location may be found by converting the difference between the longitude of the place and that of its standard meridian to time (1° = 4 minutes of time), the correction being + if the place is west of its standard meridian, − if east. **Note**: Due to a difference in height between the observer and the actual horizon, the observed time may differ by several minutes from the predicted time.

Canadian Cities				American Cities	
Belleville	44° +10E	Québec	47° −15E	Atlanta	34° +37E
Calgary	51° +36M	Regina	50° +58C	Boston	42° −16E
Charlottetown	46° +12A	Resolute	75° +20C	Chicago	42° −10C
Corner Brook	49° +22N	Rimouski	48° −26E	Cincinnati	39° +38E
Edmonton	54° +34M	Saint John	45° +24A	Denver	40° 0M
Halifax	45° +14A	St. John's	48° +1N	Fairbanks	65° +50A
Hamilton	43° +20E	Sarnia	43° +29E	Flagstaff	35° +27M
Kelowna	50° −3P	Saskatoon	52° +67C	Kansas City	39° +18C
Kingston	44° +6E	Sudbury	47° +24E	Los Angeles	34° −7P
Kitchener	43° +22E	Thunder Bay	48° +57E	Miami	26° +21E
London	43° +25E	Toronto	44° +18E	Minneapolis	45° +13C
Moncton	46° +19A	Vancouver	49° +12P	New Orleans	30° 0C
Montréal	46° −6E	Victoria	48° +13P	New York	41° −4E
Niagara Falls	43° +16E	Whitehorse	61° +60P	San Francisco	38° +10P
Ottawa	45° +3E	Windsor, Ont.	42° +32E	Seattle	48° +9P
Pangnirtung	66° +23A	Winnipeg	50° +29C	Tucson	32° +24M
Prince George	54° +11P	Yellowknife	62° +38M	Washington	39° +8E

SUNRISE AND SUNSET, 2011 JANUARY–JUNE
UNIVERSAL TIME AT GREENWICH MERIDIAN

Latitude:	+20°		+30°		+35°		+40°		+45°		+50°		+55°		+60°	
Event:	RISE	SET	RISE	SET	RISE	SET	RISE	SET	RISE	SET	RISE	SET	RISE	SET	RISE	SET
Jan.–2	6:34	17:30	6:55	17:09	7:07	16:57	7:21	16:43	7:38	16:26	7:58	16:06	8:25	15:39	9:03	15:01
2	6:35	17:33	6:56	17:12	7:08	17:00	7:22	16:46	7:38	16:30	7:58	16:10	8:25	15:43	9:02	15:06
6	6:36	17:35	6:57	17:15	7:09	17:03	7:22	16:50	7:38	16:34	7:58	16:14	8:23	15:49	8:59	15:13
10	6:37	17:38	6:57	17:18	7:08	17:07	7:22	16:53	7:37	16:38	7:56	16:19	8:21	15:55	8:55	15:20
14	6:38	17:40	6:57	17:21	7:08	17:10	7:21	16:58	7:35	16:43	7:54	16:25	8:17	16:01	8:50	15:29
18	6:38	17:43	6:56	17:25	7:07	17:14	7:19	17:02	7:33	16:48	7:50	16:31	8:13	16:08	8:43	15:38
22	6:38	17:46	6:55	17:28	7:05	17:18	7:17	17:07	7:30	16:53	7:47	16:37	8:08	16:16	8:36	15:48
26	6:37	17:48	6:54	17:32	7:03	17:22	7:14	17:11	7:27	16:59	7:42	16:43	8:02	16:24	8:28	15:58
30	6:36	17:50	6:52	17:35	7:01	17:26	7:11	17:16	7:23	17:04	7:37	16:50	7:55	16:32	8:19	16:08
Feb. 3	6:35	17:53	6:49	17:39	6:58	17:30	7:07	17:21	7:18	17:10	7:31	16:57	7:48	16:40	8:10	16:18
7	6:33	17:55	6:47	17:42	6:54	17:34	7:03	17:26	7:13	17:16	7:25	17:04	7:40	16:49	8:00	16:29
11	6:32	17:57	6:44	17:45	6:51	17:38	6:58	17:31	7:07	17:22	7:18	17:11	7:32	16:57	7:50	16:40
15	6:29	17:59	6:40	17:48	6:46	17:42	6:53	17:35	7:02	17:27	7:11	17:18	7:23	17:06	7:39	16:50
19	6:27	18:01	6:37	17:51	6:42	17:46	6:48	17:40	6:55	17:33	7:04	17:25	7:14	17:14	7:28	17:01
23	6:24	18:03	6:33	17:54	6:37	17:50	6:43	17:45	6:49	17:39	6:56	17:31	7:05	17:22	7:17	17:11
27	6:22	18:04	6:29	17:57	6:33	17:53	6:37	17:49	6:42	17:44	6:48	17:38	6:56	17:31	7:05	17:21
Mar. 3	6:19	18:06	6:24	18:00	6:27	17:57	6:31	17:54	6:35	17:50	6:40	17:45	6:46	17:39	6:54	17:31
7	6:15	18:07	6:20	18:03	6:22	18:00	6:25	17:58	6:28	17:55	6:32	17:51	6:36	17:47	6:42	17:41
11	6:12	18:08	6:15	18:05	6:17	18:04	6:19	18:02	6:21	18:00	6:23	17:58	6:26	17:55	6:30	17:51
15	6:09	18:09	6:10	18:08	6:11	18:07	6:12	18:06	6:13	18:05	6:15	18:04	6:16	18:03	6:18	18:01
19	6:05	18:11	6:06	18:11	6:06	18:11	6:06	18:11	6:06	18:11	6:06	18:11	6:06	18:11	6:06	18:11
23	6:02	18:12	6:01	18:13	6:00	18:14	5:59	18:15	5:58	18:16	5:57	18:17	5:56	18:19	5:54	18:21
27	5:58	18:13	5:56	18:15	5:55	18:17	5:53	18:19	5:51	18:21	5:49	18:23	5:46	18:27	5:42	18:31
31	5:55	18:14	5:51	18:18	5:49	18:20	5:46	18:23	5:43	18:26	5:40	18:30	5:35	18:34	5:30	18:40
Apr. 4	5:51	18:15	5:46	18:20	5:43	18:23	5:40	18:27	5:36	18:31	5:31	18:36	5:25	18:42	5:18	18:50
8	5:48	18:16	5:42	18:23	5:38	18:27	5:34	18:31	5:29	18:36	5:23	18:42	5:15	18:50	5:06	19:00
12	5:45	18:17	5:37	18:25	5:33	18:30	5:28	18:35	5:22	18:41	5:14	18:48	5:05	18:58	4:54	19:10
16	5:42	18:18	5:33	18:28	5:27	18:33	5:21	18:39	5:14	18:46	5:06	18:55	4:56	19:06	4:42	19:20
20	5:39	18:20	5:28	18:30	5:22	18:36	5:16	18:43	5:08	18:51	4:58	19:01	4:46	19:13	4:30	19:30
24	5:36	18:21	5:24	18:33	5:18	18:39	5:10	18:47	5:01	18:56	4:50	19:07	4:37	19:21	4:19	19:39
28	5:33	18:22	5:20	18:35	5:13	18:43	5:05	18:51	4:55	19:01	4:43	19:13	4:28	19:29	4:07	19:49
May 2	5:31	18:24	5:17	18:38	5:09	18:46	4:59	18:55	4:49	19:06	4:35	19:20	4:19	19:37	3:56	19:59
6	5:28	18:25	5:13	18:40	5:05	18:49	4:55	18:59	4:43	19:11	4:29	19:26	4:10	19:44	3:46	20:09
10	5:26	18:27	5:10	18:43	5:01	18:52	4:50	19:03	4:38	19:16	4:22	19:32	4:02	19:52	3:36	20:19
14	5:25	18:28	5:08	18:46	4:58	18:56	4:46	19:07	4:33	19:21	4:16	19:37	3:55	19:59	3:26	20:29
18	5:23	18:30	5:05	18:48	4:55	18:59	4:43	19:11	4:28	19:25	4:11	19:43	3:48	20:06	3:16	20:38
22	5:22	18:32	5:03	18:51	4:52	19:02	4:39	19:14	4:24	19:30	4:06	19:48	3:42	20:13	3:08	20:47
26	5:21	18:33	5:01	18:53	4:50	19:04	4:37	19:18	4:21	19:34	4:01	19:53	3:36	20:19	3:00	20:55
30	5:20	18:35	5:00	18:55	4:48	19:07	4:34	19:21	4:18	19:37	3:58	19:58	3:31	20:25	2:53	21:03
Jun. 3	5:20	18:36	4:59	18:57	4:47	19:10	4:33	19:24	4:16	19:41	3:55	20:02	3:27	20:30	2:47	21:10
7	5:20	18:38	4:59	18:59	4:46	19:12	4:31	19:26	4:14	19:44	3:53	20:05	3:24	20:34	2:42	21:16
11	5:20	18:39	4:58	19:01	4:46	19:14	4:31	19:29	4:13	19:46	3:51	20:08	3:22	20:38	2:39	21:21
15	5:20	18:40	4:58	19:02	4:46	19:15	4:31	19:30	4:13	19:48	3:50	20:11	3:21	20:41	2:36	21:25
19	5:21	18:42	4:59	19:04	4:46	19:17	4:31	19:32	4:13	19:50	3:50	20:12	3:20	20:42	2:36	21:27
23	5:22	18:42	5:00	19:04	4:47	19:17	4:32	19:33	4:14	19:51	3:51	20:13	3:21	20:43	2:36	21:28
27	5:23	18:43	5:01	19:05	4:48	19:18	4:33	19:33	4:15	19:51	3:53	20:13	3:23	20:43	2:38	21:27

SUNRISE AND SUNSET, 2011 JULY–DECEMBER
UNIVERSAL TIME AT GREENWICH MERIDIAN

Latitude: Event:	+20° RISE SET	+30° RISE SET	+35° RISE SET	+40° RISE SET	+45° RISE SET	+50° RISE SET	+55° RISE SET	+60° RISE SET
Jul. 1	5:24 18:43	5:02 19:05	4:50 19:18	4:35 19:33	4:17 19:50	3:55 20:13	3:25 20:42	2:42 21:25
5	5:25 18:44	5:04 19:05	4:51 19:18	4:37 19:32	4:19 19:49	3:58 20:11	3:29 20:40	2:47 21:22
9	5:27 18:43	5:06 19:04	4:53 19:17	4:39 19:31	4:22 19:48	4:01 20:09	3:33 20:37	2:52 21:17
13	5:28 18:43	5:08 19:03	4:56 19:15	4:42 19:29	4:25 19:46	4:05 20:06	3:38 20:33	2:59 21:11
17	5:30 18:42	5:10 19:02	4:58 19:14	4:45 19:27	4:29 19:43	4:09 20:02	3:44 20:28	3:07 21:04
21	5:31 18:41	5:12 19:00	5:01 19:11	4:48 19:24	4:33 19:39	4:14 19:58	3:50 20:22	3:15 20:56
25	5:33 18:40	5:15 18:58	5:04 19:09	4:52 19:21	4:37 19:35	4:19 19:53	3:56 20:16	3:24 20:48
29	5:34 18:39	5:17 18:56	5:07 19:06	4:55 19:17	4:41 19:31	4:25 19:48	4:03 20:09	3:33 20:39
Aug. 2	5:36 18:37	5:19 18:53	5:10 19:02	4:59 19:13	4:46 19:26	4:30 19:42	4:10 20:02	3:42 20:29
6	5:37 18:35	5:22 18:50	5:13 18:59	5:03 19:09	4:51 19:21	4:36 19:35	4:17 19:54	3:52 20:19
10	5:38 18:32	5:24 18:46	5:16 18:54	5:06 19:04	4:55 19:15	4:42 19:28	4:24 19:45	4:01 20:08
14	5:40 18:30	5:27 18:43	5:19 18:50	5:10 18:59	5:00 19:09	4:48 19:21	4:32 19:36	4:11 19:57
18	5:41 18:27	5:29 18:39	5:22 18:45	5:14 18:53	5:05 19:02	4:53 19:13	4:39 19:27	4:20 19:46
22	5:42 18:24	5:31 18:34	5:25 18:40	5:18 18:47	5:09 18:56	4:59 19:05	4:47 19:18	4:30 19:34
26	5:43 18:21	5:33 18:30	5:28 18:35	5:22 18:41	5:14 18:49	5:05 18:57	4:54 19:08	4:40 19:23
30	5:44 18:17	5:36 18:25	5:31 18:30	5:25 18:35	5:19 18:42	5:11 18:49	5:02 18:58	4:49 19:11
Sep. 3	5:45 18:14	5:38 18:21	5:34 18:25	5:29 18:29	5:24 18:34	5:17 18:41	5:09 18:48	4:59 18:59
7	5:46 18:10	5:40 18:16	5:37 18:19	5:33 18:23	5:29 18:27	5:23 18:32	5:17 18:38	5:08 18:47
11	5:46 18:07	5:42 18:11	5:40 18:13	5:37 18:16	5:33 18:19	5:29 18:23	5:24 18:28	5:17 18:35
15	5:47 18:03	5:44 18:06	5:43 18:08	5:40 18:09	5:38 18:12	5:35 18:14	5:32 18:18	5:27 18:22
19	5:48 17:59	5:46 18:01	5:45 18:02	5:44 18:03	5:43 18:04	5:41 18:06	5:39 18:08	5:36 18:10
23	5:49 17:56	5:49 17:56	5:48 17:56	5:48 17:56	5:48 17:56	5:47 17:57	5:46 17:57	5:46 17:58
27	5:50 17:52	5:51 17:51	5:51 17:50	5:52 17:50	5:53 17:49	5:53 17:48	5:54 17:47	5:55 17:46
Oct. 1	5:51 17:48	5:53 17:46	5:54 17:45	5:56 17:43	5:57 17:41	5:59 17:39	6:02 17:37	6:04 17:34
5	5:52 17:45	5:55 17:41	5:57 17:39	6:00 17:37	6:02 17:34	6:05 17:31	6:09 17:27	6:14 17:22
9	5:53 17:42	5:58 17:36	6:01 17:34	6:04 17:30	6:07 17:27	6:12 17:22	6:17 17:17	6:24 17:10
13	5:54 17:38	6:00 17:32	6:04 17:28	6:08 17:24	6:12 17:19	6:18 17:14	6:25 17:07	6:33 16:58
17	5:55 17:35	6:03 17:28	6:07 17:23	6:12 17:18	6:18 17:12	6:24 17:06	6:33 16:57	6:43 16:46
21	5:57 17:32	6:06 17:23	6:11 17:18	6:16 17:12	6:23 17:06	6:31 16:58	6:41 16:48	6:53 16:35
25	5:58 17:30	6:08 17:19	6:14 17:14	6:21 17:07	6:28 16:59	6:37 16:50	6:49 16:39	7:03 16:24
29	6:00 17:27	6:11 17:16	6:18 17:09	6:25 17:02	6:34 16:53	6:44 16:43	6:57 16:30	7:13 16:13
Nov. 2	6:02 17:25	6:14 17:13	6:21 17:05	6:30 16:57	6:39 16:47	6:51 16:36	7:05 16:21	7:24 16:03
6	6:04 17:23	6:17 17:10	6:25 17:02	6:34 16:53	6:45 16:42	6:57 16:29	7:13 16:13	7:34 15:52
10	6:06 17:22	6:21 17:07	6:29 16:58	6:39 16:48	6:50 16:37	7:04 16:23	7:21 16:06	7:44 15:43
14	6:08 17:21	6:24 17:05	6:33 16:55	6:43 16:45	6:56 16:33	7:10 16:18	7:29 15:59	7:54 15:34
18	6:10 17:20	6:27 17:03	6:37 16:53	6:48 16:42	7:01 16:29	7:17 16:13	7:37 15:53	8:04 15:25
22	6:13 17:19	6:30 17:01	6:41 16:51	6:53 16:39	7:06 16:25	7:23 16:08	7:45 15:47	8:14 15:17
26	6:15 17:19	6:34 17:00	6:45 16:50	6:57 16:37	7:11 16:23	7:29 16:05	7:52 15:42	8:23 15:10
30	6:18 17:19	6:37 17:00	6:48 16:49	7:01 16:36	7:16 16:21	7:35 16:02	7:59 15:38	8:32 15:05
Dec. 4	6:20 17:20	6:40 17:00	6:52 16:48	7:05 16:35	7:21 16:19	7:40 16:00	8:05 15:35	8:40 15:00
8	6:23 17:21	6:43 17:00	6:55 16:48	7:09 16:35	7:25 16:18	7:45 15:59	8:11 15:33	8:47 14:56
12	6:25 17:22	6:46 17:01	6:58 16:49	7:12 16:35	7:29 16:18	7:49 15:58	8:15 15:32	8:53 14:54
16	6:27 17:23	6:49 17:02	7:01 16:50	7:15 16:36	7:32 16:19	7:52 15:58	8:19 15:31	8:58 14:53
20	6:30 17:25	6:51 17:04	7:03 16:52	7:17 16:37	7:34 16:20	7:55 16:00	8:22 15:33	9:01 14:54
24	6:32 17:27	6:53 17:06	7:05 16:54	7:19 16:39	7:36 16:23	7:57 16:02	8:24 15:35	9:03 14:56
28	6:33 17:29	6:55 17:08	7:07 16:56	7:21 16:42	7:38 16:25	7:58 16:05	8:25 15:38	9:03 14:59
32	6:35 17:32	6:56 17:11	7:08 16:59	7:22 16:45	7:38 16:29	7:59 16:08	8:25 15:42	9:02 15:04

MIDNIGHT TWILIGHT AND MIDNIGHT SUN
BY ROY BISHOP

Astronomers generally desire dark skies, free of moonlight and man-made light pollution. As mentioned on p. 213, the beginning or end of *astronomical twilight* corresponds to the centre of the Sun being 18° below the horizon. At that point the amount of sunlight scattered by the upper layers of Earth's atmosphere is negligible; that is, it is less than the combined illuminance (about 2×10^{-3} lux) from starlight, airglow, and zodiacal light, the three main contributors to the light of the "dark" night sky.

For observers in countries at high latitudes (e.g. the United Kingdom, Norway, southern Argentina and Chile, and most of Canada), around the time of the summer solstice the Sun always lies less than 18° below the horizon, and the sky does not get dark at night. This "midnight twilight" phenomenon can be displayed in a graph as a function of latitude and time of year.

The following diagram indicates the brightness of the sky at local midnight at any time of the year for any latitude north of 45°N or south of 45°S. Below the lower curve the natural sky is dark. Between the two curves twilight prevails. Above the upper curve the Sun is in the sky. Place names in roman type (left-hand side) are in the Northern Hemisphere; place names in *italic* type (right-hand side) are in the *Southern Hemisphere*. On the horizontal axis use the roman-type months for the former, *italic*-type months for the latter. The diagram is simplified slightly in that the months are assumed to be of equal duration, and the seasonal pattern of months and summer solstices for Earth's two hemispheres are assumed to be identical except for a 6-month phase shift.

The latitude of the Arctic and Antarctic Circles (90° subtract the obliquity of the ecliptic = 66°34') is indicated by the dashed line. This line is *not* tangent to the Midnight Sun curve because at midnight on the summer solstice at either the Arctic or the Antarctic Circle the Sun is above the horizon. Atmospheric refraction raises the apparent Sun about 34' above the true Sun. Also, rise/set is defined as the top limb of the Sun at a sea-level horizon; thus the 16' semidiameter of the Sun must also be taken into account. To see the top limb of the Sun on the horizon at local midnight on the summer solstice, an observer must be 34' + 16' = 50' south of the Arctic Circle (or north of the Antarctic Circle), at latitude 65°44'.

By running a horizontal line across the chart at a selected latitude, the reader can determine the approximate dates when midnight twilight and, possibly, midnight Sun begin and end for any locality at north or south latitudes above 48.6°, the lower limit for midnight twilight on the summer solstice. (Remarkably, when rounded to the nearest degree, the latter figure is the latitude of the longest east–west international border: the 2000-km-long 49th parallel between the United States and western Canada.)

Some examples: The diagram shows that at Grise Fiord (a hamlet on the stunning south coast of Ellesmere Island, and Canada's most northerly community) the sky is never dark from about Mar. 10 until early October, and the midnight Sun lasts from late April until mid-August. Note that Cape Horn at midnight is bathed in dim Antarctic twilight from early November until early February. Even at the latitude of Vancouver there is a period of almost a month each year when the sky never gets astronomically dark—although the natural night sky is obliterated *every* night near any town or city unless there is an electrical power failure! Finally, note that Earth's poles are astronomically dark for less than three months of the year.

MIDNIGHT TWILIGHT AND MIDNIGHT SUN DIAGRAM

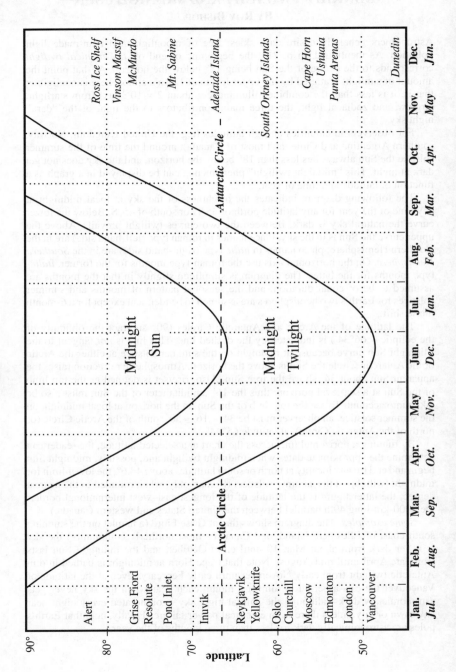

TWILIGHT
BY RAJIV GUPTA

There are three definitions for the beginning of morning and ending of evening twilight: (1) *Civil twilight*—centre of the Sun 6° below the horizon, brightest stars visible, artificial illumination required for most outdoor activities, marks the ending or beginning of night for aviation purposes; (2) *Nautical twilight*—centre of the Sun 12° below the horizon, sea horizon no longer visible; (3) *Astronomical twilight*—centre of the Sun 18° below the horizon, amount of sunlight scattered by the atmosphere is negligible.

The table below gives the beginning of morning and ending of evening astronomical twilight in UT at 0° longitude. For observers in North America the times may be handled in the same way as those of sunrise and sunset (see p. 208).

Latitude:	+20°		+30°		+35°		+40°		+45°		+50°		+55°		+60°	
M–E:	Morn.	Eve.	Morn.	Eve.	Morn.	Eve.	Morn.	Eve.	Morn.	Eve.	Morn.	Eve.	Morn.	Eve.	Morn.	Eve.
Jan. 0	5:16	18:50	5:30	18:36	5:37	18:29	5:44	18:22	5:52	18:14	6:00	18:06	6:08	17:58	6:18	17:48
10	5:19	18:56	5:32	18:43	5:39	18:36	5:45	18:30	5:52	18:23	5:59	18:16	6:06	18:09	6:15	18:00
20	5:21	19:01	5:32	18:50	5:38	18:45	5:43	18:39	5:48	18:34	5:54	18:28	6:00	18:23	6:06	18:17
30	5:20	19:06	5:29	18:57	5:34	18:53	5:38	18:49	5:41	18:46	5:45	18:42	5:48	18:39	5:51	18:36
Feb. 9	5:18	19:11	5:24	19:05	5:27	19:02	5:29	19:00	5:31	18:58	5:32	18:57	5:33	18:57	5:32	18:57
19	5:13	19:15	5:17	19:12	5:17	19:11	5:18	19:11	5:17	19:11	5:16	19:13	5:13	19:16	5:09	19:21
Mar. 1	5:07	19:18	5:07	19:18	5:06	19:19	5:04	19:21	5:01	19:24	4:57	19:29	4:51	19:36	4:41	19:46
11	4:59	19:21	4:56	19:25	4:53	19:28	4:49	19:32	4:43	19:38	4:36	19:46	4:25	19:57	4:10	20:13
21	4:50	19:24	4:44	19:32	4:38	19:37	4:32	19:44	4:23	19:52	4:12	20:04	3:56	20:20	3:34	20:43
31	4:41	19:28	4:31	19:39	4:23	19:46	4:14	19:56	4:02	20:08	3:47	20:23	3:25	20:45	2:53	21:18
Apr. 10	4:32	19:32	4:17	19:46	4:08	19:56	3:56	20:08	3:40	20:24	3:20	20:45	2:51	21:14	2:04	22:03
20	4:23	19:36	4:04	19:54	3:52	20:07	3:37	20:22	3:18	20:42	2:52	21:08	2:12	21:49	0:48	23:24
30	4:14	19:41	3:52	20:03	3:38	20:18	3:19	20:36	2:55	21:01	2:22	21:35	1:24	22:35	—	—
May 10	4:07	19:46	3:41	20:12	3:24	20:29	3:03	20:51	2:34	21:21	1:50	22:06	—	—	—	—
20	4:01	19:52	3:32	20:21	3:13	20:41	2:48	21:06	2:14	21:41	1:15	22:41	—	—	—	—
30	3:58	19:57	3:26	20:29	3:05	20:51	2:37	21:19	1:56	22:00	0:28	23:35	—	—	—	—
Jun. 9	3:56	20:02	3:23	20:36	3:00	20:59	2:30	21:29	1:44	22:15	—	—	—	—	—	—
19	3:57	20:06	3:22	20:40	2:59	21:04	2:28	21:35	1:40	22:23	—	—	—	—	—	—
29	4:00	20:07	3:25	20:41	3:02	21:05	2:31	21:35	1:44	22:22	—	—	—	—	—	—
Jul. 9	4:04	20:07	3:31	20:39	3:09	21:01	2:39	21:30	1:56	22:13	—	—	—	—	—	—
19	4:09	20:04	3:38	20:34	3:18	20:54	2:51	21:21	2:13	21:58	1:02	23:06	—	—	—	—
29	4:14	19:59	3:46	20:26	3:28	20:44	3:05	21:07	2:33	21:39	1:42	22:28	—	—	—	—
Aug. 8	4:19	19:52	3:55	20:16	3:39	20:31	3:19	20:51	2:52	21:17	2:14	21:55	0:53	23:10	—	—
18	4:24	19:44	4:03	20:04	3:50	20:17	3:33	20:34	3:11	20:55	2:41	21:25	1:53	22:11	—	—
28	4:28	19:34	4:11	19:51	4:00	20:02	3:47	20:15	3:29	20:32	3:05	20:55	2:31	21:29	1:28	22:28
Sep. 7	4:31	19:25	4:18	19:37	4:10	19:46	3:59	19:56	3:45	20:10	3:27	20:28	3:01	20:53	2:21	21:31
17	4:34	19:15	4:25	19:24	4:19	19:30	4:11	19:38	4:00	19:48	3:46	20:01	3:27	20:20	3:00	20:47
27	4:37	19:05	4:31	19:10	4:27	19:14	4:21	19:20	4:14	19:27	4:04	19:37	3:51	19:50	3:31	20:09
Oct. 7	4:39	18:56	4:37	18:58	4:35	19:00	4:32	19:03	4:27	19:08	4:21	19:14	4:12	19:23	3:59	19:35
17	4:42	18:49	4:43	18:47	4:43	18:47	4:42	18:48	4:40	18:50	4:37	18:53	4:32	18:58	4:24	19:05
27	4:45	18:43	4:49	18:38	4:51	18:36	4:52	18:35	4:52	18:35	4:52	18:35	4:50	18:36	4:47	18:39
Nov. 6	4:48	18:39	4:56	18:31	4:59	18:28	5:02	18:25	5:04	18:22	5:07	18:20	5:08	18:18	5:09	18:17
16	4:53	18:36	5:03	18:26	5:07	18:22	5:12	18:17	5:16	18:13	5:20	18:08	5:25	18:04	5:29	17:59
26	4:58	18:36	5:10	18:24	5:16	18:18	5:21	18:13	5:27	18:07	5:33	18:01	5:40	17:54	5:47	17:47
Dec. 6	5:03	18:38	5:17	18:25	5:23	18:18	5:30	18:11	5:37	18:04	5:44	17:57	5:52	17:49	6:02	17:40
16	5:09	18:42	5:23	18:28	5:30	18:21	5:37	18:13	5:45	18:06	5:53	17:58	6:02	17:49	6:12	17:39
26	5:14	18:47	5:28	18:33	5:35	18:25	5:43	18:18	5:50	18:11	5:58	18:03	6:07	17:54	6:18	17:43
Jan. 5	5:18	18:53	5:32	18:39	5:38	18:32	5:45	18:25	5:52	18:18	6:00	18:11	6:08	18:03	6:17	17:53

PLANETS AND SATELLITES

THE PLANETS FOR 2011
By Murray Paulson

INTRODUCTION

You would think that with the Internet and today's technology you would never need a telescope. In my opinion, nothing could be further from the truth. Nothing replaces that "being there" moment at the eyepiece when, with the persistence of effort, you see those subtle details obscured by distance and our atmosphere, revealed for fleeting moments in time. Seeing the changing face of the planets in real time is something that many of us find alluring. We get to be explorers in that last frontier, and we get to see the beauty of our neighbouring planets firsthand. Sometimes we even discover something new and point it out to the rest of the world, like the latest impact in Jupiter's atmosphere. There is a rôle for us to play in discovery.

When observing or imaging the planets, it is important to minimize the optical aberrations between the observer and the planet. To get the most out of your observing sessions, use high magnification plus high-quality well-collimated optics. If you are unable to change the optics, make sure they are well collimated. If you are considering change, then there is the question of what kind of telescope is best. In my opinion high-quality refractors are the best. The cost of these high-end telescopes is prohibitive, and "large" aperture means something like 200-mm aperture. The aperture may be limited, but the quality is astounding. There are other high-quality optical systems, Maksutovs, Dahl Kirkam, and other mirror configurations that work very well.

Also important in planetary viewing is resolution. One of the axioms of optics is the larger the diameter of the telescope, the higher the resolution. See TELESCOPE PARAMETERS and TELESCOPE EXIT PUPILS p. 54. In the world of amateur planetary imaging, some of the best work is being done with the larger commercial Schmidt-Cassegrain telescopes (SCTs) in the 280-mm to 355-mm range. The reason for this is that you can find good optical quality in the larger SCTs, and, when coupled with image-processing software, you can do amazing things to the images. Software can stretch the contrast that central obstructions tend to smear out. There are also good-quality Newtonian telescopes and other Cassegrain topologies. The important thing is to evaluate them for the purpose. See H. Suiter's book *Star Testing Astronomical Telescopes*[1], which provides the tools to evaluate the quality of your telescope.

With a well-collimated telescope you need good-quality eyepieces. The general rule is that the higher the quality and the fewer optical elements, the better. Every surface scatters light, and the features on the planets are subtle. Orthoscopic eyepieces seem to be the benchmark of planetary eyepieces, with the Zeiss orthos at the top of the scale. I have had the opportunity to look through some, and they produce a very clean high-contrast image. Some observers believe that University Optics orthos are also good, as are those by Pentax, Brandon, and Takahashi. Thomas Back, founder of TMB Opticals, was of the opinion that the Radian eyepieces were very good for planetary viewing. The important thing is to try a variety of eyepieces when you can (at star parties, etc.), and evaluate how they work for you. Be critical of what you see, the contrast, and the colour cast each eyepiece produces. Then check your wallet.

If you are using a non-driven telescope, a wide, flat-field eyepiece like the Nagler and now the Ethos, is indispensible. Nikon has stepped up to the plate with its new NAV SW series. I have the opinion of one reviewer that these eyepieces exhibit very little distortion and contribute no false color to the image. The large field of view of these eyepieces gives you lots of time to observe at high power before having to move the telescope again. In my experience, these eyepieces are sharp to the edge of the field. You can go the step up and get a drive for the telescope. It gives the observer

uninterrupted time to concentrate on the planetary image and to discern the details. In addition to German-equatorial drives popular for refractors and other scopes, fork equatorials for many Schmidt-Cassegrains, and platforms like Poncet for Dobsonians, are also heartily recommended.

Cleanliness of the eyepiece and diagonals is also important. These surfaces are close to the observer, and will contribute the most degradation to image contrast if they are not clean. Do your homework before you clean your eyepieces and make sure you do not damage them in the cleaning process. There are special cleaning aids and cloths you can use, but I will not go into that here.

The next optical aberration between the observer and the planet is the sky itself. If the telescope is warmer than the outside air temperature, the warm air coming off the optical surfaces in the tube assembly and the cold ambient air will mix, causing localized turbulence, which will degrade the image. Adequate thermal equalization of the telescope is critical in getting a good image. The general rule is that for less thermal mass, the shorter the cool-down period. To avoid long cool-down periods, some amateurs have resorted to a cooling fan to flush the heat out of the telescope or to blow cool air onto the mirror. Closed-tube assemblies will limit the mixing of the warm and cool air, but they do not cool quite as fast as an open-tube assembly.

The last of the thermal aberrations is the air between the telescope and the sky. Local heat sources, such as furnace flues, warm cars, paved parking lots, even someone in front of the telescope talking to you, will cause heat plumes that will degrade the seeing. One way of ascertaining if there are thermal sources affecting your seeing is to defocus your telescope while observing a bright star and see if the image has any slow-moving anomalous structure in it. This slow-moving structure is due to the heat plume aberrating the star's image. Sometimes the atmosphere is just not cooperative, and a jet stream or other phenomenon will bloat the planet's image to resemble a fuzzy tennis ball. The de-focused image will show a river of structure moving in one direction across it. There is not much you can do but to try again on another night.

The inner planets are often very close to the horizon after sunset, and this puts the observer at a disadvantage. Down this low, the shimmering of the atmosphere obscures the fine details on the inner planets. Just finding Mercury is a challenge in the twilight. Daytime observing of the inner planets is possible, but it does take some equipment and planning. The easiest way is to use a Go To telescope. Failing that, then use a polar-aligned equatorial mount with setting circles. Both options will get the telescope aimed in the right area of the sky. One note though, if the sky is hazy, the task of finding the planet in the daytime becomes significantly more difficult.

The recommended procedure is that you set up your telescope **with a solar filter** and a low-power eyepiece, and focus on the Sun. You cannot just point the telescope at the planet and expect to be able to acquire focus. It is too difficult. There is also the uncertainty that you are pointed in the right spot. Once you have a good focus on the Sun, lock the focuser, if possible, so that it doesn't move. **Do not remove the solar filter yet. I do not recommend hunting for planets within 5° of the Sun because of the hazard that accidental exposure to the Sun poses without a solar filter.** Remember that blindness is not a desirable observing attribute! SEE VIEWING A SOLAR ECLIPSE—A WARNING (p. 151).

If you are not using a Go To scope, set the coordinates on the mount to the Sun's position, and then move off to the location of the planet you are hunting. With the Go To, just enter the command to go to the planet. **Now it is safe to remove the solar filter.** When I am observing a planet that is close to the Sun, I test to make absolutely sure that the Sun is not in the field of view. Pass your hand over the eyepiece to see if it is safe, then look. The resolution of the eye is only very acute near the centre of your vision, so if you are not looking directly at the planet, you probably will not see it and will have to scan all over the field to find it. With Venus this is not a problem, but it is with Mercury and the outer planets. Once you find the planet in the field of view, centre it and try higher-power eyepieces. My eyepieces are parfocal and make it

an easy transition. A light-orange filter like the Wratten #21 will darken the light-blue sky and improve the contrast.

If the planet is not in the field, either there is an error in your polar alignment or the planet is very low in contrast. You can fish around for the planet being very careful about sweeping towards the Sun. **Do not sweep too far!** The second choice is to try to do a better polar alignment. You can do a drift alignment on the Sun or get a better north–south reference. The atmosphere heats up throughout the day, so it is most stable in the morning. Objects in the foreground will affect the seeing, such as asphalt parking lots. If possible, for best stability, observe over grass or water. Finally, Mars, Jupiter, and Saturn are observable in the daytime hours, so you are not limited to just the inner planets. They are more challenging, but are fun. It is especially fun to observe a planetary conjunction in the daytime. My favourites have been Venus and Jupiter, and Mercury and Venus.

Drawing the planets is an exercise that I encourage. I now mostly image the planets, but I am glad for the time I have put in drawing them. Drawing gives the observer the time to critically observe the planets. This is a useful activity because it gives you lots of time to see the details that come and go in the moments of good seeing, and the effort you put in to "see" the details on a planet teaches your eye/brain how to see those subtle details. You become a much better observer. As a bonus, it also provides you with a record of what you saw on that night so you can return to it years later. What you need is a set of soft and hard pencils (e.g. an HB and an H), a log book, and a template. Mars is typically drawn with a 42-mm circular template. The 42 mm corresponds to the 6792 km (4200 mile) diameter of Mars. A metric ruler can measure the sizes of features you see on Mars. The other planets' circles can be of a convenient size, but do not make them too small. Jupiter and Saturn need an oblate template to make them easier to draw. Draw major features first, then fill in the little details as you see them. Jupiter rotates very rapidly, and the features will visibly shift over a 20-min interval. It is very important that you record the time and date on the drawing, as well as the aperture and eyepiece you are using, filters if any, the general observing conditions, and your name and location. The Association of Lunar and Planetary Observers is interested in amateur contributions and is happy to receive amateur drawings.

Editor's Note: **All dates are UT and some events, as viewed from North America, may occur on the evening of the previous date. Check the THE SKY MONTH BY MONTH (p. 98) for exact times.**

MERCURY

Mercury is a planet of extremes. It is the smallest of the eight planets, is closest to the Sun and therefore the fastest moving, and comes up just short of being the hottest planet. It also has the longest solar day, lasting 2 of its orbital periods, or 176 days. In

(text continues on p. 218)

MERCURY EVENTS FOR 2011

Date	Event	Elong. from Sun °	Ang. Dia. "	Mag.	Date	Event	Elong. from Sun °	Ang. Dia. "	Mag.
Jan. 9	GEW	23	7	−0.3	Aug. 17	IC	5	11	+5.3
Feb. 25	SC	2	5	−1.7	Sep. 3	GEW	18	7	−0.2
Mar. 23	GEE	19	7	−0.2	Sep. 28	SC	1	5	−1.7
Apr. 9	IC	2	11		Nov. 14	GEE	23	7	−0.3
May 7	GEW	27	8	+0.4	Dec. 4	IC	1	10	
Jun. 13	SC	1	5	−2.3	Dec. 23	GEW	22	7	−0.4
Jul. 20	GEE	27	8	+0.3					

GEE = Greatest Elongation East; GEW = Greatest Elongation West; IC = Inferior Conjunction; SC = Superior Conjunction

ELONGATIONS OF MERCURY IN 2011

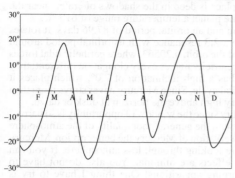

Eastern elongations occur with positive angles (evening visibility); western elongations occur with negative angles (morning visibility). Visibility depends not only on the magnitude of the elongation but on the angle between the ecliptic and the horizon. The first day of each month is indicated with tick marks on the horizontal axis. The table below gives details during the most favourable elongations visible from northern latitudes.

APPARENT DIAMETER OF MERCURY IN 2011

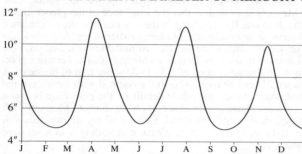

Mercury's apparent diameter is given in arcseconds. The first day of each month is indicated with tick marks on the horizontal axis.

MERCURY—MOST FAVOURABLE VIEWS IN 2011 FROM NORTHERN LATITUDES:
MARCH/APRIL (Evening); SEPTEMBER (Morning)

Date 0h UT	Mag.	Angular Diameter "	Percent Illuminated	Elongation from Sun °	Apparent RA (2011) h m	Dec ° '
Mar. 14	−1.1	5.9	79	14	0 28	+3 31
18	−0.9	6.5	64	17	0 51	+6 51
22	−0.4	7.2	48	18	1 09	+9 36
26	+0.3	8.2	31	18	1 20	+11 31
Aug. 27	+1.5	9.0	17	15	9 22	+13 08
31	+0.3	8.0	31	17	9 28	+13 56
Sep. 4	−0.4	7.1	48	18	9 42	+13 55
8	−0.8	6.4	65	17	10 02	+13 00

CONJUNCTIONS AND APPULSES INVOLVING MERCURY FOR 2011

Date (UT)	Planet	Separation	Date (UT)	Planet	Separation
Mar. 16	Jupiter	2.0°	May 17	Venus	1.4°
Apr. 19	Mars	0.6°	May 20	Mars	2.1°
May 8	Venus	1.4°	Nov. 2	Venus	2.0°
May 11	Jupiter	2.0°	Nov. 13	Venus	2.0°

the peak of its "noonday" heat, Mercury's surface warms to 427 °C, and on the far side it goes down to −163 °C. The coldest place is deep in the shadows of craters near the poles, −183 °C. These extremes give the planet a temperature range of 610 °C.

Mercury has a diameter of 4879 km and an orbital period of 87.96 days. It rotates on its axis every 58.65 days, locked in a 2:3 resonance with its orbital period around the Sun. This is due to the eccentricity of the orbit, 0.20563, where perihelic tidal forces dominate the spin period. This high eccentricity makes every elongation different; they can range from 18° to 28°. Mercury has a high inclination of 7.0°, which places it above or below the ecliptic over its orbital cycle. Since Mercury never strays more than 28° from the Sun, it is never visible very high above the horizon at dusk or dawn.

Most people have never seen Mercury since the window of opportunity is so narrow near the end of twilight. That, coupled with the general poor quality of the atmosphere close to the horizon, makes daytime observation of Mercury the better option. Mercury is then higher in the sky, where you are looking through less atmosphere. If you can observe early in the day, the thermal effects are minimal. You also do not have to get out of bed so early for those morning apparitions! One thing I have to try is observing over a body of water during the daytime. Some solar observatories do this because water doesn't radiate heat during the day, which improves the seeing. One difficulty of observing Mercury after dark is that the irradiance of the planet makes the subtle markings difficult to see. By observing in the daytime, the sky can balance against Mercury's brightness, which makes the markings easier to see. Any telescope equipped with Go To or setting circles can be used to find Mercury. See daytime observing of the planets in the introduction. Details on Mercury can be seen in a good 130-mm telescope using high magnifications of 1.5× to 3.0× per mm of diameter. A red or orange filter (Wratten 21) can be used to boost the contrast with the blue of the sky. Anecdotally, the best phases to see the subtle details on the planet are between mid-gibbous and a fat crescent phase. Some observers have imaged Mercury with 250-mm Maksutovs, which show surprising detail. Despite all my urgings that you observe Mercury in the daytime, I do take great pleasure in finding it in an elusive twilight with just my binoculars.

Mercury's mean synodic period (time between successive inferior conjunctions) is 115.88 days, so we generally get three opportunities to see it both after sunset and in the dawn sky every year. The angle of the ecliptic makes fall evening and spring morning apparitions in the higher latitudes very poor because the ecliptic is almost parallel to the horizon. The net effect is that Mercury sets shortly after the Sun in bright twilight. This rule goes for both hemispheres. One disparity between the hemispheres is that the Southern Hemisphere gets the better of the fall morning and spring evening elongations. Mercury's orbital inclination produces a more favourable geometry of Mercury's orbit as seen from the Southern Hemisphere.

2011 starts off with a greatest western elongation of Mercury culminating on Jan. 9. Mercury rises 1 h 40 min before the Sun and, helped by its orbital inclination, sits high above the ecliptic in the morning sky. On Mar. 23, we get a decent evening apparition with a greatest eastern elongation of 18.6° from the Sun. This event benefits once again from Mercury sitting above the ecliptic, which is very steep in the evening sky. Jupiter sits just 2° south, making for a nice conjunction. Mercury will set 1 h 35 min after sunset. In May, Mercury has a conjunction with Venus, Jupiter, and Mars, with the grouping occupying a span of just over 7°. Unfortunately for us Northerners, it suffers from the shallow-ecliptic syndrome, but will be brilliant from the Southern Hemisphere.

On Aug. 16–17, in a grand coincidence, both Venus and Mercury will be in conjunction with the Sun only 13 h apart. Venus will sit on the far side of the Sun (just over a degree above it), while Mercury will pass on the near side of the Sun (4.4° below it. This is followed by a fine morning apparition of Mercury on Sep. 3. Mercury will only sit 18° from the Sun at this time, but the ecliptic is very steep and the planet rises 1 h 43 min before the Sun for us Northerners.

In mid-November, the 14th to be exact, Mercury comes to a greatest eastern elongation, which is rather unfavourable due, once again, to the placement of the

ecliptic in the evening fall sky. It will be great for those in the Southern Hemisphere. The notable event will be the conjunction of Venus and Mercury, where they will lie close to 2° apart for the better part of the month. It is not a great conjunction, but worthy of a hunt with a scope in the daytime. The notable thing about this conjunction is that you will be able to see the fat gibbous disk of Mercury change to a 50-percent crescent over the first 18 days of the month. Mercury will be bright at magnitude –0.2 for most of this time. Venus will have a rather stable 10.5″ gibbous phase and will be a magnitude –3.9 beacon to help you home in on the pair. Mercury will sit just 2° below Venus in declination for most of it. This is a great event that affords you the opportunity to watch the phase of Mercury evolve from gibbous to dichotomy.

The last Mercury event of the year is the grand Christmas western elongation. We will get to see Mercury rise 2 h before the Sun, and it will shine at magnitude –0.3. Dichotomy occurs on Dec. 19 where the 50-percent phase will measure 7.35″ and it will shine at magnitude –0.1. Greatest western elongation occurs on Dec. 23. Mercury will sit more than 20° from the Sun over the time from dichotomy till well after Christmas.

One thing I have noticed about the April, August, and December apparitions of Mercury is that the planet sits still against the background stars while the Sun moves it out from inferior conjunction to greatest western elongation. Play the scenarios on a sky simulator program for fun.

VENUS

Known as both the "Morning Star" and the "Evening Star," Venus has impressed us throughout the ages with the brilliance and purity of its light. It varies from magnitude –4.9 to –3.9 and is bright enough to cast a visible shadow. If you know where to look, it is visible naked-eye in full daylight. Venus has a diameter of 12 104 km and rotates on its axis once every 243.019 days in retrograde motion. It orbits the Sun in 224.70 days at a distance of 0.723 332 au, with an inclination of 3.395°. Venus also has the most circular orbit of the planets, with an eccentricity of just 0.006 77.

In the pre-spacecraft era, people thought that our sister planet might bear habitable zones somewhat like Earth. Nothing could be further from the truth. The surface temperature on Venus is a fairly constant 460 °C, under a runaway greenhouse effect. The dense carbon dioxide atmosphere has a pressure of 92 atm (over 9000 kPa) at the surface and a density of 65 kg/m^3. This is 6.5 percent the density of water! Wind friction would be a serious thing on Venus.

The surface of Venus is veiled by thick sulphur dioxide clouds with sulphuric acid droplets; little light reaches the surface. Occasional detail is seen in the cloud structure in amateur telescopes, but for the most part it appears as a featureless white disk. The subtle structure in the cloud tops is difficult to observe, but too few observers even give it a try. The best times to look are from just before Venus' first-quarter to mid-gibbous phases. A violet filter can enhance the visibility of atmospheric structure, and imaging through a UV filter will show cloud details. The Association of Lunar and Planetary Observers is interested in your images of Venus seen this way.

Venus is easily found in a telescope in the daytime, far from the deleterious effects of our thick atmosphere near the horizon. The daytime sky presents a good contrast for Venus' bright disk, reducing the irradiance effect. This is one of my favourite daytime activities at star parties. Please review seeing planets in the daytime in the introduction of this section.

2011 starts off with Venus reaching greatest western elongation on Jan. 8. It will sit 47° from the Sun, and is exactly at dichotomy (50-percent phase). Over the next 8 months it will move at a leisurely rate of 0.227°/d on its way back toward the Sun. On the way, it passes close by Neptune on Mar. 27; only 8.5′ separates them. Unfortunately, close approach will be only visible from the Far East to Eastern Europe. In North America, the best we can do is see the pair about ½ degree apart. Venus also passes by Uranus on Apr. 22 and we can see the pair about 1° apart. I love watching

ELONGATIONS AND ANGULAR SIZE OF VENUS IN 2011

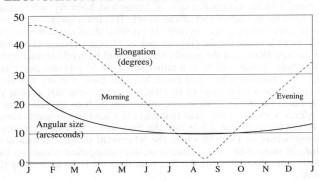

The first day of each month is indicated with tick marks on the horizontal axis.

CONJUNCTIONS AND APPULSES INVOLVING VENUS FOR 2011

Date (UT)	Planet	Separation	Date (UT)	Planet	Separation
Mar. 27	Neptune	0.2°	May 22	Mars	1.1°
Apr. 22	Uranus	0.9°	Sep. 29	Saturn	1.3°
May 8	Venus	1.4°	Nov. 2	Mercury	2.0°
May 11	Jupiter	0.6°	Nov. 13	Mercury	2.0°
May 18	Venus	1.4°			

the contrast of an inner planet and an outer planet in the eyepiece. One time I observed a Venus–Uranus conjunction from the shoulder of a highway in my Brandon refractor. The weather had been poor and I carried the scope for a week hoping that I might get an opening. The highlight of Venus' review of the planets will be on May 11, when she passes 35′ below Jupiter and 1.5° above Mercury. Contrast the brilliant white of Venus' –3.9-magnitude 11.2″ gibbous disk with Jupiter's –2.0-magnitude, 33.8″ cream-coloured disk. Mercury will be a dim magnitude-0.3 companion at dichotomy showing a 7.5″ "quarter moon" phase. It will be a highlight, but did I mention the particularly poor inclination of the spring's morning ecliptic? You may be able to catch the pair in the eyepiece just before the Sun rises. Similarly, Venus will pass by Mars and Mercury over the remainder of the month, but they will be much harder to view and the view will not be quite as spectacular.

On Aug. 16–17, Venus and Mercury will be in conjunction with the Sun only 13 h apart. Venus will sit just over 1° above the Sun and Mercury will sit 4.4° below the sun. It may be a lark to see if you can find Venus in Hα, but the conjunction is otherwise unobservable with their proximity to the Sun. The notable date here is that Venus is exactly one half cycle from the next, and last, transit of our lifetime. You have just one more chance to get to see a transit of Venus. Start planning now! Jay Anderson will undoubtedly have recommendations for the best weather prospects in next year's Handbook.

Venus and Mercury have a grand dance in November, with the pair sitting much of the month close to 2° from each other. Venus will provide the beacon to home you in on the action, so you can watch Mercury change from a gibbous disk to a half phase over the first three weeks of the month. This will be a daytime observation and a good project, if the weather holds out.

MARS

Mars is a planet that inspires us, a place we could anticipate walking on and exploring, a place where our grandchildren may go. A web of canals has ensnared us, and

generations of observers and scientists have devoted their lives to the study of the Red Planet. Despite the unveiling of Mars' mysteries, and finding neither Martians nor canals, many of us are still infatuated with the planet. About every 2 years and 40 days, we get to renew our acquaintance as Earth, on its inside path, overtakes the 4th planet. Over the 15.7-year cycle between successive closest oppositions, we have seven apparitions, with the closest approach in August–September and the farthest in February–March. Apparent sizes range from the perihelic 25.1″, as in 2003, to the aphelic 13.88″ in 2012.

Mars' mean distance from the Sun is 1.52 au, and its orbit has an eccentricity of 0.0934 with an inclination of 1.8506°. It rotates on it axis in 24 h 37 min 22.66 s. The differential between Earth and Mars's rotation period results in us seeing the same meridian on Mars 38 min later each successive night. The same feature will be visible at the same time of night in 40 days' time. You generally get to see two full rotations of Mars in stroboscopic form over one apparition where the planet is near its best. This 3-month window will start in the first quarter of 2012 for our last aphelic opposition of the current Martian cycle. Despite what you may read on the Internet, Mars will not be as big as the Moon in August!

Mars is accompanied by two small moons, Deimos and Phobos. Deimos is the smaller at 15.6 × 12 km, and its orbit has a semi-major axis of 23 463 km. It completes one orbit in 1.262 days. Phobos, at 26.2 × 22.2 km, has an orbit with a semi-major axis of 9 377 km. Phobos orbits Mars in a frantic 0.3189 days and, if viewed from the Martian surface, would rise in the west and traverse the sky to set in the east. The two moons were discovered by Asaph Hall in 1877 with the 26-inch refractor at the U.S. Naval Observatory. These two moons undoubtedly are captured asteroids. Viewing them is a real challenge because, at opposition, Mars outshines them by 14.2 and 13.1 magnitudes respectively, and they never venture very far from the planet.

2011 is not a great Mars year as we start off with the Red Planet heading to a Feb. 4 conjunction with the Sun. Over the next four months, Mars undergoes a number of conjunctions with Neptune, Uranus, Mercury, Jupiter, and Venus, which are all not visible due to the shallow angle of the ecliptic of the morning sky. The events from mid-April onward will be good as seen from the Southern Hemisphere.

Things pick up for Mars in the fall as it starts to move closer to its 2012 opposition. On Nov. 3, Mars passes 6″ in diameter, and by the end of the year it will break the 9″ barrier. If you are an early riser, you can watch as Mars starts its return to our skies. Opposition will be in early March of next year. This upcoming opposition is at aphelion, and marks the end of the shrinking apparitions of Mars. Mars will be in Leo, so it sits moderately high in the sky as it crosses the meridian in the morning hours.

In previous apparitions of similar circumstance, lots of detail was seen despite the aphelic opposition. I used magnifications up to 540× in my 12.5-inch Newtonian. When Mars is at aphelion, its atmosphere is considerably calmer and subsequently clearer of dust. This improves the contrast and hence visibility for the surface features. There also tend to be more clouds at aphelion, so watch for them near the terminator and limb (use a blue or violet filter).

The subtle details on Mars can be enhanced with colour filters at the eyepiece. If you can only afford one filter, buy the orange Wratten #21 filter. It will enhance the contrast between the darker maria areas and the light, rust-coloured deserts. In addition, it is not too dense for smaller apertures. If you have a 200-mm aperture or larger, the red filter will produce the maximum enhancement between the desert areas and the maria. Yellow and green filters help enhance the view of dust-storm activity, and green filters enhance the view of ground hazes and frosts. Blue light does not penetrate into the atmosphere, so atmospheric details and clouds are brought out by blue and violet filters. You get occasions when the atmosphere of Mars is unusually clear in blue wavelengths, and you can see surface details through a blue filter. This phenomenon is called "blue clearing." We expect that the situation of aphelion will

(text continues on p. 226)

OPPOSITIONS OF MARS, 2001–2014

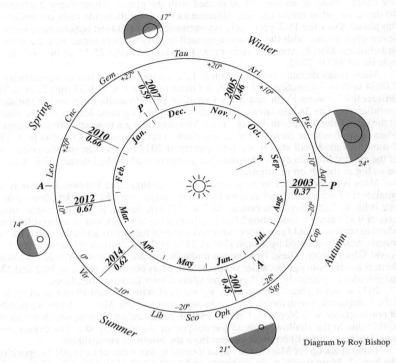

Diagram by Roy Bishop

The above diagram represents the orbits of Earth and Mars as viewed from the north ecliptic pole. Straight lines link simultaneous positions of the two planets for seven successive oppositions of Mars, beginning with that of the year 2001. The separation of the two planets (in astronomical units) at the various oppositions is indicated beside each of the connecting lines. The months inside of Earth's orbit indicate the position of Earth during the year (both planets orbit counterclockwise). For each orbit, two tick marks labelled A and P indicate the aphelion point and the perihelion point, respectively. The direction of the vernal equinox is shown (toward the late-September position of Earth). Around the orbit of Mars is indicated its declination (ranges between +27° and −28°) and the constellation in which Mars resides when at opposition.

Four views of Mars are shown—at its two equinoxes and two solstices. These views show the portion of Mars illuminated by the Sun, the location and approximate size of its north polar cap, and the apparent size of Mars (labelled in arcseconds) for oppositions occurring at these points in its orbit. The seasons of the Martian northern hemisphere are indicated around the outer margin of the diagram, and are very nearly one season ahead of those on Earth at the same orbital position. (For the southern hemisphere of Mars, the season and the configuration of the south polar cap are the same as those of the diametrically opposite view.) Note that the maximum angular diameter Mars can attain (25″) occurs near its perihelion, at a late-August opposition.

As an example of the information that can be read from this diagram: the 2012 opposition of Mars occurs in early March with Mars located near declination +10° in the constellation Leo, 0.67 au from Earth, and only about 14″ in diameter. It is summer in the Martian northern hemisphere and the north polar cap is visible but shrinking.

MARS—TABLE OF DAILY CENTRAL MERIDIANS, 2011

Date 0h UT		Date 0h UT		Date 0h UT		Date 0h UT		Date 0h UT		Date 0h UT	
JANUARY		**MARCH**		**MAY**		**JULY**		**SEPTEMBER**		**NOVEMBER**	
1	56	1	192	1	305	1	66	1	184	1	313
2	46	2	182	2	295	2	56	2	174	2	303
3	37	3	172	3	285	3	46	3	164	3	294
4	27	4	162	4	275	4	36	4	154	4	284
5	17	5	152	5	265	5	27	5	145	5	274
6	7	6	143	6	255	6	17	6	135	6	265
7	357	7	133	7	245	7	7	7	125	7	255
8	347	8	123	8	236	8	358	8	116	8	245
9	337	9	113	9	226	9	348	9	106	9	236
10	328	10	103	10	216	10	338	10	96	10	226
11	318	11	93	11	206	11	328	11	87	11	217
12	308	12	83	12	196	12	319	12	77	12	207
13	298	13	73	13	186	13	309	13	67	13	197
14	288	14	63	14	176	14	299	14	58	14	188
15	278	15	53	15	166	15	289	15	48	15	178
16	269	16	43	16	157	16	280	16	38	16	168
17	259	17	33	17	147	17	270	17	28	17	159
18	249	18	23	18	137	18	260	18	19	18	149
19	239	19	13	19	127	19	250	19	9	19	140
20	229	20	3	20	117	20	241	20	359	20	130
21	219	21	353	21	107	21	231	21	350	21	120
22	209	22	343	22	97	22	221	22	340	22	111
23	199	23	333	23	88	23	212	23	330	23	101
24	190	24	323	24	78	24	202	24	321	24	92
25	180	25	313	25	68	25	192	25	311	25	82
26	170	26	303	26	58	26	182	26	301	26	72
27	160	27	293	27	48	27	173	27	292	27	63
28	150	28	283	28	38	28	163	28	282	28	53
29	140	29	273	29	29	29	153	29	272	29	44
30	130	30	263	30	19	30	144	30	263	30	34
31	120	31	253	31	9	31	134				
FEBRUARY		**APRIL**		**JUNE**		**AUGUST**		**OCTOBER**		**DECEMBER**	
1	110	1	243	1	359	1	124	1	253	1	25
2	101	2	233	2	349	2	114	2	243	2	15
3	91	3	223	3	339	3	105	3	233	3	5
4	81	4	213	4	330	4	95	4	224	4	356
5	71	5	203	5	320	5	85	5	214	5	346
6	61	6	193	6	310	6	76	6	204	6	337
7	51	7	183	7	300	7	66	7	195	7	327
8	41	8	173	8	290	8	56	8	185	8	318
9	31	9	163	9	281	9	47	9	175	9	308
10	21	10	153	10	271	10	37	10	166	10	299
11	11	11	144	11	261	11	27	11	156	11	289
12	1	12	134	12	251	12	17	12	146	12	280
13	351	13	124	13	241	13	8	13	137	13	270
14	342	14	114	14	232	14	358	14	127	14	261
15	332	15	104	15	222	15	348	15	117	15	251
16	322	16	94	16	212	16	339	16	108	16	242
17	312	17	84	17	202	17	329	17	98	17	232
18	302	18	74	18	193	18	319	18	88	18	223
19	292	19	64	19	183	19	310	19	79	19	213
20	282	20	54	20	173	20	300	20	69	20	204
21	272	21	44	21	163	21	290	21	59	21	194
22	262	22	34	22	154	22	280	22	50	22	185
23	252	23	24	23	144	23	271	23	40	23	176
24	242	24	14	24	134	24	261	24	30	24	166
25	232	25	4	25	124	25	251	25	21	25	157
26	222	26	354	26	114	26	242	26	11	26	147
27	212	27	345	27	105	27	232	27	1	27	138
28	202	28	335	28	95	28	222	28	352	28	128
		29	325	29	85	29	213	29	342	29	119
		30	315	30	75	30	203	30	332	30	110
						31	193	31	323	31	100

MAP OF MARS

This map has south at top and north at bottom, and represents the view through a reflecting telescope (one with an even number of reflecting surfaces). It was computer-generated by Daniel Troiani, using all the data (CCD images, drawings, and photographs) from the Mars section of the Association of Lunar and Planetary Observers (ALPO) during the 2001 apparition. The map is intended to represent the appearance of Mars, as viewed from Earth through moderate-sized telescopes, during favourable apparitions, or electronic images that have been digitally processed. For recent observations of Mars, visit the Mars section of the ALPO Web site, alpo-astronomy.org.

MARS—EPHEMERIS FOR PHYSICAL OBSERVATIONS, 2011

Date 0h UT	Distance au	Mag.	Eq. Diam. "	Perc. Ill.	PA °	Incl. °
Aug. 1	2.129	+1.4	4.4	95	332	+2
Sep. 1	1.992	+1.4	4.7	93	343	+11
Oct. 1	1.814	+1.3	5.1	92	355	+17
Nov. 1	1.582	+1.1	5.9	90	6	+22
Dec. 1	1.322	+0.7	7.1	90	16	+24
Jan. 1	1.040	+0.2	9.0	92	22	+24

The above table gives information useful to observers of Mars during 2011, when Mars has an elongation greater than 40°. Data are given at 12-day intervals while Mars is greater than 10″ in equatorial diameter, otherwise data are given for the first of each month. The columns give (1) the date; (2) the distance of Mars from Earth in astronomical units; (3) the visual magnitude of Mars; (4) its apparent equatorial angular diameter; (5) the percentage of its disk illuminated; (6) the position angle of its rotation axis, measured counterclockwise from north (clockwise in telescopes having an odd number of reflections); and (7) the inclination of its rotation axis to the plane of the sky, positive if its north pole is tipped towards Earth.

CONJUNCTIONS AND APPULSES INVOLVING MARS FOR 2011

Date (UT)	Object	Separation	Date (UT)	Object	Separation
Apr. 19	Mercury	0.6°	May 20	Mercury	2.1°
May 1	Jupiter	0.4°	May 22	Venus	1.1°

ANGULAR SIZE OF MARS IN 2011

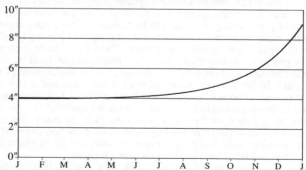

The angular size of Mars, in arcseconds, is shown in the above graph. The first day of each month is indicated with tick marks on the horizontal axis.

produce a fairly clear Martian atmosphere, so blue clearing may not be significant this time around.

On 1999 May 1, I had one very instructive view of Mars in a 200-mm achromatic refractor at the Calgary Science Centre during the peak of the opposition. Mars was 16.2″ at the time, and it was that side of Mars that is mostly desert, the Elysium Planitia region crowned with Mare Cimmerium; typically there is not much to see. The view was through an 8-element Meade Ultrawide eyepiece, which produced 200×, a bit low in my opinion, but I realized that I could see little, subtle, white clouds in the salmon-pink desert region. I had never seen them like this before, only along the limb, or near the poles. With a coloured filter, the clouds would have disappeared, swallowed up by the masking effect of the filter. It was a revelation, and I encourage observers to look through their filters, but to also have a look without them. I now have a planetary imager in the back end of the telescope, but do enjoy the view through an eyepiece. There still is something about seeing it in real time.

A useful Web resource on Mars is ralphaeschliman.com/id22.htm.

JUPITER

Jupiter is the largest of the planets in the solar system, with an equatorial diameter of 142 894 km at 5.202 au from the Sun. I have always loved the harmonic symmetry of Jupiter being 1/10 the size of the Sun and roughly 10 times the size of Earth. At close to 50″, Jupiter is one of the largest planets to view in a telescope. The notable exception is Venus at inferior conjunction, where in October 2010, it exhibited a razor-thin 62″ crescent. This year, Jupiter moves slightly away from perihelion and will exhibit a 49.7″ disk at opposition. Jupiter moves an average of 30° per year on its path around the Sun, and this year moves from Pisces east into Aries.

Jupiter does not have a solid surface, however, unlike Venus, it has high-contrast, semi-stationary cloud features that have been observed for many centuries. Jupiter rotates on its axis in 9 h 55.46 m, slower toward the poles. You can actually notice the planet rotating over a period of half an hour. If you are drawing Jupiter, draw the main features in the first 10 min, because it will noticeably change to your critical eye if you spend much longer on it. You then fill in the other details relative to the major features. A good 50-mm telescope will show the equatorial belts, the polar hoods, as well as the four Galilean moons. If you jump to a good 75-mm aperture, the moons' shadows can easily be seen, and some structure in the belts is visible along with the temperate zone belts. Forty years ago, my old 50-mm refractor showed me a brick-red Great Red Spot, but now it has faded to a very light salmon pink, so that you need a 90-mm refractor to see it under good conditions. The more aperture, the better, and the view in good 125-mm to 175-mm apochromatic refractors or high-quality 200-mm to 250-mm obstructed apertures is spectacular. All you have to do is wait for those moments of good seeing, and you will be rewarded. These apertures will show festoons and the many structures visible in the best images of Jupiter. I find that with a 125-mm refractor at magnifications much above 200×, the contrast on Jupiter starts to get soft. As you move to larger apertures, that magnification limit moves upward as well. Larger apertures will improve the contrast, colour, and amount of fine detail visible on Jupiter. In the last few years, additional red spots and a few long-lived white ovals have been observed. The southern hemisphere of Jupiter seems to have a preponderance of the ovals and red spots, and the north equatorial belt has more dark markings along its margins. As has happened in the past, the South Equatorial Belt disappeared in 2010, so it will be interesting to see how it evolves over 2011. I could see numerous thin belts in the Northern Temperate Zone, and the Northern Equatorial Belt is very dark as the Handbook publication date advances.

Since some of Jupiter's cloud features are coloured, you can improve the contrast and hence the visibility of these features with colour filters. You can improve the

(text continues on p. 229)

JUPITER—DAILY CENTRAL MERIDIANS AND TIME OF TRANSIT OF GREAT RED SPOT

The table on the next page can be used to calculate the longitude of the central meridian of the observed disk of Jupiter during the months of January, February, and May–December (when Jupiter is well placed for observation). System I is the most rapidly rotating region between the middle of the North Equatorial Belt and the middle of the South Equatorial Belt. System II applies to the rest of the planet. The rotation rate of System I is 36.577 ± 0.008 °/h and that of System II is 36.259 ± 0.008 °/h. These figures, together with the closest tabular value, can be used to determine the longitude of a system's central meridian for any given date and time (UT) of observation. **Example:** At 1:00 ADT Aug. 8 = 4:00 UT Aug. 8, the longitude of the central meridian of System I is

$$245.9 + (36.577 \times 4) = 392.2°;$$

putting this angle in the range 0°–360° by subtracting 360° leaves a longitude of 32.2°, accurate to about 0.1°.

The table may also be used to determine when the Great Red Spot (GRS) (near longitude 120° in System II) will cross the central meridian of the disk of Jupiter. **Example:** Suppose an observer in Winnipeg is viewing Jupiter on the evening of May 28 (time zone: CDT, –5 h). At 0h UT May 29 (19h CDT May 28), the table gives approximately 75° for the longitude of the central meridian in System II. A further rotation of 120° – 75° = 45° will bring the GRS to the central meridian, which will require 45° ÷ 36.259°/h =1.24 h = 1 h 14 min. Thus the GRS will transit at 1:14 UT May 29 = 20:14 CDT May 28. Note that the GRS slowly drifts in longitude, so the 120° figure is only a guide. By timing a transit of the GRS and using the table, you can update its longitude.

CONJUNCTIONS AND APPULSES INVOLVING JUPITER FOR 2011

Date (UT)	Planet	Separation	Date (UT)	Planet	Separation
Jan. 2	Uranus	0.6°	May 11	Mercury	2.0°
Mar. 16	Mercury	2.0°	May 11	Venus	1.1°
May 1	Mars	0.4°			

GALILEAN MOON DATA AT OPPOSITION

Moon	Diameter km	Apparent Size "	Magnitude	Moon	Diameter km	Apparent Size "	Magnitude
Io	3643	1.27	4.7	Ganymede	5262	1.84	4.3
Europa	3122	1.09	5.0	Callisto	4820	1.68	5.4

Jupiter—2011		
Date UT	Mag.	Equatorial Diameter "
Jan. 1.0	−2.4	39.0
Feb. 1.0	−2.2	35.7
Mar. 1.0	−2.1	34.0
Apr. 1.0	−2.1	33.2
May 1.0	−2.1	33.4
Jun. 1.0	−2.1	34.6
Jul. 1.0	−2.3	37.1
Aug. 1.0	−2.4	40.6
Sep. 1.0	−2.6	44.8
Oct. 1.0	−2.8	48.4
Nov. 1.0	−2.9	49.6
Dec. 1.0	−2.8	47.6
Jan. 1.0	−2.6	43.4

JUPITER—TABLE OF DAILY CENTRAL MERIDIANS, 2011

JANUARY

Date 0h UT	System I	II
0	109.4	39.9
1	267.1	190.0
2	64.8	340.1
3	222.5	130.1
4	20.2	280.2
5	177.8	70.2
6	335.5	220.3
7	133.2	10.3
8	290.9	160.4
9	88.5	310.4
10	246.2	100.4
11	43.9	250.5
12	201.5	40.5
13	359.2	190.6
14	156.9	340.6
15	314.5	130.6
16	112.2	280.7
17	269.9	70.7
18	67.5	220.7
19	225.2	10.7
20	22.8	160.8
21	180.5	310.8
22	338.1	100.8
23	135.8	250.8
24	293.4	40.9
25	91.1	190.9
26	248.7	340.9
27	46.4	130.9
28	204.0	280.9
29	1.7	70.9
30	159.3	221.0
31	317.0	11.0

FEBRUARY

Date 0h UT	System I	II
1	114.6	161.0
2	272.2	311.0
3	69.9	101.0
4	227.5	251.0
5	25.2	41.0
6	182.8	191.0
7	340.4	341.0
8	138.1	131.0
9	295.7	281.1
10	93.3	71.1
11	251.0	221.1
12	48.6	11.1
13	206.2	161.1
14	3.9	311.1
15	161.5	101.1
16	319.2	251.1
17	116.8	41.1
18	274.4	191.1
19	72.1	341.1
20	229.7	131.1
21	27.3	281.1
22	185.0	71.1
23	342.6	221.1
24	140.2	11.1
25	297.8	161.1
26	95.5	311.1
27	253.1	101.1
28	50.7	251.1

MAY

Date 0h UT	System I	II
1	105.3	192.6
2	262.9	342.6
3	60.6	132.7
4	218.3	282.8
5	16.0	72.8
6	173.7	222.9
7	331.4	13.0
8	129.1	163.0
9	286.8	313.1
10	84.5	103.2
11	242.2	253.2
12	39.9	43.3
13	197.6	193.4
14	355.3	343.5
15	153.0	133.5
16	310.7	283.6
17	108.5	73.7
18	266.2	223.8
19	63.9	13.9
20	221.6	164.0
21	19.3	314.0
22	177.0	104.1
23	334.8	254.2
24	132.5	44.3
25	290.2	194.4
26	87.9	344.5
27	245.7	134.6
28	43.4	284.7
29	201.1	74.8
30	358.9	224.9
31	156.6	15.0

JUNE

Date 0h UT	System I	II
1	314.3	165.1
2	112.1	315.2
3	269.8	105.4
4	67.6	255.5
5	225.3	45.6
6	23.1	195.7
7	180.8	345.8
8	338.6	135.9
9	136.3	286.1
10	294.1	76.2
11	91.8	226.3
12	249.6	16.5
13	47.4	166.6
14	205.1	316.7
15	2.9	106.9
16	160.7	257.0
17	318.4	47.1
18	116.2	197.3
19	274.0	347.4
20	71.8	137.6
21	229.6	287.7
22	27.3	77.9
23	185.1	228.0
24	342.9	18.2
25	140.7	168.4
26	298.5	318.5
27	96.3	108.7
28	254.1	258.8
29	51.9	49.0
30	209.7	199.2

JULY

Date 0h UT	System I	II
1	7.5	349.4
2	165.3	139.5
3	323.1	289.7
4	120.9	79.9
5	278.7	230.1
6	76.5	20.3
7	234.4	170.4
8	32.2	320.6
9	190.0	110.8
10	347.8	261.0
11	145.7	51.2
12	303.5	201.4
13	101.3	351.6
14	259.2	141.8
15	57.0	292.0
16	214.8	82.2
17	12.7	232.5
18	170.5	22.7
19	328.4	172.9
20	126.2	323.1
21	284.1	113.3
22	81.9	263.6
23	239.8	53.8
24	37.7	204.0
25	195.5	354.3
26	353.4	144.5
27	151.3	294.7
28	309.1	85.0
29	107.0	235.2
30	264.9	25.5
31	62.8	175.7

AUGUST

Date 0h UT	System I	II
1	220.7	326.0
2	18.5	116.2
3	176.4	266.5
4	334.3	56.8
5	132.2	207.0
6	290.1	357.3
7	88.0	147.6
8	245.9	297.8
9	43.8	88.1
10	201.7	238.4
11	359.7	28.7
12	157.6	179.0
13	315.5	329.2
14	113.4	119.5
15	271.3	269.8
16	69.3	60.1
17	227.2	210.4
18	25.1	0.7
19	183.1	151.0
20	341.0	301.3
21	138.9	91.6
22	296.9	242.0
23	94.8	32.3
24	252.8	182.6
25	50.7	332.9
26	208.7	123.2
27	6.6	273.6
28	164.6	63.9
29	322.6	214.2
30	120.5	4.6
31	278.5	154.9

SEPTEMBER

Date 0h UT	System I	II
1	76.5	305.2
2	234.5	95.6
3	32.4	245.9
4	190.4	36.3
5	348.4	186.6
6	146.4	337.0
7	304.4	127.4
8	102.4	277.7
9	260.4	68.1
10	58.3	218.4
11	216.3	8.8
12	14.3	159.2
13	172.3	309.5
14	330.4	99.9
15	128.4	250.3
16	286.4	40.7
17	84.4	191.1
18	242.4	341.4
19	40.4	131.8
20	198.4	282.2
21	356.5	72.6
22	154.5	223.0
23	312.5	13.4
24	110.5	163.8
25	268.6	314.2
26	66.6	104.6
27	224.6	255.0
28	22.6	45.4
29	180.7	195.8
30	338.7	346.2

OCTOBER

Date 0h UT	System I	II
1	136.8	136.6
2	294.8	287.0
3	92.8	77.4
4	250.9	227.8
5	48.9	18.2
6	207.0	168.7
7	5.0	319.1
8	163.0	109.5
9	321.1	259.9
10	119.1	50.3
11	277.2	200.7
12	75.2	351.1
13	233.3	141.6
14	31.3	292.0
15	189.4	82.4
16	347.4	232.8
17	145.4	23.2
18	303.5	173.6
19	101.5	324.0
20	259.6	114.5
21	57.6	264.9
22	215.7	55.3
23	13.7	205.7
24	171.8	356.1
25	329.8	146.5
26	127.8	296.9
27	285.9	87.3
28	83.9	237.7
29	241.9	28.2
30	40.0	178.6
31	198.0	329.0

NOVEMBER

Date 0h UT	System I	II
1	356.0	119.4
2	154.1	269.8
3	312.1	60.1
4	110.1	210.5
5	268.1	0.9
6	66.2	151.3
7	224.2	301.7
8	22.2	92.1
9	180.2	242.5
10	338.2	32.9
11	136.2	183.2
12	294.2	333.6
13	92.2	124.0
14	250.2	274.3
15	48.2	64.7
16	206.2	215.1
17	4.2	5.4
18	162.2	155.8
19	320.1	306.1
20	118.1	96.5
21	276.1	246.8
22	74.1	37.2
23	232.0	187.5
24	30.0	337.8
25	188.0	128.2
26	345.9	278.5
27	143.9	68.8
28	301.8	219.1
29	99.8	9.4
30	257.7	159.8

DECEMBER

Date 0h UT	System I	II
1	55.6	310.1
2	213.6	100.4
3	11.5	250.7
4	169.4	40.9
5	327.3	191.2
6	125.2	341.5
7	283.1	131.8
8	81.1	282.1
9	239.0	72.3
10	36.9	222.6
11	194.7	12.9
12	352.6	163.1
13	150.5	313.4
14	308.4	103.6
15	106.3	253.9
16	264.1	44.1
17	62.0	194.4
18	219.9	344.6
19	17.7	134.8
20	175.6	285.1
21	333.4	75.3
22	131.3	225.5
23	289.1	15.7
24	87.0	165.9
25	244.8	316.1
26	42.6	106.3
27	200.4	256.5
28	358.3	46.7
29	156.1	196.9
30	313.9	347.1
31	111.7	137.2

contrast of red spots and the belt features with a green filter, and the bluish festoons will darken with an orange or red filter. Jupiter is one of the best planets for imaging. The most recent generation of Web-camera-style dedicated imagers has improved the quality with which the amateur can image the planets. It is easy to get images that push the limits of the optical system's capability, and once captured, the dynamic range in the image can be stretched to allow all the low-contrast details to show. Amateurs are producing images only a bit lower in resolution than *Hubble* images, and these same amateurs are making discoveries on Jupiter, like Red Spot Junior in 2008 and the 2009 Jul. 19 and 2010 Jun. 3 impacts in Jupiter's atmosphere discovered by Anthony Wesley. Much like deep-sky observers who search locations that produce the darkest skies, some of these leading imagers seek places that have the most stable skies for imaging. (See Damian Peach's article on his Caribbean expeditions on his Web site, **www.damianpeach.com**.) I will not go on about imaging here because it is an area that deserves a chapter of its own, but it has a tremendous potential to push the limits of what you can see on the planets.

Jupiter starts off the year in close conjunction with Uranus. The pair sit in the constellation of Pisces and will be in closest approach on Jan. 2 with a 31″ spacing. Jupiter then moves off on its way across Pisces to a conjunction with the Sun on Apr. 6. In May, we have a nice triple conjunction with Mercury and Venus, but it is the dreaded morning ecliptic, and you will see them in bright twilight, or in an eyepiece. It may be a good excuse to visit the Southern Hemisphere, where the conjunction will be great! There Mars will be an easy find as well, 5° below the group. Back in the Northern Hemisphere, Venus will provide the homing beacon, so it will be easy to spot them. Jupiter continues its trip across the sky to arrive in Aries for opposition on Oct. 29. In December, Jupiter makes a short pass back into Pisces in the ansae of retrograde, where it stays for the balance of the year.

Jupiter has 62 moons, four of which are visible in binoculars, and one very faint one is within reach of larger amateur telescopes. All the major moons show a disk in a 90-mm or larger telescope, and if you examine them carefully, you will see the colour differences and size differences that distinguish one from the other. Callisto is quite dark, and I see it as having a bluish cast. I have confused a satellite transit of Callisto as a shadow transit until the real shadow made the scene. Callisto's albedo is slightly less than half that of Ganymede, whereas Ganymede's albedo is roughly the same as Jupiter and about 66 percent of Europa and Io's albedo. Since Io and Europa have a slightly greater albedo than Jupiter, they are "visible" as they cross in front of Jupiter. They are

ANGULAR SIZE OF JUPITER IN 2011

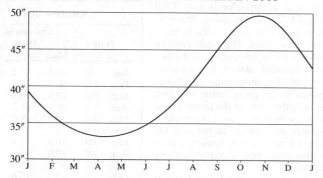

The angular size of Jupiter, in arcseconds, is shown in the above graph. The first day of each month is indicated with tick marks on the horizontal axis.

really difficult to follow across the disk, but it can be done. The inner three of these bright moons are in orbital resonance with each other. Europa has twice Io's period, and Ganymede has twice Europa's period. Callisto orbits Jupiter in 16.7 days.

The next moon in a larger orbit that amateurs may observe is Himalia, a 170-km body that has a 250-day orbital period. It shines at magnitude 14.6 around the time of opposition. Canadian amateur Alan Whitman spotted it in a 400-mm Newtonian. Of the outer moons of Jupiter, 48 move in retrograde orbits, which indicates that they may be captured asteroids.

The major moons of Jupiter are frequently involved in eclipses, occultations, and transits with Jupiter, and these are within easy reach of amateur telescopes. A complete listing of events is on pp. 240–245.

SATURN

Saturn is the second-largest planet in our solar system, and, with its system of rings, possibly the most spectacular. In the eyepiece, it usually elicits a gasp of wonder from first-time viewers. The first thing you notice is the incredible set of rings disposed around the subtly shaded ball of the planet. Saturn's rings are visible in higher-power binoculars and small spotting scopes. They subtend 44.35″ around the time of opposition. Saturn takes 29.424 years to orbit the Sun and moves only 12.22° per year in its journey around the ecliptic. The light that leaves Saturn takes a little more than an hour to reach Earth. The equatorial diameter of Saturn is 120536 km. Saturn is the most oblate of the planets, with a pole-to-equatorial-diameter ratio of 0.9020.

Saturn's incredible system of rings is composed mostly of ice particles of sizes ranging from dust to boulders. The rings are composed of many subsystems of rings with divisions. The more you zoom in on them, the more there is to see. The *Cassini* probe has shown fine structure right down to the limits of its view. Visually in Earth-bound telescopes, the rings are broken into three distinct segments. The outer ring is the A ring, with the Cassini Division as the boundary to the next ring inward, the B ring. The A ring has a very fine division about 1/5 of the way in from the edge of the ring to the Cassini Division called the Encke Gap. This division is extremely difficult to observe, requiring a large good-quality aperture, 250 mm or greater, and high magnification in the order of 500× to observe. There is also a minimum in brightness called the Encke minimum about halfway between the outer edge of the A ring and the Cassini Division. This is often confused with the Encke Gap.

The Cassini Division was discovered in 1675 by J.D. Cassini and is visible in a good 50-mm scope. This is an impressive feat since the Cassini Division is only 4700 km in width, or 0.77″ at opposition. The next ring inward is the B ring, and it is the broader and brighter of the rings. The inner edge of this ring fades a bit in brightness, and often appears of a stranded nature, like grooves in a vinyl record. The inner edge sometimes exhibits spokes in the rings' ansae (the part of the rings on either side of the planet). You need high magnification and a very clean optical system to see these subtle features. On the occasions I have seen the spokes, I have found that they may only be visible on one side of the planet.

The innermost ring is the Crepe Ring. It goes largely unnoticed because it is so dim in

Saturn—2011			
Date		**Equatorial Diam.**	**Ring Incl.**
UT	Mag.	″	°
Jan. 1.0	+0.8	17.2	+10.1
Feb. 1.0	+0.7	18.2	+10.2
Mar. 1.0	+0.5	18.9	+9.7
Apr. 1.0	+0.4	19.3	+8.8
May 1.0	+0.5	19.0	+7.8
Jun. 1.0	+0.7	18.3	+7.3
Jul. 1.0	+0.9	17.4	+7.5
Aug. 1.0	+0.9	16.5	+8.3
Sep. 1.0	+0.9	15.9	+9.6
Oct. 1.0	+0.8	15.6	+11.1
Nov. 1.0	+0.7	15.6	+12.6
Dec. 1.0	+0.8	16.0	+13.9
Jan. 1.0	+0.7	16.7	+14.8

(text continues on p. 232)

ANGULAR SIZE OF SATURN IN 2011

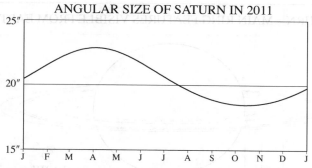

The angular size of Saturn, in arcseconds, is shown in the above graph. The first day of each month is indicated with tick marks on the horizontal axis.

INCLINATION OF SATURN'S RINGS IN 2011

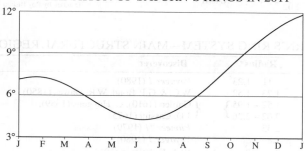

The inclination of Saturn's rings, in degrees, is shown in the above graph. The first day of each month is indicated with tick marks on the horizontal axis.

CONJUNCTIONS AND APPULSES INVOLVING SATURN FOR 2011

Date (UT)	Planet	Separation	Date (UT)	Planet	Separation
Sep. 29	Venus	1.3°			

SATURN MOON DATA AT OPPOSITION

Moon	Diameter km	Apparent Size "	Magnitude	Moon	Diameter km	Apparent Size "	Magnitude
Mimas	397	0.06	12.8	Rhea	1530	0.25	9.6
Enceladus	499	0.08	11.6	Titan	5150	0.84	8.2
Tethys	1060	0.17	10.1	Hyperion	266	0.04	14.1
Dione	1120	0.18	10.3	Iapetus	1469	0.24	10.2–11.6

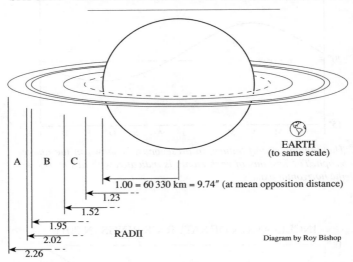

SATURN—MAIN RING FEATURES VISIBLE FROM EARTH

EARTH
(to same scale)

1.00 = 60 330 km = 9.74″ (at mean opposition distance)

1.23

1.52

1.95

2.02

2.26

RADII

A   B   C

Diagram by Roy Bishop

SATURN'S RING SYSTEM—MAIN STRUCTURAL REGIONS

Ring	Radius**	Discoverer
D	1.11 – 1.23	*Voyager 1* (1980)
C*	1.23 – 1.52	W.C. & G.P. Bond, W.R. Dawes (1850)
B*	1.52 – 1.95 ⎫	⎧ Galileo (1610), C. Huygens (1659),
A*	2.02 – 2.26 ⎭	⎩ J.D. Cassini (1675)
F	2.33	*Pioneer 11* (1979)
G	2.8	*Voyager 1* (1980)
E	3. – 8.	W.A. Feibelman (1966)

*Visible from Earth; also, the E ring can be detected when Saturn's ring system
 appears edge-on.
**In units of Saturn's equatorial radius (60 330 km)

comparison to the outer two rings and the glare from Saturn. It is a ghostly ring about
the same width as the A ring, and, where it passes in front of the planet, it appears
dark. It looks like a shadow cast on the planet, but it is actually blocking the planet's
reflected light from our view. A very clean optical system is a must to get a good view
of the C ring. If you are using a star diagonal, make sure it and your eyepieces are
clean. Contrast-robbing dust and debris on these surfaces has a much greater effect
because it is closer to the eye. You know you have seen the Crepe Ring when you
notice the black space within the ansae next to the ball of the planet is only slightly
darker than the Crepe Ring. With the low inclination of the rings this year, the Crepe
Ring should be much more obvious. The year starts off with Saturn's rings tilted at
an angle of 10°. Saturn's North Pole is tipped toward us now and the inclination will
increase from year to year. The rings will tip down as our orbital position changes the
perspective until early June, where it drops to a minimum of 7.3°. From this point
onward, the rings tip back up until year end, when they tip up at 14.8°. One ring
phenomena that I have read about is the Seeliger Effect, a brightening of the rings
around the time of opposition. It is visible for just a few days near opposition.

Saturn starts off the year 6° southeast of γ (Gamma) Virginis and begins retrograde motion on Jan. 28, when it starts its apparent westward motion. Saturn is at opposition on Apr. 4, where it will shine at magnitude 0.3 and its disk subtends 19.29″. Saturn swings close to 2.74-magnitude γ Vir in the early part of the month of June, marking the end of Saturn's retrograde motion. The closest approach is on Jun. 9, when it is separated from γ Vir by only 15.15′. After retrograde, Saturn moves down Virgo and passes above Spica near the end of the year. Saturn is in conjunction with the Sun on Oct. 13.

At a distance of 9.5 au from the Sun, Saturn does not receive enough energy to create a lively atmosphere like Jupiter's. The average observer may see an equatorial-region belt and the dark polar hood, but not much else is going on. The experienced observer may see much more, but the details are subtle. The energy levels in Saturn's atmosphere are one-quarter that of Jupiter, but it does show the occasional storm and outbreak of activity. White spots have been seen in the south tropical zone over the last number of years, and in 2009, a south equatorial disturbance was recorded. They are subtle and are more readily captured with a planetary camera.

Saturn has 61 named satellites, of which 8 are visible in amateur telescopes. Of them, only Titan shows a disk in large telescopes. At opposition this year, Titan presents a 0.835″ disk. I had extended the challenge last year, and intended to give this good study in the spring of 2009, but the recovery effort of the Buzzard Coulee meteorite occupied all of my available time. I missed my chance, but I will try again this coming apparition. Notably, Christopher Go imaged the disk of Titan and its shadow on Saturn during the 2009 apparition. His equipment comprised a C11 and a DMK 21F04 camera—excellent work; I recommend you find him on the Internet.

Iapetus is tidally locked to Saturn, and it has a very interesting property in its brightness: its leading hemisphere is as dark as coal and the other side is quite white. (The actual albedos are 0.05 and 0.5.) So when Iapetus is near elongation on the west side of Saturn, it is two magnitudes brighter than it is on the east side of Saturn. Iapetus's 79.33-day orbit puts it as far as 9.35′ from Saturn. As a finding aid, near Saturn's opposition, Iapetus is directly above (north of) Saturn on Jan. 24, Apr. 13, and Jul. 1; and directly below (south of) Saturn on Mar. 5 and May 22.

URANUS

Uranus is the faintest of the planets visible to the naked eye and the 4th-largest overall with an equatorial diameter of 51 118 km. It sits at an average distance of 19.19 au from the Sun. Sir William Hershel discovered it in 1781 with a 160-mm reflector, but it had been recorded by earlier observers as far back as Galileo, who marked it on observation drawings as a star. At magnitude 5.7, it does require a clear and transparent sky for a successful naked-eye sighting. Binoculars easily reveal Uranus, and it blossoms into a pale blue-green disk under high power in a telescope. I have never seen details on the

(text continues on p. 235)

URANUS MOON DATA AT OPPOSITION

Moon	Orbital Period d	Maximum Separation ″	Mag.	Moon	Orbital Period d	Maximum Separation ″	Mag.
Arial	2.52	13.8	14.3	Titania	8.71	31.5	13.9
Umbrial	4.14	19.2	15.0	Oberon	13.46	42.1	14.1

CONJUNCTIONS AND APPULSES INVOLVING URANUS FOR 2011

Date (UT)	Planet	Separation	Date (UT)	Planet	Separation
Jun. 2	Jupiter	0.6°	Apr. 22	Venus	0.9°

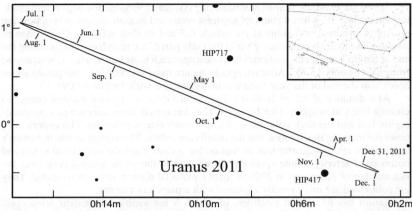

The finder chart above, provided by Dave Lane, shows the path of Uranus in Aquarius during the 9-month period April–December 2011. Coordinates are for equinox J2000.0, and the magnitude limit is approximately 9.0. Tick marks are drawn along the path at the beginning of each month. The brightest star in the chart, near the Nov. 1 position, is 6.3-magnitude HIP 417.

Along the 5-month retrograde portion of its track, from Jul. 1 to Dec. 2 and centred at its Sep. 26 opposition, Uranus ranges between 5.7 and 5.9 in magnitude.

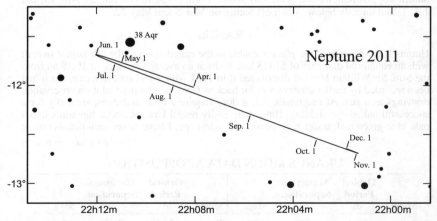

The finder chart above, provided by Dave Lane, shows the path of Neptune in Capricornus during the 8-month period April–December 2011. Coordinates are for equinox J2000.0, and the magnitude limit is approximately 9.0. Tick marks are drawn along the path at the beginning of each month. The brightest star in the chart, near the May 1 position, is 5.4-magnitude 38 Aqr.

Along the 5-month retrograde portion of its track, from Jun. 1 to Nov. 7 and centred at its Aug. 22 opposition, Neptune ranges between 7.8 and 7.9 in magnitude.

OPPOSITION MAGNITUDE OF URANUS 1810–2060

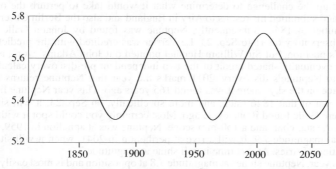

planet, but they have been seen in amateur-sized instruments. Fred Price in *The Planet Observer's Handbook* states that the only features seen on the planet are the two faint belts and that you need at least a 250-mm telescope to see anything on it. Uranus's orbital period is 84.4 years and it moves about 4.29° per year. This year it is just a binocular field east from where it was seen last year. Uranus lies at 19.08 au at the time of the Sep. 26 opposition, and will exhibit a 3.69″ disk in the eyepiece. Just for comparison, Mars around the time of solar conjunction will be 3.94″. Uranus rotates in 17.24 hours, rather leisurely compared to Jupiter and Saturn's period.

Uranus was at aphelion last year and it is now rounding the corner on its trip back towards the Sun. It will be another 40 years before it reaches perihelion and shines at magnitude 5.3. Do not wait that long to try to see it naked eye! I have included a chart showing the variation in Uranus' brightness at opposition over the period from 1810 to 2060. The year starts off with Uranus about 4° below the circlet of Pisces in a close conjunction with Jupiter. This will be very nice in a telescope with the pair only 31′ apart. Uranus moves into conjunction with the Sun on Mar. 21. One month later it moves into conjunction with Venus on Apr. 22 in the morning sky, where the pair will be less than a degree apart. Venus will act as the finder beacon in the morning twilight. Uranus arrives at opposition on Sep. 26, where it will exhibit a 3.69″ disk, shining at magnitude 5.7. Its north pole is inclined at an angle of 14.7° toward the Earth. (90° would point directly at Earth.) During the favourable late-summer/autumn observing window, it sits at −1° declination, providing a good view for northern observers.

Uranus's system of moons is within reach of medium to large amateur telescopes. I have seen Titania and Oberon in a 320-mm Newtonian, where Uranus was sitting at an altitude of 18°. The brighter, more-distant moons should be accessible in telescopes as small as 250 mm under good conditions. The fainter moons are closer to Uranus, complicating things somewhat. The use of clean optics and possibly an occulting-bar eyepiece should make the observation possible in 300-mm to 430-mm telescopes. I recommend using your favourite planetarium software to generate a finder chart for the evening you choose to search for these moons. I also encourage you to use a clean eyepiece and as much magnification as the conditions will bear to separate the moons from the planet.

NEPTUNE

Neptune is the most distant major planet in our solar system. It has an equatorial diameter of 49 532 km, making it the fifth largest, and an average distance of 30.069 au from the Sun. Neptune's position was predicted independently by two mathematicians in 1845–46, based on the observed errors between the predicted versus observed positions of Uranus. In England, John Couch Adams took the task on as an undergraduate and continued working on it after he was elected a Fellow at Cambridge in 1844. He presented his results to the British Astronomer Royal, Airy, in the fall of 1845. Airy was suspect of the results and requested more information,

but Adams took his time getting back to Airy. Meanwhile Urbain Le Verrier of France also took up the challenge to determine what it would take to perturb the orbit of Uranus, and submitted his results to Airy in England and also the Berlin Observatory in September of 1846. Subsequently, Neptune was found by Johann Galle at the Berlin Observatory on 1846 Sep. 23. Le Verrier was credited with the prediction of Neptune's position, but Sir William Hershel pointed out John Adams' work, and the two men eventually shared credit of the two independent pre-discovery calculations that led to Neptune's discovery. 2011 marks the year that Neptune returns to this **exact place** on the sky where it was found 165 years ago. This year Neptune lies less than 31' east of that 1846 track, and more specifically, on Sep. 23, it will sit 30.4' from where Galle found it one cycle ago. Most certainly you could spot it with just a Uranometria star chart and a 150-mm scope. Neptune was at aphelion in 1959, where it shone at magnitude 7.9. It will arrive at perihelion in 2041, when it will sit in the constellation of Aries. At that time it will shine at magnitude 7.7.

This year, Neptune shines at magnitude 7.8 at opposition and is most easily found with a pair of binoculars and finder chart. You need high magnification and reasonably steady skies to see the 2.35″ greenish disk. I recommend 200× and above. Remember that Jupiter's moon Ganymede shows a 1.7″ disk when Jupiter is at opposition. Neptune also has one moon that is within reach of medium amateur telescopes (250 mm and larger). Neptune's largest moon, Triton, shines at magnitude 13.4 around the time of opposition, and ranges from 17″ to 12″ from Neptune. We are observing Neptune with a rather high inclination, so Triton's orbit is an ellipse that is close to a circle. Use your favourite planetarium software to create a chart for the specific set of nights you intend to look for it. I have glimpsed it in my 250-mm telescope on many occasions. Triton is easier to find than any of Uranus's moons primarily because it is brighter, but also Neptune is two magnitudes fainter and the glare is much reduced.

The year starts off with Neptune slipping quietly into the glare of the Sun. On Feb. 17, it lies in conjunction with the Sun and sits near the western border of Aquarius. Neptune only moves 2.1° per year on its 165.84-year orbit, so it is in the same low-power field as last year. You can find the field for it just above Iota Aquarius, a fourth-magnitude star. On Mar. 27, it will be in close conjunction with Venus, an incredible 9' apart. The close approach will be visible only in the Far East, but by the time they rise here in North America it will be more like half a degree of separation. In the eyepiece, you will see the two planets, both of which are on the far side of the Sun, gibbous Venus at 13″ and Neptune at 2.2″. Neptune comes to opposition on Aug. 22, well placed for summer star parties. In September, see if you can "re-discover" Neptune on its first Neptunian anniversary since Johann Galle discovered it.

CONJUNCTIONS AND APPULSES INVOLVING NEPTUNE FOR 2011

Date (UT)	Planet	Separation	Date (UT)	Planet	Separation
Mar. 27	Venus	0.2°			

PLUTO

In 2006, Pluto was demoted from the club of planets. I understand the logic of the change of designations, but Pluto has appeared in the *Observer's Handbook* since the year after its discovery, in 1930, so I will maintain this fine tradition. Pluto's highly eccentric orbit has a mean distance of 39.5 au from the Sun, and is in a 2:3 resonance with Neptune. Presently, it is much closer than that, about 32.05 au in 2011.

A look at a plot of the brightness of Pluto over a 300-year period shows we are at the beginning of a long fade-out as it leaves perihelion. Clyde Tombaugh discovered Pluto when it was lurking at a distance of 42.3 au and 15.3 magnitude. It will be another 39 years before Pluto becomes this faint. Pluto is 2390 km in diameter, only twice the size of its largest moon, Charon (1212 km). It rotates in a retrograde direction in 6.39 days, in synchrony with Charon's orbit. Pluto has two more rather

small satellites, Nix and Hydra. Both are estimated to be from 36 to 88 km in diameter and are 9.5 magnitudes fainter than Pluto.

The year starts off with Pluto emerging from its late-December conjunction with the Sun as it moves away from the M24 star cloud. It will proceed east to just above M25 by the month of May, then do a retrograde loop back to the edge of M24. It is at opposition on Jun. 28 and shines at magnitude 14.1. After it completes its retrograde motion and turns the corner, it will head back to end the year in M25. There will be no lack of field stars to help find Pluto over the next few years. At magnitude 14.1, where it lies in the depths of Sagittarius, it is a bit of a challenge in an 8-inch scope from our northern latitudes. You will need to wait for a night of near-perfect transparency to find it, or use a larger scope. This year, M25 sits on the left-hand side of the Pluto finder chart, and should make the star hop a bit easier. This year's apparition concludes with Pluto's conjunction with the Sun on Dec. 29.

Now, if finding Pluto wasn't enough of a challenge, then the real challenge is to see if you can spot it in a mid-sized refractor. The observation is a good challenge in a 125-130-mm refractor, but the transparency and seeing must both be very good. One year, I challenged Edmonton Centre member Alister Ling to find it in his 125-mm APO, and I repeated it with my 94-mm Brandon refractor. Pluto was much higher back then. Alister did it with relative ease, but the challenge of the 94-mm made for a very tough hunt. I got it, but with great difficulty, eyestrain, and over an hour of painstaking star hopping. I welcome any comments or stories of your hunt.

The author would like to apologize to any of you who may have tried to contact him over the last apparition of the Handbook. The email ID received so few enquiries that it lapsed, and the author missed the comments that were there. Any comments or enquiries should be directed to murray.paulson@gmail.com with the word Handbook included in the subject line. This email is continuously monitored.

References

[1] Suiter, H.R., *Star Testing Astronomical Telescopes: A Manual for Optical Evaluation and Adjustment*, Willman-Bell Inc, Richmond, 1994.

FINDER CHART FOR PLUTO
BY IAN CAMERON

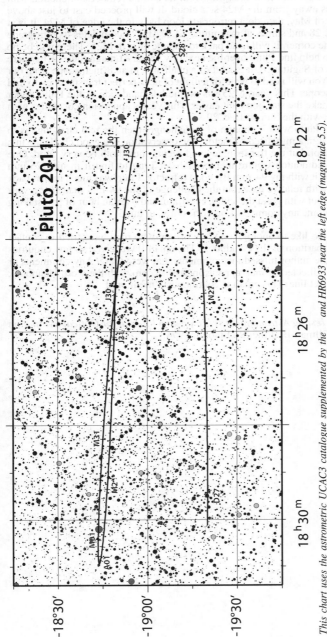

This chart uses the astrometric UCAC3 catalogue supplemented by the Tycho catalogue for the brightest stars. The UCAC3 lists CCD magnitudes that are somewhat between V and R magnitudes. Uranometria 2000 stars (Chart 339/340 in Vol. 2) are indicated in light gray and the Tirion 2000 stars (Chart 15 in 1st edition), in dark gray.

The relatively bright star Y Sgr is centrally located towards the right edge of the chart (magnitude 5.75 according to The Bright Star Catalogue)

and HR6933 near the left edge (magnitude 5.5).

Pluto is at opposition at magnitude 13.99 on Jun. 26. The chart limiting magnitude is 14.5 according to the UCAC3. The chart is generated using the open source Generic Mapping Tools (GMT4.5.2) under Mac OS 10.6.4.

PHENOMENA OF THE GALILEAN SATELLITES

The table on the following pages gives the various transits, occultations, and eclipses of the four great satellites of Jupiter during January–mid-February and mid-May–December 2011. Jupiter is not well-placed for observing from mid-February to mid-May since it is in conjunction with the Sun on Apr. 6. Double-shadow transits are indicated in **bold**. Double-satellite transits are indicated in *italics*.

Since the satellite phenomena are not instantaneous but take up to several minutes, the predicted times are for the middle of each event. The predictions were generated by the Institut de Mécanique Céleste et de Calcul des Ephémérides in Paris.

Satellites are denoted using the standard designations: I = Io; II = Europa; III = Ganymede; IV = Callisto. Events are denoted using the following abbreviations:

Ec = eclipse; Oc = occultation; Tr = transit of satellite; Sh = transit of shadow;
I = ingress; E = egress; D = disappearance; R = reappearance

The general motion of the satellites and the successive phenomena are shown in the diagram at right, which is a view of Jupiter and the orbit of one of its satellites looking down from the north side. Satellites move from east to west across the face of the planet and from west to east behind it (here "east" and "west" are used in the sense of the observer's sky, not in the Jovian sense). Before opposition, shadows fall to the west and after opposition, to the east (as in the diagram).

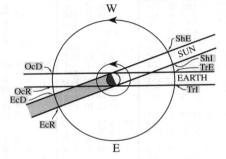

The sequence of phenomena for the outer satellite shown in the diagram, counterclockwise beginning at the lower right, is transit ingress (TrI), transit egress (TrE), shadow ingress (ShI), shadow egress (ShE), occultation disappearance (OcD), occultation reappearance (OcR), eclipse disappearance (EcD), and eclipse reappearance (EcR). The actual sequence will depend on the actual Sun–Jupiter–Earth angle and the size of the satellite's orbit.

Over three-quarters of the phenomena listed will not be visible from any one location because they occur when Jupiter is near or below the horizon or when daylight interferes. In practice, an observer usually knows when Jupiter will be conveniently placed in the night sky; if not, he or she can check THE SKY MONTH BY MONTH section (p. 98) for this information. The table can then be scanned to see if there are any events during the intended observing period. For example, an observer in Halifax would know that Jupiter is well placed near midnight in October and November with opposition occurring on Oct. 29. If planning to observe from 22:00 on Oct. 21 to 2:00 ADT on Oct. 22 (3 h behind UT), he or she could scan the table for events in the interval Oct. 21 1:00 to 5:00 UT and find that there are five events, beginning at 22:25 ADT with the appearance of Io's shadow on Jupiter's surface, followed 13 minutes later by the start of Io itself transitting in front of the planet. At 11:06, Ganymede emenges from Jupiter's limb. At 0:35 Io's shadow egresses followed 11 minutes later by the egress of Io. The configuration of the four Galilean satellites during that night is given in the diagram on the right-hand side of p. 121 in the THE SKY MONTH BY MONTH section.

A total of 1761 events (330 eclipse, 331 occultation, 548 transit, and 552 shadow) appear in the table, an average of one event every 3 h 20 min.

SATELLITES OF JUPITER, UT OF 2011 GEOCENTRIC PHENOMENA

Day	UT	Sat.	Phen.
JANUARY			
0	0:00	III	OcR
	2:21	III	EcD
	4:53	I	TrI
	5:09	III	EcR
	6:12	I	ShI
	7:07	I	TrE
	8:25	I	ShE
1	2:03	I	OcD
	5:35	I	EcR
	6:42	II	OcD
	12:08	II	EcR
	17:06	IV	OcD
	18:50	IV	OcR
	23:23	I	TrI
2	0:41	I	ShI
	1:37	I	TrE
	2:54	I	ShE
	20:32	I	OcD
3	0:04	I	EcR
	1:07	II	TrI
	3:43	II	ShI
	3:51	II	TrE
	6:22	II	ShE
	11:12	III	TrI
	14:18	III	TrE
	16:37	III	ShI
	17:52	I	TrI
	19:10	**I**	**ShI**
	19:23	III	ShE
	20:06	I	TrE
	21:23	I	ShE
4	15:02	I	OcD
	18:33	I	EcR
	20:05	II	OcD
5	1:28	II	EcR
	12:22	I	TrI
	13:39	I	ShI
	14:36	I	TrE
	15:52	I	ShE
6	9:31	I	OcD
	13:02	I	EcR
	14:28	II	TrI
	17:01	II	ShI
	17:12	II	TrE
	19:41	II	ShE
7	1:04	III	OcD
	4:12	III	OcR
	6:24	III	EcD
	6:52	I	TrI
	8:08	I	ShI
	9:06	I	TrE
	9:11	III	EcR
	10:21	I	ShE
8	4:01	I	OcD
	7:31	I	EcR
	9:26	II	OcD
	14:46	II	EcR
9	1:22	I	TrI
	2:37	I	ShI
	3:36	I	TrE
	4:50	I	ShE
	22:30	I	OcD
10	1:59	I	EcR
	2:48	IV	TrI
	3:49	*II*	*TrI*
	4:13	IV	TrE
10	6:19	II	ShI
	6:33	II	TrE
	8:59	II	ShE
	15:26	III	TrI
	18:31	III	TrE
	19:51	I	TrI
	20:40	III	ShI
	21:06	**I**	**ShI**
	22:05	I	TrE
	23:19	I	ShE
	23:24	III	ShE
11	17:00	I	OcD
	20:28	I	EcR
	22:49	II	OcD
12	4:06	II	EcR
	14:21	I	TrI
	15:35	I	ShI
	16:35	I	TrE
	17:48	I	ShE
13	11:30	I	OcD
	14:57	I	EcR
	17:10	II	TrI
	19:38	II	ShI
	19:55	II	TrE
	22:17	II	ShE
14	5:20	III	OcD
	8:27	III	OcR
	8:51	I	TrI
	10:04	I	ShI
	10:27	III	EcD
	11:05	I	TrE
	12:17	I	ShE
	13:13	III	EcR
15	6:00	I	OcD
	9:26	I	EcR
	12:12	II	OcD
	17:24	II	EcR
16	3:21	I	TrI
	4:33	I	ShI
	5:35	I	TrE
	6:46	I	ShE
17	0:29	I	OcD
	3:55	I	EcR
	6:32	II	TrI
	8:56	II	ShI
	9:17	II	TrE
	11:36	II	ShE
	19:43	III	TrI
	21:51	*I*	*TrI*
	22:48	III	TrE
	23:02	I	ShI
18	0:05	I	TrE
	0:42	**III**	**ShI**
	1:15	I	ShE
	3:26	III	ShE
	12:37	IV	OcD
	14:11	IV	OcR
	18:59	I	OcD
	22:24	I	EcR
19	1:36	II	OcD
	6:43	II	EcR
	16:21	I	TrI
	17:31	I	ShI
	18:35	I	TrE
	19:44	I	ShE
20	13:29	I	OcD
	16:53	I	EcR
	19:55	II	TrI
20	22:15	II	ShI
	22:39	II	TrE
21	0:54	II	ShE
	9:39	III	OcD
	10:51	I	TrI
	12:00	I	ShI
	12:46	III	OcR
	13:05	I	TrE
	14:12	I	ShE
	14:30	III	EcD
	17:15	III	EcR
22	7:59	I	OcD
	11:22	I	EcR
	14:59	II	OcD
	20:02	II	EcR
23	5:21	I	TrI
	6:29	I	ShI
	7:35	I	TrE
	8:41	I	ShE
24	2:29	I	OcD
	5:50	I	EcR
	9:17	II	TrI
	11:33	II	ShI
	12:02	II	TrE
	14:13	II	ShE
	23:51	I	TrI
25	*0:04*	*III*	*TrI*
	0:58	I	ShI
	2:05	I	TrE
	3:07	III	TrE
	3:10	I	ShE
	4:45	III	ShI
	7:27	III	ShE
	20:59	I	OcD
26	0:19	I	EcR
	4:23	II	OcD
	9:21	II	EcR
	18:21	I	TrI
	19:27	I	ShI
	20:35	I	TrE
	21:39	I	ShE
	22:51	IV	TrI
	23:53	IV	TrE
27	15:29	I	OcD
	18:48	I	EcR
	22:40	II	TrI
28	0:52	II	ShI
	1:25	II	TrE
	3:31	II	ShE
	12:51	I	TrI
	13:56	I	ShI
	14:02	III	OcD
	15:05	I	TrE
	16:08	I	ShE
	17:07	III	OcR
	18:33	III	EcD
	21:16	III	EcR
29	9:59	I	OcD
	13:17	I	EcR
	17:47	II	OcD
	22:40	II	EcR
30	7:21	I	TrI
	8:25	I	ShI
	9:35	I	TrE
	10:37	I	ShE
31	4:30	I	OcD
	7:46	I	EcR
31	12:04	II	TrI
	14:10	II	ShI
	14:48	II	TrE
	16:49	II	ShE
FEBRUARY			
1	1:52	I	TrI
	2:54	I	ShI
	4:06	I	TrE
	4:27	III	TrI
	5:06	I	ShE
	7:30	III	TrE
	8:48	III	ShI
	11:29	III	ShE
	23:00	I	OcD
2	2:15	I	EcR
	7:12	II	OcD
	11:59	II	EcR
	20:22	I	TrI
	21:23	I	ShI
	22:36	I	TrE
	23:35	I	ShE
3	17:30	I	OcD
	20:44	I	EcR
4	1:28	II	TrI
	3:29	II	ShI
	4:12	II	TrE
	6:08	II	ShE
	8:53	IV	OcD
	10:00	IV	OcR
	14:52	I	TrI
	15:52	I	ShI
	17:06	I	TrE
	18:04	I	ShE
	18:25	III	OcD
	21:29	III	OcR
	22:35	III	EcD
5	1:17	III	EcR
	12:00	I	OcD
	15:12	I	EcR
	20:36	II	OcD
6	1:17	II	EcR
	9:22	I	TrI
	10:21	I	ShI
	11:36	I	TrE
	12:33	I	ShE
7	6:30	I	OcD
	9:41	I	EcR
	14:52	II	TrI
	16:47	II	ShI
	17:36	II	TrE
	19:27	II	ShE
8	3:53	I	TrI
	4:50	I	ShI
	6:07	I	TrE
	7:02	I	ShE
	8:53	III	TrI
	11:55	III	TrE
	12:52	III	ShI
	15:32	III	ShE
9	1:01	I	OcD
	4:10	I	EcR
	10:01	II	OcD
	14:36	II	EcR
	22:23	I	TrI
	23:18	I	ShI
10	0:37	I	TrE
	1:31	I	ShE
10	19:31	I	OcD
	22:39	I	EcR
11	4:16	II	TrI
	6:06	II	ShI
	7:00	II	TrE
	8:45	II	ShE
	16:53	I	TrI
	17:47	I	ShI
	19:07	I	TrE
	20:00	I	ShE
	22:51	III	OcD
12	1:54	III	OcR
	2:37	III	EcD
	5:18	III	EcR
	14:01	I	OcD
	17:08	I	EcR
	23:26	II	OcD
13	3:54	II	EcR
	11:24	I	TrI
	12:16	I	ShI
	13:38	I	TrE
	14:28	I	ShE
14	8:32	I	OcD
	11:37	I	EcR
	17:40	II	TrI
	19:25	II	ShI
	20:25	II	TrE
	22:04	II	ShE
15	5:54	I	TrI
	6:45	I	ShI
	8:08	I	TrE
	8:57	I	ShE
	13:21	III	TrI
	16:21	III	TrE
	16:54	III	ShI
	19:33	III	ShE
MAY			
15	15:52	I	EcD
	18:45	I	OcR
16	7:07	III	EcD
	9:31	III	EcR
	9:51	III	OcD
	11:03	II	EcD
	12:17	III	OcR
	13:09	I	ShI
	13:49	I	TrI
	14:59	II	OcR
	15:20	I	ShE
	16:00	I	TrE
17	10:20	I	EcD
	13:15	I	OcR
18	5:35	II	ShI
	7:02	II	TrI
	7:38	**I**	**ShI**
	8:11	II	ShE
	8:19	I	TrI
	9:38	II	TrE
	9:48	I	ShE
	10:30	I	TrE
19	4:49	I	EcD
	7:45	I	OcR
	21:21	III	ShI
	23:43	III	ShE
20	0:19	III	TrI
	0:21	II	EcD
	2:06	I	ShI

SATELLITES OF JUPITER, UT OF 2011 GEOCENTRIC PHENOMENA (cont)

MAY (cont)

Date	Time	Sat	Phen
20	2:42	III	TrE
	2:49	I	TrI
	4:17	I	ShE
	4:22	II	OcR
	5:00	I	TrE
	23:18	I	EcD
21	2:15	I	OcR
	18:54	II	ShI
	20:27	II	TrI
	20:35	**I**	**ShI**
	21:20	I	TrI
	21:29	II	ShE
	22:45	I	ShE
	23:02	II	TrE
	23:30	I	TrE
22	17:47	I	EcD
	20:46	I	OcR
23	11:08	III	EcD
	13:31	III	EcR
	13:38	II	EcD
	14:21	III	OcD
	15:03	I	ShI
	15:50	I	TrI
	16:43	III	OcR
	17:14	I	ShE
	17:46	III	TrE
	18:00	I	TrE
24	12:15	I	EcD
	15:16	I	OcR
25	8:13	II	ShI
	9:32	**I**	**ShI**
	9:53	II	TrI
	10:20	I	TrI
	10:49	II	ShE
	11:42	I	ShE
	12:28	II	TrE
	12:30	I	TrE
26	6:44	I	EcD
	9:46	I	OcR
27	1:23	III	ShI
	2:56	II	EcD
	3:43	III	ShE
	4:00	I	ShI
	4:48	III	TrI
	4:50	I	TrI
	6:11	I	ShE
	7:00	I	TrE
	7:07	III	TrE
	7:09	II	OcR
28	1:13	I	EcD
	4:16	I	OcR
	21:32	II	ShI
	22:29	**I**	**ShI**
	23:18	II	TrI
	23:20	I	TrI
29	0:07	II	ShE
	0:39	I	ShE
	1:30	I	TrE
	1:52	II	TrE
	19:41	I	EcD
	22:47	I	OcR
30	15:10	III	EcD
	16:13	II	EcD
	16:57	I	ShI
	17:32	III	EcR
	17:50	I	TrI
30	18:49	III	OcD
	19:08	I	ShE
	20:00	I	TrE
	20:32	II	OcR
	21:07	III	OcR
31	14:10	I	EcD
	17:17	I	OcR

JUNE

Date	Time	Sat	Phen
1	10:51	II	ShI
	11:26	**I**	**ShI**
	12:20	I	TrI
	12:44	II	TrI
	13:26	II	ShE
	13:36	I	ShE
	14:30	I	TrE
	15:17	II	TrE
2	8:39	I	EcD
	11:47	I	OcR
3	5:24	III	ShI
	5:30	II	EcD
	5:54	**I**	**ShI**
	6:50	I	TrI
	7:43	III	ShE
	8:05	I	ShE
	9:00	I	TrE
	9:15	III	TrI
	9:55	II	OcR
	11:30	III	TrE
4	3:07	I	EcD
	6:17	I	OcR
5	0:10	II	ShI
	0:23	**I**	**ShI**
	1:20	I	TrI
	2:08	II	TrI
	2:33	I	ShE
	2:44	II	ShE
	3:30	I	TrE
	4:41	II	TrE
	21:36	I	EcD
6	0:47	I	OcR
	18:48	II	EcD
	18:51	I	ShI
	19:11	III	EcR
	19:50	I	TrI
	21:01	I	ShE
	21:32	III	EcR
	22:00	I	TrE
	23:16	III	OcD
	23:17	II	OcR
7	1:30	III	OcR
	16:04	I	EcD
	19:17	I	OcR
8	13:20	I	ShI
	13:29	**II**	**ShI**
	14:20	I	TrI
	15:30	I	ShE
	15:34	II	TrI
	16:03	II	ShE
	16:29	I	TrE
	18:06	II	TrE
9	10:33	I	EcD
	13:47	I	OcR
10	7:48	I	ShI
	8:05	II	EcD
	8:49	I	TrI
	9:25	**III**	**ShI**
10	9:58	I	ShE
	10:59	I	TrE
	11:43	III	ShE
	12:40	II	OcR
	13:40	III	TrI
	15:50	III	TrE
11	5:02	I	EcD
	8:17	I	OcR
12	2:17	I	ShI
	2:47	**II**	**ShI**
	3:19	I	TrI
	4:27	I	ShE
	4:58	II	TrI
	5:22	II	ShE
	5:29	I	TrE
	7:29	II	TrE
	23:30	I	EcD
13	2:47	I	OcR
	20:45	I	ShI
	21:22	II	EcD
	21:49	I	TrI
	22:55	I	ShE
	23:14	III	EcD
	23:58	I	TrE
14	1:33	III	EcR
	2:02	II	OcR
	3:42	III	OcD
	5:51	III	OcR
	17:59	I	EcD
	21:16	I	OcR
15	15:14	I	ShI
	16:07	**II**	**ShI**
	16:19	I	TrI
	17:24	I	ShE
	18:22	I	TrI
	18:28	I	TrE
	18:41	II	ShE
	20:53	II	TrE
16	12:28	I	EcD
	15:46	I	OcR
17	9:42	I	ShI
	10:39	II	EcD
	10:48	I	TrI
	11:52	I	ShE
	12:58	I	TrE
	13:26	III	ShI
	15:24	II	OcR
	15:42	III	ShE
	18:03	III	TrI
	20:09	III	TrE
18	6:56	I	EcD
	10:16	I	OcR
19	4:11	I	ShI
	5:18	I	TrI
	5:25	**II**	**ShI**
	6:21	I	ShE
	7:27	I	TrE
	7:46	II	TrI
	7:59	II	ShE
	10:16	II	TrE
20	1:25	I	EcD
	4:46	I	OcR
	22:39	I	ShI
	23:48	I	TrI
	23:57	II	EcD
21	0:49	I	ShE
	1:57	I	TrE
21	3:15	III	EcD
	4:45	II	OcR
	5:33	III	EcR
	8:04	III	OcD
	10:10	III	OcR
	19:53	I	EcD
	23:16	I	OcR
22	17:08	I	ShI
	18:17	I	TrI
	18:45	**II**	**ShI**
	19:17	I	ShE
	20:26	I	TrE
	21:10	II	TrI
	21:18	II	ShE
	23:40	II	TrE
23	14:22	I	EcD
	17:45	I	OcR
24	11:36	I	ShI
	12:47	I	TrI
	13:14	II	EcD
	13:46	I	ShE
	14:56	I	TrE
	17:27	III	ShI
	18:07	II	OcR
	19:42	III	ShE
	22:24	III	TrI
25	0:26	III	TrE
	8:51	I	EcD
	12:15	I	OcR
26	6:05	I	ShI
	7:16	I	TrI
	8:03	**II**	**ShI**
	8:14	I	ShE
	9:25	I	TrE
	10:33	II	TrI
	10:36	II	ShE
	13:02	II	TrE
27	3:19	I	EcD
	6:44	I	OcR
28	0:33	I	ShI
	1:46	I	TrI
	2:31	II	EcD
	2:43	I	ShE
	3:54	I	TrE
	7:17	III	EcD
	7:28	II	OcR
	9:33	III	EcR
	12:24	III	OcD
	14:25	III	OcR
	21:48	I	EcD
29	1:14	I	OcR
	19:02	I	ShI
	20:15	I	TrI
	21:11	I	ShE
	21:22	II	ShI
	22:24	I	TrE
	23:55	II	TrI
	23:56	II	ShE
30	2:25	II	TrE
	16:17	I	EcD
	19:43	I	OcR

JULY

Date	Time	Sat	Phen
1	13:30	I	ShI
	14:44	I	TrI
	15:40	I	ShE
	15:49	II	EcD
	16:53	I	TrE
1	20:49	II	OcR
	21:28	III	ShI
	23:42	III	ShE
2	2:43	III	TrI
	4:40	III	TrE
	10:45	I	EcD
	14:13	I	OcR
3	7:58	I	ShI
	9:14	I	TrI
	10:08	I	ShE
	10:41	II	ShI
	11:22	I	TrE
	13:13	II	ShE
	13:18	II	TrI
	15:46	II	TrE
4	5:14	I	EcD
	8:42	I	OcR
5	2:27	I	ShI
	3:43	I	TrI
	4:36	II	ShE
	5:06	II	EcD
	5:51	I	TrE
	7:38	I	EcR
	7:41	II	OcD
	10:09	II	OcR
	11:17	III	EcD
	13:33	III	EcR
	16:41	III	OcD
	18:38	III	OcR
	23:42	I	EcD
6	3:12	I	OcR
	20:55	I	ShI
	22:12	I	TrI
	23:05	I	ShE
7	0:00	II	ShI
	0:21	I	TrE
	2:32	II	ShE
	2:41	I	TrI
	5:08	II	TrE
	18:11	I	EcD
	21:41	I	OcR
8	15:24	I	ShI
	16:41	I	TrI
	17:33	I	ShE
	18:23	II	EcD
	18:50	I	TrE
	20:55	II	EcR
	21:01	II	OcD
	23:29	II	OcR
9	1:30	III	ShI
	3:43	III	ShE
	6:59	III	TrI
	8:51	III	TrE
	12:39	I	EcD
	16:10	I	OcR
10	9:52	I	ShI
	11:11	I	TrI
	12:02	I	ShE
	13:18	II	ShI
	13:19	I	TrE
	15:51	II	ShE
	16:02	II	TrI
	18:29	II	TrE
11	7:08	I	EcD
	10:39	I	OcR
12	4:21	I	ShI
	5:40	I	TrI
	6:30	I	ShE

SATELLITES OF JUPITER, UT OF 2011 GEOCENTRIC PHENOMENA (cont)

JULY (cont)

```
12   7:40  II  EcD
     7:48  I   TrE
    10:13  II  EcR
    10:22  II  OcD
    12:49  II  OcR
    15:18  III EcD
    17:33  III EcR
    20:55  III OcD
    22:47  III OcR
13   1:37  I   EcD
     5:08  I   OcR
    22:49  I   ShI
14   0:09  I   TrI
     0:58  I   ShE
     2:17  I   TrE
     2:38  II  ShI
     5:09  II  ShE
     5:24  II  TrI
     7:50  II  TrE
    20:05  I   EcD
    23:38  I   OcR
15  17:18  I   ShI
    18:38  I   TrI
    19:27  I   ShE
    20:46  I   TrE
    20:58  II  EcD
    23:30  II  EcR
    23:41  II  OcD
16   2:08  II  OcR
     5:31  III ShI
     7:42  III ShE
    11:11  III TrI
    12:59  III TrE
    14:34  I   ShI
    18:07  I   OcR
17  11:46  I   ShI
    13:07  I   TrI
    13:55  I   ShE
    15:15  I   TrE
    15:56  II  ShI
    18:28  II  ShE
    18:44  II  TrI
    21:10  II  TrE
18   9:02  I   EcD
    12:36  I   OcR
19   6:14  I   ShI
     7:35  I   TrI
     8:24  I   ShE
     9:43  I   TrE
    10:15  II  EcD
    12:47  II  EcR
    13:01  II  OcD
    15:27  II  OcR
    19:20  III EcD
    21:33  III EcR
20   1:07  III OcD
     2:54  III OcR
     3:31  I   EcD
     7:05  I   OcR
21   0:43  I   ShI
     2:04  I   TrI
     2:52  I   ShE
     4:12  I   TrE
     5:15  II  ShI
     7:46  II  ShE
     8:05  II  TrI
    10:30  II  TrE
    21:59  I   EcD
```

```
22   1:33  I   OcR
    19:11  I   ShI
    20:33  I   TrI
    21:20  I   ShE
    22:41  I   TrE
    23:32  II  EcD
23   2:04  II  EcR
     2:20  II  OcD
     4:46  II  OcR
     9:32  III ShI
    11:42  III ShE
    15:20  III TrI
    16:28  I   EcD
    17:03  III TrE
    20:02  I   OcR
24  13:40  I   ShI
    15:02  I   TrI
    15:49  I   ShE
    17:10  I   TrE
    18:33  II  ShI
    21:04  II  ShE
    21:24  II  TrI
    23:49  II  TrE
25  10:57  I   EcD
    14:31  I   OcR
26   8:08  I   ShI
     9:30  I   TrI
    10:17  I   ShE
    11:38  I   TrE
    12:50  II  EcD
    15:21  II  EcR
    15:38  II  OcD
    18:04  II  OcR
    23:21  III EcD
27   1:33  III EcR
     5:14  III OcD
     5:25  I   EcD
     6:57  III OcR
     9:00  I   OcR
28   2:37  I   ShI
     3:59  I   TrI
     4:46  I   ShE
     6:07  I   TrE
     7:52  II  ShI
    10:23  II  ShE
    10:44  II  TrI
    13:08  II  TrE
    23:54  I   EcD
29   3:28  I   OcR
    21:05  I   ShI
    22:28  I   TrI
    23:14  I   ShE
30   0:35  I   TrE
     2:07  II  EcD
     4:39  II  EcR
     4:57  II  OcD
     7:22  II  OcR
    13:32  III ShI
    15:41  III ShE
    18:22  I   EcD
    19:25  III TrI
    21:04  III TrE
    21:57  I   OcR
31  15:34  I   ShI
    16:56  I   TrI
    17:43  I   ShE
    19:04  I   TrE
    21:10  II  ShI
    23:41  II  ShE
```

AUGUST

```
1    0:02  II  TrI
     2:26  II  TrE
    12:51  I   EcD
    16:25  I   OcR
2   10:02  I   ShI
    11:25  I   TrI
    12:11  I   ShE
    13:32  I   TrE
    15:25  II  EcD
    17:56  II  EcR
    18:14  II  OcD
    20:39  II  OcR
3    3:23  III EcD
     5:34  III EcR
     7:19  I   EcD
     9:18  III OcD
    10:54  I   OcR
    10:57  III OcR
4    4:30  I   ShI
     5:53  I   TrI
     6:39  I   ShE
     8:00  I   TrE
    10:29  II  ShI
    13:00  II  ShE
    13:21  II  TrI
    15:44  II  TrE
5    1:48  I   EcD
     5:22  I   OcR
    22:59  I   ShI
6    0:21  I   TrI
     1:08  I   ShE
     2:29  I   TrE
     4:42  II  EcD
     7:13  II  EcR
     7:31  II  OcD
     9:56  II  OcR
    17:33  III ShI
    19:41  III ShE
    20:16  I   EcD
    23:26  III TrI
    23:50  I   OcR
7    1:00  III TrE
    17:27  I   ShI
    18:50  I   TrI
    19:36  I   ShE
    20:57  I   TrE
    23:47  II  ShI
8    2:18  II  ShE
     2:38  II  TrI
     5:01  II  TrE
    14:45  I   EcD
    18:19  I   OcR
9   11:56  I   ShI
    13:18  I   TrI
    14:05  I   ShE
    15:25  I   TrE
    18:00  II  EcD
    20:31  II  EcR
    20:48  II  OcD
    23:12  II  OcR
10   7:24  III EcD
     9:14  I   EcD
     9:34  III EcR
    12:47  I   OcR
    13:18  III OcD
    14:51  III OcR
```

```
11   6:24  I   ShI
     7:46  I   TrI
     8:33  I   ShE
     9:53  I   TrE
    13:06  II  ShI
    15:36  II  ShE
    15:56  II  TrI
    18:18  II  TrE
12   3:42  I   EcD
     7:15  I   OcR
13   0:52  I   ShI
     2:14  I   TrI
     3:02  I   ShE
     4:21  I   TrE
     7:17  II  EcD
     9:48  II  EcR
    10:04  II  OcD
    12:28  II  OcR
    21:34  III ShI
    22:11  I   EcD
    23:40  III ShE
14   1:43  I   OcR
     3:23  III TrI
     4:52  III TrE
    19:21  I   ShI
    20:42  I   TrI
    21:30  I   ShE
    22:49  I   TrE
15   2:24  II  ShI
     4:54  II  ShE
     5:12  II  TrI
     7:34  II  TrE
    16:39  I   EcD
    20:11  I   OcR
16  13:49  I   ShI
    15:10  I   TrI
    15:58  I   ShE
    17:17  I   TrE
    20:35  II  EcD
    23:06  II  EcR
    23:20  II  OcD
17   1:43  II  OcR
    11:08  I   EcD
    11:25  III EcD
    13:34  III EcR
    14:39  I   OcR
    17:12  III OcD
    18:41  III OcR
18   8:18  I   ShI
     9:38  I   TrI
    10:27  I   ShE
    11:45  I   TrE
    15:43  II  ShI
    18:13  II  ShE
    18:28  II  TrI
    20:50  II  TrE
19   5:36  I   EcD
     9:07  I   OcR
20   2:46  I   ShI
     4:05  I   TrI
     4:55  I   ShE
     6:13  I   TrE
     9:52  II  EcD
    12:23  II  EcR
    12:35  II  OcD
    14:58  II  OcR
21   0:05  I   EcD
     1:35  III ShI
```

```
21   3:34  I   OcR
     3:40  III ShE
     7:16  III TrI
     8:40  III TrE
    21:15  I   ShI
    22:33  I   TrI
    23:24  I   ShE
22   0:40  I   TrE
     5:01  II  ShI
     7:31  II  ShE
     7:43  II  TrI
    10:04  II  TrE
    18:33  I   EcD
    22:02  I   OcR
23  15:43  I   ShI
    17:01  I   TrI
    17:52  I   ShE
    19:08  I   TrE
    23:10  II  EcD
24   1:41  II  EcR
     1:50  II  OcD
     4:12  II  OcR
    13:02  I   EcD
    15:26  III EcD
    16:30  I   OcR
    17:33  III EcR
    21:02  III OcD
    22:27  III OcR
25  10:12  I   ShI
    11:28  I   TrI
    12:21  I   ShE
    13:36  I   TrE
    18:19  II  ShI
    20:49  II  ShE
    20:58  II  TrI
    23:19  II  TrE
26   7:30  I   EcD
    10:57  I   OcR
27   4:40  I   ShI
     5:56  I   TrI
     6:49  I   ShE
     8:03  I   TrE
    12:28  II  EcD
    14:58  II  EcR
    15:04  II  OcD
    17:26  II  OcR
28   1:59  I   EcD
     5:25  I   OcR
     5:36  III ShI
     7:41  III ShE
    11:04  III TrI
    12:25  III TrE
    23:08  I   ShI
29   0:23  I   TrI
     1:18  I   ShE
     2:31  I   TrE
     7:37  II  ShI
    10:07  II  ShE
    10:12  II  TrI
    12:33  II  TrE
    20:28  I   EcD
    23:52  I   OcR
30  17:37  I   ShI
    18:51  I   TrI
    19:46  I   ShE
    20:58  I   TrE
31   1:45  II  EcD
     4:16  II  EcR
```

SATELLITES OF JUPITER, UT OF 2011 GEOCENTRIC PHENOMENA (cont)

AUGUST (cont)

31 4:18 II OcD
    6:39 II OcR
    14:56 I EcD
    18:19 I OcR
    19:26 III EcD
    21:33 III EcR

SEPTEMBER

1 0:46 III OcD
   2:07 III OcR
   12:05 I ShI
   13:18 I TrI
   14:15 I ShE
   15:25 I TrE
   20:56 II ShI
   23:25 II ShE
   23:26 II TrI

2 1:46 II TrE
   9:25 I EcD
   12:47 I OcR

3 6:34 I ShI
   7:45 I TrI
   8:43 I ShE
   9:53 I TrE
   15:03 II EcD
   19:52 II OcR

4 3:53 I EcD
   7:14 I OcR
   9:37 III ShI
   11:41 III ShE
   14:46 III TrI
   16:03 III TrE

5 1:02 I ShI
   2:13 I TrI
   3:11 I ShE
   4:20 I TrE
   10:14 II ShI
   12:38 II TrI
   12:43 II ShE
   14:58 II TrE
   22:22 I EcD

6 1:41 I OcR
   19:31 I ShI
   20:40 I TrI
   21:40 I ShE
   22:47 I TrE

7 4:21 II EcD
   9:04 II OcR
   16:50 I EcD
   20:08 I OcR
   23:28 III EcD

8 1:33 III EcR
   4:26 III OcD
   5:44 III OcR
   13:59 I ShI
   15:07 I TrI
   16:08 I ShE
   17:14 I TrE
   23:32 II ShI

9 1:51 II TrI
   2:01 II ShE
   4:10 II TrE
   11:19 I EcD
   14:35 I OcR

10 8:28 I ShI
    9:34 I TrI

10 10:37 I ShE
    11:41 I TrE
    17:39 II EcD
    22:16 II OcR

11 5:47 I EcD
    9:02 I OcR
    13:38 III ShI
    15:41 III ShE
    18:23 III TrI
    19:37 III TrE

12 2:56 I ShI
    4:01 I TrI
    5:06 I ShE
    6:08 I TrE
    12:50 II ShI
    15:02 II TrI
    15:19 II ShE
    17:22 II TrE

13 0:16 I EcD
    3:29 I OcR
    21:24 I ShI
    22:27 I TrI
    23:34 I ShE

14 0:35 I TrE
    6:57 II EcD
    11:27 II OcR
    18:44 I EcD
    21:55 I OcR

15 3:29 III EcD
    5:33 III EcR
    8:01 III OcD
    9:16 III OcR
    15:53 I ShI
    16:54 I TrI
    18:03 I ShE
    19:01 I TrE

16 2:08 II ShI
    4:13 II TrI
    4:37 II ShE
    6:33 II TrE
    13:13 I EcD
    16:22 I OcR

17 10:21 I ShI
    11:21 I TrI
    12:31 I ShE
    13:28 I TrE
    20:15 II EcD

18 0:37 II OcR
    7:42 I EcD
    10:49 I OcR
    17:38 III ShI
    19:40 III ShE
    21:55 III TrI
    23:07 III TrE

19 4:50 I ShI
    5:47 I TrI
    7:00 I ShE
    7:55 I TrE
    15:26 II ShI
    17:23 II TrI
    17:55 II ShE
    19:43 II TrE

20 2:10 I EcD
    5:15 I OcR
    23:18 I ShI

21 0:14 I TrI
    1:28 I ShE

21 2:21 I TrE
    9:33 II EcD
    13:48 II OcR
    20:39 I EcD
    23:42 I OcR

22 7:31 III EcD
    9:34 III EcR
    11:32 III OcD
    12:45 III OcR
    17:47 I ShI
    18:41 I TrI
    19:57 I ShE
    20:48 I TrE

23 4:44 II ShI
    6:33 II TrI
    7:13 II ShE
    8:53 II TrE
    15:07 I EcD
    18:08 I OcR

24 12:16 I ShI
    13:07 I TrI
    14:25 I ShE
    15:14 I TrE
    22:51 II EcD

25 2:57 II OcR
    9:36 I EcD
    12:35 I OcR
    21:39 III ShI
    23:40 III ShE

26 1:22 III TrI
    2:33 III TrE
    6:44 I ShI
    7:33 I TrI
    8:54 I ShE
    9:41 I TrE
    18:02 II ShI
    19:42 II TrI
    20:31 II ShE
    22:02 II TrE

27 4:04 I EcD
    7:01 I OcR

28 1:13 I ShI
    2:00 I TrI
    3:22 I ShE
    4:07 I TrE
    12:09 II EcD
    16:06 II OcR
    22:33 I EcD

29 1:27 I OcR
    11:32 III EcD
    13:34 III EcR
    14:56 III OcD
    16:09 III OcR
    19:41 I ShI
    20:26 I TrI
    21:51 I ShE
    22:34 I TrE

30 7:20 II ShI
    8:51 II TrI
    9:49 II ShE
    11:11 II TrE
    17:02 I EcD
    19:54 I OcR

OCTOBER

1 14:10 I ShI
   14:52 I TrI
   16:20 I ShE

1 17:00 I TrE

2 1:27 II EcD
   5:15 II OcR
   11:30 I EcD
   14:20 I OcR

3 1:40 III ShI
   3:41 III ShE
   4:45 III TrI
   5:55 III TrE
   8:38 I ShI
   9:18 I TrI
   10:48 I ShE
   11:26 I TrE
   20:38 II ShI
   21:59 II TrI
   23:07 II ShE

4 0:19 II TrE
   5:59 I EcD
   8:46 I OcR

5 3:07 I ShI
   3:44 I TrI
   5:17 I ShE
   5:52 I TrE
   14:46 II EcD
   18:24 II OcR

6 0:27 I EcD
   3:12 I OcR
   15:33 III EcD
   17:34 III EcR
   18:17 III OcD
   19:30 III OcR
   21:35 I ShI
   22:11 I TrI
   23:46 I ShE

7 0:18 I TrE
   9:56 II ShI
   11:07 II TrI
   12:25 II ShE
   13:27 II TrE
   18:56 I EcD
   21:38 I OcR

8 16:04 I ShI
   16:37 I TrI
   18:14 I ShE
   18:45 I TrE

9 4:04 II EcD
   7:31 II OcR
   13:25 I EcD
   16:04 I OcR

10 5:42 III ShI
    7:41 III ShE
    8:04 III TrI
    9:16 III TrE
    10:33 I ShI
    11:03 I TrI
    12:43 I ShE
    13:11 I TrE
    23:14 II ShI

11 0:14 II TrI
    1:42 II ShE
    2:34 II TrE
    7:53 I EcD
    10:30 I OcR

12 5:01 I ShI
    5:29 I TrI
    7:11 I ShE
    7:37 I TrE
    17:23 II EcD

12 20:40 II OcR

13 2:22 I EcD
    4:56 I OcR
    19:34 III EcD
    22:49 III OcR
    23:30 I ShI
    23:55 I TrI

14 1:40 I ShE
    2:03 I TrE
    12:32 II ShI
    13:22 II TrI
    15:00 II ShE
    15:42 II TrE
    20:50 I EcD
    23:22 I OcR

15 17:59 I ShI
    18:21 I TrI
    20:09 I ShE
    20:29 I TrE

16 6:41 II EcD
    9:47 II OcR
    15:19 I EcD
    17:48 I OcR

17 9:44 III ShI
    11:21 III TrI
    11:43 III ShE
    12:27 I ShI
    12:35 III TrE
    12:46 I TrI
    14:37 I ShE
    14:55 I TrE

18 1:50 I ShI
    2:28 II TrI
    4:18 II ShE
    4:49 II TrE
    9:48 I EcD
    12:14 I OcR

19 6:56 I ShI
    7:12 I TrI
    9:06 I ShE
    9:21 I TrE
    20:00 II EcD
    22:55 II OcR

20 4:16 I EcD
    6:39 I OcR
    23:35 III EcD

21 1:25 I ShI
    1:38 I TrI
    2:06 III OcR
    3:35 I ShE
    3:46 I TrE
    15:08 II ShI
    15:35 II TrI
    17:36 II ShE
    17:56 II TrE
    22:45 I EcD

22 1:05 I OcR
    19:53 I ShI
    20:04 I TrI
    22:04 I ShE
    22:12 I TrE

23 9:18 II EcD
    12:02 II OcR
    17:14 I EcD
    19:31 I OcR

24 13:46 III ShI
    14:22 I ShI

SATELLITES OF JUPITER, UT OF 2011 GEOCENTRIC PHENOMENA (cont)

OCTOBER (cont)

Date	Time	Sat	Ph
24	14:30	I	TrI
	14:34	III	TrI
	15:43	III	ShE
	15:52	III	TrE
	16:32	I	ShE
	16:38	I	TrE
25	4:26	II	ShI
	4:42	II	TrI
	6:54	II	ShE
	7:03	II	TrE
	11:42	II	EcD
	13:57	I	OcR
26	8:51	I	ShI
	8:56	I	TrI
	11:01	I	ShE
	11:04	I	TrE
	22:37	II	EcD
27	1:09	II	OcR
	6:11	I	EcD
	8:23	I	OcR
28	3:19	I	ShI
	3:22	I	TrI
	3:37	III	EcD
	5:30	I	ShE
	5:30	I	TrE
	5:35	III	EcR
	17:44	II	ShI
	17:48	II	TrI
	20:09	II	TrE
	20:12	II	ShE
29	0:40	I	EcD
	2:50	I	EcR
	21:48	I	ShI
	21:48	I	TrI
	23:56	I	TrE
	23:58	I	ShE
30	11:54	II	OcD
	14:25	II	EcR
	19:06	I	OcD
	21:18	I	EcR
31	16:13	I	TrI
	16:17	I	ShI
	17:46	III	TrI
	17:47	**III**	**ShI**
	18:22	I	TrE
	18:27	I	ShE
	19:09	III	TrE
	19:44	III	ShE

NOVEMBER

Date	Time	Sat	Ph
1	6:54	II	TrI
	7:02	II	ShI
	9:16	II	TrE
	9:30	II	ShE
	13:32	I	OcD
	15:47	I	EcR
2	10:39	I	TrI
	10:46	I	ShI
	12:48	I	TrE
	12:56	I	ShE
3	1:01	II	OcD
	3:44	II	EcR
	7:58	I	OcD
	10:16	I	EcR
4	5:05	I	TrI
	5:15	I	ShI

Date	Time	Sat	Ph
4	7:13	III	OcD
	7:14	I	TrE
	7:25	I	ShE
	9:36	III	EcR
	20:01	II	TrI
	20:20	II	ShI
	22:23	II	TrE
	22:48	II	ShE
5	2:24	I	OcD
	4:44	I	EcR
	23:31	I	TrI
	23:43	I	ShI
6	1:40	I	TrE
	1:54	I	ShE
	14:08	II	OcD
	17:02	II	EcR
	20:50	I	OcD
	23:13	I	EcR
7	17:57	I	TrI
	18:12	I	ShI
	20:06	I	TrE
	20:22	I	ShE
	20:59	III	TrI
	21:49	III	ShI
	22:27	III	TrE
	23:45	III	ShE
8	9:08	II	TrI
	9:38	II	ShI
	11:30	II	TrE
	12:05	II	ShE
	15:16	I	OcD
	17:42	I	EcR
9	12:23	I	TrI
	12:41	I	ShI
	14:32	I	TrE
	14:51	I	ShE
10	3:16	II	OcD
	6:21	II	EcR
	9:42	I	OcD
	12:10	I	EcR
11	6:49	I	TrI
	7:10	I	ShI
	8:58	I	TrE
	9:20	I	ShE
	10:27	III	OcD
	13:38	III	EcR
	22:15	II	TrI
	22:56	II	ShI
12	0:37	II	TrE
	1:23	II	ShE
	4:07	II	EcR
	6:39	I	EcR
13	1:15	I	TrI
	1:39	I	ShI
	3:24	I	TrE
	3:49	I	ShE
	16:23	II	OcD
	19:40	II	EcR
	22:33	I	OcD
14	1:08	I	EcR
	19:42	I	TrI
	20:07	I	ShI
	21:50	I	TrE
	22:18	I	ShE
15	0:13	III	TrI
	1:46	III	TrE
	1:50	III	ShI

Date	Time	Sat	Ph
15	3:45	III	ShE
	11:22	II	TrI
	12:14	II	ShI
	13:45	II	TrE
	14:41	II	ShE
	17:00	I	OcD
	19:36	I	EcR
16	14:08	I	TrI
	14:36	I	ShI
	16:17	I	TrE
	16:46	I	ShE
17	5:31	II	OcD
	8:59	II	EcR
	11:26	I	OcD
	14:05	I	EcR
18	8:34	I	TrI
	9:05	I	ShI
	10:43	I	TrE
	11:15	I	ShE
	13:42	III	OcD
	15:21	III	OcR
	15:43	III	EcD
	17:39	III	EcR
19	0:29	II	TrI
	1:32	II	ShI
	2:53	II	TrE
	3:59	II	ShE
	5:52	I	OcD
	8:34	I	EcR
20	3:00	I	TrI
	3:34	I	ShI
	5:09	I	TrE
	5:44	I	ShE
	18:39	II	OcD
	22:18	II	EcR
21	0:18	I	OcD
	3:03	I	EcR
	21:27	I	TrI
	22:03	I	ShI
	23:36	I	TrE
22	0:13	I	ShE
	3:30	III	TrI
	5:09	III	ShI
	5:53	III	TrE
	7:47	III	ShE
	13:37	II	TrI
	14:50	II	ShI
	16:01	II	TrE
	17:17	II	ShE
	18:44	I	OcD
	21:31	I	EcR
23	15:53	I	TrI
	16:32	I	ShI
	18:02	I	TrE
	18:42	I	ShE
24	7:49	II	OcD
	11:38	II	EcR
	13:11	I	OcD
	16:00	I	EcR
25	10:19	I	TrI
	11:01	I	ShI
	12:29	I	TrE
	13:11	I	ShE
	17:01	III	OcD
	18:44	III	OcR
	19:45	III	EcD
	21:40	III	EcR

Date	Time	Sat	Ph
26	2:45	II	TrI
	4:08	II	ShI
	5:10	II	TrE
	6:34	II	ShE
	7:37	I	OcD
	10:29	I	EcR
27	4:46	I	TrI
	5:30	I	ShI
	6:55	I	TrE
	7:39	I	ShE
	20:58	II	OcD
28	0:56	II	EcR
	2:03	I	OcD
	4:58	I	EcR
	23:13	I	TrI
	23:58	I	ShI
29	1:22	I	TrE
	2:08	I	ShE
	6:51	III	TrI
	8:35	III	TrE
	9:55	III	ShI
	11:48	III	ShE
	15:54	II	TrI
	17:26	II	ShI
	18:19	II	TrE
	19:52	II	ShE
	20:30	I	OcD
	23:26	I	EcR
30	17:39	I	TrI
	18:27	I	ShI
	19:48	I	TrE
	20:37	I	ShE

DECEMBER

Date	Time	Sat	Ph
1	10:08	II	OcD
	14:16	II	EcR
	14:57	I	OcD
	17:55	I	EcR
2	12:06	I	TrI
	12:56	I	ShI
	14:15	I	TrE
	15:06	I	ShE
	20:23	III	OcD
	22:12	III	OcR
	23:46	III	EcD
3	1:41	III	EcR
	5:04	II	TrI
	6:45	II	ShI
	7:29	II	TrE
	9:10	II	ShE
	9:23	I	OcD
	12:24	I	EcR
4	6:33	I	TrI
	7:25	I	ShI
	8:42	I	TrE
	9:35	I	ShE
	23:18	II	OcD
5	3:35	II	EcR
	3:50	I	OcD
	6:53	I	EcR
6	1:00	I	TrI
	1:54	I	ShI
	3:09	I	TrE
	4:04	I	ShE
	10:17	III	OcD
	12:06	III	TrI
	13:58	III	ShI
	15:51	III	ShE

Date	Time	Sat	Ph
6	18:13	II	TrI
	20:03	II	ShI
	20:39	II	TrE
	22:17	II	OcD
	22:28	II	ShE
7	1:21	I	EcR
	19:27	I	TrI
	20:23	I	ShI
	21:36	I	TrE
	22:33	I	ShE
8	12:29	II	OcD
	16:44	I	OcD
	16:55	II	EcR
	19:50	I	EcR
9	13:54	I	TrI
	14:52	I	ShI
	16:03	I	TrE
	17:02	I	ShE
	23:50	III	OcD
10	1:43	III	OcR
	3:48	III	EcD
	5:42	III	EcR
	7:24	II	TrI
	9:21	II	ShI
	9:50	II	TrE
	11:10	I	OcD
	11:46	II	ShE
	14:19	I	EcR
11	8:21	I	TrI
	9:21	I	ShI
	10:30	I	TrE
	11:30	I	ShE
12	1:41	II	OcD
	5:38	I	OcD
	6:13	II	EcR
	8:48	I	EcR
13	2:48	I	TrI
	3:50	I	ShI
	4:58	I	TrE
	5:59	I	ShE
	13:47	III	TrI
	15:41	III	TrE
	18:01	III	ShI
	19:52	III	ShE
	20:35	I	TrI
	22:39	II	ShI
	23:01	II	TrE
14	0:05	I	OcD
	1:03	II	ShE
	3:17	I	EcR
	21:15	I	TrI
	22:19	I	ShI
	23:25	I	TrE
15	0:28	I	ShE
	14:54	II	OcD
	18:32	I	OcD
	19:33	II	EcR
	21:45	I	EcR
16	15:43	I	TrI
	16:48	I	ShI
	17:52	I	TrE
	18:57	I	ShE
17	3:22	III	OcD
	5:20	III	OcR
	7:50	III	EcD
	9:43	III	EcR
	9:47	II	TrI

SATELLITES OF JUPITER, UT OF 2011 GEOCENTRIC PHENOMENA (cont)

DECEMBER (cont)							
17	11:57	II	ShI	28	3:44	I	OcD
	12:13	II	TrE		**3:51**	**II**	**ShI**
	12:59	I	OcD		3:52	II	TrE
	14:21	II	ShE		3:55	III	ShE
	16:14	I	EcR		6:15	II	ShE
					7:07	I	EcR
18	10:10	I	TrI				
	11:17	I	ShI	29	0:57	I	TrI
	12:20	I	TrE		2:11	I	ShI
	13:26	I	ShE		3:06	I	TrE
					4:20	I	ShE
19	4:06	II	OcD		19:50	II	OcD
	7:26	I	OcD		22:12	I	OcD
	8:52	II	EcR		22:20	II	OcR
	10:43	I	EcR		22:24	II	EcD
20	4:38	I	TrI	30	0:51	I	EcR
	5:46	I	ShI		1:36	I	EcR
	6:47	I	TrE		19:25	I	TrI
	7:55	I	ShE		20:40	I	ShI
	17:22	III	TrI		21:35	I	TrE
	19:20	III	TrE		22:49	I	ShE
	22:03	III	ShI				
	22:59	II	TrI	31	10:44	III	OcD
	23:54	II	ShE		12:48	III	OcR
21	1:15	II	ShI		14:39	II	TrI
	1:25	II	TrE		15:55	III	EcD
	1:54	I	OcD		16:40	I	OcD
	3:39	II	ShE		17:07	II	TrE
	5:12	I	EcR		17:09	II	ShI
	23:06	I	TrI		17:47	III	EcR
22	0:15	I	ShI		19:33	II	ShE
	1:15	I	TrE		20:05	I	EcR
	2:24	I	ShE				
	17:20	II	OcD				
	20:21	I	OcD				
	22:12	II	EcR				
	23:41	I	EcR				
23	17:33	I	TrI				
	18:44	I	ShI				
	19:43	I	TrE				
	20:53	I	ShE				
24	7:00	I	OcD				
	9:01	III	OcR				
	11:52	III	EcD				
	12:12	I	TrI				
	13:45	III	EcR				
	14:33	II	ShI				
	14:39	II	TrE				
	14:49	I	OcD				
	16:57	II	ShE				
	18:09	I	EcR				
25	12:01	I	TrI				
	13:13	I	ShI				
	14:11	I	TrE				
	15:22	I	ShE				
26	6:34	II	OcD				
	9:17	I	OcD				
	11:31	II	EcR				
	12:38	I	EcR				
27	6:29	I	TrI				
	7:42	I	ShI				
	8:39	I	TrE				
	9:51	I	ShE				
	21:03	III	TrI				
	23:04	III	TrE				
28	1:25	II	TrI				
	2:05	III	ShI				

CONFIGURATIONS OF SATURN'S BRIGHTEST SATELLITES

By Larry D. Bogan

The diagrams on the following three pages give the relative locations of Saturn's five brightest satellites for January through August plus December 2011. The names and magnitudes of these satellites, in order of increasing distance from Saturn, are Enceladus 11.8, Tethys 10.3, Dione 10.4, Rhea 9.7, and Titan 8.4.

The curves in the diagrams show the elongations of the satellites from Saturn for day 0.0 UT to day 32.0 UT for each month. The dashed curves represent Enceladus and Dione, the first and third out from Saturn. The narrow, central, vertical band represents the disk of Saturn, and the wider band the outer edge of Saturn's A ring.

At the top of each monthly diagram is a scale drawing of Saturn, its rings, and the orbits of four of the five brightest satellites as seen through an inverting telescope (in the Northern Hemisphere). **South is up.** No orbit is shown for Enceladus, the innermost satellite, because of the small size of the scale drawing. Due to its faintness and proximity to the bright rings, Enceladus is best seen when near a maximum elongation, but even then good seeing, good optics, and an aperture of at least 250 mm are required.

During 2011, we see Saturn and its satellites from north of the ring plane. The tilt for 2011 has a minimum of 7.3° on Jun. 8 and a maximum of 14.8° on Dec. 31. The direction of motion of the satellites, as viewed with a telescope having an even number (0, 2, 4,…) of reflections in its optics, is counter-clockwise. An arrow has been placed on the orbit of Titan to indicate all satellite orbit rotation directions.

A particular configuration of the satellites may be determined by drawing a horizontal line across the monthly curves at the time (UT) of interest. The intersection of this line with the curves gives the relative elongations of the satellites. Project these elongations onto the drawing of the orbits at the top of the diagram. The east side of the A-ring vertical band has been extended up to the drawing to facilitate transfer of each elongation. A millimetre scale, a pair of dividers, or a strip of paper on which to mark enables one to do this quickly and accurately.

The direction of the orbital motion of a satellite determines on which side of its orbit (north or south) a satellite is located. Note the movement of the satellite along the diagram curves past elongation as it revolves around Saturn to determine whether to put the satellite on the north or south side of the orbit. The January diagram has an example configuration drawn on it for Jan. 4 at 10:00 p.m. EST (Jan. 5 at h UT).

Greatest Elongations and Conjunctions for Iapetus

While the magnitude of Iapetus is comparable to the five plotted satellites, it varies from 10.1 (western elongation) to 11.9 (eastern elongation). This moon's orbit is about 2.9 times the size of Titan's and is tilted 15° to Saturn's ring plane; its period is 79 days. Iapetus is easiest to find near conjunctions when it is just north or south of Saturn. The table below lists times (UT) of greatest elongations and conjunctions during 2011.

Eastern Elong.		Inferior Conj.		Western Elong.		Superior Conj.	
				Jan. 5	~6h	Jan. 24	21.0h
Feb. 14	4.2h	Mar. 5	3.1h	Mar. 24	~17h	Apr. 13	6.7h
May 2	23.7h	May 22	9.4h	Jun. 11	~5h	Jul. 1	0.6h
Jul. 21	3.6h	Aug. 10	4.3h	Aug. 30	~12h	Sep. 19	21.1h
Oct. 10	12.7h	Oct. 30	9.6h	Nov. 19	~6h	Dec. 10	9.6h
Dec. 31	0.6h						

Note: Three freeware computer programs that display the configurations of Saturn's satellites are (1) *The Planets* (Java) by Brenden Murphy (www.cpac.org.uk/solar.asp), (2) *Stellarium* for MacOS, Linux and Windows (www.stellarium.org), and (3) *Meridian* by Claude Duplessis (astrosurf.com/mordu/meridian/more.html).

CONFIGURATIONS OF SATURN'S SATELLITES
2011 JANUARY–MARCH

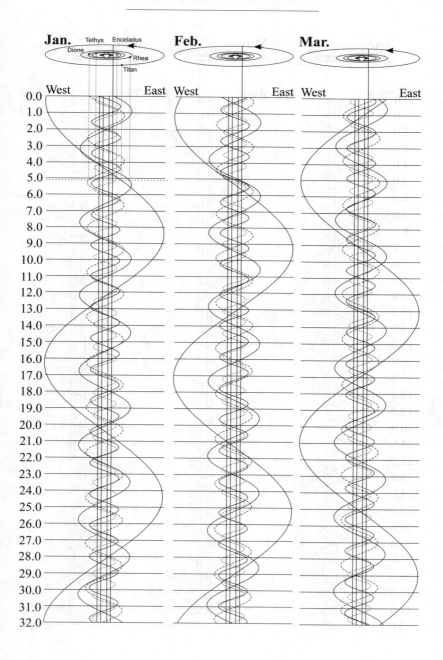

CONFIGURATIONS OF SATURN'S SATELLITES
2011 APRIL–JUNE

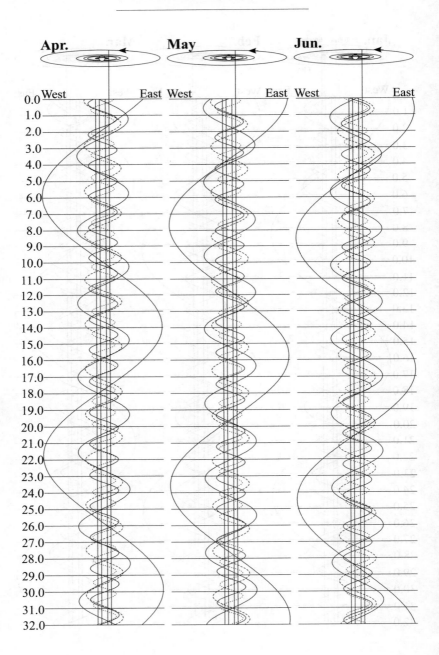

CONFIGURATIONS OF SATURN'S SATELLITES
2011 JULY–AUGUST, DECEMBER

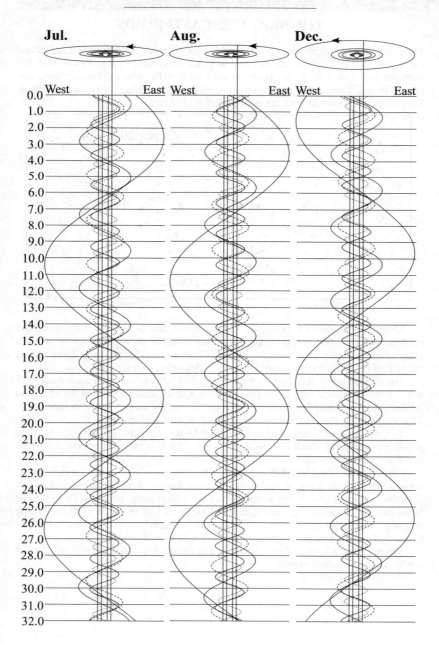

ASTEROIDS

THE BRIGHTEST ASTEROIDS

The following two pages contain ephemerides for asteroids (identified by number and name) that will be brighter than or equal to visual magnitude 10.0 and more than 90° from the Sun during 2011. The positions are based on TT, which differs by about one minute from UT (see TIME AND TIME SCALES on p. 43). "Mag" is visual magnitude. These data were derived from current osculating elements.

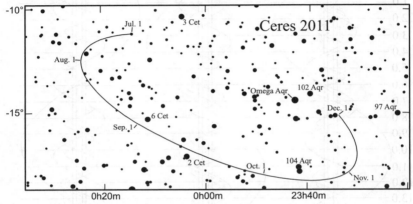

Charts displaying the motion of each asteroid can be produced by using the ephemerides provided and an appropriate star atlas, or on a computer by using a planetarium program. For example, the chart above, provided by Dave Lane, shows the path of (1) Ceres for the months of July to December of this year.

The coordinates in the chart are for equinox J2000.0, and the chart magnitude limit is 9.0; Ceres ranges in magnitude from about 8.8 at the start and end of the track and brightens to 7.6 in mid-September. At that time, it will be an easy target in binoculars. Tick marks along the path indicate Ceres' position on the given dates.

The star labelled Omega Aql can be found on the SEPTEMBER ALL-SKY MAP on p. 349 and the NOVEMBER ALL-SKY MAP on p. 350. It is the most eastern star in the line drawing of Aquarius.

Ceres was the first asteroid discovered (on the first day of the 19th century), hence its designation (1) Ceres. It was originally classified as a planet, as were the next three asteroids, (2) Pallas, (3) Juno, and (4) Vesta. For most of the 19th century, Vesta was thought to be larger than Ceres due to its greater brightness. Ceres is, in fact, the larger of the two, being almost twice the diameter of Vesta. It is Vesta's higher albedo (0.42 compared to 0.11 for Ceres) that makes Vesta the brighter of the two despite its smaller size.

See p. 23 for a listing of the diameters and current osculating orbital elements of the 30 largest main-belt asteroids.

EPHEMERIDES FOR THE BRIGHTEST ASTEROIDS IN 2011
BY BRIAN MARSDEN

Date 0h TT	RA (2000) h m	Dec ° ′	Mag.
(1) Ceres			
Jun. 28	0 12.2	−11 17	8.9
Jul. 8	0 17.9	−11 24	8.8
18	0 21.9	−11 45	8.6
28	0 23.8	−12 19	8.4
Aug. 7	0 23.6	−13 06	8.3
17	0 21.1	−14 04	8.1
27	0 16.4	−15 07	7.9
Sep. 6	0 09.9	−16 12	7.7
16	0 02.0	−17 09	7.6
26	23 53.6	−17 54	7.7
Oct. 6	23 45.6	−18 21	7.9
16	23 38.8	−18 28	8.1
26	23 33.8	−18 15	8.2
Nov. 5	23 31.0	−17 44	8.4
15	23 30.5	−16 56	8.6
25	23 32.2	−15 55	8.7
Dec. 5	23 36.0	−14 44	8.8
(2) Pallas			
Jun. 8	20 29.5	+18 26	10.0
18	20 26.0	+19 03	9.9
28	20 20.7	+19 22	9.7
Jul. 8	20 14.0	+19 16	9.6
18	20 06.3	+18 46	9.6
28	19 58.3	+17 49	9.5
Aug. 7	19 50.6	+16 28	9.5
17	19 44.0	+14 48	9.6
27	19 38.9	+12 54	9.7
Sep. 6	19 35.7	+10 52	9.8
16	19 34.4	+8 50	9.9
26	19 35.3	+6 52	10.0
(3) Juno			
Jan. 9	11 51.5	−2 40	9.9
19	11 53.8	−2 25	9.7
29	11 53.5	−1 49	9.6
Feb. 8	11 50.7	−0 52	9.4
18	11 45.6	+0 23	9.3
28	11 38.7	+1 53	9.1
Mar. 10	11 30.8	+3 31	8.9
20	11 22.8	+5 07	9.1
30	11 15.7	+6 34	9.4
Apr. 9	11 10.2	+7 47	9.6
19	11 06.7	+8 40	9.8
29	11 05.4	+9 15	10.0
(4) Vesta			
May 9	21 01.2	−17 10	7.2
19	21 12.2	−16 55	7.1
29	21 21.0	−16 51	6.9
Jun. 8	21 27.4	−17 02	6.7
18	21 31.0	−17 29	6.5
28	21 31.5	−18 15	6.4
Jul. 8	21 28.9	−19 18	6.1
18	21 23.3	−20 34	5.9
28	21 15.3	−21 56	5.7
Aug. 7	21 06.0	−23 15	5.6
17	20 56.8	−24 21	5.9
27	20 49.0	−25 10	6.1
Sep. 6	20 43.6	−25 39	6.4
16	20 41.4	−25 48	6.6

Date 0h TT	RA (2000) h m	Dec ° ′	Mag.
(4) Vesta (continued)			
Sep. 26	20 42.3	−25 41	6.8
Oct. 6	20 46.3	−25 18	7.0
16	20 52.9	−24 43	7.2
26	21 01.8	−23 57	7.4
Nov. 5	21 12.6	−23 01	7.6
(7) Iris			
Jan. 9	8 34.4	+12 11	8.1
19	8 23.7	+12 18	7.9
29	8 12.7	+12 35	8.0
Feb. 8	8 03.0	+12 56	8.3
18	7 55.9	+13 19	8.6
28	7 52.0	+13 39	8.9
Mar. 10	7 51.4	+13 54	9.2
20	7 54.0	+14 02	9.5
30	7 59.3	+14 04	9.7
Apr. 9	8 07.0	+13 57	9.9
(9) Metis			
Jul. 8	20 51.8	−24 46	10.0
18	20 43.3	−25 44	9.7
28	20 33.3	−26 38	9.6
Aug. 7	20 22.9	−27 21	9.7
17	20 13.5	−27 51	9.9
(10) Hygiea			
Mar. 30	15 38.1	−24 12	10.0
Apr. 9	15 36.0	−24 13	9.8
19	15 31.5	−24 02	9.6
29	15 25.0	−23 40	9.4
May 9	15 17.2	−23 08	9.2
19	15 09.1	−22 28	9.2
29	15 01.7	−21 45	9.4
Jun. 8	14 55.8	−21 03	9.6
18	14 52.0	−20 28	9.8
28	14 50.6	−20 01	10.0
(11) Parthenope			
Mar. 30	13 12.4	−0 09	10.0
Apr. 9	13 03.6	+0 56	9.9
(15) Eunomia			
Aug. 27	3 51.9	+33 36	9.4
Sep. 6	4 05.8	+34 50	9.3
16	4 17.6	+35 55	9.2
26	4 26.8	+36 52	9.0
Oct. 6	4 32.7	+37 39	8.8
16	4 35.0	+38 14	8.6
26	4 33.1	+38 32	8.4
Nov. 5	4 27.4	+38 30	8.3
15	4 18.5	+38 01	8.1
25	4 07.9	+37 04	7.9
Dec. 5	3 57.4	+35 42	8.0
15	3 48.9	+34 05	8.2
25	3 43.4	+32 23	8.4
(20) Massalia			
Jan. 29	12 02.0	−1 03	9.9
Feb. 8	12 00.7	−0 55	9.7
18	11 56.3	−0 27	9.5
28	11 49.4	+0 20	9.3

EPHEMERIDES FOR THE BRIGHTEST ASTEROIDS IN 2011 (cont)

Date 0h TT	RA (2000) h m	Dec ° '	Mag.
(20) Massalia (continued)			
Mar. 10	11 40.7	+1 19	9.0
20	11 31.5	+2 22	9.1
30	11 23.2	+3 20	9.4
Apr. 9	11 16.8	+4 06	9.6
19	11 13.1	+4 35	9.9
(21) Lutetia			
Jun. 18	19 07.2	−24 04	10.0
28	18 58.5	−24 39	9.7
Jul. 8	18 48.5	−25 11	9.5
18	18 38.8	−25 38	9.8
(23) Thalia			
Jun. 18	19 07.2	−24 04	10.0
28	18 58.5	−24 39	9.7
Jul. 8	18 48.5	−25 11	9.5
18	18 38.8	−25 38	9.8
(27) Euterpe			
Sep. 16	0 57.9	+3 11	9.9
26	0 50.0	+2 16	9.6
Oct. 6	0 40.7	+1 16	9.4
16	0 31.4	+0 19	9.6
26	0 23.3	−0 26	9.9
(29) Amphitrite			
Sep. 6	3 01.1	+21 20	10.0
16	3 03.7	+22 08	9.8
26	3 03.3	+22 47	9.6
Oct. 6	2 59.7	+23 13	9.4
16	2 53.2	+23 26	9.2
26	2 44.2	+23 23	8.9
Nov. 5	2 34.0	+23 04	8.7
15	2 23.9	+22 34	8.9
25	2 15.3	+21 59	9.1
Dec. 5	2 09.2	+21 26	9.4
15	2 06.3	+21 01	9.6
25	2 06.6	+20 47	9.8
(30) Urania			
Nov. 5	3 16.3	+22 13	9.8
15	3 06.2	+21 31	9.6
25	2 56.6	+20 44	9.9
(40) Harmonia			
Oct. 26	3 30.5	+13 01	9.8
Nov. 5	3 20.9	+12 33	9.5
15	3 10.2	+12 08	9.4
25	2 59.9	+11 50	9.7
Dec. 5	2 51.5	+11 44	10.0
(43) Ariadne			
May 29	18 45.6	−23 16	10.0
Jun. 8	18 41.0	−22 49	9.7
18	18 33.3	−22 21	9.4
28	18 23.7	−21 52	9.0
Jul. 8	18 14.3	−21 24	9.4
18	18 06.7	−20 58	9.7
28	18 02.4	−20 37	10.0
(44) Nysa			
Jan. 9	9 57.9	+12 14	9.6

Date 0h TT	RA (2000) h m	Dec ° '	Mag.
(44) Nysa (continued)			
Jan. 19	9 54.0	+13 00	9.4
29	9 47.3	+14 02	9.2
Feb. 8	9 38.6	+15 13	9.0
18	9 29.5	+16 23	9.1
28	9 21.5	+17 23	9.4
Mar. 10	9 15.9	+18 07	9.6
20	9 13.4	+18 31	9.9
(51) Nemausa			
Apr. 9	13 34.0	−1 38	9.9
19	13 26.0	+0 05	10.0
(68) Leto			
Nov. 5	3 08.5	+18 14	9.9
15	2 58.3	+18 11	9.8
(115) Thyra			
Oct. 26	3 49.3	+42 08	10.0
Nov. 5	3 41.2	+42 23	9.8
15	3 30.5	+41 57	9.6
25	3 19.5	+40 50	9.6
Dec. 5	3 10.4	+39 12	9.7
15	3 05.0	+37 16	10.0
(192) Nausikaa			
Jul. 28	23 07.4	−10 03	9.8
Aug. 7	23 04.9	−9 38	9.5
17	22 59.1	−9 23	9.1
27	22 50.6	−9 13	8.6
Sep. 6	22 40.8	−9 04	8.5
16	22 31.3	−8 49	8.9
26	22 23.8	−8 26	9.2
Oct. 6	22 19.6	−7 50	9.5
16	22 19.3	−7 02	9.7
26	22 22.7	−6 01	10.0
(230) Athamantis			
Oct. 16	1 44.0	+20 34	10.0
26	1 35.2	+18 58	9.9
(349) Dembowska			
Jul. 18	22 03.4	−24 50	10.0
28	21 57.3	−25 38	9.9
Aug. 7	21 49.5	−26 22	9.7
17	21 40.6	−26 57	9.7
27	21 31.8	−27 18	9.8
Sep. 6	21 24.0	−27 22	10.0
(532) Herculina			
Jul. 8	20 37.4	−23 33	10.0
18	20 29.2	−24 56	9.8
28	20 20.2	−26 14	9.8
Aug. 7	20 11.3	−27 22	10.0
(1036) Ganymed			
Sep. 6	0 25.7	+63 39	9.9
16	1 02.3	+60 01	9.6
26	1 30.2	+53 21	9.3
Oct. 6	1 48.4	+43 19	8.9
16	1 59.1	+30 41	8.6
26	2 05.1	+17 42	8.4
Nov. 5	2 09.1	+6 54	8.9
15	2 13.1	−0 41	9.6

PLANETARY AND ASTEROIDAL OCCULTATIONS
By David W. Dunham and James Stamm

As planets, satellites, asteroids, and comets move across the sky, they occasionally pass directly between an observer and a distant star, thereby producing an *occultation*. Astronomers have learned much about various solar-system bodies by carefully monitoring the changing apparent brightness of stars during the immersion and emersion phases of occultations. If the occulting body does not have an atmosphere, the occultation is virtually instantaneous; if there is an atmosphere, it causes the star's disappearance and reappearance to occur gradually. If a planet has rings or other debris in its environs, the extent and degree of transparency of this material can be precisely mapped. The rings of Uranus, the ring arcs of Neptune, and the atmosphere of Pluto were all discovered by occultation observations. In addition, if an occultation is observed at several appropriately distributed sites, it is often possible to determine the size and shape of the occulting body more accurately than by other Earth-based techniques.

Amateur astronomers can sometimes make important contributions to occultation observing campaigns. This is particularly true for asteroid occultations, for which the event path across Earth is often very narrow and uncertain in location (due to uncertainties in both the star's position and the ephemeris of the asteroid). By recording the times of the star's disappearance and reappearance as seen from several sites (i.e. by noting the edges of the asteroid's shadow as it sweeps across Earth), the asteroid's profile can be directly determined. Often timings of adequate accuracy can be made by visual observers using modest telescopes.

When observing an occultation, it is important that an observer know his or her location to within a fraction of a kilometre. Geographic longitude and latitude as well as the altitude of an observing site can be determined with a GPS receiver, from a high-quality topographic map, or from some map Web sites. If observations are to be of maximum value, the times of immersion and emersion must be determined as accurately as possible—certainly to better than 0.5 s, and better than 0.2 s for the shortest events (those less than about 10 s in duration). Photoelectric equipment with high-speed digital recording systems is well suited for this work. Attaching a low-light-level video camera to a telescope is a less expensive method for accurately timing these events. Visual observers equipped with audio recorders and shortwave time-signal receivers can also make useful contributions. Even simple measurements of the duration of an occultation made with an ordinary stopwatch can be of value. CCD observers should be aware that most of these systems are incapable of timing accuracies better than about 2 s; hence visual observation may be better. A trick that some CCD observers have used is to turn off the telescope clock drive shortly before the predicted time and let the images trail. The occultation will appear as a break in the trail that can be measured to a few tenths of a second, if the moment the drive is turned off is accurately timed.

Occultation observations are coordinated in North America by the International Occultation Timing Association (IOTA). IOTA member or not, IOTA wants to inform you and others in your area able to locate stars to 11th magnitude of last-minute prediction updates. Please email the longitude and latitude (or location from the nearest town) of convenient observing sites, telescope size(s), and an indication of whether you are mobile to dunham@starpower.net. Individuals interested in joining IOTA should refer to OCCULTATIONS BY THE MOON, p. 166 for membership information.

More information is in the *Solar System Photometry Handbook* (Willmann-Bell, Inc., 1983), *Sky & Telescope*, and occasional papers in the *Astronomical Journal*, *Icarus*, and other scientific journals.

Observations of asteroidal and planetary occultations, *including* negative observations, should be sent to reports@asteroidoccultation.com for analysis and publication by IOTA. When reporting timings, describe your geographic longitude, latitude, and altitude (to the nearest second of arc and 30 m, respectively), telescope size, timing method, the start and end time of observation, an estimate of the observer's reaction-time (if applicable) and the accuracy of the timing, and whether the reaction-time correction has been applied. For reporting, the forms at www.asteroidoccultation.com/observations/NA are preferred. Much useful information is at www.asteroidoccultation.com/observations.

The following two-page table of predictions of asteroidal and planetary satellite occultations visible from North America for 2011 is based on predictions by Edwin Goffin, Scott Donnell, Steve Preston, Derek Breit, and David Herald.

The successive columns in the table list: (1) the date and central time of the event; (2) the name of the occulting body; (3) the apparent magnitude of the asteroid or planet; (4) the catalogue number of the occulted star; (5) the apparent visual magnitude of the star; (6) the right ascension and (7) declination of the star; (8) the expected magnitude change from the combined brightness; (9) the predicted maximum duration of the occultation in seconds; and (10) the approximate region from which the occultation is predicted to be visible (locations are listed chronologically from first to last). Due to uncertainties in the catalogue positions of the stars and the ephemerides of the asteroids from which these predictions are derived, the exact region of visibility of an occultation cannot be derived until CCD observations link the star and asteroid to the new *HIPPARCOS* reference frame, usually a few weeks prior to the event. Even then, errors remain, so those near but outside the paths should try to observe. Maps and more about these events is at www.poyntsource.com/New/RASC_Events.htm.

Note that the times are for the first North American (or Hawaiian) land crossed by the occultation shadow; for other locations in North America, the time might be a few minutes later. Within a few weeks of each event, improved predictions and the latest path maps may be obtained from Steve Preston's asteroidal occultation Web site: www.asteroidoccultation.com. Much other useful information, including interactive maps to zoom in on the path, circumstances for dozens of stations in and near the path, and lists of stars that can be used to prepoint telescopes to the target stars are at www.poyntsource.com/New/Global.htm. "Occult Watcher" finds many other asteroidal occultations visible from your site; you can obtain it from www.hristopavlov.net/OccultWatcher/publish.htm, Since Occult Watcher works from an interactive Web site, IOTA uses it to coordinate asteroidal occultation observation plans.

In the following table, the **Date** is given as month number–day of month. **Ast. #** is the asteroid's number. The alternative star numbers given in the table below are from the HIPPARCOS-mission catalogs used for the predictions on IOTA's asteroidal occultation Web sites mentioned above. Tycho 2 (TYC) catalog numbers are abbreviated since they all have 0 for the 5th number and 1 for the last, and hyphens are removed; thus, TYC 19570122 is in full, TYC 1957-00122-1. Spectral types (**Sp.**) are not available for some of the stars.

Date	AST#		Sp.	Date	AST#		Sp.
1–12	1424	TYC 19570122	K5	5–29	217	HIP 87494	K0
1–16	66	TYC 13440100	K0	7–4	52	TYC 02920339	F0
1–22	635	TYC 02360185	F8	8–6	194	TYC 04161196	G0
1–24	160	HIP 46249	G5	8–15	360	TYC 07290057	B8
2–2	419	HIP 25908	A0	11–4	105	TYC 47100235	K0
2–4	773	TYC 24340946	F8	11–14	972	TYC 57740212	
2–4	635	TYC 02391257	K0	12–7	114	TYC 63470340	
2–27	38	HIP 69317	A2	12–8	593	TYC 24370787	K5
3–9	72	HIP 55379	F5	12–13	906	TYC 58190555	A5
3–12	530	TYC 13061185	A2	12–13	433	HIP 48614	A0
3–28	58	TYC 49610894		12–23	172	HIP 14450	B9
4–3	1467	HIP 56417	G5	12–28	407	HIP 54719	A5
4–24	209	TYC 61470304		12–30	748	TYC 52450766	
5–10	349	TYC 69400650					

Notes regarding some of the events in the table:

Mar. 20: Oceana is an M-class (spectra contains metallic signatures) asteroid. The star is HIP 60645, spectral type F8.

May 3: The star is TYC 5767-02253-1, spectral type G0. It has a 12.2-mag. companion 5.0″ away in position angle (PA) 186° that will not be occulted as seen from anywhere on Earth's surface.

Jul. 19: The star is ZC 3339 (Robertson's Zodiacal Catalog) = SAO 165285 = HIP 112420, spectral type Ma. This is the brightest star predicted to be occulted by a sizeable asteroid in North America during 2011. Antiope is a binary asteroid with nearly equal components (estimated diameters 88 km and 84 km) separated by 171 km in a circular orbit. The duplicity of Antiope was discovered on 2000 Aug. 10 by W. Merline et al. using the Keck II telescope with adaptive optics. IOTA plans to hold its annual meeting at Sierra College in Rocklin, Calif., north of Sacramento, on the weekend (Jul. 16–17) before this Tuesday morning event so that attendees can observe the event.

Sep. 2: The star is HIP 47035, spectral type B9. Mercury's 7.4″ disk will be 42 perecnt sunlit, so the star will be at most 4.3″ from Mercury's bright terminator when it reappears; the bright-side disappearance will be impossible to observe. The occultation will occur in strong twilight along the west coast of the USA, with lower altitude but a darker sky towards Alaska. 9.1-mag. SAO 98655 is 45″ away in PA 48°; it will not be occulted.

Oct. 22: The star is TYC 5718-00380-1, spectral type F2. The star has a 12.3-mag. companion 2.7″ away at position angle 174° that will not be occulted as seen from anywhere on Earth's surface. The companion, 1.4 mag. brighter than Thia, will remain visible while the primary star is occulted, so the mag. drop when the occultation occurs will appear to be about 3.2, rather than the 4.6 predicted without the companion star. But 3.2 is still a large, very noticeable drop.

IOTA SELECTED LIST OF NORTH AMERICAN OCCULTATIONS BY SOLAR SYSTEM OBJECTS FOR THE YEAR 2011

Date	UT	Occulting Body	(Mag.)	Star	(Mag.)	RA (2000) h m s	Dec ° ' "	ΔMag.	Dur. s	Nominal Path
Jan. 5	4:49	623 Chimaera	13.6	TYC 2453–01146–1	10.1	7 30 39	+31 11 11	3.5	4.0	NW Manitoba to Vancouver Island
8	11:47	212 Medea	12.7	TYC 1839–00696–1	10.0	4 45 14	+27 00 07	2.8	19.4	Nevada to central California
11	9:53	363 Padua	13.2	TYC 1946–01252–1	11.2	8 51 59	+25 25 01	2.2	6.1	Southern Texas to northern California
12	8:38	1424 Sundmania	14.5	SAO 80669	8.3	9 10 05	+29 33 29	6.2	5.5	Eastern Georgia to Vancouver Island
13	5:50	1212 Francette	14.2	TYC 1344–00100–1	11.1	7 00 19	+15 19 45	3.2	6.5	S Nova Scotia to N British Columbia
16	8:58	66 Maja	12.2	SAO 79763	8.7	7 52 47	+25 55 34	3.5	7.0	New Jersey to N British Columbia
22	9:21	635 Vundtia	13.8	PPM 156211	10.4	9 48 44	+02 00 32	3.5	9.2	Eastern Georgia to western Washington
22	12:08	42 Isis	11.6	TYC 1933–00197–1	11.0	7 55 38	+27 59 31	1.1	6.8	Eastern Texas to southeastern Alaska
24	4:10	160 Una	12.8	SAO 80827	9.1	9 25 45	+20 22 50	3.7	7.3	Massachusetts to northern California
25	11:29	589 Croatia	13.9	TYC 0239–01756–1	11.1	9 42 23	+03 45 01	2.9	7.4	Maryland to northwestern Alberta
Feb. 2	7:56	419 Aurelia	13.8	SAO 94620	8.8	5 31 46	+19 33 04	5.0	21.5	Delaware to southeastern Alaska
4	5:12	773 Irmintraud	14.0	SAO 59192	9.4	6 32 16	+36 20 28	4.6	8.7	Central Florida to central Mexico
4	6:56	635 Vundtia	13.6	SAO 117838	9.2	9 40 10	+02 57 53	4.4	7.4	Panama to Baja Sur
11	3:50	28 Bellona	10.6	UCAC2 37524724	11.1	7 14 44	+16 23 18	0.5	18.2	Southern Mexico to southern Alberta
27	9:06	38 Leda	13.0	SAO 182321	8.7	14 11 16	–22 49 33	4.3	31.2	Southern Mexico to southern Alberta
Mar. 4	8:21	702 Alauda	12.3	UCAC2 21314843	11.2	11 27 19	–25 47 38	1.4	14.7	Northeastern Ontario to N California
9	6:04	72 Feronia	12.0	SAO 138141	8.4	11 20 24	–01 47 49	3.6	7.2	Haiti to Oregon
12	4:54	530 Turandot	15.5	SAO 94751	8.9	5 40 46	+19 07 33	6.6	6.7	Baja to Florida Keys
20*	9:45	224 Oceana	12.1	SAO 138776	8.3	12 25 50	–04 51 43	3.8	5.1	Maine to northwest British Columbia
28	9:46	58 Concordia	12.4	PPM 196383	10.8	13 19 01	–03 26 52	1.8	9.0	Florida to Yukon Territory
Apr. 1	2:29	416 Vaticana	14.0	TYC 2403–00758–1	11.0	5 27 14	+31 27 03	3.1	3.9	Southern Nevada to Florida Keys
3	9:23	1467 Mashona	14.0	PPM 224592	10.2	11 34 00	–18 02 38	3.8	7.2	Eastern Texas to Baja Norte
8	14:11	366 Vincentina	14.0	TYC 7400–01200–1	10.0	18 17 31	–35 34 21	4.0	8.6	Hawaii
24	5:21	209 Dido	12.4	PPM 731566	10.9	14 17 14	–20 31 24	1.7	13.3	Southern Nova Scotia to Saskatchewan
30	4:27	7 Iris	10.3	TYC 0808–00566–1	10.3	8 28 59	+13 14 45	0.8	10.1	Northern Idaho to SE North Carolina
May 3*	10:58	679 Pax	13.7	SAO 163717	9.1	20 36 02	–13 49 32	4.6	3.0	Baja Norte to S Texas to Florida Keys
10	4:38	304 Olga	13.3	TYC 0919–01401–1	10.7	15 02 03	+07 56 24	2.7	6.0	Bahamas to northern California
10	10:05	349 Dembowska	11.1	PPM 736904	10.8	21 42 26	–23 02 36	0.9	7.6	Central California to central Florida
11	5:49	1437 Diomedes	16.1	TYC 1908–00370–1	11.0	7 12 43	+29 06 56	5.1	5.5	Alberta to Kansas
12	4:07	345 Tercidina	12.4	TYC 4955–00800–1	10.9	12 43 16	–06 08 58	1.7	17.6	Bahamas to northern Ontario
29	6:31	217 Eudora	12.9	SAO 141925	7.0	17 52 37	–05 15 44	5.9	10.8	Bahamas to Oregon
Jul. 4	3:03	52 Europa	12.1	PPM 158947	10.1	12 33 05	+04 31 29	2.2	17.3	Nebraska to northern Florida
17	10:08	415 Palatia	13.7	TYC 0040–00598–1	11.2	2 03 21	+04 49 17	2.6	3.1	Central Baja to South Carolina
19*	10:39	90 Antiope	12.5	ZC 3339	6.7	22 46 14	–11 09 59	5.8	39.5	Saskatchewan to northern California

* See the note for this event at the bottom of p. 255.

IOTA SELECTED LIST OF NORTH AMERICAN OCCULTATIONS BY SOLAR SYSTEM OBJECTS FOR THE YEAR 2011 (continued)

Date	UT	Occulting Body	(Mag.)	Star	(Mag.)	RA (2000) h m s	Dec ° ' "	ΔMag.	Dur. s	Nominal Path
Aug. 6	6:04	194 Prokne	10.9	SAO 122833	9.2	17 51 31	+00 37 29	1.9	17.8	Central Manitoba to Baja Sur
15	8:52	360 Carlova	13.8	SAO 95144	8.9	6 02 14	+14 52 59	4.9	3.1	Louisiana to SE North Carolina
30	10:11	697 Galilea	15.1	TYC 2412-00623-1	11.1	5 41 07	+21 15	4.0	3.0	Baja Sur to southern Ontario
Sep. 2*	13:28	Mercury	—	SAO 98654	7.9					Far-western USA, Alaska
5	6:13	95 Arethusa	13.1	TYC 5706-03276-1	11.2	18 55 11	-08 44 37	2.1	48.1	Central Manitoba to Baja Norte
10	10:09	175 Andromache	14.6	TYC 1914-01611-1	11.1	7 23 57	+24 47 34	3.5	3.4	Northern California to N Ontario
28	9:44	119 Althaea	13.4	TYC 1334-00235-1	11.0	6 43 19	+18 13 15	2.5	2.9	Washington to Newfoundland
Oct. 1	7:43	360 Carlova	13.5	TYC 0774-00138-1	10.8	7 13 04	+13 26 46	2.8	5.1	Northeastern Mexico to North Carolina
1	11:49	478 Tergeste	12.4	TYC 1179-00820-1	10.8	0 15 21	+16 42 22	1.8	5.9	Central California to Oklahoma
14	9:16	466 Tisiphone	14.3	UCAC2 42399135	11.0	7 16 44	+30 10 08	3.4	9.1	Vancouver Island to northern Quebec
22*	0:42	405 Thia	13.7	SAO 161949	9.1	18 53 59	-13 47 20	4.6	4.7	Northern Mexico to South Carolina
23	8:16	433 Eros	11.8	TYC 3390-00294-1	9.9	6 53 03	+46 43 07	2.1	2.0	Eastern Oregon to NW Manitoba
Nov. 3	9:53	356 Liguria	12.5	TYC 1946-00052-1	11.2	8 54 34	+26 52 18	1.6	7.5	Northern California to N Nova Scotia
4	10:16	105 Artemis	12.6	SAO 130262	9.4	3 03 39	-02 38 53	3.3	7.6	NW Manitoba to Vancouver Island
5	3:58	704 Interamnia	11.7	TYC 5729-02083-1	10.3	19 49 37	-10 22 04	1.7	14.6	Southern California to Missouri
14	0:17	972 Cohnia	14.4	PPM 204638	10.2	20 56 32	-09 47 58	4.2	3.4	Central Mexico to central Florida
24	05:51	1309 Hyperborea	15.8	TYC 5242-00991-1	11.0	23 01 48	-01 20 15	4.8	6.3	Northern California to Iowa
25	07:29	63 Ausonia	11.1	TYC 1811-00638-1	11.0	3 44 15	+29 10 16	0.8	8.1	Delaware to central California
27	06:36	162 Laurentia	13.6	TYC 1415-00353-1	9.4	9 58 19	+19 56 38	4.2	7.1	Central Mexico to southern Florida
Dec. 1	09:28	57 Mnemosyne	11.4	TYC 0134-00671-1	9.8	6 00 57	+03 08 54	1.8	10.1	NW Manitoba to Vancouver Island
7	01:44	114 Kassandra	14.2	PPM 238544	11.1	21 13 36	-15 07 34	3.2	3.4	Cent. British Columbia to NW Saskatchewan
8	13:01	593 Titania	12.2	SAO 59642	9.3	6 57 38	+30 30 00	3.0	7.9	Baja Sur to northern Alberta
10	10:48	156 Xanthippe	13.1	TYC 1315-01964-1	11.0	6 23 04	+16 35 11	2.3	9.0	SE South Carolina to S California
13	01:32	906 Repsolda	14.8	SAO 165400	9.8	22 57 15	-14 49 03	5.0	2.9	Central California to central Manitoba
13	10:49	433 Eros	10.1	SAO 61753	8.9	9 54 51	+37 24 54	1.5	3.8	Southwestern Alaska to South Carolina
15	01:56	112 Iphigenia	13.0	TYC 1871-00287-1	10.8	5 52 08	+27 03 55	2.3	6.2	Northeastern Manitoba to Oregon
18	10:04	593 Titania	11.9	TYC 2440-00225-1	10.0	6 49 44	+32 41 13	2.1	7.2	Eastern Cuba to northeastern Manitoba
23	09:16	172 Baucis	12.5	SAO 56158	7.9	3 06 32	+33 37 31	4.6	9.7	Hawaii
26	01:49	329 Svea	13.3	TYC 4773-01413-1	11.1	5 55 45	-02 03 47	2.3	6.0	Bahamas to Baja Norte
28	11:28	407 Arachne	13.9	SAO 138052	8.2	11 12 10	-00 24 35	5.7	11.6	Yukon to Yucatan
30	03:15	748 Simeisa	15.7	PPM 207129	10.3	23 05 01	-03 35 56	5.4	4.0	Central California to Wisconsin

*See the note for this event at the bottom of p. 255.

METEORS, COMETS, AND DUST

METEORS
By Margaret Campbell–Brown and Peter Brown

A *meteor* (from the Greek *meteoros*, meaning high in the air) is the light, heat, ionization, and, occasionally, sound phenomena produced when a solid body (a *meteoroid*) collides with molecules in Earth's upper atmosphere. These collisions heat the surface of the object; then at a height typically between 120 km and 80 km the meteoroid begins to ablate, or lose mass. Typically, ablation takes the form of vapourization, although melting and quasicontinuous fragmentation may also contribute. It is these ablated meteoric atoms that collide with air molecules to produce atomic excitations, or ionization, leading to the emission of light we see in the night sky. Typical visual meteors are produced by meteoroids the size of a small pebble, although the relationship between mass–brightness and velocity is complex (Figure 1). The faintest meteors visible to the naked eye are due to meteoroids the size of the tip of a ballpoint pen; the brightest meteors are due to meteoroids whose diameters roughly match the thickness of a pen.

Larger and low-velocity meteoroids are favoured to pass through Earth's atmosphere, although rarely as a single monolithic body. When these ponderable masses reach the ground, they are called *meteorites*. At the other extreme, very small meteoroids (micrometres in size) efficiently radiate heat from their surface and do not reach ablation temperatures; such particles reach Earth's surface without having been fully ablated, although most are heated many hundreds of degrees.

Meteoroids can be divided broadly into two groups: stream and sporadic meteoroids. *Stream* meteoroids follow similar orbits around the Sun, many of which can be linked to a particular parent object, in most cases a comet. When Earth intersects the orbit of a stream, a meteor shower occurs. Since all the meteoroids in a stream move along nearly identical orbits, their paths in the atmosphere are parallel. This creates a perspective effect: the meteor trails on the celestial sphere appear to radiate from a fixed location, called the meteor *radiant*. *Sporadic* meteoroids, in contrast, are much more loosely associated and are not part of tightly grouped streams.

Meteor showers are named for the constellation from which they appear to radiate. Official rules for naming showers have been adopted by IAU commission #22 and can be found at **www.ta3.sk/IAUC22DB/MDC2007/Dokumenty/shower_nomenclature.php**. When several showers have radiants in the same constellation, nearby bright stars are used in naming.

The sporadic complex as seen at Earth, however, is structured and shows definite directionalities as well as annual variations in activity levels. Sporadic meteor radiants are concentrated in six major source regions throughout the sky. These sources are in fixed locations with respect to the Sun. Variations in the strengths of these sources throughout the year have been observed; it is the elevation of these sources at a particular location plus the intrinsic strength of each source at a given time of the year that determine the average background sporadic rate. Figure 2 shows the distribution of sporadic radiants in Sun-centred coordinates. The expected sporadic rate varies as a function of the altitude of the apex of Earth's way throughout the year, but is generally in the range of 8–13 meteors per hour for visual observers. The apex is the instantaneous direction of travel of Earth around the Sun; it is the point on the ecliptic that transits at 6:00 local apparent solar time (see pp. 45–46).

In general, meteoroid streams are formed when particles are ejected from comets as they approach the Sun. The parent objects of many showers have been identified from the similarity of the orbits of the object and the stream. Cometary associations include the η-Aquariids and Orionids, which are derived from 1P/Halley, the Leonids, which originate from 55P/Tempel-Tuttle, and the Perseids, from 109P/Swift-Tuttle. Several asteroids are known to be associated with meteor streams: 3200 Phaethon

and the Geminid stream and 2003 EH1 linked to the Quadrantid shower are the most prominent examples. All of these particles have orbits that coincide closely with that of the parent object, but their orbits are gradually shifted through radiative effects and planetary perturbations. Such effects lead to a broadening of the stream over time, resulting in an increased duration of the meteor shower as seen from Earth—older streams tend to be more long-lived—and eventually transform stream meteoroids into sporadic meteoroids.

The visual strength of a meteor shower is measured by its Zenithal Hourly Rate (ZHR), defined as the number of meteors a single average observer would see if the radiant were directly overhead and the sky dark and transparent with a limiting stellar magnitude of +6.5 (conditions that are rarely met in reality). A more physical measure is the flux of a meteoroid stream, measured in numbers of meteors of absolute brightness (referenced to a range of 100 km) brighter than +6.5 per square kilometre per second perpendicular to the radiant direction. While an observer will tend to see the largest number of meteors by looking at the shower radiant, the most useful counts are obtained by looking some distance away from the radiant.

Most data on meteor showers are currently gathered visually by amateur observers. It is crucial to observe from a dark-sky location with a clear view of the sky, and to allow at least 20 min before the start of observations to allow dark adaptation of the eyes. One should choose an area of the sky to observe, preferably with an elevation greater than 40°. The limiting magnitude should be carefully recorded for each session,

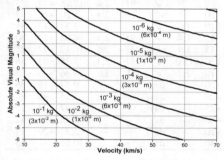

FIGURE 1 *Magnitude as a function of velocity for meteoroids of different sizes. Uncertainties in the mass scale are largest at high velocities and small masses, and may be as large as an order of magnitude in mass at the extremes.*

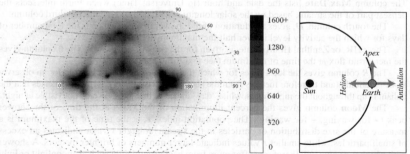

FIGURE 2 *Plot of the radiant distribution of meteors as seen by the Canadian Meteor Orbit Radar throughout the entire year, in Sun-centred ecliptic coordinates. The Sun is at (0,0), the helion, and the Earth's orbital velocity points to the centre of the plot, the apex. The antihelion point is at (180,0). The small concentrations visible near the centre of the plot are major showers (the Geminids and Eta Aquariids in particular). The intensity of the plot reflects the number of radiants per 2 deg². The rate of sporadic meteors as a function of time depends on which of the sporadic sources are above the horizon at the time of observation. The diagram at right shows the meaning of the coordinate system.*

along with the UT and the centre of the field of view of the observer. The most basic observations should include an estimate of the brightness of the meteor, the time of observation, and a shower association (based on the radiant and apparent speed of the meteor). Information on collecting and reporting scientifically useful observations can be found at the International Meteor Organization's Web site, **www.imo.net.**

TABLE OF METEOR SHOWERS FOR 2011

The table lists the major visual showers as well as those detectable by radio methods during the day. Of the strongest annual showers, the Moon is favourable only for the Quadrantids. The October Draconids are expected to show a strong outburst with a peak ZHR of order several hundred near 20 UT Oct. 8, with noticeable activity lasting several hours centred around this time. The peak favours European longitudes, but the full Moon will severely curtail the visual impact of the shower.

Shower	Max Date UT	λ 2000	D	ZHR	θ ×10⁻⁶	R	Moon %	r	RA h m	Dec °	v km/s
Quadrantids	Jan. 4 1h	283.16	0.6	120	8.4	✓	0	2.1	15 20	+49	43
April Lyrids	Apr. 22 23h	32.3	1.3	20	4.6	✓	69–	2.9	18 10	+34	48
η-Aquariids	May 6 13h	45.5	5	60	6.4	>03	10+	2.4	22 30	–2	66
S. δ-Aquariids	Jul. 29 15h	126	8	20	6.2	>23	1–	3.2	22 44	–16	43
Perseids	Aug. 13 6h	140.0	2	90	6.0	✓	99+	2.1	3 08	+58	60
Oct. Draconids	Oct. 8 20h	195	<0.1	?	?	✓	91+	2.6	17 28	+54	23
Orionids	Oct. 21 22h	208	2	20	2.2	>23	28+	2.4	6 20	+16	67
S. Taurids	Nov. 5 23h	223	15	10	1.0	✓	80+	2.3	3 34	+14	31
N. Taurids	Nov. 12 22h	230	15	15	1.4	✓	95–	2.3	4 00	+22	30
Leonids	Nov. 18 4h	235.3	1	15	1.9	>00	53–	2.5	10 12	+22	71
Geminids	Dec. 14 18h	262.2	1	120	11.0	✓	81–	2.3	7 28	+33	36
Ursids	Dec. 23 2h	270.7	0.5	10	2.2	✓	2–	3.0	14 36	+75	35
N D ω-Cetids	May 5 16h	49	30	≈20		day	—	—	0 47	+19	36
S D ω-Cetids	May 7 1h	46	20	≈20		day	—	—	1 24	–6	36
D ζ-Perseids	Jun. 5 3h	74	19	≈25		day	—	—	3 47	+23	29
D Arietids	Jun. 9 20h	78.5	16	≈60		day	—	—	2 52	+26	41
D β-Taurids	Jun. 26 2h	94	9	≈20		day	—	—	5 31	+20	29
D Sextantids	Sep. 29 16h	186	12	≈40		day	—	—	10 17	–1	33

The column **Max Date** lists the date and hour (in Universal Time) when Earth intersects the densest part of the stream, based on the solar longitude λ (J2000.0) given in the third column.

The fourth column, **D**, gives the duration of the shower in days, which is the total number of days for which the activity level is over half the maximum activity.

The **ZHR**, or Zenithal Hourly Rate, is given for the peak of the shower. The θ column gives the meteoroid flux at the time of maximum (see text for explanation).

The **R** column gives the local times for which the radiant is above the horizon for an observer at 45°N latitude (and therefore meteors from the shower are visible); a ✓ symbol indicates that the radiant is up throughout the night hours, while "day" indicates that the shower is not visible at night.

The **Moon** column gives the percent illumination of the Moon at the time of the shower peak (+ for waxing, – for waning). The population index, **r**, at the time of the maximum is a measure of the size distribution of particles in the stream. A larger **r** value indicates an excess of small particles, while smaller **r** values indicate larger numbers of brighter meteors. A shower with a higher **r** value will therefore suffer more from background light such as moonlight or light pollution. Sporadic meteors at observable visual magnitudes have an **r** value near 3.0.

The **RA** and **Dec** are given in the next two columns: They give the position in the sky of the radiant at the time of the shower peak. The position of the radiant will vary from these values away from the time of the peak; tables published by the International Meteor Organization in their annual shower calendar provide details of radiant drift. The last column, **v**, gives the apparent atmospheric speed of the meteors in the shower.

RADIO DETECTION OF METEORS
By Philip Gebhardt

The term *meteor* applies not only to the streak of light produced by a meteoroid, but also to the column of ionized atoms and molecules along the path behind the meteoroid. These meteor trails are capable of scattering radio signals from terrestrial stations. Radio detection rates tend to be higher than visual observation rates because particles down to 10^{-5} kg can be detected visually, while particles down to 10^{-10} kg can be detected by radio. Assuming a density of 1 t/m^3, these mass limits correspond to diameters of about 3 mm and 0.06 mm, respectively.

Two types of meteor trails exist: *underdense* and *overdense*; they are determined by the density of free electrons. Reradiated signals from underdense trails (fewer than 2×10^{14} electrons per metre) rise above the receiver noise almost instantaneously and then decay exponentially. The duration of many meteor bursts is about a second or less. Reflected signals from overdense trails may have higher amplitude and longer duration, but destructive interference due to reflection from different parts of the trail can produce fluctuations in the signal.

Data for selected meteor showers appear in the Table of Meteor Showers on the previous page. These data are for visual observations and should only be considered as guidelines for radio purposes. The sporadic meteor rate (visual and radio) peaks about 6:00 local time (i.e. on the advancing side of Earth in its orbit) and is minimum near 18:00. The rate will vary from a few per hour for off-peak times for sporadic meteors to several hundred per hour during a very active shower. Unlike visual observation, radio detection of sporadic meteors or shower meteors can be undertaken in daylight and during inclement weather. Six daytime showers are listed in the Table of Meteor Showers. Frequencies between 20 MHz and 150 MHz are typically used for meteor detection. Both amplitude and duration of meteor bursts are frequency dependent—they decrease with increasing frequency. At the lower frequencies, however, galactic as well as human-made noise (particularly in urban areas) become limiting factors. Also, as the wavelength becomes comparable to the width of the meteor trail, the echo strength decreases.

The commercial FM broadcast band (88 MHz to 108 MHz) provides a good introductory opportunity for meteor detection. The abundance of over-the-horizon stations transmitting 24 hours a day ensures that a meteor burst can be heard from a suitably positioned meteor regardless of the time of day.

The technique involves listening on a frequency not used by a local FM station. A receiver with a digital frequency readout is therefore an asset. Frequencies throughout North America are assigned at 200-kHz intervals between 88.1 MHz and 107.9 MHz. Alternatively, a TV set (channels 2 through 6) can be used, provided the set is connected to an antenna rather than through cable TV. Long bursts can be heard from WWV (20 MHz, Fort Collins, Colorado) or CHU (14.670 MHz, Ottawa, Ontario), provided there is no ionospheric propagation between the station and your receiving site. In all cases, an outdoor antenna is preferable. It is also possible to listen using the FM radio in your car. Note that other means of signal propagation may be heard, but only meteor signals have their characteristic fast rise-time and short duration.

Further information can be found on the following Web sites www.imo.net/calendar/2011 and www.spaceweather.com/glossary/nasameteorradar.html.

Also see *Sky & Telescope, 94* (December 1997), No. 6, p. 108.

FIREBALLS
BY ALAN HILDEBRAND

Exceptionally bright meteors (above magnitude –5) that are spectacular enough to light up a wide area and attract public attention are generally referred to as *fireballs*. The main reasons to report the observation of a fireball are the following: (1) to assist with meteorite recovery; (2) to help provide orbital information for recovered meteorites; (3) to rule out other catastrophic events, such as airplane crashes and satellite re-entries; and (4) to help calibrate infrasound arrays deployed to monitor the Comprehensive Test Ban Treaty.

Rapid recovery of freshly fallen meteorites—as well as careful handling and storage—before they have been exposed too long to the terrestrial atmosphere is highly desirable. This allows meteorite researchers to study water-soluble minerals (such as salt), organic phases, and physical properties (such as porosity and seismic velocities). Rapid recovery is also essential for the study of short-lived radioactive isotopes induced by space exposure.

Fireballs no brighter than magnitude –6 can produce small meteorites. A slow fireball with or without terminal breakup is a good candidate for dropping meteorites. A delayed sonic boom associated with a fireball indicates that it is relatively nearby and often that it has penetrated into the lower atmosphere with an associated meteorite fall.

The scientific value of a meteorite is significantly greater when its prefall orbit is known. Under favourable circumstances, visual data can be used to obtain an approximate atmospheric trajectory, which, coupled with satellite or video observations, can be used to derive a prefall orbit.

The Meteorites and Impacts Advisory Committee (MIAC) of the Canadian Space Agency maintains an informative Web site: miac.uqac.ca. The preferred method for submitting fireball reports is via the Web:

Canada (only): miac.uqac.ca/MIAC/fireball.php
United States (AMS): www.amsmeteors.org/fireball/report.html
Global (IMO): www.imo.net/fireball/report.html
North American Meteor Network (NAMN):
    www.namnmeteors.org/fireball/namnreport.html

Reports of fireballs seen over Canada can also be faxed to the Canadian Fireball Reporting Centre at (403) 284-0074. Reports should include the following information (making notes immediately, at least of the precise time, is recommended):

(1) The name, telephone number/email, and address of the observer(s).

(2) The time of occurrence (and uncertainty in this time); an accurate time is required to search instrumental databases.

(3) The location of the observer at the time the fireball was seen (preferably in precise longitude and latitude).

(4) The beginning and ending points of the fireball, in terms of either right ascension and declination or azimuth and elevation. Indicate whether the true beginning was observed and whether the ending point was blocked by an object on the horizon.

(5) An estimate of the apparent magnitude; or compare the fireball brightness to that of the Moon. Was the ground lit up?

(6) The duration of the fireball and the persistent train (if any).

(7) A qualitative description of the event (e.g. colour, flares, fragmentation, dust clouds persisting after the fireball, and sound). If sound was heard, report the time delay between the fireball and the arrival of the sound or the precise time of the sound arrival as well as that of the fireball.

(8) The existence of any video, audio, or photographic records.

METEORITE IDENTIFICATION
BY RICHARD K. HERD AND CHRISTOPHER D.K. HERD

Meteorites are rocks from space that have fallen on Earth. Some have lain for many thousands of years before discovery. Fossil meteorites are found in ancient strata; others, found at the surface, are recent arrivals or may have lain there for many thousands of years before discovery. Those witnessed to traverse Earth's atmosphere, and recovered based on those observations, are called meteorite *falls*; less than 1100 have ever been documented. Those with no record of arrival are meteorite *finds* when recognized, and are far more numerous. Meteorites are named for where they are found. The Meteoritical Society (Met. Soc.) is the main worldwide organization for meteorite specialists, called *meteoriticists*. It is responsible for approval of new meteorites. Its nomenclature committee guidelines (www.meteoriticalsociety.org/bulletin/nc-guidelines.htm) ensure that new meteorites are named to avoid confusion and ambiguity with existing meteorites, and that type specimens of all new meteorites are preserved in collections accessible to researchers.

Over 47000 meteorites are known; more than 50000 exist. Over 34000 are from Antarctica, over 9200 are numbered meteorites from the Saharan and Arabian deserts, and about 3800 (numbered and unnumbered) meteorites worldwide comprise the rest. See *Field Guide to Meteors and Meteorites* by O.R. Norton and L.A. Chitwood, Springer-Verlag, 2008, *Meteorites from A to Z* (3rd ed) by M.R. Jensen and W.B Jensen, published by Michael R. Jensen, 2008, and the Meteoritical Bulletin database at: tin.er.usgs.gov/meteor. The latter allows a rapid search based on meteorite name, or any number of qualifiers.

Over 70 identified meteorites are known from Canada, but there is a backlog in describing them for Met. Soc. approval. There have been six falls since 1994: St-Robert, Québec, 1994 Jun. 14; Kitchener, Ontario, 1998 Jul. 12; Tagish Lake, British Columbia, 2000 Jan. 18; Buzzard Coulee, Saskatchewan, 2008 Nov. 20; Grimsby, Ontario 2009 Sep. 25, and another in 2005 that is not yet official. One of the most significant recent finds is of iron meteorites associated with a late Holocene crater near Whitecourt, Alberta, the first such recognized in Canada.

Often there is confusion over when and where meteorites have fallen or have been preserved, and also over what they are and look like, even though Web sites now provide ready access to meteorite research, photos, and data. All are significantly different than Earth rocks. Samples sent to experts for identification, even by other scientists, are usually "meteorwrongs"—terrestrial rocks or minerals, human-made slag, metals, alloys, or concrete—that rarely resemble meteorites.

Meteorites probably begin as streams of fragments *(meteoroids)* that are debris from collisions between larger objects. The calculated orbits of several falls intersect the asteroid belt; their ultimate origin in space and time may be elsewhere. Among the majority of meteorites, links have been suggested between other types or groups of meteorites and specific asteroids or asteroid types, based on the meteorites' reflectance spectra and density. A source in the asteroid belt is most likely; however, the exact provenance of most is uncertain. Yet they are an unparalleled source of information about our solar system, from its primitive beginnings to its present. Many preserve pre-solar mineral grains made in stars that were part of our local stellar nursery. Decay products of short-lived radionuclides produced in the early solar system, and primordial organic compounds possibly derived from cold molecular clouds, have been identified, yielding detailed information about the origin of the solar system and the biological precursors of life.

The diversity of planetary bodies represented by meteorites is unmatched by planetary exploration missions. They are thus invaluable, and represent space exploration "without the commute," providing complementary information to planetary missions, and insights into the overall physical and chemical processes that have acted to form the Sun and its planets and their satellites. With increased space exploration, their current, somewhat arcane, classification schemes will undoubtedly change considerably to realistically reflect their planetological contexts, as geological fieldwork provides for Earth rocks. In theory, any rocky solar-system body is a potential source of meteorites already in collections. About 68 meteorites are similar to Apollo samples, and are from the Moon; see: curator.jsc.nasa.gov/antmet/lmc/index.cfm and www.meteorites.wustl.edu/lunar/moon_meteorites.htm. Fifty-five meteorites are derived from Mars; see curator.jsc.nasa.gov/antmet/mmc/index.cfm and www.imca.cc/mars/martian-meteorites.htm. These meteorites, also known as the SNCs (shergottite-nakhlite-chassignite, after their main representatives, Shergotty, Nakhla, and Chassigny), are linked to the Red Planet by trapped gas within them that matches the composition of Mars' unique atmosphere, as measured by the 1976 *Viking* landers.

Popular ideas about when and where meteorites fall are connected with the observation of *meteors*, the brief streaks of light produced when high-speed, interplanetary particles enter Earth's upper atmosphere. Sporadic meteors and *meteor showers* do not produce meteorites; their fragile cometary debris fragments are reduced to dust high in the atmosphere. Earth collects over 100 tonnes of cosmic dust debris per day. In contrast, stronger, larger space rocks can survive a fiery passage through the atmosphere and result in meteorites. These first appear as bright *fireballs*, are slowed to terminal speeds by atmospheric friction, and cease to show a bright trail long before they reach Earth's surface. Fireballs, which may seem very close, are usually quite high in the atmosphere, 50 km or more from the observer. Even if an extraterrestrial object does reach the surface, it is likely to plunge into the 70 percent that is water or to be lost among forests, jungles, or mountainous regions. In only uncommonly recorded cases have meteorites struck or landed within a few metres of humans (see "Possible Hazards of Meteorite Falls" by C.E. Spratt, *JRASC*, *85* (October 1991), p. 263). Rare meteoroids of masses exceeding several tonnes are not slowed appreciably by Earth's atmosphere, and produce impact craters. Large impacts may have dramatically altered the history of life on our planet, but they do not result in meteorites—the kinetic energy is sufficiently high to vapourize the impacting body completely and to deform and melt the target area in seconds. Crater diameters are typically ten times the diameter of the impacting body. Glassy *tektites* found scattered over several continents may be evidence of such impacts, but they do not have meteorite compositions or characteristics, instead reflecting the composition of the target materials struck by the meteoroid.

Meteorites are divided into three groups that vary widely both in appearance and properties: *stones* or *stony meteorites*, *stony-irons*, and *irons* or *iron meteorites* (known in the past as *aerolites*, *siderolites*, and *siderites*, respectively). All usually contain metallic nickel-iron compounds (with traces of other metals) and are mildly to strongly magnetic, depending on the amount of nickel-iron relative to other minerals. Those that have lain on Earth's surface for long periods may be rusted almost beyond recognition; some require laboratory tests to confirm their identity. Specimens generally have a quite soft, dull black to brown fusion crust formed by friction during atmospheric passage; more prevalent on stones and stony-irons, it may have partially flaked off or been weathered away. Meteorites only rarely contain bubble-like cavities; they are never almost perfectly spherical and smooth. During atmospheric entry, only their surface is affected. Surfaces of irons and stony-irons are dimpled rather than bulbous. They rust easily so there may be no bright metal showing. Stony meteorites do not show protuberances; weathered

varieties are rusty, even on broken surfaces. Fresh stony meteorites may have a whitish "concrete-like" rock interior, with bright metal specks. Their crusts are black or smoky grey, varying from quite glassy to dull; telltale lines and bubbled patches orient their flight through the air. More metallic samples may have a shield-like shape, as a result of aerodynamic sculpting and may therefore also be oriented.

Stones are the most abundant; they resemble some terrestrial rocks but are denser. Most (called *chondrites*) consist of spheres of silicate minerals (called *chondrules*) visible on broken, cut, or polished surfaces, and scattered grains of metal. The oldest, most primitive, and least altered meteorites are found among the chondrites. Rare stony meteorites without chondrules are called *achondrites*; these are thought to be melt products from chondrites, or samples of younger volcanic planetary surfaces. In August 1996, NASA scientists announced the discovery of fossil and chemical evidence of bacterial life in the Allan Hills 84001 meteorite—an ancient achondrite from Mars. Other scientists disagree that the weight of evidence points to ancient life on Mars; however, the rock retains evidence of the conditions necessary for life in the form of minerals precipitated by warm water. This controversy has resulted in renewed interest in missions to Mars and in finding water and life on Mars and elsewhere, even in extreme conditions on Earth. Irons and stony-irons are dense, with up to equal amounts of silicates and iron. Most irons are thought to be core material of planetary bodies formed by melting chondrites, whereas stony-irons (in particular the *pallasites*) may be samples of the core-mantle boundary of such planetary bodies.

Rare *carbonaceous chondrites* are grey to black, some resembling charcoal with silicate inclusions. The dark colour is from iron oxides and sulphides. They contain a few percent carbon in very fine-grained carbonates, carbides, graphite, diamonds, and primitive organic molecules. They may have had biologically significant roles in providing seeds for the origin of life; recent significant insights into this process have come from study of the unique Tagish Lake meteorite. The study of these samples, along with interplanetary dust particles and samples of Comet Wild-2 from the NASA *Stardust* mission, has become important in deciphering the origins of meteorites and, therefore, of our solar system and everything in it. We are all composed of recycled stardust.

In Canada, expertise in meteorite identification and classification exists at several government and university institutions. The largest meteorite collections are the National Meteorite Collection, maintained by the Geological Survey of Canada (GSC), the Royal Ontario Museum collection, and the Alberta Meteorite Collection at the University of Alberta. The curators of these collections, and other experts on meteorite identification and research, are members of the Astromaterials Discipline Working Group (ADWG); see regional contacts at: www.eas.ualberta.ca/adwg. If a suspected meteorite passes initial criteria, such as magnetic character, presence of a fusion crust, etc., digital photos are typically requested for follow-up. Further examination and any analysis may be negotiated with the expert, but an expert opinion is free of charge. Experts can assist in enabling classification of any new meteorite. Meteorites of Canadian origin are subject to the provisions of the Cultural Property Export and Import Act and may not be exported from Canada without a permit.

METEORITE IMPACT CRATERS OF NORTH AMERICA
BY JOHN SPRAY

Earth has endured the hypervelocity impact of planetary materials since its inception 4.57 Ga ago, just like any other planet in our solar system. However, in contrast to the Moon, Mercury, Mars, and many asteroids, the Earth shows relatively few impact craters on its surface. On Earth, currently 174 are proven; see the Earth Impact Database, 2007 at **www.unb.ca/passc/ImpactDatabase**. The Moon's surface is saturated with craters, as is Mercury's, and 42000 craters have been catalogued on Mars. Our inventory is limited because Earth (like Venus) is an active planet. This means that most craters are destroyed or buried due to plate tectonics, volcanic activity, and weathering. Of the 174 known craters on Earth, 57 are known from North America (see the following table), 29 of which are in Canada, 27 in the United States, and 1 in Mexico (see the map at the end of this section.) This total thus represents about a third of the world inventory. North American craters range in diameter from as small as 170 m, for the largest of the Odessa crater field (Texas), up to ~250 km for Sudbury (Ontario).

The principal criteria for determining if a geological feature is an impact structure formed by the hypervelocity impact of a meteorite or comet are listed below. Criteria are divided into *megascopic* (overview—bird's eye/satellite scale), *macroscopic* (can be seen easily with the naked eye), and *microscopic* (requires a microscope to see) features:

1. Presence of shatter cones that are in situ (macroscopic evidence);
2. Presence of multiple planar deformation features (PDFs) in minerals within in situ lithologies (microscopic evidence);
3. Presence of high-pressure mineral polymorphs within in situ lithologies (microscopic evidence and requiring proof via X-ray diffraction, etc.). Examples include the high-pressure polymorphs of SiO_2 coesite and stishovite.

4. Morphometry. On some planetary bodies, such as the Moon and Mars, we rely on the shape of the impact structure to determine its presence and type. This is a megascopic quality (i.e. too big to be seen unaided by the human eye, thus requiring remote sensing, etc.). On Earth, recognizing impact structures solely by their morphometry is complicated by two factors: (a) weathering, erosion, burial processes, and tectonic deformation; and (b) certain terrestrial features having comparable shape (e.g. volcanoes, salt diapirs, glacigenic features), *such that a circular structure alone is not sufficient to claim impact-structure status*;

5. Presence of an impact-melt sheet and/or dikes, and impact-melt breccias that were generated due to hypervelocity impact (macroscopic). Melt sheets may be overlain by so-called fallback breccias (referred to as "suevite" by some workers), and material blasted out of the crater may form ejecta blankets about the original central cavity. For large impact events, ejecta can be distributed globally;

6. Pseudotachylyte—is a rock generated by faulting at either microscopic or macroscopic scales. Some pseudotachylytes are associated with endogenic seismic faulting (e.g. earthquakes due to isostatic rebound and plate tectonics), so they are not exclusively impact generated; however, in association with features 1-3 above, they can be a contributory criterion.

In terms of relative importance, criteria 1–3 above are definitive, with contributory evidence being added by 4–6. For well-preserved buried structures, as revealed by detailed geophysical techniques (especially seismic data), some workers consider this as strong evidence in favour of an impact origin. Normally, buried craters are verified by drilling and sampling for evaluation using criteria 1–3 above.

TABLE OF METEORITE IMPACT CRATERS OF NORTH AMERICA

#	Name, Location	Lat. (N) ° '	Long. (W) ° '	Diam. km	Age* Ma	Surface Expression	Visible Geologic Features
1	Ames, Oklahoma, USA	36 15	98 12	16.	470. (30)	buried 3 km	none
2	Avak, Alaska, USA	71 15	156 38	12.	3–95.	buried 30 m	none
3	Barringer (Meteor) Crater, Arizona, USA	35 02	111 01	1.2	0.049 (0.003)	rimmed polygonal crater	fragments of meteorite, highly shocked sandstone
4	Beaverhead, Montana, USA	44 36	113 00	60.	≈600.	oval area of crushed sandstone, and shatter cones	shatter cones
5	Brent, Ontario	46 05	78 29	3.8	396. (20)	sediment-filled shallow depression	fracturing
6	Calvin, Michigan, USA	41 50	85 57	8.5	450. (10)	buried 400 m	none
7	Carswell, Saskatchewan	58 27	109 30	39.	115. (10)	discontinuous circular ridge	shatter cones, breccia, impact melt
8	Charlevoix, Québec	47 32	70 18	54.	342. (15)	semicircular trough, central peak	breccia, shatter cones, impact melt
9	Chesapeake Bay, Virginia, USA	37 17	76 01	90.	35.5 (0.3)	buried 400–500 m, ring structure	none
10	Chicxulub, Mexico	21 20	89 30	170.	64.98 (0.05)	buried 1 km, ring of sink holes	none (related to the K/T mass-extinction event)
11	Clearwater East, Québec	56 05	74 07	26.	290. (20)	circular lake	sedimentary float
12	Clearwater West, Québec	56 13	74 30	36.	290. (20)	island ring in circular lake	impact melt, breccias
13	Cloud Creek, Wyoming, USA	43 07	106 45	7.	190. (30)	buried 1.1 km	none
14	Couture, Québec	60 08	75 20	8.	430. (25)	circular lake	breccia float
15	Crooked Creek, Missouri, USA	37 50	91 23	7.	320. (80)	oval area of disturbed rocks, shallow marginal depression	breccia, shatter cones
16	Decaturville, Missouri, USA	37 54	92 43	6.	<300.	slight oval depression	breccia, shatter cones
17	Deep Bay, Saskatchewan	56 24	102 59	13.	99. (4)	circular bay	sedimentary float
18	Des Plaines, Illinois, USA	42 03	87 52	8.	<280.	buried, 15–100 m	none
19	Eagle Butte, Alberta	49 42	110 30	10.	<65.	minor structural disturbance	shatter cones
20	Elbow, Saskatchewan	50 59	106 43	8.	395. (25)	buried, small mound	none
21	Flynn Creek, Tennessee, USA	36 17	85 40	3.8	360. (20)	sediment-filled shallow depression with small central peak	breccia, shatter cones
22	Glasford, Illinois, USA	40 36	89 47	4.	<430.	buried 350 m	none
23	Glover Bluff, Wisconsin, USA	43 58	89 32	8.	<500.	disturbed dolomite exposed	shatter cones
24	Gow, Saskatchewan	56 27	104 29	5.	<250.	lake and central island	breccia, impact melt
25	Haughton, Nunavut	75 22	89 41	23.	39.	shallow circular depression	shatter cones, breccia
26	Haviland, Kansas, USA	37 35	99 10	0.015	<0.001	excavated depression	fragments of meteorite
27	Holleford, Ontario	44 28	76 38	2.4	550. (100)	sediment-filled shallow depression	sedimentary fill
28	Île Rouleau, Québec	50 41	73 53	4.	<300.	island is central peak of submerged structure	shatter cones, breccia dykes
29	Kentland, Indiana, USA	40 45	87 24	13.	<97.	central peak exposed in quarries, rest buried	breccia, shatter cones, disturbed rocks

* Numbers in parentheses are possible errors.

TABLE OF METEORITE IMPACT CRATERS OF NORTH AMERICA (cont)

#	Name, Location	Lat. (N) ° '	Long. (W) ° '	Diam. km	Age* Ma	Surface Expression	Visible Geologic Features
30	La Moinerie, Québec	57 26	66 37	8.	400. (50)	lake-filled depression	breccia float
31	Manicouagan, Québec	51 23	68 42	100.	214. (1)	circumferential lake, central peak	impact melt, breccia
32	Manson, Iowa, USA	42 35	94 33	35.	73.8 (0.3)	none, central elevation buried 30 m	none
33	Maple Creek, Saskatchewan	49 48	109 06	6.	<75.	buried, small mound	disturbed rocks
34	Marquez, Texas, USA	31 17	96 18	12.7	58. (2)	circular area of disturbed rock	shatter cones
35	Middlesboro, Kentucky, USA	36 37	83 44	6.	<300.	circular depression	disturbed rocks
36	Mistastin, Labrador	55 53	63 18	28.	36.4. (4)	elliptical lake and central island	breccia, impact melt
37	Montagnais, Nova Scotia	42 53	64 13	45.	50.5 (0.8)	none, under water (115 m) and sediment	none
38	New Québec, Québec	61 17	73 40	3.4	1.4 (0.1)	rimmed, circular lake	raised rim, impact melt
39	Newporte, North Dakota, USA	48 58	101 58	3.2	<500.	none, buried 3 km	none
40	Nicholson, NWT	62 40	102 41	12.5	<400.	irregular lake with islands	breccia
41	Odessa, Texas, USA	31 45	102 29	0.17	<0.05	sediment-filled depression with very slight rim, 4 others buried & smaller	fragments of meteorite
42	Pilot, NWT	60 17	111 01	6.	445. (2)	circular lake	fracturing, breccia float
43	Presqu'île, Québec	49 43	74 48	24.	<500.	none, heavily eroded	shatter cones
44	Red Wing, North Dakota, USA	47 36	103 33	9.	200. (25)	none, buried 1.5 km	none
45	Rock Elm, Wisconsin, USA	44 43	92 14	6.	<505.	circular rim depression, central dome	shatter cones, breccia
46	St. Martin, Manitoba	51 47	98 32	40.	220. (32)	none, partially buried	impact melt
47	Serpent Mound, Ohio, USA	39 02	83 24	8.	<320.	circular area of disturbed rock, slight central peak	breccia, shatter cones
48	Sierra Madera, Texas, USA	30 36	102 55	13.	<100.	central hills, annular depression, outer ring of hills	breccia, shatter cones
49	Slate Islands, Ontario	48 40	87 00	30.	≈450.	islands are central peak of submerged structure	shatter cones, breccia dykes
50	Steen River, Alberta	59 30	117 38	25.	91. (7)	none, buried 200 m	none
51	Sudbury, Ontario	46 36	81 11	250.	1850. (3)	deformed elliptical basin	breccia, impact melt, shatter cones, breccia dykes
52	Upheaval Dome, Utah, USA	38 26	109 54	10.	<170.	circular area of disturbed rock	breccia dykes
53	Viewfield, Saskatchewan	49 35	103 04	2.5	190. (20)	buried 1 km	none
54	Wanapitei, Ontario	46 45	80 45	7.5	37. (1.2)	lake-filled depression	breccia float
55	Wells Creek, Tennessee, USA	36 23	87 40	12.	200. (100)	basin with central hill, inner and outer annular valleys, ridges	breccia, shatter cones
56	West Hawk Lake, Manitoba	49 46	95 11	2.4	351. (20)	circular lake	none
57	Wetumpka, Alabama, USA	32 31	86 10	6.5	81. (1.5)	arcuate outer ridge, central depression	breccia

*Numbers in parentheses are possible errors.

MAP OF NORTH AMERICAN METEORITE IMPACT STRUCTURES

Of the 170-plus impact structures identified on Earth, 57 are in North America (29 in Canada, 27 in the United States, and 1 in Mexico). These are identified on the above map; the numbers correspond to the listing in the table on the previous pages. Although the oceans cover 70 percent of Earth, only two impact structures have been identified on the seafloor (#37 and Mjølnir, in the Barents Sea). Also, with the exception of structure #51, all of those shown occurred within approximately the last 10 percent of Earth's history. Evidence of many earlier craters has been erased by geologic processes. It is possible, however, to calculate a terrestrial cratering rate by focusing only on geologically stable areas of Earth (known as cratons), with low erosion and sedimentation rates. One such area is the North American craton. These rate calculations indicate that Earth has received at least 10 000 impacts sufficient to result in craters greater than 20 km in diameter over the last 3.5 billion years. Very early in Earth history, the cratering rate was even higher, perhaps as high as 100 times the current rate. Doubtless some of these impacts have had profound influence upon the evolution of life on this planet. For example, Chicxulub (#10), the very large structure in Mexico, is linked to a major extinction event 65 million years ago. Some impact craters are the source of considerable economic resources: in North America, hydrocarbons are extracted from #1, 2, 6, 34, 39, 44, 48, 50, 53; #7 produces uranium; and #51 is the site of a world-class nickel and copper mining camp.

COMETS IN 2011
By Brian G. Marsden

Listed below are the periodic comets expected at perihelion in 2011. The orbital elements are given with sufficient precision to allow an ephemeris computation good to about 1′. The angular elements are referred to the ecliptic and mean equinox J2000.0.

Comet	Perihelion Date T TT	Dist. q au	Eccen. e	Rev. Per. P a	Arg. Peri. ω °	Asc. Node Ω °	Incl. i °
9P	Jan. 12.37	1.5103	0.5165	5.5	178.92	68.91	10.52
P/2003 S2	Mar. 3.52	2.4561	0.3599	7.5	283.90	87.70	7.63
P/2005 U1	Mar. 10.89	2.3606	0.2543	5.6	325.32	51.64	1.27
P/2006 U1	Apr. 15.81	0.5109	0.8160	4.6	64.23	240.47	8.42
P/2004 T1	Apr. 24.86	1.7077	0.5082	6.5	336.41	51.44	11.04
231P	May 16.68	3.0328	0.2466	8.1	42.47	133.10	12.33
164P	Jun. 2.34	1.6753	0.5414	7.0	325.85	88.33	16.26
213P	Jun. 16.23	2.1225	0.3796	6.3	3.33	312.67	10.24
130P	Jun. 24.78	2.0981	0.4067	6.6	224.37	89.81	7.31
62P	Jun. 30.39	1.3836	0.5974	6.4	30.23	90.31	9.71
123P	Jul. 4.47	2.1289	0.4484	7.6	102.82	46.60	15.36
69P	Jul. 17.24	2.2712	0.4147	7.6	343.44	104.88	22.04
27P	Aug. 3.81	0.7479	0.9187	27.9	195.98	250.64	28.96
97P	Aug. 21.00	2.5966	0.4594	10.5	228.21	185.21	17.89
228P	Aug. 23.84	3.4305	0.1772	8.5	114.79	31.07	7.92
45P	Sep. 28.75	0.5296	0.8246	5.2	326.24	89.01	4.25
48P	Sep. 29.30	2.3011	0.3677	6.9	207.96	117.27	13.66
115P	Oct. 6.98	2.0351	0.5210	8.8	120.07	176.60	11.71
73P	Oct. 16.75	0.9428	0.6922	5.4	198.86	69.84	11.38
P/1996 R2	Oct. 17.06	2.6119	0.3107	7.4	333.99	40.20	2.60
49P	Oct. 19.08	1.4238	0.6004	6.7	332.79	118.88	19.05
41P	Nov. 12.15	1.0495	0.6601	5.4	62.18	141.06	9.23
P/2004 H3	Nov. 23.28	2.4503	0.3726	7.7	346.49	220.95	25.13
P/2004 R3	Nov. 28.43	2.1325	0.4427	7.5	5.56	318.73	7.97
37P	Dec. 11.02	1.5753	0.5407	6.4	329.39	315.03	8.96
71P	Dec. 15.78	1.5675	0.4985	5.5	208.83	59.61	9.48
36P	Dec. 29.59	3.0879	0.2609	8.5	201.60	182.39	9.93

For an explanation of these elements, see p. 22; the elements are for an epoch within 20 days of perihelion.

The returns of 36P/Whipple, 45P/Honda-Mrkos-Pajdušáková, 48P/Johnson, 115P/Maury, 130P/McNaught-Hughes, 213P/Van Ness, 231P/LINEAR-NEAT and P/1996 R2 (Lagerkvist) are favourable, and those of 9P/Tempel, 49P/Arend-Rigaux, 123P/West-Hartley, 228P/LINEAR, P/2003 S2 (NEAT), P/2004 H3 (Larsen), P/2004 R3 (LINEAR-NEAT) and P/2004 T1 (LINEAR-NEAT) are fair. The returns of 37P/Forbes, 97P/Metcalf-Brewington and P/2005 U1 (Read) are poor, and those of 27P/Crommelin, 41P/Tuttle-Giacobini-Kresák, 62P/Tsuchinshan, 69P/Taylor, 71P/Clark, 73P/Schwassmann-Wachmann, 164P/Christensen and P/2006 U1 (LINEAR) are very poor.

For current ephemerides for all comets listed here, visit
www.cfa.harvard.edu/iau/Ephemerides/Comets

OBSERVING COMETS
BY DAVID H. LEVY

Each comet has its own unique, changing appearance. Observationally, comets are very much like deep-sky objects. Even in large telescopes an observer can confuse a comet with a galaxy or a diffuse planetary nebula. Comets near a telescope's limit are virtually impossible to spot without an accurate position extracted from a detailed atlas like *Uranometria* or *Millennium*. It is difficult to define a telescope's limiting magnitude for comets because the more diffuse a comet, the more difficult it is to find. Typically, under a dark sky a 150-mm telescope will catch a 9th-magnitude comet, a 200-mm telescope will see 10th, and a 400-mm should capture a 13th-magnitude comet.

If you are sure you have discovered a comet, follow the procedure in REPORTING OF ASTRONOMICAL DISCOVERIES, p. 10. For more information on comet observing and hunting, read *David Levy's Guide to Observing and Discovering Comets* (Cambridge, 2003).

Magnitude Estimates

The brightness of the coma can be estimated using a variety of methods, the most common of which is the "In-Out" method:

(1) Study the coma until you are familiar with its "average" brightness, an easy process if the coma is of uniform brightness but rather difficult if there is a strong central condensation.

(2) With the help of a variable-star chart or some source in which star magnitudes are listed, find a comparison star at approximately the same altitude as the comet.

(3) Defocus the star to the size of the in-focus coma.

(4) Compare the star's out-of-focus brightness with that of the coma.

Repeat the last three steps with a second star, or more if needed, until an interpolation can be made.

Physical Characteristics

An estimate of a comet's magnitude is more useful if an estimate of the coma diameter is made at the same time. An observer seeing a 3′ coma, for example, will estimate much brighter than one who sees only a 1′ coma at the same time. The simplest way of estimating coma size is to draw the coma with the embedded and surrounding field stars and then compare the drawing to an atlas, using its scale to determine the size.

A nightly measurement of a comet's degree of condensation is a good way of studying its changing behaviour. A comet undergoing an outburst of dust from its nucleus might begin its display by showing almost overnight the development of an increased condensation. Use an integer scale from 0 to 9, where 0 means a diffuse coma with absolutely uniform brightness, 3 means a diffuse coma with gradually increasing brightness toward the centre, 6 involves a definite central condensation, and 9 refers to an almost stellar image.

Because of the changing Earth–Sun–comet geometry and the changing activity in a comet, the length and position angle of a tail should be measured. A rough way to measure the length of a tail is to sketch it and compare with a detailed atlas, as with the coma. Observers can also measure the position angle using an atlas and a protractor.

Visual Comet Hunting

The key ingredient to a successful comet search is perseverance, especially in this time of automated searches. The chances for a visual discovery have plummeted in the last few years. Although there are stories of people finding comets very quickly (Mark Whitaker discovered Comet Whitaker-Thomas 1968 V after three nights of comet hunting), these

are the exception. Don Machholz searched for some 1700 hours for each of his first two comets, and I spent more than 917 hours before my first discovery. In contrast, neither Alan Hale nor Tom Bopp was comet hunting when they independently discovered what later became the Great Comet of 1997.

It is important to know the sky well before beginning a comet search program, but it is more important to know the difference between the fuzzy appearances of comets compared to galaxies, nebulae, and clusters. Observing all the objects in Messier's Catalogue (see p. 319) provides an excellent education in what these distant objects look like, and observing as many known comets as possible is good preparation for recognizing an interloper. Generally, comets lack the bilateral symmetry of spiral galaxies and the mottled appearance of globular clusters. More important, they usually have unsharp edges, fading off into space so that it is often difficult to tell where the comet ends and the sky begins.

Although most comet hunters still use traditional star atlases to check their suspects, some are moving into a new mode of comet hunting. These hunters have attached encoders to their telescopes that allow an instant reading of the suspect's position in right ascension and declination. If the telescope has been properly set up, this approach is faster. However, a sense of the nature of the fuzzy object in the field of view is still important since thousands of nonstellar objects dot the sky.

Comets may appear at any time, but they are usually found within 90° of the Sun. Good areas to search are in the evening western sky during the week after full Moon and in the morning eastern sky before dawn around new Moon. Although comet hunters differ in their approaches to searching, one way is to use an altazimuth mount and make horizontal sweeps. In the western sky, begin near the end of evening twilight at the horizon, sweep across, then return to the point of origin, move upward about half a field of view and sweep again, etc. In the morning reverse the process.

The confirmation image of Levy's most recently-discovered comet, P/2006 T1. It will make a close pass to the Earth at the end of 2011. The comet is at the upper right corner of the photograph; Saturn is the very bright object at lower left. The image was taken using Flaire, Levy's 14-inch Meade SCT with a HyperStar lens and a Canon 20Da camera.

Photographic and Electronic Comet Hunting

While still possible, it is now very difficult to discover comets photographically because the sky is so well covered by the professional surveys. With film and a wide-angle camera like a Schmidt camera, take photographs of selected areas of sky, then repeat these exposures after at least 45 min. Using a stereomicroscope or a blink microscope, it is then possible to spot moving objects. Through a stereomicroscope, the comet will appear to "float" above or "sink" below the stellar background. If a blink microscope is used, the comet will appear to jump back and forth.

Using a CCD, take at least three images of each field, then examine either visually or using a moving-object detection program. Visual inspection is like blinking, so

moving objects appear to move steadily through the three pictures, then jump back and begin moving again.

Finally, it is possible to discover comets over the Internet. Since images from the *SOHO* spacecraft are made available soon after they are taken, amateur astronomers can scan these images for Sun-grazing comets. RASC member Michael Boschat won the 2001 Ken Chilton Prize for his discoveries of several *SOHO* comets in this way.

Designation of Comets

At the International Astronomical Union's 22nd General Assembly in The Hague in 1994, Commission 20 of the IAU approved a resolution that changes the way comets are designated. Under the old system, a comet was designated according to its order of discovery or recovery in a given year (e.g. 1982i, Comet Halley, was the ninth comet to appear in 1982). After cometary information was complete for a given year, each comet also received a Roman numeral designation based on the order of perihelion passage (e.g. Halley at its last return was also known as 1986 III). Although the new designation went into effect in January 1995, it is retroactive to every comet for which a reasonable orbit is available.

Under the new system, a comet is assigned only one designation which is similar, although not identical, to the provisional designation system for asteroids. With this system the year is divided into periods called *half-months* beginning with A (the first half of January) and concluding with Y (the last half of December), omitting the letter I. In addition, there is a letter indicating the comet's status: C for a long-period comet, P for a "periodic comet" (defined as having a period of less than 200 years), X for a comet for which a reasonable orbit cannot be computed, and D for a disappeared comet. Once the orbit of a periodic comet is well known, that comet receives a permanent number according to the order in which the comet's periodicity was recognized. Thus Comet Hale-Bopp, as the first comet to be found in the O part of 1995, is labelled C/1995 O1. Comet Shoemaker-Levy 9 was 1993e; its new designation as the second comet to be found in the F part of 1993 is D/1993 F2. The new designation for Comet Halley is 1P/Halley.

When a comet becomes well known, the vast majority of scientists, press, and public ignore the official designation, preferring instead to use more easily remembered names. Our experience with comets Hale-Bopp and Hyakutake (C/1996 B2) showed clearly that people were more comfortable with proper names. However, with 2 comets named Hyakutake, almost 1500 named *SOHO*, and well over 100 named LINEAR, we need to become familiar with the official designation in order to separate one comet from another.

A handful of comets are named not for their discoverers but for the persons who computed their orbits. The most famous of these is P/Halley, which has been well observed since at least 240 BC. It was finally identified as a comet appearing every 76 years or so by Edmund Halley in 1705. Two others are 2P/Encke and 27P/Crommelin.

In the event that the cometary nature of an object is established after it was originally given an asteroidal designation, the original designation remains. When Gene and Carolyn Shoemaker and I discovered Asteroid 1990 UL3 using the Palomar 18-in. telescope, for example, its orbit appeared to be more cometary than asteroidal. A few weeks after discovery, Steve Larson and I took a series of images through the Kuiper 61-in. telescope that clearly showed a tail, and the identification was changed to periodic comet Shoemaker-Levy 2. The mixed designation C/1990 UL3 applies.

Editor's Note: David Levy is the discoverer of 22 comets: 9 by visual searches and 13 photographically at Palomar under the combined name Shoemaker-Levy.

INTERPLANETARY DUST
BY ROY BISHOP

Outside of the astronomical community it is not generally realized that the inner solar system contains a vast cloud of dust. The particles in this cloud are concentrated near the plane of the ecliptic and toward the Sun, their spatial particle density in the ecliptic falling off somewhat more rapidly than the reciprocal of their distance from the Sun. Measurements from spacecraft indicate that the cloud extends well beyond the orbit of Mars but is negligible in the vicinity of Jupiter's orbit and beyond.

The particles composing the cloud have a continuum of sizes, from pebble-sized clumps down to specks with diameters comparable to the wavelength of visible light and smaller. The smaller particles are the more numerous, although the mass distribution appears to peak near 10^{-8} kg, corresponding to a particle diameter of a few tenths of a millimetre. The total mass of the cloud is small, amounting to perhaps 10^{-14} of the mass of the solar system. It is as if the satellites of Mars had been pulverized and spread throughout the inner solar system.

Like the planetary system, the interplanetary dust cloud is not static; its particles generally move in orbits about the Sun. In addition, the particles undergo continual fragmentation due to collisions, sputtering associated with bombardment by the solar wind, electrostatic bursting, and sublimation. This progression toward smaller and smaller sizes is of crucial significance for the cloud, since particles with diameters appreciably less than a tenth of a millimetre have a sufficiently large surface-to-volume ratio that the radiation pressure of sunlight has a significant effect upon their motion — aberration of sunlight results in a small backward force that slows the dust particles (the Poynting–Robertson Effect), and they slowly spiral inward toward the Sun. During a total solar eclipse in 1983, instruments carried by a balloon detected a ringlike concentration of dust only a couple of solar diameters from the Sun. Its inner edge apparently marks the point at which solar heat vapourizes the infalling particles. The resulting tiny gas molecules, like the smallest particles of dust, are blown out of the solar system by the dominant radiation pressure and interactions with the solar wind.

Because of the above-mentioned influences on the sizes and motions of the dust particles, the estimated mean life of a cloud particle is about 10^4 years. Since this is much less than the age of the solar system, it is obvious that the cloud must be in a dynamic equilibrium — that is, it must be gaining new material as it loses the old. Part of the coma and tail of a comet is the result of significant quantities of dust ejected from its nucleus, and it is believed that comets provide most of the new dust to the cloud (see *Sky & Telescope*, Jun. 2010, p. 16). Since comet nuclei are believed to consist of the undifferentiated matter from which the solar system formed, much of the dust of the interplanetary cloud is most likely composed of this same low-density, fragile, primitive material.

To an observer on Earth the most noticeable aspect of the dust cloud is meteors — larger particles of the cloud that encounter Earth at high speeds and vapourize in the upper atmosphere. In addition, sunlight scattered by the dust cloud appears as a faint (fortunately!) glow in the vicinity of the ecliptic. This glow is brightest toward the Sun, is due primarily to particles with diameters between a few micrometres and a millimetre, and is referred to as the *zodiacal light*. A slight brightening in the sky opposite the Sun, called the *gegenschein* (German for "counterglow"), is due to a phase effect (analogous to full Moon) and also, possibly, to a concentration of dust at the L3 Lagrangian point of the Earth–Sun system. The integrated visual magnitude of the dust is about −8.5, making it the brightest solar-system object in the sky after the Sun and Moon. As astronomical objects the zodiacal light and the gegenschein are unusual in

that they can be seen only with the unaided eye. Because of their large angular sizes and indistinct borders, both are invisible in binoculars or a telescope.

The Zodiacal Light

Poetic references to the zodiacal light go back several centuries (e.g. see *The Observatory*, *108* (1988), p. 181). The 19th-century poet Edward FitzGerald is noted for his translation of the famous poem "Rubaiyat" by the Persian Omar Khayyam. In one of the stanzas Khayyam's reference to the morning was altered by FitzGerald into haunting references to the zodiacal light: "Dreaming when Dawn's Left Hand was in the Sky" (in midnorthern latitudes the zodiacal light and the first glow of the early autumn dawn combine to produce a large, glowing, ghostly figure having an upraised left arm); and "Before the phantom of False morning died" (the zodiacal light soon vanishes in the glow of the true dawn).

When conditions are favourable, the zodiacal light is indeed a mysterious and beautiful sight. Because the zodiacal light is brightest nearest the Sun, it is best seen within half an hour following the end of evening twilight and in the half hour prior to the beginning of morning twilight (for times of twilight, see p. 207), and when the ecliptic is at a steep angle relative to the horizon. In the tropics the ecliptic is always at a steep angle to the horizon. In midnorthern latitudes the optimum geometry occurs in the evening western sky in February and March, and in the morning eastern sky in September and October. The zodiacal light appears as a huge, softly radiant pyramid of white light with its base near the horizon and its axis centred on the zodiac. In its brightest parts it exceeds the luminance of the central Milky Way.

Despite its brightness, most people have not seen the zodiacal light. As mentioned above, certain times of night and year are more favourable than others. In addition, moonlight, haze, or light pollution rule out any chance of seeing this phenomenon. Even with a dark, transparent sky the inexperienced observer may confuse the zodiacal light with twilight and thus ignore it, or may not notice it because he or she is expecting a much smaller object.

The Gegenschein

The zodiacal light extends all around the zodiac with a shallow minimum in brightness some 120° to 150° from the Sun; nevertheless, this "zodiacal band" or "light bridge" is exceedingly faint and is visible only from high-altitude sites having very dark, transparent skies. However, the slight brightening in the vicinity of the antisolar point can be seen from most dark observing sites, provided the air is transparent.

The gegenschein is very faint. Haze, moonlight, bright nearby stars, planets, or light pollution will hide it completely. Most observers, including experienced ones, have not seen it. The gegenschein is sufficiently faint that, except from high-altitude sites with very dark skies, a person will not notice it without making a special effort to *look* for it. It is a ghostly apparition best seen near midnight, and in midnorthern latitudes, in the autumn or winter when the antisolar point is nearest the zenith. To avoid interference from bright stars or the Milky Way, the periods late September to early November and late January to early February are best. At these times the gegenschein is in Pisces and Cancer, respectively. It appears as a faint yet distinct, somewhat elliptical glow perhaps 10° in diameter. The luminance of the gegenschein is about 10^{-4} cd/m^2, some 10 orders of magnitude dimmer than the brightest light the human eye can tolerate.

Don't determine the antisolar point before you look—imagination is too powerful. Find the antisolar point by locating the gegenschein, and *then* check your star charts!

STARS

CONSTELLATIONS—NAMES AND ABBREVIATIONS

Nominative & Pronunciation	Genitive & Pronunciation	Abbr.	Meaning
Andromeda, ăn-drŏm′ē-dà	Andromedae, ăn-drŏm′ē-dē′	And	Daughter of Cassiopeia
Antlia, ănt′lĭ-à	Antliae, ănt′lē-ē′	Ant	The Air Pump
Apus, ā′pŭs	Apodis, ăp′ä-dĭs	Aps	Bird of Paradise
Aquarius, à-kwâr′ē-ŭs	Aquarii, à-kwâr′ē-ī′	Aqr	The Water-bearer
Aquila, à-kwĭl′à	Aquilae, à-kwĭl′ē	Aql	The Eagle
Ara, ā′rà	Arae, ā′rē	Ara	The Altar
Aries, âr′ēz	Arietis, à-rī′ē-tĭs	Ari	The Ram
Auriga, ô-rī′gà	Aurigae, ô-rī′jē	Aur	The Charioteer
Bootes, bō-ō′tēz	Bootis, bō-ō′tĭs	Boo	The Herdsman
Caelum, sē′lŭm	Caeli, sē′lī	Cae	The Chisel
Camelopardalis kà-mĕl′ō-pàr′dà-lĭs	Camelopardalis kà-mĕl′ō-pàr′dà-lĭs	Cam	The Giraffe
Cancer, kăn′sēr	Cancri, kăn′krē	Cnc	The Crab
Canes Venatici kā′nēz vē-năt′ĭ-sī	Canum Venaticorum kā′nŭm vē-năt′ĭ-kôr′ŭm	CVn	The Hunting Dogs
Canis Major, kā′nĭs mā′jēr	Canis Majoris, kā′nĭs mā-jôr′ĭs	CMa	The Big Dog
Canis Minor, kā′nĭs mī′nēr	Canis Minoris, kā′nĭs mī-ñôr′ĭs	CMi	The Little Dog
Capricornus, kăp′rĭ-kôr-nŭs	Capricorni, kăp′rĭ-kôr-nī	Cap	The Goat
Carina, kà-rī′-nà	Carinae, kà-rī′-nē	Car	The Keel
Cassiopeia, kăs′ĭ-ō-pē′yà	Cassiopeiae, kăs′ĭ-ō-pē′yē	Cas	The Queen
Centaurus, sĕn-tôr′ŭs	Centauri, sĕn-tôr′ī	Cen	The Centaur
Cepheus, sē′fē-ŭs	Cephei, sē′fē-ī′	Cep	The King
Cetus, sē′tŭs	Ceti, sē′tī	Cet	The Whale
Chamaeleon, kà-mē′lē-ŭn	Chamaeleontis, kà-mē′lē-ŏn′tĭs	Cha	The Chameleon
Circinus, sûr′sĭ-nŭs	Circini, sûr′sĭ-nī	Cir	The Compasses
Columba, kō-lŭm′bà	Columbae, kō-lŭm′bē	Col	The Dove
Coma Berenices kō′mà bĕr′ĕ-nī′sēz	Comae Berenices kō′mē bĕr′ĕ-nī′sēz	Com	Berenice's Hair
Corona Australis kō-rō′nà ôs-trā′lĭs	Coronae Australis kō-rō′nē ôs-trā′lĭs	CrA	The Southern Crown
Corona Borealis kō-rō′nà bôr′ē-ăl′ĭs	Coronae Borealis kō-rō′nē bôr′ē-ăl′ĭs	CrB	The Northern Crown
Corvus, kôr′vŭs	Corvi, kôr′vī	Crv	The Crow
Crater, krā′tēr	Crateris, krā-tēr′ĭs	Crt	The Cup
Crux, krŭks	Crucis, kroo′sĭs	Cru	The Cross
Cygnus, sĭg′nŭs	Cygni, sĭg′nī	Cyg	The Swan
Delphinus, dĕl-fī′nŭs	Delphini, dĕl-fī′nī	Del	The Dolphin
Dorado, dō-rá′dō	Doradus, dō-rá′dŭs	Dor	The Swordfish
Draco, drā′kō	Draconis, drā′kō′nĭs	Dra	The Dragon
Equuleus, ē-kwoo′lē-ŭs	Equulei, ē-kwoo′lē-ī′	Equ	The Little Horse
Eridanus, ē-rĭd′à-nŭs	Eridani, ē-rĭd′à-nī′	Eri	The River
Fornax, fôr′năks	Fornacis, fôr-nās′ĭs	For	The Furnace
Gemini, jĕm′ĭ-nī	Geminorum, jĕm′ĭ-nôr′ŭm	Gem	The Twins
Grus, grŭs	Gruis, groo′ĭs	Gru	The Crane (bird)
Hercules, hûr′kū-lēz	Herculis, hûr′kū-lĭs	Her	The Son of Zeus
Horologium, hŏr′ō-lō′jĭ-ŭm	Horologii, hŏr′ō-lō′jĭ-ī	Hor	The Clock
Hydra, hī′drà	Hydrae, hī′drē	Hya	The Water Snake (♀)
Hydrus, hī′drŭs	Hydri, hī′drī	Hyi	The Water Snake (♂)
Indus, ĭn′dŭs	Indi, ĭn′dī	Ind	The Indian

CONSTELLATIONS—NAMES AND ABBREVIATIONS (continued)

Nominative & Pronunciation	Genitive & Pronunciation	Abbr.	Meaning
Lacerta, là-sûr'tà	Lacertae, là-sûr'tē	Lac	The Lizard
Leo, lē'ō	Leonis, lē'ō'nĭs	Leo	The Lion
Leo Minor, lē'ō mī'nēr	Leonis Minoris lē'ō'nĭs mī-nôr'ĭs	LMi	The Little Lion
Lepus, lē'pŭs	Leporis, lĕp'ôr-ĭs	Lep	The Hare
Libra, lē'brà	Librae, lē'brē	Lib	The Balance
Lupus, lōō'pŭs	Lupi, lōō'pī	Lup	The Wolf
Lynx, lĭnks	Lyncis, lĭn'sĭs	Lyn	The Lynx
Lyra, lī'rà	Lyrae, lī'rē	Lyr	The Lyre
Mensa, mĕn'sà	Mensae, mĕn'sē	Men	The Table
Microscopium mī'krō-skō'pē-ŭm	Microscopii mī'krō-skō'pē-ī'	Mic	The Microscope
Monoceros, mō-nŏs'ēr-ŏs	Monocerotis, mō-nŏs'ēr-ō'tĭs	Mon	The Unicorn
Musca, mŭs'kà	Muscae, mŭs'ē	Mus	The Fly
Norma, nôr'mà	Normae, nôr'mē	Nor	The Square
Octans, ŏk'tănz	Octantis, ŏk'tăn'tĭs	Oct	The Octant
Ophiuchus, ō'fē-ū'kŭs	Ophiuchi, ō'fē-ū'kī	Oph	The Serpent-bearer
Orion, ō-rī'ōn	Orionis, ôr'ē-ō'nĭs	Ori	The Hunter
Pavo, pā'vō	Pavonis, pà-vō'nĭs	Pav	The Peacock
Pegasus, pĕg'à-sŭs	Pegasi, pĕg'à-sī	Peg	The Winged Horse
Perseus, pûr'sē-ŭs	Persei, pûr'sē-ī'	Per	Rescuer of Andromeda
Phoenix, fē'nĭks	Phoenicis, fē-nī'cĭs	Phe	The Phoenix
Pictor, pĭk'tēr	Pictoris, pĭk-tor'ĭs	Pic	The Painter
Pisces, pī'sēz	Piscium, pĭsh'ē-ŭm	Psc	The Fishes
Piscis Austrinus, pī'sĭs ôs-trī'nŭs	Piscis Austrini, pī'sĭs ôs-trī'nī	PsA	The Southern Fish
Puppis, pŭp'ĭs	Puppis, pŭp'ĭs	Pup	The Stern
Pyxis, pĭk'sĭs	Pyxidis, pĭk'sĭ-dĭs	Pyx	The Compass
Reticulum, rē-tĭk'-ū-lŭm	Reticuli, rē-tĭk'-ū-lī	Ret	The Reticle
Sagitta, sà-jĭt'à	Sagittae, sà-jĭt'ē	Sge	The Arrow
Sagittarius, săj'ĭ-târ'ē-ŭs	Sagittarii, săj'ĭ-târ'ē-ī'	Sgr	The Archer
Scorpius, skôr'pē-ŭs	Scorpii, skôr'pē-ī	Sco	The Scorpion
Sculptor, skŭlp'tēr	Sculptoris, skŭlp'tôr'ĭs	Scl	The Sculptor
Scutum, skū'tŭm	Scuti, skōō'tī	Sct	The Shield
Serpens, sûr'pĕnz	Serpentis, sûr-pĕn'tĭs	Ser	The Serpent
Sextans, sĕks'tănz	Sextantis, sĕks-tăn'tĭs	Sex	The Sextant
Taurus, tôr'ŭs	Tauri, tôr'ī	Tau	The Bull
Telescopium tĕl'à-skō'pē-ŭm	Telescopii, tĕl'à-skō'pē-ī	Tel	The Telescope
Triangulum, trī-ăng'gū-lŭm	Trianguli, trī-ăng'gū-lī'	Tri	The Triangle
Triangulum Australe trī-ăng'gū-lŭm ôs-trā'lē	Trianguli Australis trī-ăng'gū-lī' ôs-trā'lĭs	TrA	The Southern Triangle
Tucana, tōō-kăn'à	Tucanae, tōō-kăn'ē	Tuc	The Toucan
Ursa Major, ûr'sà mā'jēr	Ursae Majoris, ûr'sē mà-jôr'ĭs	UMa	The Great Bear
Ursa Minor, ûr'sà mī'nēr	Ursae Minoris, ûr'sē mī-nôr'ĭs	UMi	The Little Bear
Vela, vē'là	Velorum, vē-lôr'ŭm	Vel	The Sails
Virgo, vûr'gō	Virginis, vûr'jĭn-ĭs	Vir	The Maiden
Volans, vō'lănz	Volantis, vō-lăn'tĭs	Vol	The Flying Fish
Vulpecula, vŭl-pĕk'ū-là	Vulpeculae, vŭl-pĕk'ū-lē'	Vul	The Fox

ā dāte; ă tăp; â câre; à gàgà; ē wē; ĕ mĕt; ē makēr; ī īce; ĭ bĭt; ō gō; ŏ hŏt; ô ôrb; ōō mōōn; ū ūnite; ŭ ŭp; û ûrn

In terms of area (based on the official IAU boundaries), of the 88 constellations the 3 largest are Hydra (1303 square degrees), Virgo (1294), and Ursa Major (1280); the 3 smallest: Sagitta (80), Equuleus (72), and Crux (68). A complete list of the areas of the constellations appears in the 1972 edition of *The Handbook of the British Astronomical Association*, and was reproduced in the June 1976 issue of *Sky & Telescope* (p. 408).

FINDING LIST OF SOME NAMED STARS

Name & Pronunciation	Con.	RA	Name & Pronunciation	Con.	RA
Acamar, ā′kà-màr	θ Eri	2	Gienah, jē′nà	γ Crv	12
Achernar, ā′kẽr-nàr	α Eri	1	Hadar, hăd′ar	β Cen	14
Acrux, ā′krŭks	α Cru	12	Hamal, hăm′al	α Ari	2
Adara, à-dā′rà	ε CMa	6	Kaus Australis,	ε Sgr	18
Al Na′ir, ăl-nâr′	α Gru	22	kôs ôs-trā′lĭs		
Albireo, ăl-bĭr′ē-ō	β Cyg	19	Kochab, kō′kăb	β UMi	14
Alcor, ăl-kôr′	80 UMa	13	Markab, màr′kăb	α Peg	23
Alcyone, ăl-sī′ō-nē	η Tau	3	Megrez, me′grĕz	δ UMa	12
Aldebaran,	α Tau	4	Menkar, mĕn′kàr	α Cet	3
ăl-dĕb′à-ràn			Menkent, mĕn′kĕnt	θ Cen	14
Alderamin,	α Cep	21	Merak, mē′răk	β UMa	11
ăl-dĕr′à-mĭn			Merope, mĕr′ō-pē	23 Tau	3
Algeiba, ăl-jē′bà	γ Leo	10	Miaplacidus,	β Car	9
Algenib, ăl-jē′nĭb	γ Peg	0	mī′à-plăs′ĭ-dŭs		
Algol, ăl′gŏl	β Per	3	Mintaka, mĭn-tà′kà	δ Ori	5
Alioth, ăl′ĭ-ŏth	ε UMa	12	Mira, mī′rà	o Cet	2
Alkaid, ăl-kād′	η UMa	13	Mirach, mī′răk	β And	1
Almach, ăl′măk	γ And	2	Mirfak, mir′făk	α Per	3
Alnilam, ăl-nī′lăm	ε Ori	5	Mizar, mi′zàr	ζ UMa	13
Alphard, ăl′fàrd	α Hya	9	Nunki, nŭn′kē	σ Sgr	18
Alphecca, ăl-fĕk′à	α CrB	15	Peacock, pē′kŏk	α Pav	20
Alpheratz, ăl-fē′răts	α And	0	Phecda, fĕk′dà	γ UMa	11
Altair, ăl-târ′	α Aql	19	Polaris, pō-lâr′ĭs	α UMi	2
Ankaa, ăn′kà	α Phe	0	Pollux, pŏl′ŭks	β Gem	7
Antares, ăn-tā′rēs	α Sco	16	Procyon, prō′sĭ-ŏn	α CMi	7
Arcturus, ark-tū′rŭs	α Boo	14	Pulcherrima,	ε Boo	14
Atria, ā′trĭ-a	α TrA	16	pŭl-kĕr′ĭ-mà		
Avior, ă-vĭ-ôr′	ε Car	8	Rasalgethi,	α Her	17
Bellatrix, bĕ-lā′trĭks	γ Ori	5	ràs′ăl-jē′thē		
Betelgeuse, bĕt′ĕl-jūz	α Ori	5	Rasalhague, ràs′ăl-hāg	α Oph	17
Canopus, kà-nō′pŭs	α Car	6	Regulus, rĕg′ū-lŭs	α Leo	10
Capella, kàp-pĕl′à	α Aur	5	Rigel, rī′gĕl	β Ori	5
Caph, kăf	β Cas	0	Rigil Kentaurus,	α Cen	14
Castor, kàs′tẽr	α Gem	7	rī′jĭl kĕn-tô′rŭs		
Cor Caroli, kôr kăr′ō-lī	α CVn	12	Sabik, sā′bĭk	η Oph	17
Deneb, dĕn′ĕb	α Cyg	20	Scheat, shē′ăt	β Peg	23
Denebola, dĕ-nĕb′ō-la	β Leo	11	Schedar, shĕd′àr	α Cas	0
Diphda, dĭf′dà	β Cet	0	Shaula, shô′là	λ Sco	17
Dubhe, dŭb′ē	α UMa	11	Sirius, sĭr′ĭ-ŭs	α CMa	6
Elnath, ĕl′năth	β Tau	5	Spica, spī′kà	α Vir	13
Eltanin, ĕl-tā′nĭn	γ Dra	17	Suhail, sŭ-hāl′	λ Vel	9
Enif, ĕn′ĭf	ε Peg	21	Thuban, thōō′ban	α Dra	14
Fomalhaut, fō′măl-ôt	α PsA	22	Vega, vē′gà	α Lyr	18
Gacrux, gà′krŭks	γ Cru	12	Zubenelgenubi,	α Lib	14
Gemma, jĕm′à	α CrB	15	zōō-bĕn′ĕl-jĕ-nū′bē		

Key to pronunciation on p. 277

THE BRIGHTEST STARS
BY ROBERT F. GARRISON AND TOOMAS KARMO

In the following table the 314 brightest stars (allowing for variability) are listed. Data for visual doubles are for the brighter component (A); the last column describes the companion(s). Where the double is too close to be resolved conveniently, data are for combined light (AB).

Apparent Visual Magnitude ($m_v = V$): Apparent magnitudes, with "v" appended for variables, are from *HIPPARCOS*. (For variables, these data are occasionally in mild conflict with published magnitude ranges.) The photoelectric system is from H.L. Johnson and W.W. Morgan, *Ap. J., 117* (1953). The (yellow) V filter corresponds roughly to the response of the eye. The probable error of a V value is at most 0.03.

Colour Index ($B-V$): Since B on this system is the brightness of a star through a blue filter, the difference $B-V$, here taken from *HIPPARCOS*, measures apparent colour (as possibly reddened by interstellar dust; although, in general, $B-V$ and spectral type are well correlated). The probable error of a $B-V$ value is at most 0.02.

Spectral Classification (**MK Type**): The "temperature type" (O, B, A, F, G, K, M) is given first, followed by a finer subtype (0–9) and a "luminosity class" (Roman numerals I–V, with "a" or "b" added occasionally to indicate slightly brighter or fainter stars within the class). O stars are hottest, M stars coolest; Ia stars are the most luminous supergiants, III stars are giants, and V stars are dwarfs. (V stars form the largest class in the cosmos, comprising the main sequence.) Other MK symbols include "e" for hydrogen emission; "f" for broad, nonhydrogen emission in hot stars; "m" for strong metallic absorption; "n" or "nn" for unusually broad absorption (a signature of rotation); "p" for peculiarities; "s" for a mixture of broad and sharp lines; and ":" for a minor uncertainty. The types are the best available from Garrison's unpublished spectrograms and the literature. Where a single star (e.g. α CMa A) is given two types (e.g. A0 and A1), with the second type flagged "m", the first is the type that best characterizes the hydrogen lines, the second the type that best characterizes the metal lines.

Parallax (**π**): Parallaxes, in milliarcseconds (mas), are from *HIPPARCOS*.

Absolute Visual Magnitude (M_V) and *Distance in Light-Years (D)*: Absolute magnitudes and distances are determined from parallaxes, except where a colon follows the absolute magnitude; in these cases, both quantities are determined from a calibration of the spectral classification. Corrections are made for interstellar absorption, by comparing, under an unpublished intrinsic-colour calibration from Garrison, spectral classification with $B-V$.

Proper Motion (**μ**) and *Position Angle* (**PA**): Proper motion and PA are derived from D. Hoffleit and C. Jaschek, *Bright Star Catalogue*, Yale, 1982. Proper motion is the absolute value of the vector resultant from BSC individual-coordinate proper motions. PA is the direction of the proper motion, as an angle measured from north through east.

Radial Velocity (**RV**): Radial velocities are from BSC. "SB" indicates a spectroscopic binary, an unresolved system whose duplicity is revealed by periodic Doppler oscillations in its spectrum and for which an orbit is generally known. If the lines of both stars are detectable, "SB2" is used; "+" and "–" indicate, respectively, motion away from and toward the observer. "V" indicates a variable velocity in a star not observable as a spectroscopic binary. (In most "V" cases the orbit is unknown.)

Remarks: Remarks include data on variability and spectra, particulars on any companions, and traditional names. Our principal source for variability ranges is P.N. Kholopov et al., *Combined General Catalogue of Variable Stars*, 4.1 ed., 1998 (online as VizieR GCVS4). Our sources for traditional names include BSC and M.E. Bakich, *Cambridge Guide to the Constellations*, Cambridge University Press, 1995. Navigation-star names are **bold**.

TABLE OF BRIGHTEST STARS

Star Name	RA (2011.5) h m	Dec ° ′	V	B – V	MK Type	π mas	Mv	D ly	μ ″/yr	PA °	RV km/s	Remarks	Name
Sun	—	—	-26.75	0.63	G2 V	—	4.8	8 lm	—	—	varies		Sun
α And	0 09.0	+29 09	2.07	-0.04	B9p IV: (HgMn)	34	-0.5	97	0.209	139	-12 SB		Alpheratz
β Cas	0 09.8	+59 13	2.28v	0.38	F2 III	60	1.2	54	0.555	109	+11 SB	var.: 2.25–2.31, 0.10 d	Caph
γ Peg	0 13.8	+15 15	2.83v	-0.19	B2 IV	10	-2.4	300	0.008	176	+4 SB	var.: 2.78–2.89, 0.15 d	Algenib
β Hyi	0 26.3	-77 11	2.82	0.62	G1 IV	134	3.4	24	2.255	82	23		
α Phe	0 26.8	-42 15	2.40	1.08	K0 IIIb	42	-0.3	77	0.442	152	+75 SB		Ankaa
δ And A	0 39.9	+30 55	3.27	1.27	K3 III	32	0.9	101	0.161	122	-7 SB		
α Cas	0 41.2	+56 36	2.24	1.17	K0 IIa	14	-2.5	230	0.058	117	-4 V?		Schedar
β Cet	0 44.2	-17 55	2.04	1.02	K0 III	34	-1.0	96	0.234	81	13		Diphda
η Cas A	0 49.8	+57 53	3.46	0.59	G0 V	168	4.6	19	1.218	115	+9 SB	B:7.51,K4 Ve,13.0″PA:62°→323°,1779→2008	Achird
γ Cas	0 57.4	+60 47	2.15v	-0.05	B0 IVnpe (shell)	5	-5.0	600	0.026	90	-7 SB	var.:1.6–3.0; B:8.21″,PA:255°→259°,1888→2002	Cih
β Phe AB	1 06.6	-46 39	3.32	0.88	G8 III	16	0.3:	150	0.030	279	-1	AB similar in light, spectrum, 1″	
η Cet	1 09.2	-10 07	3.46	1.16	K1.5 III CN1	28	-0.1	120	0.250	122	12		
β And	1 10.4	+35 41	2.07	1.58	M0 IIIa	16	-1.9	200	0.210	121	+3 V		Mirach
δ Cas	1 26.6	+60 18	2.66v	0.16	A5 IV	33	0.2	99	0.303	99	+7 SB	ecl.? 2.68–2.76, 759 d	Ruchbah
γ Phe	1 28.9	-43 16	3.41v	1.54	K7 IIIa	14	-1.6	230	0.108	184	+26 SB	irreg. var.: 3.39–3.49	
α Eri	1 38.1	-57 11	0.45	-0.16	B3 Vnp (shell)	23	-2.9	144	0.204	105	+16 V		Achernar
τ Cet	1 44.6	-15 53	3.49	0.73	G8 V	274	5.7	12	1.921	296	-16		
α Tri	1 53.7	+29 38	3.42	0.49	F6 IV	51	1.8	64	0.230	177	-13 SB		Mothallah
ε Cas	1 55.2	+63 44	3.35	-0.15	B3 V:p (shell)	7	-2.5	400	0.036	114	-8 V		Segin
β Ari	1 55.3	+20 52	2.64	0.16	A4 V	55	1.3	60	0.145	138	-2 SB		Sheratan
α Hyi	1 59.1	-61 31	2.86	0.29	F0n III–IV	46	1.1	71	0.271	83	+1 V		
γ And A	2 04.6	+42 23	2.10	1.37	K3 IIb	9	-3.0	350	0.066	136	-12 SB	B: 5.4, B9 V, 9.5″; C: 6.2, A0 V; BC 0.3″	Almach
α Ari	2 07.8	+23 31	2.01	1.15	K2 IIab	49	0.5	66	0.238	127	-14 SB		Hamal
β Tri	2 10.2	+35 02	3.00	0.14	A5 IV	26	0.1	120	0.153	104	+10 SB2		
ο Cet A	2 19.9	-2 56	6.47v	0.97	M5–10 IIIe	8	3.0	400	0.232	183	+64 V	LPV, 2–10; B: VZ Cet, 9.5v, Bpe, 0.5″	Mira
γ Cet AB	2 43.9	+3 17	3.47	0.09	A2 Va	40	1.3	82	0.203	224	-5 V	A: 3.57; B: 6.23, 18″ PA:283°→298°,1825→2006	
α UMi A	2 46.6	+89 19	1.97v	0.64	F5–8 Ib	8	-4.1	400	0.046	95	-17 SB	low-amp. Cep., 4.0 d; B: 8.2, F3 V, 18″	Polaris
θ Eri A	2 58.7	-40 16	3.28	0.17	A5 IV	28	-0.3	100	0.065	294	+12 SB2	B:4.35,A1 Va,8.4″PA:82°→90°,1835→2002	Acamar
α Cet	3 02.9	+4 08	2.54	1.63	M2 III	15	-1.7	220	0.075	189	-26		Menkar
γ Per	3 05.6	+53 33	2.91	0.72	G8 III + A2 V	13	-0.8:	200	0.002	180	+3 SB	composite spectrum	
ρ Per	3 05.9	+38 53	3.32v	1.53	M4 II	10	-1.3	320	0.165	124	28	semiregular var.: 3.3–4.0	
β Per	3 08.9	+41 00	2.09v	0.00	B8 V + F:	35	-0.5	93	0.004	124	+4 SB	ecl.: 2.12–3.39, 2.9 d; composite	Algol
α Per	3 25.2	+49 54	1.79	0.48	F5 Ib	6	-4.9	600	0.033	131	-2 V	in open cluster	Mirfak
δ Per	3 43.7	+47 49	3.01	-0.12	B5 IIIn	6	-3.1	500	0.042	139	+4 SB		
δ Eri	3 43.8	-9 44	3.52	0.92	K0 IV	111	3.4	29	0.752	352	-6		Rana

TABLE OF BRIGHTEST STARS (continued)

Star Name	RA (2011.5) h m	Dec ° '	MK Type	B-V	mv	π mas	Mv	D ly	μ "/yr	PA °	RV km/s	Remarks	Name
γ Hyi	3 47.1	-74 12	M2 III	1.59	3.26	15	-1.0	210	0.128	24	16		
η Tau	3 48.2	+24 08	B7 IIIn	-0.09	2.85	9	-1.6:	400	0.048	157	+10 V?	in Pleiades	Alcyone
ζ Per A	3 54.9	+31 55	B1 Ib	0.27	2.84	3	-6.0:	1000:	0.011	146	+20 SB		
γ Eri	3 58.6	-13 29	M1 IIIb	1.59	2.97	15	-1.6	220	0.124	153	62		Zaurak
ε Per A	3 58.6	+40 03	B0.5 IV	-0.20	2.90	6	-3.4	500	0.029	145	+1 SB2	calcium, chromium weak	
λ Tau A	4 01.3	+12 31	B3 V	-0.10	3.41v	9	-2.3	400	0.011	218	+18 SB2	ecl.: 3.37-3.91, 4.0 d; B: A4 IV	
α Ret A	4 14.6	-62 27	G8 II-III	0.92	3.33	20	-0.5	160	0.068	43	+36 SB?	B: 7.39, B9.5 V, 8.8" PA:9°→10°,1780→2007	
ε Tau	4 29.3	+19 12	K0 III	1.01	3.53	21	0.1	160	0.114	108	39	in Hyades	Ain
θ² Tau	4 29.3	+15 54	A7 III	0.18	3.40	22	0.2	150	0.105	103	+40 SB	in Hyades	
α Dor AB	4 34.2	-55 01	A0p V: (Si)	-0.08	3.30	19	0.2	180	0.051	89	26	A: 3.8; B: 4.3, B9 IV ; 0.3"; orbit 12 y	
α Tau A	4 36.6	+16 32	K5 III	1.54	0.87v	50	-0.8	65	0.200	161	+54 SB	irregular var.: 0.75-0.95	Aldebaran
π³ Ori	4 50.5	+6 59	F6 V	0.48	3.19	125	3.7	26	0.463	88	+24 SB2		
ι Aur	4 57.7	+33 11	K3 II	1.49	2.69v	6	-3.6	500	0.018	167	18	var.: 2.63-2.78	Hasseleh
ε Aur A	5 02.8	+43 50	A9 Iae + B	0.54	3.03v	2	-8.0:	2000?	0.004	166	-3 SB	ecl.: 2.92-3.83, 9892 d	Almaaz
ε Lep	5 05.9	-22 21	K4 III	1.46	3.19	14	-2.0	230	0.073	166	-1		
η Aur	5 07.3	+41 15	B3 V	-0.15	3.18	15	-1.2	220	0.073	157	+7 V?		Hoedus II
β Eri	5 08.4	-5 04	A3 IVn	0.16	2.78	37	0.4	89	0.128	231	-9		Cursa
μ Lep	5 13.4	-16 12	B9p IV: (HgMn)	-0.11	3.29v	18	-0.4	180	0.043	129	28	var.: 2.97-3.41, 2 d	
β Ori A	5 15.1	-8 11	B8 Ia	-0.03	0.18	6	-6.6	800	0.004	236	+21 SB	B: 6.8, B5 V, 9"; C: 7.6; BC: 0.1"	Rigel
α Aur Aa+Ab	5 17.5	+46 01	G6:III + G2:III	0.80	0.08	77	-0.8	42	0.430	169	+30 SB	composite; A: 0.6; B: 1.1, 0.0—0.1"	Capella
η Ori AB	5 25.1	-2 23	B0.5 V + B	-0.24	3.35v	4	-3.9	900	0.003	288	+20 SB2	ecl.:3.31-3.60, 8.0 d; A: 3.6; B: 5.0, 1.8" (2006)	
γ Ori	5 25.7	+6 22	B2 III	-0.22	1.64	13	-2.8	240	0.018	221	+18 SB?		Bellatrix
β Tau	5 27.0	+28 37	B7 III	-0.13	1.65	25	-1.3	130	0.178	172	+9 V		El Nath
β Lep A	5 28.7	-20 45	G5 II	0.81	2.81	20	-0.7	160	0.090	185	-14		Nihal
δ Ori A	5 32.6	-0 17	O9.5 II	-0.18	2.25v	4	-5.4	900	0.002	252	+16 SB	B: 7.4, 2.2" PA:268°→339°,1875→1993	Mintaka
α Lep	5 33.2	-17 49	F0 Ib	0.21	2.58	3	-5.5	1000	0.006	279	24	ecl.: 2.14-2.26, 5.7 d	Arneb
β Dor	5 33.7	-62 29	F7-G2 Ib	0.64	3.76v	3	-4.2	1000	0.007	8	+7 V	Cepheid var.: 3.46-4.08, 9.8 d	
λ Ori A	5 35.8	+9 56	O8 IIIf	-0.16	3.39	3	-4.6	1000	0.006	191	34	B: 5.61, B0 V 4.1" PA:45°→44°,1779→2008	Meissa
ι Ori A	5 36.0	-5 54	O9 III	-0.21	2.75	2	-5.6	1000	0.005	284	+22 SB2	B:73,B7 IIIp(He wk),11.3" PA:134°→141°,1779→2002	
ε Ori	5 36.8	-1 12	B0 Ia	-0.18	1.69	2	-6.6	1000	0.004	236	+26 SB		Alnilam
ζ Tau	5 38.3	+21 09	B2 IIIpe (shell)	-0.15	2.97v	8	-2.8	400	0.023	177	+20 SB	ecl., var.: 2.88-3.17, 133 d; B: 5.0, 0.007"	
α Col A	5 40.1	-34 04	B7 IV	-0.12	2.65	12	-1.9	270	0.026	178	+35 V?		Phakt
ζ Ori A	5 41.3	-1 56	O9.5 Ib	-0.20	1.74	4	-5.5	800	0.002	207	+18 SB	B:4.2,B0 III, 2.4" PA:152°→166°,1822→2008	Alnitak
λ Lep	5 47.5	-14 49	A2 Vann	0.10	3.55	46	1.7	70	0.023	263	+20 SB?		
κ Ori	5 48.3	-9 40	B0.5 Ia	-0.17	2.07	5	-5.0:	820	0.006	211	+21 V?		Saiph
β Col	5 51.4	-35 46	K1.5 III	1.15	3.12	38	0.2	86	0.405	7	+89 V		Wasn

TABLE OF BRIGHTEST STARS (continued)

Star Name	RA (2011.5) h m	Dec ° '	MK Type	B–V	m_v	π mas	M_v	D ly	μ "/yr	PA °	RV km/s	Remarks
α Ori	5 55.8	+7 24	M2 Iab	1.50	0.45v	8	−5.0:	520	0.028	68	+21 SB	semiregular var: 0.0–1.3 **Betelgeuse**
β Aur	6 00.4	+44 57	A1 IV	0.08	1.90v	40	−0.2	82	0.055	269	−18 SB2	ecl: 1.89–1.98, 4.0 d (mags. equal) Menkalinan
θ Aur AB	6 00.5	+37 13	A0p II: (Si)	−0.08	2.65	19	−1.0	170	0.097	149	+30 SB	B: 7.2, G2 V, 3.9" PA:7°→306°,1871→2008
η Gem	6 15.6	+22 30	M3 III	1.60	3.31v	9	−1.8	300	0.068	259	+19 SB	ecl, var: 3.2–3.9, 233 d; B: 8.8, 1.7" (2006) Propus
ζ CMa	6 20.8	−30 04	B2.5 V	−0.16	3.02	10	−2.2	340	0.006	59	+32 SB	Furud
β CMa	6 23.2	−17 58	B1 II–III	−0.24	1.98v	7	−4.0	500	0.014	253	+34 SB	var: 1.93–2.00, 0.25 d Mirzam
μ Gem	6 23.7	+22 30	M3 IIIab	1.62	2.87v	14	−1.5	230	0.125	154	55	irregular var: 2.75–3.02 Tejat Posterior
α Car	6 24.2	−52 42	A9 Ib	0.16	−0.62	10	−5.4	310	0.034	50	21	**Canopus**
ν Pup	6 38.1	−43 12	B8 IIIn	−0.10	3.17	8	−2.4	400	0.010	234	+28 SB	
γ Gem	6 38.4	+16 23	A1 IVs	0.00	1.93	31	−0.6	100	0.061	136	−13 SB	Alhena
ε Gem	6 44.6	+25 07	G8 Ib	1.38	3.06	4	−5.0	900	0.016	195	+10 SB	Mebsuta
α CMa A	6 45.7	−16 44	A0mA1 Va	0.01	−1.44	379	1.5	9	1.324	204	−8 SB	B: 8.5, WDA: 8.4" (2009); orbit 50.1 y **Sirius**
ξ Gem	6 45.9	+12 53	F5 IV	0.44	3.35	57	2.2	57	0.224	211	+25 V?	Alzirr
α Pic	6 48.3	−61 57	A6 Vn	0.22	3.24	33	0.7	100	0.275	345	21	
τ Pup	6 50.2	−50 38	K1 III	1.21	2.94	18	−1.9	180	0.079	157	+36 SB	
ε CMa A	6 59.1	−28 59	B2 II	−0.21	1.50	8	−4.1	400	0.002	27	27	**Adhara**
σ CMa	7 02.2	−27 57	K7 Ib	1.73	3.49v	3	−4.7	1000	0.008	284	22	irregular var: 3.43–3.51
o² CMa	7 03.5	−23 51	B3 Ia	−0.08	3.02	1	−6.6	3000	0.007	262	+48 SB	
δ CMa	7 08.9	−26 25	F8 Ia	0.67	1.83	2	−7.2	2000	0.008	291	+34 SB	Wezen
L₂ Pup	7 13.9	−44 40	M5 IIIe	1.33	4.42v	16	1.5	200	0.346	18	+53 V?	long-period var: 2.6–6.2 HR2748
π Pup	7 17.5	−37 07	K3 Ib	1.62	2.71	3	−5.1	1100	0.012	284	16	
δ Gem AB	7 20.8	+21 58	F0 IV	0.37	3.50	55	2.2	59	0.029	241	+4 SB	B: 8.2, K3 V5.4" PA:184°→225°,1781→2006 Wasat
η CMa	7 24.6	−29 20	B5 Ia	−0.08	2.45	1	−7.5	3000	0.008	283	+41 V	Aludra
β CMi	7 27.8	+8 16	B8 V	−0.10	2.89	19	−0.8	170	0.065	233	+22 SB	Gomeisa
σ Pup A	7 29.6	−43 20	K5 III	1.51	3.25	18	−1.6	180	0.195	342	+88 SB	B: 8.6, G5: V, 22.1" PA:90°→74°,1826→2007
α Gem A	7 35.3	+31 52	A1mA2 Va	0.03	1.93	63	0.6	52	0.199	239	+6 SB	4"; orbit 445 y; max = 6.5", in 1880; **Castor**
α Gem B	7 35.3	+31 52	A2mA5 V:	0.03	2.97	63	1.0	52	0.199	239	−1 SB	min = 1.8", in 1965; 4.6" (2008)
α CMi A	7 39.9	+5 12	F5 IV–V	0.43	0.40	286	2.8	11	1.248	214	−3 SB	B: 10.3, WD: 2.3" (2010); orbit 41 y **Procyon**
β Gem	7 46.0	+28 00	K0 IIIb	0.99	1.16	97	1.1	34	0.629	265	+3 V	**Pollux**
ξ Pup	7 49.8	−24 53	G6 Iab-Ib	1.22	3.34	2	−7.5:	3300	0.033	240	+3 SB	Asmidiske
χ Car	7 57.1	−53 01	B3 IVp (cf. Remarks)	−0.18	3.46	8	−2.0	387	0.042	306	+19 V	Si II strong
ζ Pup	8 04.0	−40 02	O5 Iafn	−0.27	2.21	2	−6.1	1000	0.033	290	−24 V?	Naos
ρ Pup	8 08.0	−24 20	F2mF5 II: (var)	0.46	2.83v	52	1.4	63	0.100	299	+46 SB	delta Del spec.; var: 2.68–2.87, 0.14 d
γ² Vel	8 09.9	−47 22	WC8 + O9 I:	−0.14	1.75v	4	−5.8	800	0.007	304	+35 SB2	var: 1.81–1.87
β Cnc	8 17.1	+9 09	K4 III	1.48	3.53	11	−1.2	290	0.068	220	22	Tarf
ε Car	8 22.7	−59 33	K3:III + B2:V	1.20	1.86v	5	−4.8	600	0.030	301	2	ecl.?: 1.82–1.94 Avior

TABLE OF BRIGHTEST STARS (continued)

Star Name	RA h m	Dec ° '	m_v	B–V	MK Type	π mas	M_v	D ly	μ "/yr	PA °	RV km/s	Remarks
o UMa A	8 31.2	+60 41	3.35v?	0.86	G5 III	18	−0.3	180	0.171	230	20	var.?: 3.30?-3.36?
δ Vel AB	8 45.0	−54 45	1.93	0.04	A1 Va	41	0.0	80	0.082	164	+2 V?	B: 5.0, 1.0" PA:177°→338°,1894→2001
ε Hya ABC	8 47.4	+6 23	3.38	0.68	G5:III + A:	24	0.0	140	0.198	254	+36 SB	composite A: 3.8; B: 4.7, 0.2"; C: 7.8, 3"
ζ Hya	8 56.0	+5 54	3.11	0.98	G9 II-III	22	−0.2	150	0.101	277	23	
ι UMa A	9 00.0	+48 00	3.12	0.22	A7 IV n	68	2.2	48	0.501	242	+9 SB	BC 10.8,M1 V,4.5" PA:349°→24°,1831→1983 Talitha
λ Vel	9 08.4	−43 29	2.23v	1.66	K4 Ib-IIa	6	−4.8	600	0.026	299	18	var.: 2.14-2.30
a Car	9 11.3	−59 01	3.43v	−0.19	B2 IV-V	8	−2.2	420	0.028	283	+23 SB2	ecl.?: 3.41-3.44 HR3659
β Car	9 13.3	−69 46	1.67	0.07	A1 III	29	−1.1	111	0.183	304	−5 V?	Miaplacidus
ι Car	9 17.4	−59 19	2.21v	0.19	A7 Ib	5	−4.4	700	0.019	285	13	var: 2.23-2.28 Tureis
α Lyn	9 21.8	+34 21	3.14	1.55	K7 IIIab	15	−1.3	220	0.223	273	38	
κ Vel	9 22.5	−55 04	2.47	−0.14	B2 IV-V	24	−3.9	500	0.012	315	+22 SB	
α Hya	9 28.2	−8 43	1.99	1.44	K3 II-III	18	−2.1	180	0.034	327	−4 V?	Alphard
N Vel	9 31.6	−57 05	3.16	1.54	K5 III	14	−1.3	240	0.034	268	−14	HR3803
θ UMa	9 33.6	+51 37	3.17	0.48	F6 IV	74	2.6	44	1.094	240	+15 SB	A: occ. bin. (mags. equal)
o Leo AB	9 41.8	+9 50	3.52v	0.52	F5 II + A5?	24	0.1	140	0.149	254	+27 SB	Subra
l Car	9 45.6	−62 34	3.69v	1.01	F9-G5 Ib	2	−5.8	2000	0.016	281	+4 V	Cepheid var.: 3.28-4.18, 36 d HR3884
ε Leo	9 46.5	+23 43	2.97	0.81	G1 II	13	−1.6	250	0.048	252	+4 V?	Ras Elased Australis
ν Car AB	9 47.4	−65 08	2.92	0.29	A6 II	2	−2.5	330	0.012	305	14	A:3.0I;B:5.99,B7 III,5.0" PA:126°→129°,1836→2000
φ Vel	9 57.3	−54 37	3.52	−0.07	B5 Ib	2	−5.5	2000	0.013	293	14	
η Leo	10 08.0	+16 42	3.48	−0.03	A0 Ib	2	−5.5	2000	0.006	189	+3 V	
α Leo A	10 09.0	+11 55	1.36	−0.09	B7 Vn	42	−0.6	78	0.248	271	+6 SB	A: 4.5, 0.1" PA:84°→309°,1937→1993 **Regulus**
ω Car	10 14.0	−70 06	3.29	−0.07	B8 IIIn	9	−2.1	370	0.032	275	+7 V	
ζ Leo	10 17.3	+23 22	3.43	0.31	F0 IIIa	13	−1.1	260	0.023	124	−16 SB	Adhafera
q Car	10 17.5	−61 23	3.39v	1.54	K3 IIa	4	−4.2	700	0.027	276	8	irregular var.: 3.36-3.44 HR4050
λ UMa	10 17.8	+42 51	3.45	0.03	A1 IV	24	0.4	130	0.170	255	+18 V	Tania Borealis
γ Leo A	10 20.6	+19 47	2.61	1.13	K1 IIb Fe-0.5	26	−0.7	130	0.342	116	−37 SB	4.6" (2008); orbit 510.3 y; Algieba
γ Leo B	10 20.6	+19 47	3.16	1.42	G7 III Fe-1	26	−1.9	130	0.358	119	−36 V	max ≈ −5", around 2100
μ UMa	10 23.0	+41 26	3.06	1.60	M0 IIIp	13	−1.5	250	0.088	290	−21 SB	Ca II emission Tania Australis
p Car	10 32.4	−61 45	3.30v	−0.09	B4 Vne	7	−2.0	330	0.021	287	26	irregular var.: 3.27-3.37 HR4140
θ Car	10 43.4	−64 27	2.74	−0.22	B0.5 Vp	7	−3.1	400	0.022	291	+24 SB	nitrogen enhanced
μ Vel AB	10 47.3	−49 29	2.69	1.07	G5 III + F8:V	28	−0.9	116	0.085	125	+6 SB	A:2.72; B:5.9,2.1" PA:55°→51°,1880→1995
ν Hya	10 50.2	−16 15	3.11	1.23	K2 III	24	−0.3	140	0.215	24	−1	
β UMa	11 02.5	+56 19	2.34	0.03	A0mA1 IV–V	41	0.4	79	0.087	70	−12 SB	Merak
α UMa AB	11 04.4	+61 41	1.81	1.06	K0 IIIa	26	−1.3	124	0.138	239	−9 SB	A: 1.86; B: 4.8, A8 V, 0.5" (2007) Dubhe
ψ UMa	11 10.3	+44 26	3.00	1.14	K1 III	22	−0.5	147	0.075	245	−4	
δ Leo	11 14.7	+20 28	2.56	0.13	A4 IV	57	1.3	58	0.197	133	−20 V	Zosma

TABLE OF BRIGHTEST STARS (continued)

Star Name	RA (2011.5) h m	Dec	m_v	B−V	MK Type	π mas	M_v	D ly	μ "/yr	PA °	RV km/s	Remarks	
θ Leo	11 14.8	+15 22	3.33	0.00	A2 IV (K-line var.)	18	−0.2	180	0.104	216	+8 V		Chort
ν UMa	11 19.1	+33 02	3.49	1.40	K3 III Ba0.3	8	−3.2	400	0.036	309	−9 SB	B:9.5, 7.4″ PA:147°→149°,1830→2005	Alula Borealis
ξ Hya	11 33.6	−31 55	3.54	0.95	G7 III	25	0.0	130	0.211	259	−5 V		
λ Cen	11 36.3	−63 05	3.11	−0.04	B9.5 IIn	8	−2.5	410	0.039	258	−1 V		
β Leo	11 49.6	+14 30	2.14	0.09	A3 Va	90	1.9	36	0.511	257	0 V		Denebola
γ UMa	11 54.4	+53 38	2.41	0.04	A0 Van	39	0.2	84	0.094	86	−13 SB		Phad
δ Cen	12 09.0	−50 47	2.58v	−0.13	B2 IVne	8	−3.1	400	0.034	249	+11 V	irregular var.: 2.51−2.65	
ε Crv	12 10.7	−22 41	3.02	1.33	K2 III	11	−2.3	300	0.073	278	5		Minkar
δ Cru	12 15.8	−58 49	2.79v	−0.19	B2 IV	9	−2.6	360	0.039	255	+22 V?	var.: 2.78−2.84, 0.15 d	
δ UMa	12 16.0	+56 58	3.32	0.08	A2 Van	40	1.4	81	0.102	88	−13 V		Megrez
γ Crv	12 16.4	−17 36	2.58	−0.11	B8 III	20	−0.9	160	0.163	276	−4 SB	sp. var.?	Gienah Ghurab
α Cru A	12 27.2	−63 10	1.25	−0.20	B0.5 IV	10	−4.0	320	0.030	236	−11 SB	5.4″ (1826); 4.0″ (2007)	Acrux
α Cru B	12 27.2	−63 10	1.64	−0.18	B1 Vn	10	−3.6	320	0.031	248	−1	PA unchanged	Acrux
δ Crv A	12 30.5	−16 35	2.94	−0.01	B9.5 IVn	37	−2.0	88	0.255	236	+9 V	B: 8.26, K2 V, 24.7″ PA:unch.,1782→2006	Algorab
γ Cru	12 31.8	−57 11	1.59v	1.60	M3.5 III	37	−0.7	88	0.269	174	21	var.: 1.60−1.67	Gacrux
β Crv	12 35.0	−23 28	2.65	0.89	G5 II	23	−0.5	140	0.059	179	−8		Kraz
α Mus	12 37.9	−69 12	2.69v	−0.18	B2 IV−V	11	−2.3	310	0.043	248	+13 V	var.: 2.68−2.73, 0.090 d	
γ Cen A	12 42.2	−49 01	2.95	−0.02	A1 IV	25	−0.1	130	0.190	268	−6 SB	[orbit 84 y; min = 0.2″; 0.5″ (2007)	
γ Cen B	12 42.2	−49 01	2.85	−0.02	A0 IV	25	−0.1	130	0.190	268	−6 SB	0.4″ (2010) max = 1.7″ (1931)	
γ Vir AB	12 42.2	−1 31	2.74	0.37	F1 V + F0mF2 V	85	2.2	39	0.567	271	−20 SB	A: 3.48; B: 3.50; 0.8″ (2007); 0.9″ (2010)	Porrima
β Mus AB	12 47.0	−68 10	3.04	−0.18	B2 V + B2.5 V	10	−2.2:	420	0.041	233	+42 V	A:3.5l; B:4.00,10″ PA:317°→48°,1880→2007	
β Cru	12 48.4	−59 45	1.25v	−0.24	B0.5 III	9	−4.0	350	0.042	246	+16 SB	var.: 1.23−1.31, 0.24 d	Becrux
ε UMa	12 54.5	+55 54	1.76v	−0.02	A0p IV: (CrEu)	40	−0.2	81	0.109	95	−9 SB?	var.: 1.76−1.78, 5.1 d	Alioth
δ Vir	12 56.6	+3 20	3.39	1.57	M3 III	16	−0.5	200	0.474	263	−18 V?		Auva
α² CVn A	12 56.6	+38 15	2.85	−0.06	A0p (SiEu)	30	0.4	110	0.242	282	−3 V	B:5.6,F0 V,188″ PA:224°→230°,1777→2009	CorCaroli
ε Vir	13 02.7	+10 54	2.85	0.93	G9 IIIab	32	0.4	100	0.274	274	−14		Vindemiatrix
γ Hya	13 19.5	−23 14	2.99	0.92	G8 IIIa	25	−0.6	130	0.081	127	−5 V?		
ι Cen	13 21.2	−36 46	2.75	0.07	A2 Va	56	1.4	59	0.351	255	0		
ζ UMa A	13 24.4	+54 52	2.23	0.06	A1 Va	42	0.3	78	0.122	102	−6 SB2	B:3.94, A1mA7IV−V,14.4″; period≥5000y?	Mizar
α Vir	13 25.8	−11 13	0.98v	−0.24	B1 V	12	−3.6	260	0.054	232	+1 SB2	var.: 0.95−1.05, 4.0 d; mult. 3.1, 4.5, 7.5	Spica
ζ Vir	13 35.3	−0 39	3.38	0.11	A2 IV	45	1.6	73	0.287	277	−13		Heze
ε Cen	13 40.6	−53 31	2.29	−0.17	B1 III	9	−3.3	400	0.028	232	3		
η UMa	13 48.0	+49 15	1.85	−0.10	B3 V	32	−1.8	101	0.127	264	−11 SB?		Alkaid
ν Cen	13 50.2	−41 45	3.41	−0.22	B2 IV	7	−2.4	500	0.035	227	+9 SB		
μ Cen	13 50.3	−42 32	3.47v	−0.17	B2 IV−V pne	6	−2.8	500	0.034	220	+9 SB	variable shell: 2.92−3.47	
η Boo	13 55.2	+18 20	2.68	0.58	G0 IV	88	2.4	37	0.370	190	0 SB		Mufrid

TABLE OF BRIGHTEST STARS (continued)

Star Name	RA (2011.5) h m	Dec ° '	m_v	B−V	MK Type	π mas	M_v	D ly	μ "/yr	PA °	RV km/s	Remarks
ζ Cen	13 56.3	−47 21	2.55	−0.18	B2.5 IV	8	−2.9	400	0.072	232	+7 SB2	
β Cen AB	14 04.6	−60 26	0.58v	−0.23	B1 III	6	−5.5	500	0.030	221	+6 SB	var: 0.61–0.66, 0.16 d; B: 3.9, 0.9" (1991) **Hadar**
π Hya	14 07.0	−26 44	3.25	1.09	K2 IIIb	32	0.2	101	0.049	163	27	
θ Cen	14 07.4	−36 26	2.06	1.01	K0 IIIb	54	0.1	61	0.738	225	1	**Menkent**
α Boo	14 16.2	+19 07	−0.05	1.24	K1.5 III Fe−0.5	89	−0.6	37	2.281	209	−5 V?	high space velocity **Arcturus**
ι Lup	14 20.1	−46 07	3.55	−0.18	B2.5 IVn	9	−1.7	400	0.014	266	22	
γ Boo	14 32.5	+38 16	3.04	0.19	A7 IV+	38	1.0	85	0.189	322	−37 V	**Seginus**
η Cen	14 36.2	−42 12	2.33v	−0.16	B1.5 IV pne	11	−2.8	310	0.049	226	0 SB	variable shell: 2.30–2.41
α Cen B	14 40.4	−60 53	1.35	0.90	K1 V	742	6.2	4	3.678	281	−21 V?	[AB 9"; orbit 79.9 y; min = 2"(1955); max 22"
α Cen A	14 40.4	−60 53	−0.01	0.71	G2 V	742	4.2	4	3.678	281	−25 SB	[C: Proxima, 12.4, M5e, 2.2° **Rigil Kentaurus**
α Lup	14 42.7	−47 26	2.30v	−0.15	B1.5 III	6	−4.1	500	0.026	220	+5 SB	var: 2.29–2.34, 0.26 d
α Cir	14 43.4	−65 01	3.18	0.26	A7p (Sr)	61	1.9	54	0.302	218	+7 SB?	B: 8.6, K5 V, 15.1" PA:263°→227°,1826→2002
ε Boo AB	14 45.5	+27 02	2.35	1.34	K0 II−III+A0 V	16	−2.6	210	0.054	289	−17 V	A:2.50;B:4.66,2.8" PA:300°→342°,1780→2006 **Izar**
β UMi	14 50.7	+74 07	2.07	1.46	K4 III	26	−1.1	126	0.036	286	+17 V	**Kochab**
α² Lib	14 51.5	−16 05	2.75	0.15	A3 III−IV	42	0.7	77	0.130	237	−23 SB	**Zubenelgenubi**
β Lup	14 59.3	−43 11	2.68	−0.18	B2 IV	6	−3.5	500	0.057	221	0 SB	
κ Cen	14 59.9	−42 09	3.13	−0.21	B2 V	6	−2.8	500	0.033	215	+8 SB	
β Boo	15 02.4	+40 21	3.49	0.96	G8 IIIa (cf. Remarks)	15	−0.7	220	0.056	235	−20	**Nekkar**
σ Lib	15 04.7	−25 20	3.25v	1.67	M2.5 III	11	−1.9	290	0.087	237	−4	Ba 0.4, Fe −0.5 semiregular var.: 3.20–3.46 **Brachium**
ζ Lup	15 13.1	−52 09	3.41	0.92	G8 III	28	0.1	120	0.128	237	−10	
δ Boo	15 16.0	+33 16	3.46	0.96	G8 III Fe−1	28	0.6	117	0.143	144	−12 SB	
β Lib	15 17.6	−9 25	2.61	−0.07	B8 IIIn	20	−1.0	160	0.101	275	−35 SB	**Zubeneschemali**
γ TrA	15 20.0	−68 43	2.87	0.01	A1 IIIn	18	−0.8	180	0.067	243	−3 V	
γ UMi	15 20.7	+71 48	3.00	0.06	A3 III	7	−0.1:	150	0.031	308	−4 V	**Pherkad**
δ Lup	15 22.1	−40 41	3.22	−0.23	B1.5 IVn	6	−2.8	500	0.036	207	0 V?	
ε Lup AB	15 23.5	−44 44	3.37	−0.19	B2 IV−V	6	−2.5	500	0.024	232	+8 SB2	A:3.56;B:5.04,0.3" PA:285°→118°,1883→2009
ι Dra	15 25.2	+58 56	3.29	1.17	K2 III	32	0.8	102	0.020	311	−11	**Ed Asich**
α CrB	15 35.2	+26 41	2.22v	0.03	A0 V (composite)	44	0.3	75	0.151	127	+2 SB	ecl.: 2.21–2.32, 17 d **Alphecca**
γ Lup AB	15 35.9	−41 12	2.80	−0.22	B2 IVn	6	−2.8	600	0.035	207	+2 V	A: 3.5; B: 3.6, 0.8" (2009); similar spectra
α Ser	15 44.8	+6 23	2.63v?	1.17	K2 IIIb CN1	45	0.9	73	0.143	72	+3 V?	var? **Unuk al Hai**
μ Ser	15 50.2	−3 28	3.54	−0.04	A0 III	21	0.3	160	0.094	253	−9 SB	
β TrA	15 56.2	−63 28	2.83	0.32	F0 IV	81	2.3	40	0.438	205	0	
π Sco A	15 59.6	−26 09	2.89	−0.18	B1 V + B2 V	7	−3.0	500	0.028	198	−3 SB2	A: occ. bin.: 3.4 + 4.5, 0.0003" sep.
τ CrB	16 00.0	+25 53	10.08v	1.34	gM3: + Bep	0	−9.3	—	0.013	327	−29 SB	recurrent nova 1866 (mag. 3), 1946 (mag. 2)
η Lup A	16 00.9	−38 26	3.42	−0.21	B2.5 IVn	7	−2.5	500	0.040	213	+8 V	A:3.47; B:7.70,14.4" PA:22°→20°,1834→2007
δ Sco AB	16 01.0	−22 39	2.29	−0.12	B0.3 IV	8	−4.4:	400	0.027	202	−7 SB	AB: sep. <1"; C: 4.9, B2 IV−V, 8" **Dschubba**

TABLE OF BRIGHTEST STARS (continued)

Star Name	RA (2011.5) h m	Dec ° '	m_v	$B-V$	MK Type	π mas	M_v	D ly	μ "/yr	PA °	RV km/s	Remarks
β Sco AB	16 06.1	−19 50	2.56	−0.06	B0.5 V	6	−4.2	500	0.022	196	−1 SB	A: 2.78; B: 5.04, −0.3"; C: 4.93, 14" Graffias
δ Oph	16 15.0	−3 43	2.73	1.58	M1 III	19	−0.8	170	0.153	198	−20 V	Yed Prior
ε Oph	16 18.9	−4 43	3.23	0.97	G9.5 IIIb	30	0.8	110	0.089	64	−10 V	Yed Posterior
σ Sco A	16 21.9	−25 37	2.91v	0.13	B1 III	4	−4.8:	520	0.025	201	+3 SB	var: 2.86−2.94, 0.25 d; B: 8.3, B9 V, 20.0" (1999)
η Dra A	16 24.2	+61 29	2.73	0.91	G8 IIIab	37	0.7	88	0.064	338	−14 SB?	B: 8.7, 4.8" PA:150°→139°,1843→1996
α Sco A	16 30.1	−26 27	1.06v	1.86	M1.5 Iab	5	−5.8	600	0.024	197	−3 SB	irregular var: 0.88−1.16; B: 5.37, 2.5" Antares
β Her	16 30.7	+21 28	2.78	0.95	G7 IIIa	22	−0.5	150	0.100	260	−26 SB	Kornephoros
τ Sco	16 36.6	−28 14	2.82	−0.21	B0 V	8	−3.1	400	0.026	198	+2 V	
ζ Oph	16 37.8	−10 35	2.54	0.04	O9.5 Vn	7	−4.3	500	0.026	28	−15 V	
ζ Her AB	16 41.7	+31 35	2.81	0.65	G1 IV	93	2.5	35	0.614	310	−70 SB	A: 2.90; B: 5.53, G7 V, 1.1" (2007), orbit 34 y
η Her	16 43.3	+38 54	3.48	0.92	G7.5 IIIb Fe-1	29	0.1	112	0.089	158	+8 V?	
α TrA	16 49.9	−69 03	1.91	1.45	K2 IIb-IIIa	8	−5.0	400	0.044	141	−3	Atria
ε Sco	16 50.9	−34 19	2.29	1.14	K2 III	50	0.1	65	0.661	247	−3	
μ¹ Sco	16 52.7	−38 04	3.00v	−0.20	B1.5 IVn	4	−4.1	800	0.031	202	−25 SB2	ecl.: 2.94−3.22, 1.4 d
κ Oph	16 58.2	+9 21	3.17	1.16	K2 III	38	1.1	86	0.293	268	−56	
ζ Ara	16 59.6	−56 00	3.12	1.55	K4 III	6	−4.5	600	0.037	200	−6	
ζ Dra	17 08.8	+65 42	3.17	−0.12	B6 III	10	−2.0	340	0.033	310	−17 V	Aldhibah
η Oph AB	17 11.0	−15 44	2.43	0.06	A2.5 Va	39	0.8	84	0.102	22	−1 SB	A: 3.0; B: 3.5, A3 V, 0.6" (2009), orbit 87.6 y Sabik
η Sco	17 13.0	−43 15	3.32	0.44	F2 V:p (Cr)	46	1.4	72	0.286	175	−27	
α Her AB	17 15.2	+14 23	2.78v	1.16	M5 Ib-II	9	−3.5:	1400	0.035	348	−33 V	semiregular var: 2.7−4.0; B: 5.4, 4.8" Rasalgethi
π Her	17 15.4	+36 48	3.16	1.44	K3 IIab	9	−2.2	370	0.029	276	−26	
δ Her	17 15.5	+24 50	3.12	0.08	A1 Vann	42	1.2	79	0.159	188	−40 SB	B: 8.8,9" PA:163°→286°,1779→2008 Sarin
θ Oph	17 22.7	−25 01	3.27v	−0.19	B2 IV	6	−3.1	600	0.021	188	−2 SB	occ. bin.: 3.4, 5.4; var.: 3.25−3.31, 0.14 d
β Ara	17 26.3	−55 32	2.84	1.48	K3 Ib-IIa	5	−4.1	600	0.032	182	0	
γ Ara A	17 26.4	−56 23	3.31	−0.15	B1 Ib	3	−5.7:	650	0.011	170	−3 V	broad lines for Ib; B: 10.0,17.8" PA:324°→328°,1835→2002
β Dra A	17 30.7	+52 18	2.79	0.95	G2 Ib-IIa	9	−2.9	360	0.026	301	−20 V	B: 11.5, 4.4" PA:13°→12°,1889→1934 Rastaban
υ Sco	17 31.5	−37 18	2.70	−0.18	B2 IV	6	−3.5	500	0.032	182	8 SB	
α Ara	17 32.7	−49 53	2.84	−0.14	B2 Vne	13	−1.8	240	0.075	199	0 SB	
λ Sco	17 34.4	−37 07	1.62v	−0.23	B1.5 IV	5	−3.6:	360	0.029	178	−3 SB2	ecl.?, var.: 1.62−1.68, 0.21 d Shaula
α Oph	17 35.5	+12 33	2.08	0.16	A5 Vnn	70	1.3	47	0.255	157	+13 SB?	Rasalhague
θ Sco	17 38.1	−43 00	1.86	0.41	F1 III	12	−3.0	270	0.016	90	1	Sargas
ξ Ser	17 38.2	−15 24	3.54	0.26	F0 IIIb	31	0.9	110	0.076	216	−43 SB	
κ Sco	17 43.3	−39 02	2.39v	−0.17	B1.5 III	7	−3.6	500	0.030	194	−14 SB	var: 2.41−2.42, 0.20 d
β Oph	17 44.0	+4 34	2.76	1.17	K2 III	40	0.7	82	0.164	345	−12 V	Cebalrai
μ Her A	17 46.9	+27 43	3.42	0.75	G5 IV	119	3.6	27	0.808	202	−16 V	BC: 9.78, 34.9" PA:240°→248°,1781→2007
ι¹ Sco	17 48.4	−40 08	2.99	0.51	F2 Ia	2	−8.0:	4000?	0.006	171	−28 SB	

TABLE OF BRIGHTEST STARS (continued)

Star Name	RA (2011.5) h m	Dec ° '	m_V	B–V	MK Type	π mas	M_V	D ly	μ "/yr	PA °	RV km/s	Remarks
G Sco	17 50.6	–37 03	3.19	1.19	K2 III	26	–0.6	130	0.064	58	25	HR6630
γ Dra	17 56.9	+51 29	2.24	1.52	K5 III	22	–1.1	150	0.025	213	–28	Eltanin
ν Oph	17 59.7	–9 46	3.32	0.99	G9.5 IIIa	21	0.0	150	0.118	184	13	
γ² Sgr	18 06.5	–30 25	2.98	0.98	K0 III	34	0.1	96	0.192	196	+22 SB	Nash
η Sgr A	18 18.4	–36 45	3.10v	1.50	M3.5 IIIab	22	–0.1	150	0.210	218	+1 V?	irreg. var: 3.05–3.12; B: 8.33, G8: IV.; 4"
δ Sgr	18 21.7	–29 49	2.72	1.38	K2.5 IIIa	11	–3.3	300	0.050	127	–20	Kaus Meridionalis
η Ser	18 21.9	–2 54	3.23	0.94	K0 III-IV	53	1.4	62	0.890	218	+9 V?	
ε Sgr	18 24.9	–34 23	1.79	–0.03	A0 II.n (shell?)	23	–1.4	140	0.129	194	–15	Kaus Australis
α Tel	18 27.8	–45 58	3.49	–0.18	B3 IV	13	–1.0	250	0.048	198	0 V?	
λ Sgr	18 28.7	–25 25	2.82	1.02	K1 IIIb	42	0.4	77	0.190	193	–43	Kaus Borealis
α Lyr	18 37.3	+38 48	0.03	0.00	A0 Va	129	0.6	25	0.348	35	–14 V	**Vega**
φ Sgr	18 46.4	–26 59	3.17	–0.11	B8 III	14	–1.0	230	0.052	89	+22 SB	
β Lyr	18 50.5	+33 23	3.52v	0.00	B7 Vpe (shell)	4	–4.1	900	0.002	180	–19 SB	Sheliak; ecl.: 3.25–4.36, 13 d
σ Sgr	18 56.0	–26 17	2.05	–0.13	B3 IV	15	–2.4	220	0.056	166	–11 V	Nunki
ξ² Sgr	18 58.4	–21 05	3.52	1.15	K1 III	9	0.1	400	0.035	111	–20	
γ Lyr	18 59.4	+32 42	3.25	–0.05	B9 II	5	–3.3	600	0.007	288	–21 V	Sulaphat
ζ Sgr AB	19 03.3	–29 52	2.60	0.06	A2 IV-V + A4:V:	37	1.1	90	0.014	266	+22 SB	Ascella; A:3.2; B: 3.5, 0.2" (2008), orbit 21.1 y
ξ Aql A	19 05.5	+13 53	2.99	0.01	A0 Vann	39	0.9	83	0.095	184	–25 SB	
λ Aql	19 06.9	–4 52	3.43	–0.10	B9 Vnp (kB7/HeA0)	26	0.6	130	0.090	193	–12 V	
τ Sgr	19 07.7	–27 39	3.32	1.17	K1.5 IIIb	27	–0.4	120	0.255	192	+45 SB	
π Sgr ABC	19 10.4	–21 00	2.88	0.38	F2 II-III	7	–3.1	400	0.035	180	–10	Albaldah; A:3.7; B:3.8 0.1" (1989); C:6.0,AB–C<1"?
δ Dra	19 12.6	+67 41	3.07	0.99	G9 III	33	0.6	100	0.130	44	25	Nodus Secundus
δ Aql	19 26.1	+3 08	3.36	0.32	F2 IV	65	2.6	50	0.267	72	–30 SB	Deneb Okab
β Cyg A	19 31.2	+27 59	3.36	1.09	K3 II + B9.5 V	8	–2.3	390	0.002	153	–24 V	Albireo; B: 5.11, ~37"; Aa,Ac: Δm = 1.5, 0.4"
δ Cyg AB	19 45.3	+45 10	2.86	0.00	B9.5 III	19	–0.7	170	0.069	45	–20 SB	B: 6.4, F1 V: 2.5" PA:72°→222°,1783→2007
γ Aql	19 46.8	+10 39	2.72	1.51	K3 II	7	–2.6:	330	0.016	83	–2 V	Tarazed
α Aql	19 51.3	+8 54	0.76	0.22	A7 Vnn	194	2.1	17	0.662	54	–26	**Altair**
η Aql	19 53.1	+1 02	3.87v	0.63	F6-G1 Ib	3	–4.3	1000	0.009	131	–15 SB	Cepheid var.: 3.48–4.39, 7.2 d
γ Sge	19 59.3	+19 31	3.51	1.57	M0 III	12	–0.9	270	0.070	69	–33	
θ Aql	20 11.9	–0 47	3.24	–0.07	B9.5 III	11	–1.4	290	0.037	79	–27 SB2	
β Cap A	20 21.7	–14 45	3.05	0.79	K0: II: + A5: V:n	9	–1.4	300	0.039	86	–19 SB	Dabih; A: mult.: 4.0 + 4.3 + 4.8 + 6.7, <1"
γ Cyg	20 22.6	+40 18	2.23	0.67	F8 Ib	2	–4.1:	520	0.001	27	–8	Sadr
α Pav	20 26.6	–56 42	1.94	–0.12	B2.5 V	18	–2.1	180	0.087	169	+2 SB	Peacock
α Ind	20 38.4	–47 15	3.11	1.00	K0 III CN-1	32	0.1	101	0.090	39	–1	
α Cyg	20 41.8	+45 19	1.25	0.09	A2 Ia	1	–7.5:	1500	0.005	11	–5 V	**Deneb**
η Cep	20 45.5	+61 53	3.41	0.91	K0 IV	70	2.7	47	0.827	6	–87	

TABLE OF BRIGHTEST STARS (continued)

Star Name	RA (2011.5) h m	Dec ° '	m_V	$B-V$	MK Type	π mas	M_V	D ly	μ "/yr	PA °	RV km/s	Remarks
β Pav	20 46.0	−66 10	3.42	0.16	A6 IV	24	0.6	140	0.041	295	10	
ε Cyg	20 46.7	+34 01	2.48	1.02	K0 III	45	0.7	72	0.484	47	−11 SB	Gienah
ζ Cyg	21 13.4	+30 16	3.21	0.99	G8 IIIa Ba 0.5	22	0.2	150	0.052	181	+17 SB	
α Cep	21 18.9	+62 38	2.45	0.26	A7 Van	67	1.4	49	0.159	71	−10 V	Alderamin
ε Cep	21 28.8	+70 37	3.23v	−0.20	B1 III	5	−4.0:	820	0.016	38	−8 SB	var.: 3.16–3.27, 0.19 d; B: 7.8;13.1″ (2007) Alfirk
β Aqr	21 32.2	−5 31	2.90	0.83	G0 Ib	5	−3.5	612	0.020	105	7	Sadalsuud
ε Peg	21 44.8	+9 56	2.38v	1.52	K2 Ib	5	−5.2	700	0.030	81	+5 V	irregular var.: 0.7–3.5 (flare in 1972) Enif
δ Cap	21 47.7	−16 04	2.85v	0.18	A3mF2 IV:	85	2.2	39	0.394	138	−6 SB	occ. bin.: 2.81–3.05, 1.0 d, 3.2 + 5.2
γ Gru	21 54.6	−37 19	3.00	−0.08	B8 IV–Vs	16	−1.1	200	0.104	99	−2 V?	
α Aqr	22 06.4	−0 16	2.95	0.97	G2 Ib	4	−4.3	800	0.016	104	+8 V?	Sadalmelik
α Gru	22 09.0	−46 54	1.73	−0.07	B7 Vn	32	−0.9	101	0.198	139	12	Alnair
θ Peg	22 10.8	+6 15	3.52	0.09	A2mA1 IV–V	34	1.0	97	0.277	83	−6 SB2	Baham
ζ Cep	22 11.3	+58 16	3.39	1.56	K1.5 Ib	4	−4.2	700	0.015	58	−18 SB	
α Tuc	22 19.3	−60 12	2.87	1.39	K3 III	16	−2.2	200	0.071	237	+42 SB	
δ Cep A	22 29.6	+58 28	4.07v	0.78	F5–G2 Ib	3	−4.4	1000	0.012	67	−16 SB	prototype Cepheid var.: 3.48–4.37, 5.4 d
ζ Peg	22 42.0	+10 54	3.41	−0.09	B8.5 III	16	−0.7	210	0.080	96	+7 V?	Homam
β Gru	22 43.3	−46 49	2.07v	1.61	M5 III	19	−1.4	170	0.138	92	2	irregular var.: 2.0–2.3
η Peg	22 43.5	+30 17	2.93	0.85	G8 II + F0 V	15	−1.2	210	0.025	148	+4 SB	Matar
ε Gru	22 49.2	−51 15	3.49	0.08	A2 Va	25	0.4	130	0.126	120	0 V	
ι Cep	22 50.1	+66 16	3.50	1.05	K0 III	28	0.6	115	0.137	209	−12	
μ Peg	22 50.6	+24 40	3.51	0.93	G8 III	28	0.8	120	0.152	104	14	Sadalbari
δ Aqr	22 55.3	−15 46	3.27	0.07	A3 IV–V (wk λ4481)	20	−0.1	160	0.047	242	+18 V	Skat
α PsA	22 58.3	−29 34	1.17	0.14	A3 Va	130	1.6	25	0.373	116	7	Fomalhaut
β Peg	23 04.3	+28 09	2.44v	1.66	M2 II–III	16	−1.7	200	0.236	53	+9 V	irregular var.: 2.31–2.74 Scheat
α Peg	23 05.3	+15 16	2.49	0.00	A0 III–IV	23	−0.9	140	0.073	121	−4 SB	Markab
γ Cep	23 39.8	+77 42	3.21	1.03	K1 III–IV	72	2.1	45	0.168	337	−42	Alrai

TABLE OF BRIGHTEST STARS BY MAGNITUDE

The following table contains the Sun and the 50 stars with an apparent magnitude brighter than 2.0 that appear in the previous table. A subset of data from that table is included, although the spectral classifications have been simplified due to space constraints. As in the previous table, the components of visual binary stars are listed separately. Where more than one star has the same apparent magnitude, they have been sorted by right ascension.

Rank	Star Name	RA (2011.5) h m	Dec ° '	m_V	$B-V$	MK Type	M_V	D ly	
	Sun	—	—	−26.75	0.63	G2 V	4.8	8 lm	Sun
1	α CMa A	6 45.7	−16 44	−1.44	0.01	A0 V	1.5	9	Sirius
2	α Car	6 24.2	−52 42	−0.62	0.16	A9 Ib	−5.4	310	Canopus
3	α Boo	14 16.2	+19 07	−0.05	1.24	K1.5 III	−0.6	37	Arcturus
4	α Cen A	14 40.4	−60 53	−0.01	0.71	G2 V	4.2	4	Rigil Kentaurus A
5	α Lyr	18 37.3	+38 48	0.03	0.00	A0 V	0.6	25	Vega
6	α Aur Aa+Ab	5 17.5	+46 01	0.08	0.80	G6+G2:III	−0.8	42	Capella
7	β Ori A	5 15.1	−8 11	0.18	−0.03	B8 Ia	−6.6	800	Rigel
8	α CMi A	7 39.9	+5 12	0.40	0.43	F5 IV–V	2.8	11	Procyon
9	α Eri	1 38.1	−57 11	0.45	−0.16	B3 V	−2.9	144	Achernar
9	α Ori	5 55.8	+7 24	0.45v	1.50	M2 Iab	−5.0:	520	Betelgeuse
11	β Cen AB	14 04.6	−60 26	0.58v	−0.23	B1 III	−5.5	500	Hadar
12	α Aql	19 51.3	+8 54	0.76	0.22	A7 V	2.1	17	Altair
13	α Tau A	4 36.6	+16 32	0.87v	1.54	K5 III	−0.8	65	Aldebaran
14	α Vir	13 25.8	−11 13	0.98v	−0.24	B1 V	−3.6	260	Spica
15	α Sco A	16 30.1	−26 27	1.06v	1.86	M1.5 Iab	−5.8	600	Antares
16	β Gem	7 46.0	+28 00	1.16	0.99	K0 IIIb	1.1	34	Pollux
17	α PsA	22 58.3	−29 34	1.17	0.14	A3 V	1.6	25	Fomalhaut
18	α Cru A	12 27.2	−63 10	1.25	−0.20	B0.5 IV	−4.0	320	Acrux A
18	β Cru	12 48.4	−59 45	1.25v	−0.24	B0.5 III	−4.0	350	Becrux
18	α Cyg	20 41.8	+45 19	1.25	0.09	A2 Ia	−7.5:	1500	Deneb
21	α Cen B	14 40.4	−60 53	1.35	0.90	K1 V	6.2	4	Rigil Kentaurus B
22	α Leo A	10 09.0	+11 55	1.36	−0.09	B7 V	−0.6	78	Regulus
23	ε CMa A	6 59.1	−28 59	1.50	−0.21	B2 II	−4.1	400	Adhara
24	γ Cru	12 31.8	−57 11	1.59v	1.60	M3.5 III	−0.7	88	Gacrux
25	λ Sco	17 34.4	−37 07	1.62v	−0.23	B1.5 IV	−3.6:	360	Shaula
26	γ Ori	5 25.7	+6 22	1.64	−0.22	B2 III	−2.8	240	Bellatrix
26	α Cru B	12 27.2	−63 10	1.64	−0.18	B1 V	−3.6	320	Acrux B
28	β Tau	5 27.0	+28 37	1.65	−0.13	B7 III	−1.3	130	El Nath
29	β Car	9 13.3	−69 46	1.67	0.07	A1 III	−1.1	111	Miaplacidus
30	ε Ori	5 36.8	−1 12	1.69	−0.18	B0 Ia	−6.6	1000	Alnilam
31	α Gru	22 09.0	−46 54	1.73	−0.07	B7 V	−0.9	101	Alnair
32	ζ Ori A	5 41.3	−1 56	1.74	−0.20	O9.5 Ib	−5.5	800	Alnitak
33	γ² Vel	8 09.9	−47 22	1.75v	−0.14	WC8+O9	−5.8	800	
34	ε UMa	12 54.5	+55 54	1.76v	−0.02	A0 IV	−0.2	81	Alioth
35	α Per	3 25.2	+49 54	1.79	0.48	F5 Ib	−4.9	600	Mirfak
35	ε Sgr	18 24.9	−34 23	1.79	−0.03	A0 II	−1.4	140	Kaus Australis
37	α UMa AB	11 04.4	+61 41	1.81	1.06	K0 IIIa	−1.3	124	Dubhe
38	δ CMa	7 08.9	−26 25	1.83	0.67	F8 Ia	−7.2	2000	Wezen
39	η UMa	13 48.0	+49 15	1.85	−0.10	B3 V	−1.8	101	Alkaid
40	ε Car	8 22.7	−59 33	1.86v	1.20	K3:III+B2:V	−4.8	600	Avior
40	θ Sco	17 38.1	−43 00	1.86	0.41	F1 III	−3.0	270	Sargas
42	β Aur	6 00.4	+44 57	1.90v	0.08	A1 IV	−0.2	82	Menkalinan
43	α TrA	16 49.9	−69 03	1.91	1.45	K2 IIb–IIIa	−5.0	400	Atria
44	γ Gem	6 38.4	+16 23	1.93	0.00	A1 IV	−0.6	100	Alhena
44	α Gem A	7 35.3	+31 52	1.93	0.03	A1 V	0.6	52	Castor A
44	δ Vel AB	8 45.0	−54 45	1.93	0.04	A1 V	0.0	80	
47	α Pav	20 26.6	−56 42	1.94	−0.12	B2.5 V	−2.1	180	Peacock
48	α UMi A	2 45.6	+89 19	1.97v	0.64	F5–8 Ib	−4.1	400	Polaris
49	β CMa	6 23.2	−17 58	1.98v	−0.24	B1 II–III	−4.0	500	Mirzam
50	α Hya	9 28.2	−8 43	1.99	1.44	K3 II–III	−2.1	180	Alphard

THE NEAREST STARS
By Todd J. Henry

The nearest stars hold a special fascination for any of us who have gazed skyward. Astronomers study the Sun's neighbours because they are the nearest, and therefore brightest, examples of their types. For many kinds of stars, the fundamental framework of stellar astronomy is built upon direct measurements of luminosities, colours, temperatures, and masses of nearby stars. Their surrounding environments are remote destinations to explore from Earth, and any planets orbiting them could someday become outposts of humankind because the nearest stars are the first step beyond our own solar system.

The definition of a "nearby" star system is that its distance is accurately known to be within a designated horizon. Distances may be measured geometrically, via astrometry using the technique of trigonometric parallax, or estimated using myriad combinations of photometric and spectroscopic data. Here we adopt distances based on trigonometric parallaxes only, as they are the most reliable and are independent of assumptions about the type of star under scrutiny. With modern techniques, we now know the distances to a few of the nearest stars to better than 0.1 percent accuracy.

The list presented here includes the Sun's nearest stellar neighbours and their companions within the astronomically convenient horizon of 5.0 parsecs, or 16.3 light-years (ly). The definition of a parsec is based upon the size of the Earth's orbit: as the Earth swings around the Sun, nearby stars shift back and forth relative to more distant, background objects because of our changing perspective, much as a thumb held at arm's length will seem to shift relative to a distant background when you close one eye, then the other. This shift is called parallax. The size of the shift depends entirely upon the star's distance, and astronomers have defined the distance at which a star's parallax is 1.00 arcsecond to be 1.00 parsec. As the distance increases, the shift decreases linearly. Thus, a star at 5.00 parsecs will exhibit a trigonometric parallax of 0.200 arcseconds, or 200 milliarcseconds (mas). The shifts are slight—even Proxima Centauri's full parallactic shift of 769 mas is only about 1/2300th the width of the full Moon.

To be included in the list, a stellar system must have a trigonometric parallax of at least 200 mas with an error of less than 10 mas published in the refereed literature, meaning that the distance is known to 5 percent or better. There are, effectively, four broad categories of nearby star parallaxes: (1) A wonderful compendium of ground-based parallax efforts through 1995 is *The General Catalogue of Trigonometric Stellar Parallaxes* (a.k.a. the *Yale Parallax Catalog*, or *YPC*) by van Altena et al. The *YPC* includes nearly 16000 parallax measurements of more than 8000 stars. Stars as bright as Sirius and as faint as 20th magnitude can be found in the *YPC*, with most parallaxes accurate to 3–13 mas. (2) ESA's *HIPPARCOS* space astrometry mission targeted nearly 120000 relatively bright stars at a precision of typically 0.5–4 mas, with a compendium of results published in 1997. In 2007, van Leeuwen published a new reduction of the *HIPPARCOS* data, and those results have been used to generate the parallaxes given here. (3) Since then, several teams have continued using traditional telescopes on the ground to measure parallaxes for both new and known stars within five parsecs, primarily by Gatewood's group at the Allegheny Observatory and the RECONS group at the Cerro Tololo Inter-american Observatory. (4) In space, the *Hubble Space Telescope* has been used to determine parallaxes of several of the Sun's neighbours, while measuring stellar masses or searching for exoplanets (primarily by Benedict's group). This year's version of the list again uses a comprehensive combination of trigonometric parallaxes from various sources to arrive at a weighted mean parallax for each system, which simply means that higher-quality parallaxes are mathematically given more weight in the averaging process.

Individual component parallaxes have been combined for all systems except for the nearest one, which is, in fact, a triple including Proxima and the two components of α Centauri. The *YPC* includes 43 of the 49 extrasolar systems, while *HIPPARCOS* improved upon many of those, but added no new systems. RECONS added five of the six remaining systems, and Tinney added the other, LP 944-20. In total, 105 different parallaxes have been used to generate the distances given. The RECONS group (**www.recons.org**) is keeping a tally of all trigonometric parallax efforts since the *YPC* and *HIPPARCOS*, and the reader is encouraged to contact the author about any overlooked publications.

Including the Sun, there are 50 known stellar systems in the 5-parsec sphere, made up of 67 stars, 4 brown dwarfs, and 7 extrasolar planets (plus, of course, the 8 planets in our solar system). Curiously, there are one-third more systems in the southern sky (28) than in the north (21), even though historically far more astronomical observations have been made in the northern sky. Sixteen of the systems include stellar or brown-dwarf companions, while an additional five (including our solar system) have planets. The smallest type of star, known as red dwarfs of spectral type M, dominate our galaxy, accounting for 73 percent of the 5-parsec sample (49 of 67 stars—all stars without types in the list are type M, but individual spectral types are not available because of close separations in multiple systems, hence the "J" for joint in some spectral types). None of these red dwarfs is visible with the unaided eye. In some ways, our galaxy mimics a meadow full of creatures large and small, but it is the small insects that dominate the population. Missing are the largest beasts, the most massive stars of spectral types O and B. Such stars are exceedingly rare and have lifetimes of only a few million years. The visually brightest star in the night sky is Sirius, which is the brighter star in the fifth-nearest system, and the only A-type star listed. Near Sirius in the sky is Procyon (the 14th-nearest system), nearly as bright and the only F-type star listed. Both Sirius and Procyon have white-dwarf companions that are the leftover embers of more-massive counterparts. These stars have already reinvented themselves, having changed from stars larger than Sirius and Procyon to reveal only their cores as white dwarfs by sloughing off their outer layers long ago. In the past, the light of Sirius and Procyon would be lost in the glares of their much larger, and brighter, components. In all, there are five white dwarfs, denoted by "D" in the list, nearer than five parsecs. The two stars most similar to our Sun are the only other two G dwarfs, α Centauri A and τ Ceti. Finally, eight stars are of K type, including α Centauri B, 61 Cygni A and B, and the naked-eye stars ε Indi, o Eridani A, and ε Eridani. The latter star is particularly interesting because it is circled by a band of cold dust and at least one planet, with some reports of two additional planets inferred because of gaps in the dusty disk. Other systems with planets include CD –46 11540 and CD –49 13515, each with one detected planet, the Ross 780 (GJ 876) system, for which a fourth planet was reported in 2010. Also worthy of note is Kapteyn's Star, which is a rare subdwarf—an ancient, subluminous star of spectral luminosity class VI—that is moving quickly through the solar neighbourhood. It has the largest radial velocity of the systems in the list, and has the second-fastest proper motion, only surpassed by Barnard's Star, the second-nearest system.

We continue to find more of the Sun's neighbours, even so close to home. Recent and ongoing sky surveys provide a wealth of solar neighbourhood candidates for those who cleverly dig through the databases for gems. DENIS (DEep Near-Infrared Survey, in the southern hemisphere) has provided two recent additions, the red dwarf DENIS 1048-3956 and the brown dwarf DENIS 0255–4700. To the author's knowledge, the latter object is the faintest object outside the solar system for which an absolute visual magnitude has been measured, with $M_V = 24.44$. Following in the footsteps of Giclas and Luyten, who both did breakthrough work in studies of nearby stars via proper-

motion searches, the SCR (SuperCOSMOS-RECONS) effort trawls an electronic database generated by scanning glass plates of the entire sky. The 23rd-nearest system, an M/T dwarf pair known as SCR 1845-6357, was found during an early SCR search, and efforts are continuing.

This year's list is similar to the 2010 version in layout. Names are given in the first column with new emphasis on discovery names or variable-star names, the latter if for no other reason than it gives some idea as to the system's location in the sky. Component designations within a single system are listed as A, B, or C, and are enclosed by parentheses if there are different names for individual members. Known planets are listed as "+nP" in the companion column, where n is the number of planets. Astrometric information is given next, including **RA** and **Dec** for equinox J2000.0, the weighted mean parallax (π) in mas, the derived distance (**D**) in light-years, and the proper motion (μ) in mas/y with the position angle of the motion (θ) (north is 0°, east is 90°). Spectroscopic information is then listed, including the systemic radial velocity (V_{rad}) and spectral type (**Sp.**) for each component, when known. Photometric information is provided in the form of the visual magnitude (m_v), while the derived absolute magnitude (M_v) closes out the data. An absolute magnitude is a valuable measurement of an object's intrinsic brightness, and reflects how bright an object would appear if it were at a standard distance of 10 parsecs.

Finally, there are two new candidates for the five parsec sample this year, but neither has yet been formally added to the list. UGPS 0722–05 is a brown dwarf of type T, reported to have a parallax of 246 mas with an error of 33 mas. At a distance of 4.07 parsecs, it may be close enough to be included in the list, but the very large error in the parallax precludes its inclusion until a more accurate measurement is available. DENIS 0817–6155 is another brown dwarf of type T, reported to have a parallax of 203 mas with an error of 13 mas. At a distance of 4.93 parsecs, it is very near the 5.00-parsec edge, so we will also wait for a more accurate parallax before adding it to the current list. With improved parallaxes, these two brown dwarfs may soon join the handful of systems added since the *YPC* and *HIPPARCOS* results.

The nearest entry after the completion of those compendia remains GJ 1061 at a distance of 3.68 parsecs, ranked as the 20th-nearest system. Since the turn of the century, four new systems—SCR 1845–6357 (23rd), SO 0253+1652 (24th), DENIS 1048–3956 (27th), and DENIS 0255–4700 (48th)—have been added to the census. All five of the new systems contain faint red or brown dwarfs with spectral types M5.0V to L7.5V, one of which has a T6.0V companion, SCR 1845–6357B. The other two T dwarfs in the sample were found as companions to ε Indi in 2003 and 2004.

In 1999, the first planet around Ross 780 was announced, and thus the first reliable exoplanet discovery within five parsecs made it into the *Observer's Handbook* in 2000. Research on individual nearby stars has recently been reinvigorated because the nearest stellar systems are prime targets for more sensitive exoplanet searches, and ultimately, life. The population of nearby stars remains a compelling area of research because we have yet to answer the fundamental questions, what types of stars form at what rates? and, how much mass in the galaxy can be found in stars? That so many faint, yet nearby, objects have slipped through previous surveys of our neighbourhood hints at more to come. Undoubtedly, the more complete our reconnaissance of the solar neighbourhood, the better we will understand the nature of stars that make up the galaxy, and our Sun's place among them.

TABLE OF NEAREST STARS

Name		RA (2000) h m	Dec ° '	π mas	err mas	D ly	μ mas/y	θ °	V_rad km/s	Sp.	m_V	M_V
Sun	+8P									G2V	−26.72	4.83
1 Proxima Cen	(C)	14 30	−62 41	768.85	0.29	4.24	3853	281.5	−16	M5.0V	11.05	15.48
α Cen	A	14 40	−60 50	747.23	1.17	4.36	3710	277.5	−26	G2V	0.01	4.38
	B	14 40	−60 50				3724	284.8	−18	K0.0V	1.34	5.71
2 Barnard's		17 58	+04 42	545.51	0.29	5.98	10358	355.6	−111	M3.5V	9.57	13.25
3 Wolf 359		10 56	+07 01	419.10	2.10	7.78	4696	234.6	+19	M5.5V	13.53	16.64
4 Lalande 21185		11 03	+35 58	393.25	0.57	8.29	4802	186.9	−85	M2.0V	7.47	10.44
5 Sirius	A	06 45	−16 43	380.02	1.28	8.58	1339	204.1	−9	A1V	−1.43	1.47
	B	06 45	−16 43							DA2	8.44	11.34
6 BL Cet	(A)	01 39	−17 57	373.70	2.70	8.73	3368	080.4	+29	M5.5V	12.61	15.47
UV Cet	(B)	01 39	−17 57						+32	M6.0V	13.06	15.92
7 Ross 154		18 50	−23 50	337.22	1.97	9.67	666	106.8	−10	M3.5V	10.44	13.08
8 Ross 248		23 42	+44 11	316.37	0.55	10.31	1617	177.0	−78	M5.5V	12.29	14.79
9 ε Eri	+1P	03 33	−09 27	311.22	0.09	10.48	977	271.1	+16	K2.0V	3.73	6.20
10 CD −36 15693		23 06	−35 51	305.08	0.70	10.69	6896	078.9	+9	M1.0V	7.34	9.76
11 Ross 128		11 48	+00 48	298.14	1.37	10.94	1361	153.6	−31	M4.0V	11.16	13.53
12 EZ Aqr	A	22 39	−15 18	289.50	4.40	11.27	3254	046.6	−50	M5.0VJ	13.03	15.34
	B	22 39	−15 18								13.27	15.58
	C	22 39	−15 18								15.07	17.38
13 61 Cyg	A	21 07	+38 45	286.08	0.48	11.40	5281	051.9	−66	K5.0V	5.20	7.48
	B	21 07	+38 45				5172	052.6	−64	K7.0V	6.03	8.31
14 Procyon	A	07 39	+05 13	285.17	0.64	11.44	1259	214.7	−4	F5 IV–V	0.37	2.65
	B	07 39	+05 13							DA	10.70	12.98
15 BD +59 1915	A	18 43	+59 38	283.83	1.46	11.49	2238	323.6	−1	M3.0V	8.90	11.17
	B	18 43	+59 38				2313	323.0	+1	M3.5V	9.69	11.96
16 GX And	(A)	00 18	+44 01	279.87	0.60	11.65	2918	081.9	+12	M1.5V	8.08	10.31
GQ And	(B)	00 18	+44 01						+11	M3.5V	11.06	13.29
17 ε Ind	A	22 03	−56 47	276.07	0.28	11.81	4704	122.7	−40	K3.0V	4.68	6.89
	B	22 04	−56 47				4823	121.1		T1.0V		
	C	22 04	−56 46							T6.0V		
18 DX Can		08 30	+26 47	275.80	3.00	11.83	1290	242.2	−5	M6.0V	14.90	17.10
19 τ Cet		01 44	−15 56	273.97	0.17	11.91	1922	296.4	−17	G8.5V	3.49	5.68
20 GJ 1061		03 36	−44 31	272.01	1.30	11.99	831	118.8	−20	M5.0V	13.09	15.26
21 YZ Cet		01 13	−17 00	269.08	2.99	12.12	1372	061.9	+28	M4.0V	12.10	14.25
22 Luyten's		07 27	+05 14	266.23	0.66	12.25	3738	171.2	+18	M3.5V	9.85	11.98
23 SCR 1845–6357	A	18 45	−63 58	259.50	1.11	12.57	2558	074.7		M8.5V	17.40	19.47
	B	18 45	−63 58							T6.0V		
24 SO 0253+1652		02 53	+16 53	259.41	0.89	12.57	5050	137.9		M6.5V	15.14	17.21
25 Kapteyn's		05 12	−45 01	255.67	0.91	12.76	8670	131.4	+245	M2.0VI	8.85	10.89
26 AX Mic		21 17	−38 52	253.44	0.80	12.87	3455	250.6	+28	K9.0V	6.67	8.69
27 DENIS 1048–3956		10 48	−39 56	248.53	1.18	13.12	1530	229.2		M8.5V	17.39	19.37
28 Kruger 60	A	22 28	+57 42	248.06	1.39	13.15	990	241.6	−34	M3.0V	9.79	11.76
	B	22 28	+57 41							M4.0V	11.41	13.38
29 Ross 614	A	06 29	−02 49	244.44	0.92	13.34	930	131.7	+17	M4.0V	11.18	13.12
	B	06 29	−02 49							M5.5V	14.26	16.20
30 Wolf 1061		16 30	−12 40	234.38	1.50	13.92	1189	184.5	−21	M3.5V	10.10	11.95
31 van Maanen's		00 49	+05 23	232.70	1.81	14.02	2978	155.5	+54	DZ7	12.40	14.23
32 CD −37 15492		00 05	−37 21	230.32	0.90	14.16	6100	112.5	+23	M1.5V	8.54	10.35
33 Wolf 424	A	12 33	+09 01	227.90	4.60	14.31	1811	277.4		M5.0VJ	13.25	15.04
	B	12 33	+09 01								13.24	15.03
34 TZ Ari		02 00	+13 03	224.80	2.90	14.51	2097	147.8	−29	M4.0V	12.31	14.07
35 G 208–44	(A)	19 54	+44 25	220.68	0.97	14.78	731	143.1		M5.5VJ	13.46	15.17
G 208–44	(C)	19 54	+44 25								16.75	18.46
G 208–45	(B)	19 54	+44 25							M6.0V	14.01	15.72

TABLE OF NEAREST STARS (continued)

Name		RA (2000) Dec h m ° '		π mas	err mas	D ly	μ mas/y	θ °	V_{rad} km/s	Sp.	m_V	M_V
36	BD +68 946		17 36 +68 20	220.47	0.83	14.79	1309	194.2	–29	M3.0V	9.17	10.89
37	LHS 292		10 48 –11 20	220.30	3.60	14.81	1644	158.5	–7	M6.5V	15.73	17.45
38	CD –46 11540	+1P	17 29 –46 54	220.11	1.39	14.82	1050	146.9	–10	M2.5V	9.37	11.08
39	L 145–141		11 46 –64 50	216.12	1.09	15.09	2688	97.4		DQ6	11.50	13.17
40	Ross 780	+4P	22 53 –14 16	214.47	0.57	15.21	1174	125.1	–2	M3.5V	10.18	11.84
41	G 158–27		00 07 –07 32	213.00	3.60	15.31	2041	203.6	–42	M5.0V	13.77	15.41
42	LHS 288		10 44 –61 13	209.70	2.65	15.55	1657	348.1		M5.5V	13.92	15.53
43	BD +44 2051	(A)	11 05 +43 32	205.67	0.93	15.86	4511	282.1	+69	M1.0V	8.77	10.34
	WX UMa	(B)	11 06 +43 31				4531	281.9		M5.5V	14.44	16.01
44	BD +50 1725		10 11 +49 27	205.53	0.49	15.87	1452	249.7	–26	K7.0V	6.59	8.15
45	BD +20 2465		10 20 +19 52	204.60	2.80	15.94	506	264.0	+12	M2.5V	9.32	10.87
46	CD –49 13515	+1P	21 34 –49 01	202.03	1.00	16.14	819	183.2	+4	M1.5V	8.66	10.19
47	LP 944–20		03 40 –35 26	201.40	4.21	16.19	439	47.6		M9.0V	18.69	20.21
48	DENIS 0255–4700		02 55 –47 01	201.37	3.89	16.20	1149	119.5		L7.5V	22.92	24.44
49	o Eri	A	04 15 –07 39	200.65	0.23	16.26	4088	213.2	–42	K1.0V	4.43	5.94
		B	04 15 –07 39				4073	212.4		DA4	9.52	11.03
		C	04 15 –07 39							M4.0V	11.24	12.75

Editor's Note: For more information, see A.H. Batten, "Our Changing Views of the Solar Neighbourhood," *JRASC, 92* (1998), pp. 231–237.

DOUBLE AND MULTIPLE STARS
By Brian D. Mason

Approximately 85 percent of stars are found in double or multiple systems. While the first detection of double systems dates back to the early 17th century, it was not until systematic work with large-aperture telescopes was done (notably by Sir William Herschel) that the physical rather than the optical nature of these systems was ascertained. The larger the aperture of the telescope, the closer the stars that can be separated under good conditions. The resolving power in arcseconds can be estimated as $120/D$, where D is the diameter of the telescope objective in millimetres. Astronomers using long-baseline optical interferometry have measured double-star separations less than a milliarcsecond ($0.001''$).

The double stars in the following table were selected to cover a wide variety of interests. While wide or slowly moving pairs are good for evaluating optical performance or estimating seeing, with the preponderance of inexpensive, large-aperture telescopes and the availability of interferometry for the amateur (see the *Journal of Double Star Observations* (hereafter JDSO) Vol. 4, 111, 2008, by R. Caloi), as well as access to larger magnitude-difference systems (see JDSO **3**, 159, 2007 by J. Daley), closer systems, some with larger magnitude differences, have been added to the list.

The list covers many decades of separation with small and large Δm. Of the 135 listed systems, 19 have separations less than $1''$ and 19 more between $1''$ and $2''$. At more moderate separations, there are 21 between $2''$ and $3''$, 20 between $3''$ and $5''$, 22 between $5''$ and $7''$, 25 between $7''$ and $10''$ and 9 with separations greater than $10''$. Of these more moderate separations, those with both small and large magnitude difference are well-represented. The pairs are well distributed in right ascension. A third of the objects are found south of the equator, giving adequate coverage of southern declinations.

Since many of the stars selected exhibit significant motion, the predicted position angles and separations are given for both 2011.0 and 2012.0. PA (Position Angle) is the angular direction of the fainter star (B) from the brighter (A), measured counterclockwise from north (*clockwise* in an optical system having an *odd* number of reflections). Note that data for 2011.0 have been changed for some systems due to improvements in orbit calculations or more recent measurements. For systems with no orbit determination, the most recently measured position is tabulated. Also included are notes on selected systems. If no 2012.0 data are provided, there is no calculation (orbit or linear) of the motion (if any) of this double. The 2011.0 data are the most recently published.

The JDSO (www.jdso.org) is a good source for free information on double and multiple stars.

Notes on some double and multiple stars in the table:

ζ **Phe:** The AB-C pair listed here is rather diffcult to observe due to the moderate magnitude difference at a relatively close separation. The AB pair ($\rho = 0.5''$, Δm = 2.8, P = 210 y) is also a challenge.

γ **Per:** A favourite of astronomers, the brightest eclipsing binary in the sky, Algol, has been known to be variable for hundreds of years. The second-brightest eclipsing binary, γ Per was not known until its first observed eclipse in 1990! This system, seen both spectroscopically and interferometrically, is also a visual double, and is near maximum separation. It is observable with a large telescope, and a significant colour difference should be noted for this pair consisting of a cool giant and a hot dwarf. The June 1991 *Sky & Telescope* article by Roger Griffin, while older, is an excellent astronomical adventure tale of the first observed eclipse.

β **Ori:** Rigel has a very-slow-moving companion. This, and the very slight proper motion, make it diffcult to determine physicality, but the spectral types are consistent.

α CMa: The companion to Sirius is a difficult target, usually observable only during periods of exceptional seeing, when you can use the highest magnification and move the primary off the field of view. The white-dwarf secondary, predicted by Bessel and first observed by Alvan Clark, remains a challenging target for visual observers. A new book about Sirius and its companion by Jay Holberg, *Sirius: Brightest Diamond in the Sky*, is excellent.

α CMi: Like Sirius, Procyon has a white-dwarf companion. It was first detected in 1840 by the variation in the proper motion of the star, but not resolved until 1896 by Shaeberle with the 36-in. refractor of Lick Observatory.

ξ UMa: Many "firsts" are associated with this system. It was one of the first discovered systems (Herschel), one of the first systems whose motion led to the discovery of the physical (rather than optical) nature of double stars (Struve), and the first to have an orbit calculated for it (Savary). Always relatively wide and with an obvious position-angle change of 6° per year, this is a system that will never fail to please, observing season to observing season.

α Cen: Our closest neighbour is a quick-moving double star. The brighter component is a near twin of the Sun, while the B component is cooler. The C component, Proxima, slightly closer to the Sun, is an extremely faint red dwarf, 2.2° away. According to R.G. Aitken, this was discovered by Father Richaud while observing a comet at Pondicherry, India, in December 1689.

ι¹ Nor: A small Δm and slow motion makes this a good seeing check for high-resolution techniques in the southern hemisphere. This pair was resolved first by T.J.J. See with the Lowell 24-in. during the telescope's brief sojurn near Mexico City.

μ Dra: This pair of near-equal-magnitude slow-moving components, is a good seeing test for a more modest-resolution detection system.

β Cyg: Also known as Albireo. If a neophyte doubts the colour of stars, this jewel of the summer sky should change that view. Appearing as brilliant yellow and a deep blue, this wide double has shown no apparent motion. The A component has two close companions, discovered by speckle interferometry; one at a separation of about 0.4″ and the other at 0.1″.

β Del: A well-observed close pair, this short-period binary has completed over five orbits since the first resolution by S.W. Burnham in 1873. Burnham resolved it with 6 different Clark refractors with diameters ranging between 6 and 40 in.

30 Peg: The large Δm requires a dark sky. There is an equally faint companion at 227° and 17.5″.

TABLE OF DOUBLE AND MULTIPLE STARS

Star	RA (2000) h	m	Dec °	′	Magnitudes comb.	A	B	2011.0 PA °	Sep. ″	2012.0 PA °	Sep. ″	Period a
34 Psc	0	10.0	+11	09	5.0	5.5	9.4	162	7.88			
ζ Phe*	1	08.4	−55	15	4.0	4.0	8.2	242	6.80			
φ Psc	1	13.7	+24	35	4.6	4.7	9.1	229	7.75			
κ Tuc	1	15.8	−68	53	4.9	5.0	7.7	319	4.98	318	4.98	857
γ Ari	1	53.5	+19	18	3.8	4.5	4.6	1	7.41			
α Psc	2	02.0	+02	46	3.8	4.1	5.2	264	1.77	263	1.77	933
γ And A-BC	2	03.9	+42	20	2.2	2.3	5.0	63	9.48			
γ And BC	2	03.9	+42	20	4.8	5.1	6.3	98	0.21	96	0.17	64
ι Tri	2	12.4	+30	18	5.0	5.3	6.7	67	3.83			
ι Cas AB	2	29.1	+67	24	4.5	4.6	6.9	229	2.61	229	2.61	620
ι Cas AC	2	29.1	+67	24	4.5	4.6	9.1	116	7.19			
α UMi	2	31.8	+89	16	2.1	2.1	9.1	232	18.19			
ν Cet	2	35.9	+05	36	5.0	5.0	9.1	79	7.50			
84 Cet	2	41.2	−00	42	5.8	5.8	9.7	306	3.30			
γ Cet	2	43.3	+03	14	3.4	3.5	6.2	298	2.32			
ε Ari	2	59.2	+21	20	4.6	5.2	5.6	210	1.39			
γ Per*	3	04.8	+53	30	2.7	2.9	4.4	245	0.23	244	0.25	15
α For	3	12.1	−28	59	3.9	4.0	7.2	300	5.26	300	5.28	269

*See the preceding note.

TABLE OF DOUBLE AND MULTIPLE STARS (continued)

Star	RA (2000) h m	Dec ° ′	Magnitudes comb.	A	B	2011.0 PA °	Sep. ″	2012.0 PA °	Sep. ″	Period a
94 Cet	3 12.8	−01 12	5.1	5.1	11.0	196	2.19	195	2.18	1420
HR 997	3 18.7	−18 34	5.8	5.9	8.2	122	7.95	122	7.96	
32 Eri	3 54.3	−02 57	4.5	4.8	5.9	353	7.20			
HR 1230	4 10.0	+80 42	5.2	5.6	6.3	147	0.69	148	0.69	372
14 Ori	5 07.9	+08 30	5.4	5.8	6.7	298	0.89	296	0.90	197
β Ori*	5 14.5	−08 12	0.3	0.3	6.8	204	9.25			
14 Aur	5 15.4	+32 41	5.0	5.0	9.0	9	10.06			
16 Aur	5 18.2	+33 22	4.8	4.8	10.6	56	4.41			
HR 1771	5 21.8	−24 46	5.1	5.4	6.6	99	3.50			
118 Tau	5 29.3	+25 09	5.4	5.8	6.7	208	4.44			
33 Ori AB	5 31.2	+03 18	5.4	5.7	6.7	29	1.89			
λ Ori	5 35.1	+09 56	3.3	3.5	5.5	50	4.90			
ζ Ori	5 40.7	−01 57	1.7	1.9	3.7	166	2.22	166	2.21	1509
52 Ori	5 48.0	+06 27	5.3	6.0	6.0	219	1.06			
β Mon AB	6 28.8	−07 02	4.0	4.6	5.0	127	6.60			
β Mon AC	6 28.8	−07 02	4.2	4.6	5.4	125	9.88			
β Mon BC	6 28.8	−07 02	4.4	5.0	5.4	100	2.90			
HR 2384	6 29.8	−50 14	5.3	6.0	6.2	260	0.56	259	0.54	53
α CMa*	6 45.1	−16 43	−1.5	−1.5	8.5	89	9.16	86	9.49	50
12 Lyn AB	6 46.2	+59 27	4.8	5.4	6.0	68	1.88	68	1.88	908
12 Lyn AC	6 46.2	+59 27	4.8	5.4	7.1	308	8.90			
38 Gem	6 54.6	+13 11	4.7	4.8	7.8	325	6.98	325	6.99	1944
HR 2674	7 03.3	−59 11	5.5	5.8	6.8	86	1.41			
δ Gem	7 20.1	+21 59	3.5	3.6	8.2	227	5.58	227	5.56	1200
α Gem	7 34.6	+31 53	1.6	1.9	3.0	57	4.72	56	4.80	445
HR 2949	7 38.8	−26 48	3.8	4.4	4.6	317	10.20			
α CMi*	7 39.3	+05 14	0.4	0.4	10.8	241	2.63	257	2.97	41
κ Gem	7 44.4	+24 24	3.7	3.7	8.2	241	7.03			
ζ Cnc AB	8 12.2	+17 39	4.9	5.3	6.3	34	1.07	31	1.09	60
ζ Cnc AB-C	8 12.2	+17 39	4.6	4.9	6.3	68	5.92	68	5.92	1115
HR 3432	8 37.3	−62 51	5.5	5.5	11.0	237	5.76			
ι Cnc	8 46.7	+28 46	4.0	4.1	6.0	309	30.62			
ε Hya	8 46.8	+06 25	3.4	3.5	6.7	306	2.89	306	2.89	990
ι UMa	8 59.2	+48 03	3.1	3.1	9.2	200	2.69	202	2.72	818
σ² UMa	9 10.4	+67 08	4.8	4.9	8.9	350	4.18	349	4.21	1141
38 Lyn	9 18.8	+36 48	3.8	3.9	6.1	225	2.62			
HR 3752	9 25.5	−61 57	5.8	5.8	9.6	330	8.77			
ψ Vel	9 30.7	−40 28	3.6	3.9	5.1	106	0.93	110	1.00	34
11 LMi	9 35.7	+35 49	4.8	4.8	12.5	51	6.24	50	6.29	201
γ Sex	9 52.5	−08 06	5.1	5.4	6.4	49	0.57	47	0.56	78
γ Leo	10 20.0	+19 50	2.1	2.4	3.6	126	4.62	126	4.62	510
μ Vel	10 46.8	−49 25	2.7	2.8	5.7	56	2.59	56	2.59	138
54 Leo	10 55.6	+24 45	4.3	4.5	6.3	112	6.45			
ξ UMa*	11 18.2	+31 32	3.8	4.3	4.8	204	1.61	197	1.63	60
ν UMa	11 18.5	+33 06	3.5	3.5	10.1	149	7.35			
57 UMa	11 29.1	+39 20	5.3	5.4	10.7	355	5.38			
α¹ Cru	12 26.6	−63 06	0.6	1.3	1.6	114	3.96			
24 Com	12 35.1	+18 23	4.8	5.1	6.3	271	19.85			
γ Vir	12 41.7	−01 27	2.8	3.5	3.5	19	1.59	14	1.78	169
β Mus	12 46.3	−68 06	3.0	3.5	4.0	54	0.95	55	0.93	194
θ Vir	13 09.9	−05 32	4.4	4.4	9.4	342	6.94			
α Com	13 10.0	+17 32	4.4	4.9	5.5	12	0.63	12	0.57	26
ζ UMa	13 23.9	+54 56	2.0	2.2	3.9	153	14.30			
84 Vir	13 43.1	+03 32	5.5	5.6	8.3	227	2.73			
τ Boo	13 47.3	+17 27	4.5	4.5	11.1	66	1.24	73	1.12	2000
HR 5386	14 23.4	+08 27	4.8	5.0	6.8	192	5.90			
φ Vir	14 28.2	−02 14	4.9	4.9	10.0	112	5.26			
α Cen*	14 39.6	−60 50	−0.2	0.1	1.2	251	6.09	257	5.44	80
π¹ Boo	14 40.7	+16 25	4.5	4.9	5.8	112	5.49			

* See the preceding note.

TABLE OF DOUBLE AND MULTIPLE STARS (continued)

Star	RA (2000) h m	Dec ° ′	Magnitudes comb. A B	2011.0 PA °	2011.0 Sep. ″	2012.0 PA °	2012.0 Sep. ″	Period a
ζ Boo	14 41.1	+13 44	3.8 4.5 4.6	293	0.50	292	0.47	123
ε Boo	14 45.0	+27 04	2.4 2.6 4.8	343	3.01			
ξ Boo	14 51.4	+19 06	4.6 4.8 7.0	307	5.96	306	5.88	152
44 Boo	15 03.8	+47 39	4.8 5.2 6.1	61	1.49	62	1.36	206
π Lup	15 05.1	−47 03	3.8 4.6 4.6	67	1.68			
η CrB	15 23.2	+30 17	5.0 5.6 6.0	177	0.63	185	0.66	42
δ Ser	15 34.8	+10 32	3.8 4.2 5.2	173	3.99	172	3.98	1038
ζ² CrB	15 39.4	+36 38	4.6 5.0 5.9	306	6.34			
ι¹ Nor*	16 03.5	−57 47	4.7 5.2 5.8	225	0.38	217	0.35	27
ξ Sco AB	16 04.4	−11 22	4.3 5.2 4.9	357	0.96	359	0.99	46
ξ Sco AC	16 04.4	−11 22	4.2 4.9 7.3	44	7.55	44	7.55	1514
11 Sco	16 07.6	−12 45	5.7 5.8 9.8	263	2.79			
κ Her	16 08.1	+17 03	4.8 5.1 6.2	13	27.17	13	27.15	
ν Sco	16 12.0	−19 28	4.0 4.4 5.3	1	1.34			
σ CrB	16 14.7	+33 52	5.2 5.6 6.5	238	7.13	238	7.14	726
ρ Oph	16 25.6	−23 27	4.6 5.1 5.7	338	2.90	338	2.89	
α Sco	16 29.4	−26 26	0.9 1.0 5.4	277	2.63	277	2.62	1218
λ Oph	16 30.9	+01 59	3.8 4.2 5.2	38	1.45	39	1.44	
HR 6246	16 49.6	+13 16	5.7 5.7 10.0	45	5.34			
μ Dra*	17 05.3	+54 28	4.9 5.7 5.7	5	2.38	4	2.39	672
η Oph	17 10.4	−15 44	2.4 3.1 3.3	234	0.58	234	0.58	88
α Her	17 14.6	+14 23	3.3 3.5 5.4	103	4.64	103	4.64	3600
36 Oph	17 15.3	−26 36	3.9 4.3 5.1	142	4.97	142	4.99	471
41 Ara	17 19.1	−46 38	5.6 5.6 8.9	256	9.96	257	10.02	693
95 Her	18 01.5	+21 36	4.3 4.9 5.2	256	6.32			
τ Oph	18 03.1	−08 11	4.8 5.3 5.9	285	1.61	286	1.59	257
70 Oph	18 05.5	+02 30	4.1 4.2 6.2	130	5.82	129	5.95	88
HR 6749-50	18 06.8	−43 25	4.9 5.7 5.7	2	1.72	1	1.72	450
59 Ser	18 27.2	+00 12	5.3 5.4 7.6	320	3.77			
HR 6997	18 36.6	+33 28	5.4 5.4 9.4	204	7.41			
ε¹ Lyr	18 44.3	+39 40	4.8 5.2 6.1	347	2.35	347	2.34	1725
ε² Lyr	18 44.3	+39 40	4.6 5.3 5.4	78	2.37	77	2.37	724
β Cyg*	19 30.7	+27 58	2.9 3.2 4.7	55	34.60			
16 Cyg	19 41.8	+50 32	5.3 6.0 6.2	133	39.70	133	39.71	18212
δ Cyg	19 45.0	+45 08	2.8 2.9 6.3	219	2.69	219	2.70	780
ε Dra	19 48.2	+70 16	3.9 4.0 6.9	19	3.16			
π Aql	19 48.7	+11 49	5.8 6.3 6.8	105	1.40			
ζ Sge	19 49.0	+19 09	5.0 5.0 9.0	311	8.19			
ψ Cyg	19 55.6	+52 26	4.9 5.0 7.5	178	2.96			
16 Vul	20 02.0	+24 56	5.2 5.8 6.2	125	0.79			
κ Cep	20 08.9	+77 43	4.4 4.4 8.3	120	7.12			
β Cap	20 21.0	−14 47	3.1 3.2 6.1	267	206.00			
β Del*	20 37.5	+14 36	3.7 4.1 5.0	35	0.29	53	0.22	27
52 Cyg	20 45.6	+30 43	4.2 4.2 8.7	70	6.02			
γ Del	20 46.7	+16 07	3.9 4.4 5.0	265	9.05	265	9.03	3249
HR 8040	20 58.5	+50 28	5.5 5.9 6.8	26	1.93			
ε Equ	20 59.1	+04 18	5.4 6.0 6.3	284	0.46	283	0.41	101
12 Aqr	21 04.1	−05 49	5.6 5.8 7.5	196	2.45			
τ Cyg	21 14.8	+38 03	3.7 3.8 6.6	227	0.79	221	0.82	50
μ Cyg	21 44.1	+28 45	4.5 4.8 6.2	317	1.64	318	1.62	789
λ Oct	21 50.9	−82 43	5.4 5.6 7.3	63	3.50			
ξ Cep	22 03.8	+64 38	4.3 4.5 6.4	274	8.35	274	8.36	3800
30 Peg*	22 20.5	+05 47	5.4 5.4 11.5	15	5.97			
ζ² Aqr	22 28.8	−00 01	3.7 4.3 4.5	170	2.16	169	2.18	487
δ Cep	22 29.2	+58 25	4.0 4.2 6.1	187	40.80			
o Cep	23 18.6	+68 07	4.8 5.0 7.3	222	3.34	222	3.35	1505
72 Peg	23 34.0	+31 20	5.1 5.7 6.1	105	0.53	106	0.53	246
σ Cas	23 59.0	+55 45	4.9 5.0 7.2	327	3.16			

* See the preceding note.

COLOURED DOUBLE STARS
BY MICHEL DUVAL

In the third edition of this section, 59 new coloured double stars have been added to those from the second edition. About half of the stars in the section have actually been observed so far with a small Maksutov telescope of 125-mm diameter at 60× magnification. The same subjective appreciations are also given in the table concerning their beauty (!!!: very beautiful, !!: beautiful, !: nice), and the difficulty to separate them visually in the telescope (T: tight, VT: very tight, F: faint). β Cyg, α CVn, and ε Boo are better known as Albireo, Cor Caroli ("Heart of Charles"), and Izar, respectively.

Coloured double stars with a small angular separation and/or a large difference in magnitudes between the two components will be more difficult to separate and their colours more difficult to perceive (when the magnitude difference is high, the brightest star may saturate the eye and decrease the perception of the faint one). Different observers may also perceive colours differently depending on their eye physiology and local seeing conditions.

The RA, Dec, and visual magnitudes of the A-B components of the double stars are indicated in the table, using the updated (2006) values of S. Haas when available and rounding up star separations to the corresponding unit. François Chevrefils of the Centre francophone de la SRAC in Montréal is thanked for verifying this information. The abbreviations used for colours in the table are: B: Blue, E: Emerald, G: Green, Gd: Gold, L: Lilac, O: Orange, R: Red, T: Topaz, W: White, Y: Yellow,

The table is still limited to coloured double stars that can be observed with small instruments (75- to 150-mm diameter) by beginning observers. The use of larger magnifications and/or larger instruments will, of course, allow the observation of tighter, fainter coloured double stars not included in this table. It is always a pleasure to admire these coloured gems of the sky, especially at the beginning of a night of observation and during public star parties to initiate newcomers to the beauties of the sky.

TABLE OF COLOURED DOUBLE STARS

Star	RA (2000) h	m	Dec ° '	Magnitudes A	B	Sep. "	Colour A	B	Notes Beau.	Diff.
WINTER										
λ Ari	1	58	+23 36	5.0	6.7	37	Y	B	!!	
γ And	2	04	+42 19	2.3	5.4	10	O	B	!!!	
66 Cet	2	13	−02 24	5.7	7.7	16	O	B		F
59 And	2	11	+39 02	6.0	6.7	17	Y	B	!!	
η Per	2	51	+55 53	3.8	8.5	28	O	B	!!	F
30 Tau	3	48	+11 09	5.0	10.0	9	Y	B		
32 Eri	3	54	−2 57	4.8	5.9	7	T	B	!!!	T
ε Per	3	58	+40 01	3.0	9.0	9	Y	G		VT
φ Tau	4	20	+27 21	5.1	7.5	49	Y	B		F
χ Tau	4	22	+25 38	5.4	8.5	19	Y	G		F
Σ627 Ori	5	00	+3 37	6.6	7.0	21	Y	G	!!	
ρ Ori	5	13	+2 52	4.6	8.5	7	O	B	!	
Σ680 Tau	5	19	+20 08	6.0	10.0	9	Y	B		F
σ Ori	5	39	−2 37	3.9	6.5	42	O	B	!!	
26 Aur	5	39	+30 30	6.0	8.0	12	Y	B	!	F
ε Mon	6	24	+4 36	4.5	6.5	13	Y	B	!	F
5 Lyn	6	27	+58 25	5.2	9.8	32	Y	B		
20 Gem	6	32	+17 47	6.3	6.9	20	Y	B	!	

TABLE OF COLOURED DOUBLE STARS (continued)

Star	RA (2000) h	m	Dec ° ′	Magnitudes A	B	Sep. ″	Colour A	B	Notes Beau.	Diff.
WINTER (continued)										
38 Gem	6	54	+13 11	5.0	7.8	7.7	Y	B	!!	T
h3945 CMa	7	17	−23 19	4.8	5.8	27	Y	B	!!!	
δ Gem	7	20	+21 59	3.5	8.5	6	Y	R	!!	T
κ Gem	7	44	+24 24	3.6	8.1	7	O	B		F,VT
Σ1149 CMi	7	49	+3 13	7.8	9.2	22	Y	B	!	F
Σ1183 Mon	8	06	−9 14	6.2	7.8	31	Y	G	!	F
ι Cnc	8	47	+28 46	4.0	6.6	31	Y	B	!!	
SPRING										
Σ1321 UMa	9	14	+52 41	8.0	8.0	18	Y	B		
Σ1327 Cnc	9	15	+27 55	8.0	9.0	7	Y	B		
Σ1360 Leo	9	30	+10 35	8.0	9.0	14	B	G		
6 Leo	9	32	+9 43	5.4	9.3	37	O	G		
γ Leo	10	20	+19 50	2.4	3.6	5	O	Y		VT
54 Leo	10	56	+24 45	4.3	6.3	6	Y	B		T
88 Leo	11	32	+14 22	6.4	9.1	15	Y	B		
2 CVn	12	16	+40 40	5.9	8.7	11	Gb	B		
17 Vir	12	22	+5 18	6.6	10	21	B	O		
δ Crv	12	30	−16 31	3.0	9.0	25	Y	R		
24 Com	12	35	+18 23	5.1	6.3	20	Gd	B	!!	
32 Cam	12	49	+83 25	5.0	6.0	21	Y	B		
35 Com	12	53	+21 15	5.2	9.8	28	Y	B		
α CVn	12	56	+38 19	2.9	5.6	19	B	G	!!!	
54 Vir	13	13	−18 50	6.8	7.2	5	Y	B		
π Boo	14	41	+16 25	4.9	5.8	6	B	O		
ε Boo	14	45	+27 04	2.6	4.8	3	O	B		VT
ξ Boo	14	51	+19 06	4.8	7.0	6	Y	O		VT
δ Ser	15	35	+10 32	4.2	5.2	4	B	O		
ζ CrB	15	39	+36 38	5.0	6.0	6	Y	B	!!!	
SUMMER										
β Sco	16	05	−19 48	2.6	4.9	14	B	O	!	
K Her	16	08	+17 03	5.0	6.0	28	Y	R		
α Her	17	15	+14 23	3.5	5.4	5	R	G		VT
o Oph	17	18	−24 17	5.4	6.9	10	O	Y		
ρ Her	17	23	+37 09	4.5	5.5	4	G	G		
ψ Dra	17	42	+72 09	4.9	6.1	30	Y	L		
95 Her	18	01	+21 36	5.0	5.1	6	G	B		
59 Ser	18	27	+0 12	5.4	7.7	4	Y	G		
Σ2348 Dra	18	34	+52 11	5.5	8.7	25	Y	B		
ζ Lyr	18	45	+37 36	4.3	5.9	44	Y	G		
o Dra	18	51	+59 23	4.8	7.8	34	G	L		
11 Aql	18	59	+13 37	5.3	9.3	19	Y	B	!!	
β Cyg	19	31	+27 58	3.1	5.1	35	Y	B	!!!	
57 Aql	19	54	−08 14	6.0	6.0	36	Y	G		
17 Cyg	19	46	+33 44	5.0	9.0	26	R	B		
OΣ394 Cyg	20	00	+36 25	7.0	10.0	11	O	B		
26 Cyg	20	01	+50 06	5.0	9.0	41	Y	B		
σ Cap	20	19	−19 07	5.4	9.4	56	O	B		
52 Cyg	20	45	+30 43	4.0	9.0	6	Y	B		

TABLE OF COLOURED DOUBLE STARS (continued)

Star	RA (2000) h	m	Dec ° ′	Magnitudes A	B	Sep. ″	Colour A	B	Notes Beau.	Diff.
AUTUMN										
γ Del	20	47	+16 07	4.4	5.0	9	O	G		T
β Cep	21	29	+70 34	3.2	8.6	13	W	B	!	
41 Aqr	22	14	−21 04	5.6	6.7	5	Y	B		VT
δ Cep	22	29	+58 25	4.2	6.1	41	Y	B	!!	
57 Peg	23	10	+08 41	5.1	9.7	32	Y	B		F
Σ2991 Peg	23	13	+11 04	6.0	10.0	33	Y	B		
Ψ₁ Aqr	23	16	−9 05	4.5	10.0	49	Y	B		
94 Aqr	23	19	−13 27	5.3	7.0	12	Y	G	!!	
Σ3053 Cas	0	02	+66 06	5.9	7.3	15	O	B		
Σ24 And	0	18	+26 08	8.0	8.0	5	Y	B		
42 Psc	0	22	+13 29	6.4	10.3	29	T	E		
12 Cet	0	30	−3 57	6.0	10.8	12	Y	B		
55 Psc	0	39	+21 26	5.6	8.5	7	O	B	!!	F
η Cas	0	49	+57 49	3.5	7.2	13	W	G	VT	
Σ80 Cet	0	59	+0 47	8.0	9.0	28	Y	B		
SOUTHERN										
γ Cru	12	31	−57 07	2.0	7.0	127	O	B		
μ Cru	12	54	−57 11	4.0	5.0	35	W	Y		

CARBON STARS
BY RON OSTROMECKI

Carbon stars are variable, late-stage red giants with periodicities ranging from around 70 days to over 400 days. Carbon in the outer atmosphere of the star absorbs blue light, resulting in the red appearance. Magnitude estimation can be tricky because of a phenomenon called the Purkinje Effect, which can lead to overstating the brightness of the star. Dashes indicate unavailable data. The new MK spectral type should be prefixed with "C–".

Star	RA (2010) h m	Dec ° '	Δm_v	B–V	Tycho 2 Type	Star	RA (2010) h m	Dec ° '	Δm_v	B–V	Tycho 2 Type
WZ Cas	0 1.6	+60 24	9.4–11.4	3.12	—	UZ Pyx	8 47.0	–29 45	7–7.5	2.39	J4
SU And	0 5.0	+43 35	8–8.5	2.81	N5	X Cnc	8 55.8	+17 12	5.6–7.5	3.37	N4.5
Z Psc	0 16.5	+25 48	8.8–10.1	2.86	N5	T Cnc	8 57.0	+19 49	7.6–10.5	4.32	N5
ST Cas	0 18.0	+50 19	11.6–12.4	2.48	N5	RT UMa	9 19.0	51 22	8.6–9.6	3.69	—
VX And	0 20.5	+44 46	7.8–9.3	5.59	J4.5	Y Hya	9 51.4	–23 03	8.3–12	4.17	N4.5
R And	0 24.5	+38 38	5.8–14.9	2.08	—	SZ Car	10 0.2	–60 16	10–12.1	2.81	N4.5
NQ Cas	0 25.0	+54 21	10.6–11.5	1.83	J4.5	AB Ant	10 12.3	–35 23	6.8–6.9	2.47	N4.5
AQ And	0 28.0	+35 39	9.9–11.8	3.65	N5	U Hya	10 38.0	–13 25	7–9.4	2.80	N5
WW Cas	0 34.0	+57 47	9.1–11.7	2.10	—	VY UMa	10 45.6	67 23	5.9–7	2.59	N5
W Cas	0 55.3	+58 36	7.8–12.5	3.60	—	TZ Car	10 46.4	–65 40	10.2–11.9	2.43	J4.5
R Scl	1 27.3	–32 30	9.1–12.9	4.40	N5	V Hya	10 52.0	–21 17	10.9–16	5.55	—
V Ari	2 15.4	+12 17	9.8–10.8	2.15	H3.5	SY Car	11 16.0	–57 59	10.8–11.6	2.48	N5
R For	2 29.6	–26 04	7.5–13	2.21	—	S Cen	12 25.0	–49 30	9.2–10.7	2.04	R4
TYC5285Cœt	2 35.5	–9 25	8.1	1.23	—	SS Vir	12 25.6	0 44	6–9.6	4.20	N4.5
DY Per	2 35.9	+56 11	10.6–13.2	—	R4	Y CVn	12 45.5	+45 24	7–10	3.40	J4.5
V623 Cas	3 12.0	+57 56	9–9.8	2.30	J5	RU Vir	12 47.4	4 07	7.9–14.2	4.50	—
Y Per	3 28.7	+44 12	8.1113.3	2.52	—	RY Dra	12 56.8	+65 57	6.1–8	3.70	J4
V466 Per	3 42.0	+51 32	10.9–12.7	4.25	—	TT CVn	13 0.0	+47 36	10.4–11.1	1.99	H4
U Cam	3 42.4	+62 40	11–12.8	3.95	N5	V CrB	15 49.8	+39 33	6.9–12.6	3.12	—
AC Per	3 45.6	+44 49	11.8–12.4	3.09	N5	RR Her	16 4.5	+50 28	8.8–12.5	3.00	—
UV Cam	4 6.5	+61 49	7.5–8.1	2.26	J4	V Oph	16 27.2	–12 27	7.3–11.6	4.38	—
T Cae	4 47.6	–36 11	9–10.8	2.59	N5	SU Sco	16 41.1	–32 24	11.7–13.2	3.36	N5
ST Cam	4 51.9	+68 11	9.2–12	3.38	N5	TW Oph	17 30.2	–19 29	11.6–13.8	4.34	N5
TT Tau	4 51.9	+28 32	10.2–12.2	3.22	N5	SZ Sgr	17 45.4	–18 40	11–11.9	2.89	N5.5
V346 Aur	4 53.3	+38 31	11.5–12.5	3.56	—	SX Sco	17 48.2	–35 42	10.5–11.6	3.82	N5
R Lep	5 0.0	–14 48	5–11.7	4.93	—	T Dra	17 56.5	+58 13	7.2–13.5	2.70	—
EL Aur	5 4.0	+50 39	11.5–12.3	3.77	N5	FO Ser	18 19.8	–15 37	8.4–8.7	2.03	J4
W Ori	5 5.7	+1 11	8.2–12.4	3.81	N5	SS Sgr	18 30.9	–16 54	10.9–11.3	3.82	N5
TX Aur	5 9.4	+39 01	8.5–9.2	3.71	N4.5	T Lyr	18 32.6	+37 00	7.8–9.6	5.46	J4
SY Eri	5 10.3	–5 30	10.4–11.4	2.62	N5	HK Lyr	18 43.1	+36 58	7.8–9.6	3.50	N5
UV Aur	5 22.5	+32 31	7.4–10.6	2.10	—	RV Sct	18 44.8	–13 12	8.7–9	2.63	R4
S Aur	5 27.1	+34 10	8.2–13.3	1.81	N5	S Sct	18 50.8	–7 54	9.6–10.9	3.32	N5
RT Ori	5 33.6	+7 10	9.7–11.8	2.97	N5	UV Aql	18 58.9	+14 22	11.1–12.4	4.39	—
SZ Lep	5 36.0	–25 44	7.4–7.9	2.40	N3.5	V Aql	19 4.8	–5 41	6.6–8.4	4.00	N5
S Cam	5 41.8	+68 48	8.1–11.6	2.95	N6	V1942 Sgr	19 19.6	–15 54	6.7–7	2.73	N5
TU Tau	5 45.7	24 26	5.9–9.2	2.75	N4	UX Dra	19 21.4	+76 34	5.6–7.1	2.91	N5
Y Tau	5 46.1	20 42	6.5–9.2	3.44	N5	AW Cyg	19 29.2	+46 03	11–14.5	3.87	—
FU Aur	5 48.6	+30 38	11–12.2	2.77	N6	AQ Sgr	19 34.8	–16 22	9.1–11.4	3.26	N5
TU Gem	6 11.3	+26 01	9.4–12.5	3.36	N5	TT Cyg	19 41.2	+32 38	10.2–11.9	3.15	N5
GK Ori	6 18.2	+8 31	9.5–11	2.00	N5	AX Cyg	19 57.5	+44 17	7.8–8.8	4.40	N5
V Aur	6 24.6	+47 42	8.5–13	3.87	—	V1469 Aql	20 1.6	+9 33	8.5–8.6	2.04	—
BL Ori	6 25.9	+14 43	7.9–9.7	2.55	N5	SV Cyg	20 9.7	+47 52	11.7–13.2	3.15	—
RV Aur	6 35.2	+42 30	11.8–13.6	3.47	—	RY Cyg	20 10.7	+35 58	8.5–10.3	2.82	—
UU Aur	6 37.0	+38 27	7.8–10	3.10	N5	RS Cyg	20 13.7	+38 45	6.5–9.5	2.80	N5.5
VW Gem	6 42.6	+31 27	8.1–8.5	2.68	—	RT Cap	20 17.6	–21 17	8.9–11.7	4.42	—
GY Mon	6 53.5	–4 35	9.4–11.6	2.64	N5	WX Cyg	20 18.8	+37 29	8.8–13.2	2.59	J6
NP Pup	6 54.8	–42 23	6.2–6.5	2.50	N4.5	U Cyg	20 19.9	+47 55	5.9–12.1	2.81	—
RV Mon	6 58.7	+6 10	9.7–11.9	3.20	—	V778 Cyg	20 36.4	+60 08	11.6–13.5	—	J4
V614 Mon	7 1.4	–3 16	7–7.3	1.96	J3.5	V Cyg	20 41.6	+40 10	7.7–13.9	4.04	—
RY Mon	7 7.3	–7 34	7.5–9.2	4.38	—	S Cep	21 35.1	+78 37	7.4–12.9	4.45	—
W CMa	7 8.4	–11 56	6.3–7.9	2.66	N5	V460 Cyg	21 42.4	+35 33	5.6–7	2.75	N5
R CMi	7 9.0	+10 00	7.5–11.6	2.55	—	RV Cyg	21 43.6	+38 03	10.8–12.4	4.52	N5
BM Gem	7 21.5	+24 59	11.5–12.1	2.80	J5	BD Vul	20 37.6	26 30	9.3–12.7	3.74	—
RU Cam	7 22.7	+69 39	8.1–9.8	1.16	—	RX Peg	21 56.7	+22 54	9.7–11.6	3.18	J4.5
BE CMa	7 24.0	–22 59	11–12.3	2.46	J4.5	RZ Peg	22 6.2	+33 32	7.6–13.6	2.65	—
NQ Gem	7 32.3	+24 39	7.4–8	2.27	—	DG Cep	22 44.5	+61 46	11.5–12.5	3.17	—
W CMi	7 49.3	+5 22	8.7–9	3.23	—	TV Lac	22 56.6	+54 17	11.5–12.3	2.94	N5
RT Pup	8 5.7	–38 48	10.2–11.2	2.43	J4.5	VY And	23 2.3	+45 56	9.6–11.8	3.81	—
RU Pup	8 7.8	–22 56	10.3–12.2	3.61	N5	EW And	23 27.5	+49 34	10.8–11.8	3.33	—
RY Hya	8 20.5	+2 45	12.2–13	3.77	N5	ST And	23 39.0	+35 49	7.7–11.8	3.53	—
AC Pup	8 23.1	–15 56	8.9–10.1	3.04	N5	TX Psc	23 46.8	+3 32	4.8–5.2	2.78	N5
YY Pyx	8 28.6	–27 17	9–9.4	4.52	—						

VARIABLE STARS

BY ARNE A. HENDEN AND ELIZABETH O. WAAGEN

Variable stars reveal many stellar properties. Depending upon their type, variables can tell us their mass, radius, temperature, luminosity, internal and external structure, composition, and evolutionary history. In addition, the systematic observation of variable stars is an area in which amateur astronomers can make a valuable contribution to astronomy.

For beginning observers, charts of the fields of four different types of bright variable stars are shown below. On each chart the magnitudes (with decimal point omitted) of several suitable comparison stars are shown. A brightness estimate of the variable is made using two comparison stars, one brighter, one fainter than the variable. The magnitude, date, and time of each observation are recorded. When a number of observations have been made, a graph of magnitude versus date can be plotted. The shape of this "light curve" depends upon the type of variable. Further information about variable star observing is available from the American Association of Variable Star Observers (AAVSO), 49 Bay State Road, Cambridge MA 02138, USA (email: aavso@aavso.org; Web site: www.aavso.org).

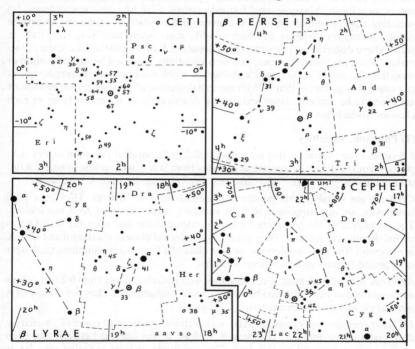

Table 1 is a list of long-period variables, brighter than magnitude 8.0 at maximum and north of –20°. The first column (the Harvard designation of the star) gives the position for the year 1900: the first four characters give the hours and minutes of right ascension, the next three the declination in degrees. The **Max.** column gives the mean maximum magnitude. The **Min.** column gives the mean minimum magnitude. The period (**Per.**) is in days. **Epoch** gives the predicted date of the earliest maximum

occurring this year; by adding multiples of the period to this epoch, the dates of subsequent maxima can be found. These variables may reach maximum two or three weeks before or after the epoch and may remain at maximum for several weeks. This table has been prepared with AAVSO observations.

Table 2 lists stars that are representative of some other types of variables. The data for the preparation of the predicted epoch of maximum for Cepheids are taken from the online edition of the *General Catalogue of Variable Stars*, at www.sai.msu.su/groups/cluster/gcvs/gcvs, the data for eclipsing binaries are from the online edition of *Rocznik Astronomiczny Obserwatorium Krakowskiego 2005*, at www.oa.uj.edu.pl/ktt/rocznik/rcznk.html, and the data for RR Lyr are based on private communication with N.N. Samus (2005) and maxima from the GEOS RR Lyr Database (2009) found at dbrr.ast.obs-mip.fr.

DESCRIPTION OF VARIABLE-STAR TYPES

Variable stars can be divided into two main classes: intrinsic variables, in which the variation is due to changes of a single star, and extrinsic variables, in which the variation is due to interaction of multiple stars or objects within a stellar system. There are many cases of overlapping variability types, such as a Mira pulsating variable as part of an eclipsing binary system. Intrinsic variables fall into three main classes: (1) pulsating stars, in which periodic expansion and contraction of the stellar surface occur; (2) eruptive variables, in which solarlike flares occur; and (3) rotating stars, in which shape distortion or star spots cause variation. Extrinsic variables consist of two main classes; (4) binary systems, in which variability is caused by orbital motion or mass transfer, and (5) cataclysmic variables, in which accretion onto a compact object can cause it to go into outburst. With modern detectors, about one percent of all stars are found to be variable. Brief and general descriptions of the major types in each class are given below.

(1) Pulsating Variables

δ *Scuti stars* are variables that have both radial and nonradial pulsation modes with periods from 0.01 to 0.2 days and amplitudes from barely measurable to nearly a full magnitude. They are of A-F spectral types. Typical representative: CY Aquarii.

Cepheids are variables that pulsate with periods of 1 to 70 days. They have high luminosity, and the amplitude of light variation ranges from 0.1 to 2 magnitudes. The prototypes of the group are located in open clusters and obey the well-known period–luminosity relation. They are of late F spectral class at maximum and G to K at minimum. The later (cooler) the spectral class of a Cepheid at minimum, the longer is its period. Typical representative: δ Cephei.

RR Lyrae stars are pulsating, giant variables with periods ranging from 0.2 to 1.2 days and amplitude of light variation between 0.5 and 2 magnitudes. They are usually of A spectral class. Typical representative: RR Lyrae.

RV Tauri stars are supergiant variables with a characteristic light curve of alternating deep and shallow minima. The periods, defined as the interval between two deep minima, range from 30 to 150 days. The amplitude of light variation may be as much as 3 magnitudes. Many show long-term cyclic variation of 500 to 9000 days. Generally, the spectral classes range from F-G at maximum to K-M at minimum light. Typical representative: R Scuti.

Long-period–Mira Ceti variables are giant variables that vary with visual amplitudes from 2.5 to 5 magnitudes or more. They have well-defined periodicity, ranging from

(text continues on p. 306)

TABLE 1—LONG-PERIOD VARIABLE STARS NORTH OF −20°

Variable		Max. m_v	Min. m_v	Per. d	Epoch 2011	Variable		Max. m_v	Min. m_v	Per. d	Epoch 2011
0017+55	T Cas	7.9	11.9	445	Aug. 20	1425+39	V Boo	7.0	11.3	258	Apr. 9
0018+38	R And	6.9	14.3	409	Nov. 20	1432+27	R Boo	7.2	12.3	223	May 28
0211+43A	W And	7.4	13.7	397	Sep. 16	1517+31	S CrB	7.3	12.9	361	Sep. 17
0214−03	o Cet	3.4	9.3	332	Sep. 13	1546+39	V CrB	7.5	11.0	358	Jan. 1
0228−13	U Cet	7.5	12.6	235	Jul. 9	1546+15	R Ser	6.9	13.4	357	Sep. 4
0231+33	R Tri	6.2	11.7	266	Feb. 5	1606+25	RU Her	8.0	13.7	484	Apr. 11
0430+65	T Cam	8.0	13.8	374	Aug. 24	1621+19	U Her	7.5	12.5	406	Sep. 7
0455−14	R Lep	6.8	9.6	432	May 6	1621−12	V Oph	7.5	10.2	298	Aug. 12
0509+53	R Aur	7.7	13.3	459	Oct. 28	1632+66	R Dra	7.6	12.4	245	Feb. 27
0549+20A	U Ori	6.3	12.0	372	Mar. 8	1647+15	S Her	7.6	12.6	307	Jun. 25
0617−02	V Mon	7.0	13.1	335	Mar. 14	1702−15	R Oph	7.6	13.3	302	Oct. 21
0653+55	R Lyn	7.9	13.8	379	Jul. 4	1717+23	RS Her	7.9	12.5	219	Apr. 16
0701+22A	R Gem	7.1	13.5	370	Jan. 1	1805+31	T Her	8.0	12.8	165	Mar. 11
0703+10	R CMi	8.0	11.0	338	Sep. 25	1811+36	W Lyr	7.9	12.2	196	Jun. 6
0727+08	S CMi	7.5	12.6	332	Oct. 10	1833+08	X Oph	6.8	8.8	334	Oct. 16
0811+12	R Cnc	6.8	11.2	362	Aug. 28	1901+08	R Aql	6.1	11.5	270	Mar 1
0816+17	V Cnc	7.9	12.8	272	Jun. 27	1910−17	T Sgr	8.0	12.6	392	Sep. 9
0848+03	S Hya	7.8	12.7	257	Aug. 29	1910−19	R Sgr	7.3	12.5	269	May 29
0850−08	T Hya	7.8	12.6	288	Sep. 10	1934+49	R Cyg	7.5	13.9	426	Apr. 19
0939+34	R LMi	7.1	12.6	372	Feb. 6	1940+48	RT Cyg	7.3	11.8	190	Feb. 16
0942+11	R Leo	5.8	10.0	313	May 22	1946+32	χ Cyg	5.2	13.4	407	Feb. 10
1037+69	R UMa	7.5	13.0	302	Sep. 26	2016+47	U Cyg	7.2	10.7	465	May 18
1214−18	R Crv	7.5	13.8	317	Sep. 10	2044−05	T Aqr	7.7	13.1	202	Apr. 15
1220+01	SS Vir	6.8	8.9	355	Jul. 4	2108+68	T Cep	6.0	10.3	390	Mar. 2
1231+60	T UMa	7.7	12.9	257	Feb. 16	2137+53	RU Cyg	8.0	9.4	234	Apr. 27
1233+07	R Vir	6.9	11.5	146	Mar. 5	2301+10	R Peg	7.8	13.2	378	Feb. 4
1239+61	S UMa	7.8	11.7	226	May 20	2307+59	V Cas	7.9	12.2	228	Jan. 19
1315+46	V CVn	6.8	8.8	192	May 26	2315+08	S Peg	8.0	13.0	319	Aug. 26
1327−06	S Vir	7.0	12.7	378	Feb. 9	2338−15	R Aqr	6.5	10.3	387	Jan. 29
1344+40	R CVn	7.7	11.9	328	Jul. 3	2353+50	R Cas	7.0	12.6	431	May 19
1425+84	R Cam	8.3	13.2	270	Feb. 6	2357−15	W Cet	7.6	14.4	351	Jun. 12

TABLE 2—OTHER TYPES OF VARIABLE STARS

Variable		Max. m_v	Min. m_v	Type	Sp. Cl.	Period d	Epoch 2011 UT
0053+81	U Cep	6.7	9.8	Ecl.	B8 + gG2	2.493 0937	Jan. 3.03*
0301+40	β Per	2.1	3.3	Ecl.	B8 + G	2.867 321	†
0355+12	λ Tau	3.5	4.0	Ecl.	B3	3.952 952	Jan. 1.06*
0530−05	T Ori	9.5	12.3	INA	B8–A3EpV		
0539+09	FU Ori	8.7	9.8	FU	F2peI–II		
0619+07	T Mon	5.6	6.6	Cep	F7–K1	27.024 649	Jan. 5.86
0658+20	ζ Gem	3.6	4.2	Cep	F7–G3	10.150 73	Jan. 9.12
0749+22	U Gem	8.6	15.5	UGSS	Pec(UG) + M4.5V		
1416+19	T Tau	9.6	10.8	INT	F8Ve–K1IV–Ve(T)		
1846+33	β Lyr	3.4	4.3	Ecl.	B8	12.940 922	Jan. 2.66*
1922+42	RR Lyr	6.9	8.0	RR Lyr	A2–F1	0.567 912#	Jan. 1.04
1946+35	CI Cyg	8.9	12.2	ZAND	Pec Bep + M5III		
1947+00	η Aql	3.5	4.3	Cep	F6–G4	7.176 641	Jan. 7.74
2138+43	SS Cyg	8.0	12.5	UGSS	K5V + (Pec)UG		
2225+57	δ Cep	3.5	4.4	Cep	F5–G2	5.366 341	Jan. 4.50

* Minimum
† Algol; predictions for all minima in 2011 are given in THE SKY MONTH BY MONTH section (p. 98).
# Changing period; revised for 2011.

80 to 1000 days. They show characteristic emission spectra of late spectral classes M, C, and S. Typical representative: o Ceti (Mira).

Semiregular variables are giants or supergiants showing appreciable periodicity accompanied by intervals of irregularities of light variation. The periods range from 30 to 1000 days with visual amplitudes not more than 1 to 2 magnitudes in general. Typical representative: R Ursae Minoris.

(2) Eruptive Variables

Eruptive variables are those with flares occurring in their chromospheres, along with shell mass ejections and other stellar-wind phenomena. The ejected matter can cause brightness drops as well.

FU Orionis variables are young stars with accompanying cometary nebulae. Usually they have large-amplitude fluctuations that may take years to complete. Typical representative: FU Orionis.

T Tauri variables are young stars that have not yet reached the Zero Age Main Sequence. They are characterized by irregular variations of several magnitudes, often accompanied by emission lines and Algol-like fadings, probably due to dust. Typical representative: T Tauri.

UV Ceti stars are late-type dwarfs that display flare activity. The flares can range from several tenths of a magnitude to many magnitudes in size, lasting a few minutes. Typical representative: UV Ceti.

R Coronae Borealis stars are highly luminous variables that have nonperiodic drops in brightness from 1 to 9 magnitudes due to the formation of "carbon soot" in the star's atmosphere. The duration of minima varies from a few months to years. Members of this group have F to K and R spectral class. Typical representative: R Coronae Borealis.

Irregular variables are stars that at times show only a trace of periodicity or none at all. Often, poorly studied stars are placed in this category. Typical representative: RX Leporis.

(3) Rotating Variables

Rotating variables are stars with nonuniform surface brightness, caused by star spots, mass outflow, or even shape distortion.

γ Cassiopeiae variables are rapidly rotating B stars with mass outflow, forming equatorial rings or disks that can cause temporary fading episodes. Typical representative: γ Cassiopeiae.

RS Canum Venaticorum variables are rapidly rotating stars, usually close binary systems that undergo small amplitude changes in light that may be due to dark or bright spots on their surface. Eclipses may also be present in such systems. Typical representative: RS Canum Venaticorum.

(4) Binary Systems

Binary systems are composed of two or more stars or planets around a star, in which the orbital plane is oriented such that one object crosses the disk of another object. These are usually divided into four main classes: detached, semi-detached, contact, and transitting. The first three relate to whether two stars overfill their Roche lobes or are completely isolated from one another.

Detached systems are those in which the two stars are completely isolated from one another. Light curves usually show constant light between eclipses; eclipse depth

can be quite large, depending on the relative brightness of the stellar pair. Typical representative: β Persei (Algol).

Semi-detached systems have one member (the donor) overflowing its Roche lobe, with mass accreting onto the second star. Typical representative: U Cephei.

Contact binaries have both members within a common envelope. These stars often exhibit ellipsoidal variations, with the light curves continuously varying throughout the orbit. Typical representative: β Lyrae.

Transitting systems are a new class of binary, in which a planet crosses the disk of the parent star. These variations are quite small (a few hundredths of a magnitude at best), but give a great deal of information about the host star and about the transitting planet. Typical representative: HD 209458.

(5) Cataclysmic Variables

This category contains both explosive and nova-like variables. These typically show outbursts caused by thermonuclear runaway on either the star surface or on an accretion disk. They are a product of accretion from one star of a binary system onto the other star, usually a compact object such as a white dwarf or neutron star.

Novae are close binary systems that consist of a normal star and a white dwarf and increase 7 to 16 magnitudes in brightness in one to several hundred days. After the outburst, the star fades slowly, returning to initial brightness in several years or decades. Near maximum brightness, the spectrum is generally similar to A or F giants. Typical representative: CP Puppis (Nova 1942).

Supernovae increase in brightness by 20 or more magnitudes due to a gigantic stellar explosion. The general appearance of the light curve is similar to novae. Typical representative: CM Tauri (supernova of AD 1054, and now the central star of the Crab Nebula).

U Geminorum types are dwarf novae that have long intervals of quiescence at minimum with sudden rises to maximum. Depending upon the star, the amplitude of eruptions ranges from 2 to 6 magnitudes, and the duration between outbursts tens to thousands of days. Most of these stars are spectroscopic binaries with periods of a few hours. Typical representative: SS Cygni.

Z Camelopardalis types are variables similar to U Gem stars in their physical and spectroscopic properties. They show cyclic variations interrupted by intervals of constant brightness ("stillstands") lasting for several cycles, approximately one-third of the way from maximum to minimum. Typical representative: Z Camelopardalis.

SU Ursae Majoris types are dwarf novae similar to U Gem and Z Cam stars in their physical and spectroscopic properties. They have frequent, faint, and narrow eruptions that last from one to a few days, along with infrequent, bright, and long eruptions—"superoutbursts" that last 10 to 20 days. During superoutbursts, there are small-amplitude, periodic variations—"superhumps," 2 percent to 3 percent longer than the orbital period of the system. Typical representative: SU Ursae Majoris.

TEN STAR STEPS TO VARIABLE-STAR OBSERVING

For the past two years, the "Star of the Year" has been ε Aurigae, the bright and puzzling star with a 27.1-year eclipse cycle that even after 175 years of observation and study is still a source of mystery to astronomers. What's the mystery? Simply this: what is causing the eclipse? Is it a second star buried in a huge doughnut-shaped disk of dust, or is it something completely different? A team from the AAVSO, Denver University, Adler Planetarium, Johns Hopkins University, and the California Academies of Science, and supported by the National Science Foundation, has created the Citizen Sky project to involve citizen (volunteer) observers worldwide in solving this mystery through making observations of ε Aurigae, analyzing them, developing

theories, helping other observers participate, and more, as part of a team or on their own. Citizen Sky is now a reality; learn about it (and sign up) by visiting the Web site www.CitizenSky.org. Whether you have never observed a star before, you are a very experienced variable-star observer, or are somewhere in between, you can participate in Citizen Sky—you are wanted and needed to help solve the mystery. In fact, you are needed badly because, at third magnitude, ε Aurigae is too bright for many professional astronomers' equipment and good visual observations will be extremely valuable. To observe, you don't need a telescope or even binoculars, and you don't need dark skies—all you need are your eyes and the interest. If you cannot observe, you can participate by analyzing the data collected by others. The eclipse started in August 2009, but, since it lasts for two years, you have plenty of time to become involved!

To teach observers who have never estimated the brightness of a star (or to refresh observers who haven't used their unaided eyes to make an estimate for a while), a **10 Star Training Tutorial** package has been developed as part of Citizen Sky. All the stars in it can be observed with the unaided eye, and by the time you have worked through the first nine, you are ready to observe the tenth one, ε Aurigae. This tutorial teaches you how to: use a star chart, use a variable-star chart, measure a star's brightness (make an estimate), and report your observations. It includes step-by-step instructions, lots of visual aids, star charts showing the ten stars in their constellations, a sky chart showing you where these constellations are, directions on submitting your observations to the AAVSO using the Internet or the paper form provided, and more. The tutorial may be downloaded as a PDF file from www.CitizenSky.org/content/10-star-training.

The stars in the tutorial, in order of observing, are: α Ori, η Gem, γ Cas, β Per, β Lyr, R Lyr, μ Cep, δ Cep, η Aql, and ε Aur. Each one is a little more challenging to observe than the ones before it. If you start now with α Ori, by next summer you will be ready for ε Aur, with the eclipse in full swing and lasting for another year before the star climbs back up to maximum. If you can't observe all of them, just do the best you can with the ones you can observe.

Five of these stars have been featured in this Handbook as Star of the Year: α Ori in 2003, β Per in 1995, μ Cep in 2004, δ Cep in 1994, and ε Aur in 2008 and 2009. In addition, these same five stars plus γ Cas and β Lyr have been featured as Variable Star of the Month or Variable Star of the Season on the AAVSO Web site.

η Gem (variable type SRA+EA) is a semiregular variable that is also an eclipsing binary. So, not only are there two stars orbiting each other, but one of them is a variable star in itself, expanding and contracting in a complicated pulsation pattern. η Gem varies in brightness between 3.15 and 3.90 V, and its pulsation period is 232.9 days. With a spectral classification of M3IIIab, η Gem is a red giant—an old star that was originally much like our Sun. It may become a nova, and then a white dwarf.

R Lyr (variable type SRB) is also a semi-regular variable. Another similarity to η Gem is its spectral classification—M5III—so it, too, is a red giant that was originally like our Sun and that may become a nova, then a white dwarf. It is different in that it is not a binary system (it has no companion star) and its variation in brightness is much larger, between 3.88 and 5.00 V. Also, its period of variation is not clearly defined, and can alternate between being very regular and completely irregular, but it averages around 46.0 days.

η Aql (variable type DCEP, brightness range 3.48-4.39 V) is very different from the other two. It is a classical Cepheid variable, so it expands and contracts with a regular period of 7.176641 days. Cepheids are very important stars—they are the stars that were first used to measure accurately the distance between galaxies. Its spectral classification is F6Ib-G4Ib, which means it is a yellow-white supergiant, a star much more massive than our Sun, and it may end its life as a supernova, and then a neutron star.

By the way, once you have mastered the ten stars and are contributing to science through your observations, you may want more variable stars to observe. Please visit our Web site and/or write to us at aavso@aavso.org for more information. We look forward to hearing from you!

STAR CLUSTERS
By Anthony Moffat and Peter Jedicke

The study of star clusters is crucial to the understanding of stellar structure and evolution. For most purposes, it can be assumed that the stars in a given cluster formed nearly simultaneously from the same parent cloud of gas and dust. Thus the basic factor that distinguishes one star in a cluster from another is the quantity of matter each contains. When comparing one cluster with another, it is essentially only the age and the chemical composition of their stars that differ. But what makes one cluster *appear* different from another in the sky is mainly the degree of concentration and regularity, the spread in magnitude and colour of the member stars, all of which vary mainly with age, and the total number of stars. Extremely young clusters are often irregular in shape, with clumps of newly formed stars pervaded by lanes of obscuring dust and bright nebulosity (e.g. the Orion Nebula around the Trapezium Cluster). The oldest clusters, which have not yet dissipated and have not been torn apart by external forces, tend to be symmetrical in shape, with only the slower-burning, low-mass stars remaining visible; the massive stars will have spent their nuclear fuel and passed to the degenerate graveyard of white dwarfs, neutron stars, or black holes, depending upon their original mass.

The star clusters in the following tables were selected as the most conspicuous. Two types can be recognized: *open* and *globular*. Open clusters often appear as irregular aggregates of tens to thousands of stars, sometimes barely distinguishable from random fluctuations of the general field. Ranging in age from very young to very old, open clusters are concentrated toward the disk of the Milky Way and generally contain stars of chemical abundance like the Sun.

Sometimes we observe loose, extended groups of very young stars. Using precise methods of photometry, spectroscopy, and kinematics, we see that these stars often have a common, but not necessarily strictly coeval, origin. Such loose concentrations of stars are called *associations*. Dynamically, they are generally unbound over time scales of the order of ten million years, being subject to the strong tidal forces of passing clouds and the background Milky Way Galaxy. Often, they contain subconcentrations of young open clusters (e.g. the double cluster h and χ Persei of slightly different ages despite their proximity, in the association Per OB1, which stretches over some 6° of the sky), with a strong gradient in age as the star formation process rips through them from one edge to another. In view of their sparse nature, we do not consider it appropriate here to list any of the 100-plus catalogued Milky Way associations.

Globular clusters, on the other hand, are highly symmetric, extremely old and rich agglomerations of up to several million stars, distributed throughout the galactic halo but concentrated toward the centre of the Milky Way Galaxy. Compared to the Sun and other disk stars, they tend to be much less abundant in elements heavier than hydrogen and helium. For the larger and brighter globular clusters, the observer's goal is to see them well enough to distinguish a generous sprinkling of individual stars against a diffuse glowing background. Large telescope apertures and good skies will help resolve globular clusters. Higher powers are helpful for identification of smaller, more distant globular clusters.

The following table lists all well-defined open clusters in the Milky Way Galaxy with diameters greater than 40′ and/or integrated magnitudes brighter than 5.0, as well as the richest clusters and some of special interest. The apparent integrated photographic magnitude (m_{pg}) is from Collinder, the angular diameter (**Diam.**) is generally from Trumpler, and the photographic magnitude of the fifth-brightest star (m_5) is from Shapley, except where in italics, which are new data. The distance (**Dist.**) is mainly from Becker and Fenkart (*Astr. Astrophys. Suppl. 4* (1971), p. 241). The earliest spectral type

of cluster stars (**Sp**) is a measure of the age as follows: expressed in millions of years, O5 = 2, B0 = 8, B5 = 70, A0 = 400, A5 = 1000, F0 = 3000, and F5 = 10 000. Complete source lists of open clusters can be found at **obswww.unige.ch/webda**.

OPEN CLUSTERS

NGC/ other†	RA (2000) Dec h m	° '	Mag. m_{pg}	Diam. '	m_5	Dist. 10^3 ly	Sp	Remarks
188	0 44.0	+85 21	9.3	14	14.6	5.0	F2	Oldest known
752	1 57.8	+37 41	6.6	45	9.6	1.2	A5	
869	2 19.0	+57 10	4.3	30	9.5	7.0	B1	h Per
884	2 22.4	+57 07	4.4	30	9.5	8.1	B0	χ Per, M supergiants
Perseus	3 22	+48 36	2.3	240	5	0.6	B1	Moving cl.; α Per
Pleiades	3 47.1	+24 08	1.6	120	4.2	0.41	B6	M45, best known
Hyades	4 20	+15 38	0.8	400	3.9	0.15	A2	Moving cl. **, in Taurus
1912	5 28.6	+35 50	7.0	18	9.7	4.6	B5	M38
1976/80	5 35.4	−5 23	2.5	50	5.5	1.3	O5	Trapezium, very young
2099	5 52.4	+32 32	6.2	24	9.7	4.2	B8	M37
2168	6 08.8	+24 21	5.6	29	9.0	2.8	B5	M35
2232	6 26.5	−4 45	4.1	20	7	1.6	B1	
2244	6 32.4	+4 52	5.2	27	8.0	5.3	O5	Rosette, very young
2264	6 41.0	+9 53	4.1	30	8.0	2.4	O8	S Mon
2287	6 47.1	−20 44	5.0	32	8.8	2.2	B4	M41
2362	7 18.8	−24 56	3.8	7	9.4	5.4	O9	τ CMa
2422	7 35.6	−14 30	4.3	30	9.8	1.6	B3	
2437	7 41.8	−14 49	6.6	27	10.8	5.4	B8	M46
2451	7 45.4	−37 58	3.7	37	6	1.0	B5	
2516	7 58.3	−60 54	3.3	50	10.1	1.2	B8	
2546	8 12.5	−37 39	5.0	45	7	2.7	B0	
2632	8 40.1	+20 00	3.9	90	7.5	0.59	A0	Praesepe, M44
IC 2391	8 40.3	−53 03	2.6	45	3.5	0.5	B4	
IC 2395	8 41.0	−48 11	4.6	20	10.1	2.9	B2	
2682	8 50.4	+11 50	7.4	18	10.8	2.7	F2	M67, very old
3114	10 02.6	−60 07	4.5	37	7	2.8	B5	
IC 2602	10 43.3	−64 23	1.6	65	6	0.5	B1	θ Car
Tr 16	10 45.2	−59 42	6.7	10	10	9.6	O3	η Car and Nebula
3532	11 06.4	−58 39	3.4	55	8.1	1.4	B8	
3766	11 36.1	−61 37	4.4	12	8.1	5.8	B1	
Coma	12 25.1	+26 06	2.9	300	5.5	0.3	A1	Very sparse
4755	12 53.6	−60 20	5.2	12	7	6.8	B3	κ Cru, "Jewel Box"
6067	16 13.3	−54 13	6.5	16	10.9	4.7	B3	G, K supergiants
6231	16 54.0	−41 48	3.5	16	7.5	5.8	O9	O supergiants, WR stars
Tr 24	16 57.0	−40 40	3.5	60	7.3	5.2	O5	
6405	17 40.1	−32 13	4.6	26	8.3	1.5	B4	M6
IC 4665	17 46.7	+5 44	5.4	50	7	1.1	B8	
6475	17 53.9	−34 48	3.3	50	7.4	0.8	B5	M7
6494	17 56.9	−19 01	5.9	27	10.2	1.4	B8	M23
6523	18 03.1	−24 23	5.2	45	7	5.1	O5	M8, Lagoon Nebula
6611	18 18.9	−13 47	6.6	8	10.6	5.5	O7	M16, nebula
IC 4725	18 31.7	−19 15	6.2	35	9.3	2.0	B3	M25, Cepheid U Sgr
IC 4756	18 39.3	+5 27	5.4	50	8.5	1.4	A3	
6705	18 51.1	−6 17	6.8	12.5	12	5.6	B8	M11, very rich
Mel 227	20 11.2	−79 19	5.2	60	9	0.8	B9	
IC 1396	21 38.9	+57 30	5.1	60	8.5	2.3	O6	Tr 37
7790	23 58.4	+61 13	7.1	4.5	11.7	10.3	B1	Cepheids CEa, CEb, and CF Cas

† IC = Index Catalogue, Tr = Trumpler, Mel = Melotte ** Basic for distance determination

The table below lists all the globular clusters in the Messier list and most of the globular clusters with a total apparent visual magnitude brighter than about 8.0. A table of Milky Way Galaxy globular-cluster data is available on W.E. Harris's Web site: physwww.mcmaster.ca/~harris/WEHarris.html. The apparent diameter (**Diam.**) is from Cragin, Lucyk, and Rappaport (*Deep Sky Field Guide To Uranometria 2000.0*, Willmann-Bell, 1993). The concentration class (**Conc.**) is from I to XII, where I is the most compact and XII the least. The integrated spectral type (**Int. Sp. T.**) varies mainly with the abundances. An observer who can see stars down to the magnitude given in the *V*(**HB**) ("horizontal-branch" magnitude) column has a good chance of being able to resolve the globular cluster; this information is from Djorgovski and Meylan (*Structure and Dynamics of Globular Clusters*, Astronomical Society of the Pacific, 1993, p. 341).

GLOBULAR CLUSTERS

NGC	M/ other	RA (2000) h m	Dec ° '	Mag. m_v	Diam. '	Conc.	Int. Sp. T.	Dist. 10^3 ly	V(HB)
104	47 Tuc	0 24.0	−72 04	3.95	30.9	III	G4	15	14.06
288		0 52.8	−25 35	8.09	13.8	X		29	15.44
362		1 03.2	−70 50	6.40	12.9	III	F9	28	15.40
1851		5 14.0	−40 02	7.14	11.0	II	F7	46	16.10
1904	79	5 24.1	−24 31	7.73	8.7	V	F5	42	16.20
2808		9 11.9	−64 51	6.20	13.8	I	F7	30	16.19
3201		10 17.6	−46 24	6.75	18.2	X	F6	17	14.75
4590	68	12 39.5	−26 44	7.84	12.0	X	F2	33	15.60
4833		12 59.5	−70 52	6.91	13.5	VIII	F3	20	15.45
5024	53	13 12.9	+18 10	7.61	12.6	V	F6	60	16.94
5139	ω Cen	13 26.8	−47 28	3.68	36.3	VIII	F5	17	14.52
5272	3	13 42.2	+28 22	6.19	16.2	VI	F6	35	15.65
5904	5	15 18.5	+2 04	5.65	17.4	V	F7	26	15.11
6093	80	16 17.0	−22 58	7.33	8.9	II	F6	33	15.86
6121	4	16 23.6	−26 31	5.63	26.3	IX	F8	14	13.35
6171	107	16 32.5	−13 03	7.93	10.0	X	G0	21	15.70
6205	13	16 41.7	+36 27	5.78	16.6	V	F6	21	14.95
6218	12	16 47.1	−1 56	6.70	14.5	IX	F8	24	14.90
6254	10	16 57.1	−4 05	6.60	15.1	VII	F3	20	14.65
6266	62	17 01.2	−30 06	6.45	14.1	IV	F9	22	15.90
6273	19	17 02.6	−26 16	6.77	13.5	VIII	F7	28	16.95
6333	9	17 19.2	−18 30	7.72	9.3	VIII	F5	27	16.10
6341	92	17 17.1	+43 08	6.44	11.2	IV	F2	26	15.05
6356		17 23.6	−17 49	8.25	7.2	III	G4	50	17.50
6388		17 36.3	−44 44	6.72	8.7	III	G2	37	16.90
6397		17 40.7	−53 40	5.73	25.7	IX	F4	9	12.90
6402	14	17 37.6	−3 14	7.59	11.7	VIII	F4	29	17.50
6541		18 08.0	−43 42	6.30	13.1	III	F6	13	15.10
6626	28	18 24.5	−24 52	6.79	11.2	IV	F8	19	15.68
6637	69	18 31.4	−32 20	7.64	7.1	V	G2	28	16.20
6656	22	18 36.3	−23 54	5.10	24.0	VII	F5	10	14.15
6681	70	18 43.2	−32 17	7.87	7.8	V	F5	29	15.60
6715	54	18 55.0	−30 28	7.60	9.1	III	F7	89	17.71
6752		19 10.9	−59 58	5.40	20.4	VI	F4	17	13.85
6779	56	19 16.6	+30 11	8.27	7.1	X	F5	33	16.20
6809	55	19 40.1	−30 57	6.32	19.0	XI	F4	20	14.35
6838	71	19 53.8	+18 46	8.19	7.2	†	G1	13	14.44
6864	75	20 06.0	−21 55	8.52	6.0	I	F9	61	17.45
6981	72	20 53.5	−12 32	9.27	5.9	IX	F7	55	16.99
7078	15	21 30.1	+12 10	6.20	12.3	IV	F3	34	15.86
7089	2	21 33.5	−0 50	6.47	12.9	II	F4	40	16.05
7099	30	21 40.4	−23 10	7.19	11.0	V	F3	26	15.10

† Originally thought to be an open cluster; never assigned a concentration class

AN EXAMPLE: NGC 5139
RECENT REVELATIONS ABOUT
THE AMAZING CLUSTER OMEGA CENTAURI

Omega Centauri tops most observers' lists as the finest of all globular clusters. Canadian amateur astronomers who visit the more southerly latitudes where Omega Centauri can be seen in the spring or summer almost always return with a tale of being staggered by their first view of it. When it was photographed in the 1890s with a 33-cm refractor, Harvard University astronomer Solon Bailey counted "more than 6000 stars" and then commented on "a background of nebulous light…caused by stars too faint for counting." Estimates of how many stars Omega Centauri actually contains have gone up steadily ever since, until in 2007, Sandro Villanova et al. (ApJ 663:296) generated a colour-magnitude diagram (CMD) from measurements, made by the *Hubble Space Telescope (HST)*, of "more than a million stars."

The CMD—almost as beautiful as the visual appearance of the cluster itself—shows a distinct split where stars turn off the upper end of the main sequence. The implications of this forking of the curve are enormous: the stars in Omega Centauri did not all form at once, as has always generally been presumed for globular clusters, but in at least two distinct time periods, separated by a billion years or more. Furthermore, analysis of how much matter in those stars is not hydrogen or helium (what astronomers call the metal content) indicates that the stars coalesced out of different clouds of gas. So Omega Centauri is not just a simple globe of stars all belonging to one happy family.

The discovery of an intermediate-mass black hole in the core of Omega Centauri is another surprise. Eva Noyola et al. (ApJ 676:1008) analyzed the velocities of selected stars, as measured by *HST* and the Gemini Observatory, out from the centre of Omega Centauri. The pattern, dropping off from 23 km/s at centre, is best explained by the gravitational influence of a concentrated object of about 40000 solar masses: a black hole.

Separate eras of star formation and the presence of a central black hole are not traditionally associated with globular clusters. Remembering also that observers have long seen Omega Centauri to have a pronounced elliptical shape, astronomers now consider Omega Centauri to be the core of a dwarf spheroidal galaxy that has been wrestling with the Milky Way for aeons.

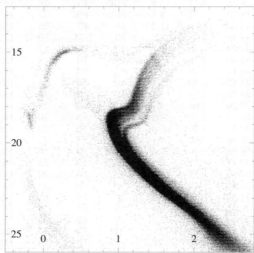

A colour-magnitude diagram plots the apparent visual brightness of each star in a globular cluster on the vertical axis against each star's colour index (its magnitude in a blue filter minus its magnitude in a yellow filter). The main sequence is the diagonal line of stars running up from bottom right. The "fork" that branches upward from there is evidence that Omega Centauri is composed of at least two distinct sets of stars that formed about a billion years apart.

AMATEUR SUPERNOVA HUNTING
BY REV. ROBERT EVANS

The first discovery of a supernova by an amateur astronomer was by G. Romano of Italy (SN 1957B in NGC 4564); this discovery was photographic. The first visual discovery was by J. Bennett of South Africa (SN 1968L in M83). In Australia in 1980, the author began systematic visual searching using a simple 250-mm backyard telescope and made two discoveries the following year. K. Okazaki of Japan, who discovered two supernovae, one each in 1983 and 1984, was one of several Japanese amateurs to mount systematic photographic searches at that time.

By the late 1980s, most of the supernovae brighter than 15th magnitude were being found visually by amateurs. In the early 1990s, professional astronomers started using supernova studies to address major problems in cosmology; at that time, they depended largely upon amateur searches to provide them with the best and brightest supernovae in nearby galaxies. These nearby supernovae provided much of the benchmark information needed for studying supernovae at remote distances, which led to independent estimates for the expansion, age, and fate of the universe.

CCD Supernova Hunting

In the last few years, the cost of charge-coupled devices (CCDs) has fallen to the point where many amateurs can afford to use them on computer-controlled telescopes. Some of these amateurs are hunting supernovae with resounding success. There are a number of advantages to using telescopes with CCDs and computer control:

(1) You can observe in locations with some light pollution or in the presence of fairly strong moonlight.

(2) With a computer to direct the telescope to individual galaxies, it is no longer necessary to know the sky well.

(3) With appropriate computer control of the telescope, you can sit in a warm room facing the computer screen.

(4) If your equipment is good enough, it will find supernovae without your presence.

(5) Stars as faint as 18th or 19th magnitude become accessible, which includes most supernovae in nearby galaxies plus the brighter supernovae in many distant galaxies, out to about 300 million light-years.

Using a CCD brings so many thousands of galaxies within range that you will never have enough time to observe them all! However, you will need reference materials for all the galaxies on your observing list—even if you make the reference images yourself—so that you can tell when a new object appears near a galaxy.

Visual Supernova Hunting

Visual supernova hunting has a number of advantages over using a CCD:

(1) The equipment is less expensive than that needed for CCD work.

(2) An experienced visual observer usually knows the location and the normal appearance of many target galaxies and can thus work through observations of galaxies at ten times the speed of anyone using a CCD on an amateur telescope. Professional-standard CCDs are quicker but are still much more expensive than those used by amateurs.

(3) You become very familiar with the night sky. (Personally, I think this is a great benefit of visual searching.)

(4) Amateurs who rely on computers to find galaxies are deceived by technology into being ignorant of the sky. Thus, when the technology fails (as it does from time

to time), the search halts, since the observer does not know where to locate target galaxies. A visual observer who knows the sky is immune to this problem.

There are, however, special requirements:

(1) A reasonably dark observing site is needed.

(2) Your telescope needs to be easily manageable so that you can locate objects quickly, and the aperture needs to be big enough so that you can see down to about 15th magnitude. You can then observe all the nearby galaxies (out to, say, 100 million light-years). You will then be able to see most supernovae in galaxies out to about 25 million light-years and the brighter supernovae out to 100 million light-years or more. But, naturally, your chances of success decrease with the distance of the galaxy. Fainter supernovae in any given galaxy may be more numerous than the brighter ones, although the latter are the most interesting, scientifically.

(3) As in CCD searches, charts or suitable photographs of all your target galaxies are needed, so that you can tell when a new object appears.

Verification and Reporting

Verification of any suspected new discovery is vitally important. The first step is to check any suspect against all available photographs, CCD images, or charts of that galaxy. Measure carefully the offset of the new star from the nucleus of the galaxy. Watch the object for any possible movement against nearby stars. Note the time of your discovery (UT). It is necessary to have a team of other observers who can make independent observations of the new object, and who will do so immediately, if asked. These other observers must also have enough galaxy resources so that they can eliminate anything that is not a supernova, and they should be spread out over a number of locations in case bad weather puts any one observer out of action.

The Central Bureau for Astronomical Telegrams has issued instructions describing how much verification is needed about any possible new supernova, and these should be consulted (see www.cfa.harvard.edu/iau/cbat.html). CCD observers need at least 5 observations covering 24 hours. A visual observer should have independent observations by people who know what they are doing. And, even after the Central Bureau has been notified, spectra will probably need to be obtained through one of the main observatories before the bureau will finally announce a discovery.

When notifying the Central Bureau, provide full details of all observations of the new object: the name and location of the person making the report, the discoverer's name and location, details of the reference materials consulted, details concerning the equipment used, universal time of all observations, name and position of the galaxy, offset and brightness of the supernova, and similar details about each verifying observation. Observers who are not already known at the bureau should be especially thorough in detailing and supporting their report. All discoveries can be emailed to the Central Bureau at cbat@cfa.harvard.edu.

Much helpful advice is available in the *AAVSO Supernova Search Manual*, which is available from the AAVSO, 49 Bay State Road, Cambridge MA 02138, USA, for the cost of postage only. It can also be viewed at www.aavso.org/observing/programs/sn/supernovasm.shtml.

Editor's Note: Robert Evans, who made his first supernova discovery in 1981, holds the record for visual discoveries of supernovae: 42. Ten of these were found using a 250-mm telescope, 8 using a 310-mm telescope, 20 with a 410-mm instrument (all "backyard" variety Newtonians), and 3 using the 1.02-m telescope at Siding Spring Observatory (Australian National University). In addition, he has discovered four supernovae (plus a comet) on U.K. Schmidt films taken as part of a special supernova search, all in 1996, and one on a European Southern Observatory Red Survey Schmidt film.

EXPIRED STARS

By Roy Bishop

Stars are where the action is, and the action is fuelled by gravitation and thermonuclear fusion. Gravitation, the midwife and undertaker, forms a star, heats it to the temperatures necessary to ignite successive stages of fusion reactions, and when nuclear fuel runs out, crushes the ashes of the star into one of three final states: white dwarf, neutron star, or black hole. Thermonuclear fusion, powered by the strong nuclear interaction between protons and neutrons, merely delays the onset of further collapse and higher temperatures. In the case of our Sun, the first and by far the longest delay, the "hang-up" provided by hydrogen-to-helium fusion, is already half over.

White Dwarfs

Stars comparable to our Sun have insufficient gravity to reach the temperatures necessary to form nuclei heavier than carbon or oxygen. When the thermal support pressure generated by fusion wanes, gravity gradually crushes the central portion of the star. If the mass of this core is less than 1.4 solar masses (a limit discovered by a leading astrophysicist of the 20th century, Subramanyan Chandrasekhar), the collapse halts at a very hot, Earth-sized remnant known as a white dwarf. At this point, the squeeze of gravity is offset by *electron degeneracy pressure*, an intrinsic aspect of the wave–particle nature of matter and the same pressure responsible for the stability and size of an atom. However, in the case of a white dwarf, the pressure is such that the electrons are not tied to individual atomic nuclei but occupy the whole star. In this sense, the star has become a giant atom. In physics jargon: electrons are fermions (i.e. they obey Fermi–Dirac quantum statistics) and hence abide by the Pauli Exclusion Principle, which dictates that no two electrons can occupy the same quantum state. This results in an immense pressure, sufficient to prevent further collapse, provided the mass is less than the Chandrasekhar limit. White-dwarf diameters are about 1 percent that of our Sun, which has a nearly water-like average density (1 g/cm^3). Thus a cubic centimetre of white-dwarf material has a mass near 100^3 g or one tonne (like a Toyota Yaris crushed into a sugar cube).

Because of their immense thermal energy and small surface area, white dwarfs cool extremely slowly. The universe is not yet old enough for any white dwarf to have cooled sufficiently to become a "black dwarf." Also, white dwarfs are intrinsically very faint; thus only those close to the solar system can be seen.

Only one white dwarf is easily observable with a small telescope: **Omicron 2 Eridani B** (also designated 40 Eridani B), located 16.5 light-years from Earth. Omicron 2 Eridani A, the bright (mag. 4.4) companion to the dim (mag. 9.5) white dwarf, is shown on the JANUARY ALL-SKY CHART on p. 345: o^2 Eri A is the eastern (left-hand) member of the close pair of stars located due west of the word "Rigel." Omicron 2 Eridani B, the white dwarf, is located only 83″ east-southeast of o^2 Eri A (position angle ≈110°). Remarkably, stars A and B are accompanied by a third star, a faint (mag. 11.2) red-dwarf star, o^2 Eri C, which resides only 9″ north of B. (There is a brighter and closer white dwarf, the companion of Sirius, α CMa B, but it is usually lost in the glare of Sirius. See THE NEAREST STARS (p. 290) and DOUBLE AND MULTIPLE STARS (p. 295) for more information on both of these stellar systems.)

For the observer with a small telescope, o^2 Eri B is the only Earth-sized object visible in the depths of interstellar space, the only visible object with a mass density far exceeding that of ordinary matter, the only accessible star no longer powered by nuclear reactions, and the only star that has expired and can still be seen.

Neutron Stars

For a large star of about eight or more solar masses, energy-releasing reactions end in its centre with the fusion of silicon nuclei into iron. Iron has the most tightly bound nucleus (per nuclear particle) and hence is no good as a fuel for further fusion. Electron degeneracy pressure supports the inert iron core until silicon fusion in a surrounding shell supplies enough additional iron to push the inert core over the Chandrasekhar limit. Gravity then overwhelms electron degeneracy pressure, and the core collapses in less than a second, so quickly that, momentarily, the outer layers of the star stay where they were. Gravitation-induced temperatures in the core rise past 10^{10} K, sufficient to disassemble heavy nuclei synthesized over the life of the star. This absorbs energy, accelerating the collapse. Also, electrons attain sufficient energy to combine with protons to form neutrons and neutrinos, another energy-absorbing reaction that also removes electrons, further hastening the collapse.

Provided the infalling mass is less than about three solar masses, like a hammer striking an anvil, when the core reaches a diameter of about 20 km, the infall is violently arrested by a combination of *neutron* degeneracy pressure and the short-range repulsive nature of the strong nuclear force, the same agents that govern the size and structure of the nuclei of atoms of ordinary matter. With a diameter 500 times smaller than that of a white dwarf, the density at this stage is 500^3 larger, 100 million tonnes per cubic centimetre (like an aircraft carrier crushed to the size of the ball of a ballpoint pen). That is the density of ordinary atomic nuclei. The star's core has effectively become a gigantic nucleus, composed primarily of neutrons.

The abrupt rebound of the nearly rigid central core reverses the infall of the adjacent layers, turning the implosion into a spectacular explosion, a Type II supernova. The explosion mechanism is complex and not yet well understood, but appears to involve interactions with the immense numbers of neutrinos generated in the neutron production, and possibly acoustic waves generated by vibrations of the core as it is pummeled by infalling material within a second of its formation. The gravitational energy released in the sudden collapse of the couple of solar masses now locked in the central neutron star is about 10^{46} J. This is far more energy than our Sun will produce in its entire 10-billion-year lifetime.

Over the next several thousand years, the remnants of the outer layers of the star form an expanding, glowing cloud of gas and dust, seeding interstellar space with the heavy chemical elements (oxygen, silicon, iron, uranium, etc.) synthesized in its outer layers both before and during the supernova explosion. The potassium ions moving in the neurons of your brain as you read these words emerged from such a conflagration some 5 billion years ago.

No neutron stars are visible in a small telescope, although one is *indirectly* visible in the **Crab Nebula**, M1. The Crab supernova was a bright, naked-eye star in the skies of Earth in the year 1054 AD, although it had taken 6000 years for the light of the explosion to reach our planet. The nebula we see today is the expanding debris cloud as it was nearly 1000 years after the initial explosion.

The Crab Nebula glows across the electromagnetic spectrum, from radio waves to gamma rays, powered by the rapid but decreasing spin of the neutron star at its centre. The glow of the debris cloud is like the glow of a red-hot disk brake slowing the spin of a wheel. The visible light from the cloud is *synchrotron radiation* emitted by electrons as they spiral in the tangled magnetic field of the neutron star. Nowhere else in the heavens is such an exotic light visible in a small telescope, polarized light with the brilliance of a thousand suns, emitted not by atoms but by free electrons being flung about by a spinning neutron star. The neutron star itself is known as a *pulsar* because it flashes 30 times per second, in step with its spin. However, even if the Crab pulsar were bright enough to be visible in a small telescope, the flashing would not be

apparent because, as in a motion picture or cathode-ray tube monitor, the flicker is too rapid for the eye to follow.

Colour photographs of the Crab Nebula reveal a celestial gift: a package of bluish synchrotron radiation wrapped in the loops of a tattered red ribbon—fragments of the shattered star, fluorescing in hydrogen-alpha light. Unfortunately, the luminance of the fluorescence is below the threshold for vision in the red part of the spectrum. Thus all we can see is the ghostly cloud of synchrotron radiation.

The Crab Nebula is located 1° northwest of the star ζ Tau, at the tip of the east horn of Taurus. In the JANUARY ALL-SKY CHART on p. 345, the nebula is the tiny circle of dots 5 mm to the right of the cross marking the summer solstice (SS). In a telescope the nebula appears merely as a small glowing cloud, but to the knowledgeable observer, this synchrotron radiation brake of a spinning neutron star is an object for profound contemplation.

Black Holes

Stars whose masses are greater than about 20 solar masses likely retain more than 3 solar masses in their imploding cores. This is sufficient that gravitation will overwhelm not only the degeneracy pressure of electrons, but also the highly incompressible nature of nuclear matter. Within seconds, spacetime itself closes around the imploding stellar core, removing all but the core's gravitational field from the observable universe. The star has become a black hole.

The earliest and best candidate for a stellar black hole is **Cygnus X-1.** Discovered by Dr. Tom Bolton of the University of Toronto, it is one of the strongest galactic X-ray sources in the sky. Cygnus X-1 is the invisible companion of a star that can be seen in a small telescope: HDE 226868, an O9.7Iab star, a very luminous, very hot supergiant located about 8000 ly from the Sun. It orbits its nearby, unseen companion with a 5.6-day period. The mass of the companion is between 10 and 16 solar masses, far too large for it to be a white dwarf or neutron star. X-rays are generated as material from the supergiant falls toward the invisible companion. The X-rays extend to energies of 100 keV and vary on time scales as short as milliseconds, indicative of a very compact companion.

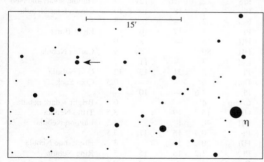

At 9th magnitude, the supergiant HDE 226868 is visible in any small telescope. It is less than half a degree from the 4th-magnitude star η Cygni, which is the star in the neck of the swan, next to the "C" in CYGNUS on the SEPTEMBER ALL-SKY CHART on p. 349. Any low magnification will more than encompass the field shown in the **finder chart** above. North is upward, η Cygni is at the lower right, and HDE 226868 is indicated by the small arrow. The chart magnitude limit is about 13. Although HDE 226868 is a blue supergiant, in telescopes of sufficient aperture this star appears orange because of interstellar dust between us and the star.

All that is to be seen is the hot supergiant, but the view will be worth the search if you know that at this same location in the field of your telescope lurks one of the most likely candidates for a black hole, a knot in the fabric of spacetime where a giant star has vanished. No painting, computer simulation, or Hollywood movie can match this observation.

NEBULAE AND GALAXIES

GALACTIC NEBULAE
By William Herbst

The following objects were selected from the brightest and largest of the various classes to illustrate the different types of interactions between stars and interstellar matter in our galaxy. *Emission regions* (HII) are excited by the strong ultraviolet flux of young, hot stars and are characterized by the lines of hydrogen in their spectra. *Reflection nebulae* (Ref) result from the diffusion of starlight by clouds of interstellar dust. At certain stages of their evolution, stars become unstable and explode, shedding their outer layers into what becomes a *planetary nebula* (Pl) or a *supernova remnant* (SN). *Protostellar nebulae* (PrS) are objects still poorly understood; they are somewhat similar to the reflection nebulae, but their associated stars, often variable, are very luminous infrared stars that may be in the earliest stages of stellar evolution. Also included in the selection are three *extended complexes* (Comp) of special interest for their rich population of dark and bright nebulosities of various types. In the table S is the optical surface brightness in magnitude per square arcsecond of representative regions of the nebula, and $m*$ is the magnitude of the associated star.

NGC	M	Con	RA (2000) h m	Dec ° ′	Type	Size ′	S mag/sq″	$m*$	Dist. 10^3 ly	Remarks
1435		Tau	3 47.5	+24 05	Ref	15	20	4	0.4	Merope nebula
1535		Eri	4 14.2	−12 45	Pl	0.5	17	12		
1952	1	Tau	5 34.5	+22 01	SN	5	19	16v	4	"Crab" + pulsar
1976	42	Ori	5 35.3	−5 24	HII	30	18	4	1.5	Orion Nebula
2070		Dor	5 38.6	−69 05	HII	20	—	13	200	Tarantula Nebula
ζ Ori		Ori	5 40.8	−1 56	Comp	2°			1.5	Incl. "Horsehead"
2068	78	Ori	5 46.8	+0 02	Ref	5	20		1.5	
IC 443		Gem	6 17.6	+22 36	SN	40			2	
2244		Mon	6 32.4	+4 52	HII	50	21	7	3	Rosette Nebula
2261		Mon	6 39.1	+8 43	PrS	2		12v	4	Hubble's Variable Neb.
2392		Gem	7 29.2	+20 54	Pl	0.3	18	10	10	Clown Face Nebula
2626		Vel	8 35.6	−40 38	Ref	2	—	10	3	
3132		Vel	10 07.0	−40 25	Pl	1	17	10	—	Eight-Burst
3324		Car	10 37.5	−58 38	HII	15	—	8	9	
3372		Car	10 45.1	−59 41	HII	80	—	6v	9	Carina Nebula
3503		Car	11 01.3	−60 43	Ref	3	—	11	9	
3587	97	UMa	11 14.8	+55 01	Pl	3	21	13	12	Owl Nebula
—		Cru	12 51	−63	Dark	6°	—	—	0.5	Coal Sack
5189		Mus	13 33.5	−65 58	Pl	2.6	—	10	—	
ρ Oph		Oph	16 25.6	−23 27	Comp	4°			0.5	Bright + dark nebula
6514	20	Sgr	18 02.4	−23 02	HII	15	19		3.5	Trifid Nebula
6523	8	Sgr	18 03.6	−24 23	HII	40	18		4.5	Lagoon Nebula
6543		Dra	17 58.6	+66 37	Pl	0.4	15	11	3.5	
6618	17	Sgr	18 20.9	−16 11	HII	20	19		3	Horseshoe Nebula
6720	57	Lyr	18 53.6	+33 03	Pl	1.2	18	15	5	Ring Nebula
6726		CrA	19 01.7	−36 54	PrS	5	—	7	0.5	
6853	27	Vul	19 59.5	+22 43	Pl	7	19	13	3.5	Dumbbell Nebula
6888		Cyg	20 12.3	+38 25	HII	15				
γ Cyg		Cyg	20 22.2	+40 16	Comp	6°				HII + dark nebula
6960/95		Cyg	20 45.6	+30 42	SN	150			2.5	Cygnus loop
7000		Cyg	20 58.9	+44 19	HII	100	22		3.5	North America Nebula
7009		Aqr	21 04.1	−11 23	Pl	0.5	16	12	3	Saturn Nebula
7027		Cyg	21 07.1	+42 14	Pl	0.2	15	13		
7129		Cep	21 43.0	+65 06	Ref	3	21	10	2.5	Small cluster
7293		Aqr	22 29.6	−20 48	Pl	13	22	13		Helix Nebula

THE MESSIER CATALOGUE
BY ALAN DYER

Charles Messier's Catalogue provides a selection of the best and brightest deep-sky wonders for Northern Hemisphere viewers. Messier compiled his list in the late 1700s to aid prospective comet hunters. Some of these objects he discovered himself, some were first seen by other astronomers of the day, while a few (the Pleiades and the Beehive) were known since antiquity. The Messier numbers do not follow an ordered sequence across the sky. Rather, they are numbered in the order he discovered and catalogued them. Although he intended to, Messier never did publish a list with entries renumbered in order of right ascension.

In our version of the Messier Catalogue, we've listed the objects by season *for the evening observer*, grouping the objects within their respective constellations. The constellations are then listed roughly in order of increasing right ascension, that is constellations farther to the east and which rise later in the night are farther down the list. This is to help plan the sequence of an evening's Messier hunt.

The identity of some Messier objects is controversial. There is evidence that M91 and M102 are mistaken observations of M58 and M101, respectively. M104 and M109 were found by a colleague, Pierre Mechain, and reported to Messier for inclusion in his Catalogue. NGC 205, one of the companion galaxies to M31, the Andromeda Galaxy, was apparently found by Messier but never included in his Catalogue. Modern-day observers have dubbed this object M110. In our list, we have included 110 entries, including two objects that some have suggested as alternative candidates for M91 and M102.

Modern-day Messier hunters often wonder what telescopes Messier used. The largest were 190-mm and 200-mm reflectors. However, their speculum metal mirrors would have had the equivalent light-gathering power of a modern 80-mm to 100-mm reflector. He also used a number of 90-mm refractors. Today, a dark site and a good 80-mm refractor or 100-mm reflector should be sufficient for completing the entire list. Objects M6 and M7 are the most southerly, while M74 and M76 are often considered the faintest and most difficult. M83's low altitude and diffuse appearance make it a challenge for Canadian observers north of 50° latitude.

The columns contain the Messier number, the object's NGC (New General Catalogue) number, the constellation, the type of object, its equinox J2000.0 coordinates, visual magnitude m_v, and angular size in minutes of arc (planetary nebula sizes are given in seconds of arc ($''$)). Entries marked "!!" are showpiece objects. OC = open cluster; GC = globular cluster; PN = planetary nebula; EN = emission nebula; RN = reflection nebula; E/RN = combination of emission and reflection nebula; SNR = supernova remnant; G = galaxy (E = elliptical, I = irregular, SA = normal spiral, SB = barred spiral, S0 = lenticular). Data are taken from *The Deep Sky Field Guide to Uranometria 2000.0* (published by Willmann-Bell, Inc., 1993), compiled by Murray Cragin, James Lucyk, and Barry Rappaport from a variety of contemporary catalogues. Some sizes have been rounded to two significant figures. Also recommended as an excellent guide is *The Messier Objects*, by Stephen James O'Meara (Cambridge University Press, 1998).

The RASC offers observing certificates for members who observe the 110 objects in the Messier list, the 110 objects in the Finest NGC list (pp. 323–325), or The David Levy Deep-Sky Gems list (pp. 326–329). For beginners or observers using binoculars the Society also offers the "Explore the Universe" Certificate and the Isabel Williamson Lunar Certificate. Contact your local Centre or the RASC National Office (see p. 10) for details.

NUMERICAL LISTING OF MESSIER OBJECTS

M#	Sky	Con	M#	Sky	Con	M#	Sky	Con	M#	Sky	Con	M#	Sky	Con
1	WIN	Tau	23	SUM	Sgr	45	WIN	Tau	67	SPR	Cnc	89	SPR	Vir
2	AUT	Aqr	24	SUM	Sgr	46	WIN	Pup	68	SPR	Hya	90	SPR	Vir
3	SPR	CVn	25	SUM	Sgr	47	WIN	Pup	69	SUM	Sgr	91	SPR	Com
4	SUM	Sco	26	SUM	Sct	48	WIN	Hya	70	SUM	Sgr	92	SUM	Her
5	SPR	Ser	27	SUM	Vul	49	SPR	Vir	71	SUM	Sge	93	WIN	Pup
6	SUM	Sco	28	SUM	Sgr	50	WIN	Mon	72	AUT	Aqr	94	SPR	CVn
7	SUM	Sco	29	SUM	Cyg	51	SPR	CVn	73	AUT	Aqr	95	SPR	Leo
8	SUM	Sgr	30	AUT	Cap	52	AUT	Cas	74	AUT	Psc	96	SPR	Leo
9	SUM	Oph	31	AUT	And	53	SPR	Com	75	SUM	Sgr	97	SPR	UMa
10	SUM	Oph	32	AUT	And	54	SUM	Sgr	76	AUT	Per	98	SPR	Com
11	SUM	Sct	33	AUT	Tri	55	SUM	Sgr	77	AUT	Cet	99	SPR	Com
12	SUM	Oph	34	AUT	Per	56	SUM	Lyr	78	WIN	Ori	100	SPR	Com
13	SUM	Her	35	WIN	Gem	57	SUM	Lyr	79	WIN	Lep	101	SPR	UMa
14	SUM	Oph	36	WIN	Aur	58	SPR	Vir	80	SUM	Sco	102	SPR	Dra?
15	AUT	Peg	37	WIN	Aur	59	SPR	Vir	81	SPR	UMa	103	AUT	Cas
16	SUM	Ser	38	WIN	Aur	60	SPR	Vir	82	SPR	UMa	104	SPR	Vir
17	SUM	Sgr	39	SUM	Cyg	61	SPR	Vir	83	SPR	Hya	105	SPR	Leo
18	SUM	Sgr	40	SPR	UMa	62	SUM	Oph	84	SPR	Vir	106	SPR	CVn
19	SUM	Oph	41	WIN	CMa	63	SPR	CVn	85	SPR	Com	107	SUM	Oph
20	SUM	Sgr	42	WIN	Ori	64	SPR	Com	86	SPR	Vir	108	SPR	UMa
21	SUM	Sgr	43	WIN	Ori	65	SPR	Leo	87	SPR	Vir	109	SPR	UMa
22	SUM	Sgr	44	SPR	Cnc	66	SPR	Leo	88	SPR	Com	110	AUT	And

SEASONAL LISTING OF MESSIER OBJECTS

M#	NGC	Con	Type	RA (2000) h m	Dec ° '	m_v	Size '	Remarks
The Winter Sky								
1	1952	Tau	SNR	5 34.5	+22 01	8.4	6 × 4	!! famous Crab Neb. supernova remnant
45	—	Tau	OC	3 47.0	+24 07	1.2	110	!! Pleiades; look for subtle nebulosity
36	1960	Aur	OC	5 36.1	+34 08	6.0	12	bright but scattered group; use low pow.
37	2099	Aur	OC	5 52.4	+32 33	5.6	20	!! finest of three Auriga clusters; very rich
38	1912	Aur	OC	5 28.7	+35 50	6.4	21	look for small cluster NGC 1907 0.5° S
42	1976	Ori	E/RN	5 35.4	−5 27	—	65 × 60	!! Orion Nebula; finest in northern sky
43	1982	Ori	E/RN	5 35.6	−5 16	—	20 × 15	detached part of Orion Nebula
78	2068	Ori	RN	5 46.7	+0 03	—	8 × 6	bright featureless reflection nebula
79	1904	Lep	GC	5 24.5	−24 33	7.8	8.7	200-mm telescope needed to resolve
35	2168	Gem	OC	6 08.9	+24 20	5.1	28	!! look for sm. cluster NGC 2158 0.25° S
41	2287	CMa	OC	6 47.0	−20 44	4.5	38	4° south of Sirius; bright but coarse
50	2323	Mon	OC	7 03.2	−8 20	5.9	16	between Sirius & Procyon; use low mag.
46	2437	Pup	OC	7 41.8	−14 49	6.1	27	!! contains planetary nebula NGC 2438
47	2422	Pup	OC	7 36.6	−14 30	4.4	29	coarse cluster 1.5° west of M46
93	2447	Pup	OC	7 44.6	−23 52	≈6.2	22	compact, bright cluster; fairly rich
48	2548	Hya	OC	8 13.8	−5 48	5.8	54	former "lost" Messier; large, sparse cl.

SEASONAL LISTING OF MESSIER OBJECTS (continued)

M#	NGC	Con	Type	RA (2000) h m	Dec ° '	m_v	Size '	Remarks
The Spring Sky								
44	2632	Cnc	OC	8 40.1	+19 59	3.1	95	!! Beehive or Praesepe; use low power
67	2682	Cnc	OC	8 50.4	+11 49	6.9	29	one of the oldest star clusters known
40	—	UMa	2 stars	12 22.4	+58 05	8.0	—	double star Winnecke 4; separation 50″
81	3031	UMa	G-SAab	9 55.6	+69 04	6.9	24 × 13	!! bright spiral visible in binoculars
82	3034	UMa	G-I0	9 55.8	+69 41	8.4	12 × 6	!! the "exploding" galaxy; M81 0.5° S
97	3587	UMa	PN	11 14.8	+55 01	9.9	194″	!! Owl Nebula; distinct grey oval
101	5457	UMa	G-SABcd	14 03.2	+54 21	7.9	26 × 26	!! Pinwheel Gal.; diffuse face-on spiral
108	3556	UMa	G-SBcd	11 11.5	+55 40	10.0	8.1 × 2.1	nearly edge-on; paired with M97 0.75° SE
109	3992	UMa	G-SBbc	11 57.6	+53 23	9.8	7.6 × 4.3	barred spiral near γ UMa
65	3623	Leo	G-SABa	11 18.9	+13 05	9.3	8.7 × 2.2	!! bright elongated spiral
66	3627	Leo	G-SABb	11 20.2	+12 59	8.9	8.2 × 3.9	!! M65 and NGC 3628 in same field
95	3351	Leo	G-SBb	10 44.0	+11 42	9.7	7.8 × 4.6	bright barred spiral
96	3368	Leo	G-SABab	10 46.8	+11 49	9.2	6.9 × 4.6	M95 in same field
105	3379	Leo	G-E1	10 47.8	+12 35	9.3	3.9 × 3.9	bright elliptical near M95 and M96
53	5024	Com	GC	13 12.9	+18 10	7.5	12.6	150-mm telescope needed to resolve
64	4826	Com	G-SAab	12 56.7	+21 41	8.5	9.2 × 4.6	!! Black Eye Gal.; eye needs big scope
85	4382	Com	G-SA0⁺	12 25.4	+18 11	9.1	7.5 × 5.7	bright elliptical shape
88	4501	Com	G-SAb	12 32.0	+14 25	9.6	6.1 × 2.8	bright multiple-arm spiral
91	4548	Com	G-SBb	12 35.4	+14 30	10.2	5.0 × 4.1	some lists say M91 = M58, not NGC 4548
98	4192	Com	G-SABab	12 13.8	+14 54	10.1	9.1 × 2.1	nearly edge-on spiral near star 6 Com. B.
99	4254	Com	G-SAc	12 18.8	+14 25	9.9	4.6 × 4.3	nearly face-on spiral near M98
100	4321	Com	G-SABbc	12 22.9	+15 49	9.3	6.2 × 5.3	face-on spiral with starlike nucleus
49	4472	Vir	G-E2	12 29.8	+8 00	8.4	8.1 × 7.1	very bright elliptical
58	4579	Vir	G-SABb	12 37.7	+11 49	9.7	5.5 × 4.6	bright barred spiral; M59 and M60 1° E
59	4621	Vir	G-E5	12 42.0	+11 39	9.6	4.6 × 3.6	bright elliptical paired with M60
60	4649	Vir	G-E2	12 43.7	+11 33	8.8	7.1 × 6.1	bright elliptical with M59 and NGC 4647
61	4303	Vir	G-SABbc	12 21.9	+4 28	9.7	6.0 × 5.9	face-on two-armed spiral
84	4374	Vir	G-E1	12 25.1	+12 53	9.1	5.1 × 4.1	!! w/ M86 in Markarian's Chain
86	4406	Vir	G-E3	12 26.2	+12 57	8.9	12 × 9	!! w/ many NGC galaxies in Chain
87	4486	Vir	G-E0-1	12 30.8	+12 24	8.6	7.1 × 7.1	the one with famous jet and black hole
89	4552	Vir	G-E	12 35.7	+12 33	9.8	3.4 × 3.4	elliptical; resembles M87 but smaller
90	4569	Vir	G-SABab	12 36.8	+13 10	9.5	10 × 4	bright barred spiral near M89
104	4594	Vir	G-SA	12 40.0	−11 37	8.0	7.1 × 4.4	!! Sombrero Galaxy; look for dust lane
3	5272	CVn	GC	13 42.2	+28 23	5.9	16.2	!! contains many variable stars
51	5194/5	CVn	G-SABc	13 29.9	+47 12	8.4	8 × 7	!! Whirlpool Galaxy; superb in big scope
63	5055	CVn	G-SAbc	13 15.8	+42 02	8.6	14 × 8	!! Sunflower Galaxy; bright, elongated
94	4736	CVn	G-SAab	12 50.9	+41 07	8.2	13 × 11	very bright and comet-like
106	4258	CVn	G-SABbc	12 19.0	+47 18	8.4	20 × 8	!! superb large, bright spiral
68	4590	Hya	GC	12 39.5	−26 45	7.7	12	150-mm telescope needed to resolve
83	5236	Hya	G-SABc	13 37.0	−29 52	7.6	16 × 13	large and diffuse; superb from far south
102	5866?	Dra	G-SA0⁺	15 06.5	+55 46	9.9	6.6 × 3.2	or is M102 = M101? (look for 5907)
5	5904	Ser	GC	15 18.6	+2 05	5.7	17.4	!! one of the sky's finest globulars
The Summer Sky								
13	6205	Her	GC	16 41.7	+36 28	5.7	16.6	!! Hercules Cluster; NGC 6207 0.5° NE
92	6341	Her	GC	17 17.1	+43 08	6.4	11.2	9° NE of M13; fine but often overlooked
9	6333	Oph	GC	17 19.2	−18 31	7.6	9.3	smallest of Ophiuchus globulars
10	6254	Oph	GC	16 57.1	−4 06	6.6	15.1	rich globular cluster; M12 is 3° NW
12	6218	Oph	GC	16 47.2	−1 57	6.8	14.5	loose globular cluster near M10
14	6402	Oph	GC	17 37.6	−3 15	7.6	11.7	200-mm telescope needed to resolve
19	6273	Oph	GC	17 02.6	−26 16	6.7	13.5	oblate globular; M62 4° south
62	6266	Oph	GC	17 01.2	−30 07	6.7	14.1	asymmetrical; in rich field

SEASONAL LISTING OF MESSIER OBJECTS (continued)

M#	NGC	Con	Type	RA (2000) Dec		m_v	Size	Remarks
				h m	° ′		′	
Summer Sky (cont)								
107	6171	Oph	GC	16 32.5	−13 03	8.1	10.0	small, faint globular
4	6121	Sco	GC	16 23.6	−26 32	5.8	26.3	bright globular near Antares
6	6405	Sco	OC	17 40.1	−32 13	4.2	33	!! Butterfly Cluster; best at low power
7	6475	Sco	OC	17 53.9	−34 49	3.3	80	!! excellent in binocs or rich-field scope
80	6093	Sco	GC	16 17.0	−22 59	7.3	8.9	very compressed globular
16	6611	Ser	EN + OC	18 18.6	−13 58	—	35 × 28	Eagle Neb. w/ open cl.; use neb. filter
8	6523	Sgr	EN	18 03.8	−24 23	—	45 × 30	!! Lagoon Nebula w/ open cl. NGC 6530
17	6618	Sgr	EN	18 20.8	−16 11	—	20 × 15	!! Swan or Omega Nebula; use neb. filter
18	6613	Sgr	OC	18 19.9	−17 08	6.9	10	sparse cluster; 1° south of M17
20	6514	Sgr	E/RN	18 02.3	−23 02	—	20 × 20	!! Trifid Nebula; look for dark lanes
21	6531	Sgr	OC	18 04.6	−22 30	5.9	13	0.7° NE of M20; sparse cluster
22	6656	Sgr	GC	18 36.4	−23 54	5.1	24	spectacular from southern latitude
23	6494	Sgr	OC	17 56.8	−19 01	5.5	27	bright, loose open cluster
24	—	Sgr	starcloud	18 16.5	−18 50	4.6	95 × 35	rich star cloud; best in big binoculars
25	IC 4725	Sgr	OC	18 31.6	−19 15	4.6	32	bright but sparse open cluster
28	6626	Sgr	GC	18 24.5	−24 52	6.8	11.2	compact globular near M22
54	6715	Sgr	GC	18 55.1	−30 29	7.6	9.1	not easily resolved
55	6809	Sgr	GC	19 40.0	−30 58	6.4	19.0	bright, loose globular cluster
69	6637	Sgr	GC	18 31.4	−32 21	7.6	7.1	small, poor globular cluster
70	6681	Sgr	GC	18 43.2	−32 18	8.0	7.8	small globular 2° east of M69
75	6864	Sgr	GC	20 06.1	−21 55	8.5	6	small and distant; 59 000 ly away
11	6705	Sct	OC	18 51.1	−6 16	5.8	13	!! Wild Duck Cl.; the best open cluster?
26	6694	Sct	OC	18 45.2	−9 24	8.0	14	bright, coarse cluster
56	6779	Lyr	GC	19 16.6	+30 11	8.3	7.1	within a rich starfield
57	6720	Lyr	PN	18 53.6	+33 02	8.8	>71″	!! Ring Nebula; an amazing smoke ring
71	6838	Sge	GC	19 53.8	+18 47	8.0	7.2	loose globular; looks like an open cluster
27	6853	Vul	PN	19 59.6	+22 43	7.3	>348″	!! Dumbbell Nebula; a superb object
29	6913	Cyg	OC	20 23.9	+38 32	6.6	6	small, poor open cluster 2° S of γ Cygni
39	7092	Cyg	OC	21 32.2	+48 26	4.6	31	very sparse cluster; use low power
The Autumn Sky								
2	7089	Aqr	GC	21 33.5	−0 49	6.4	12.9	200-mm telescope needed to resolve
72	6981	Aqr	GC	20 53.5	−12 32	9.3	5.9	near the Saturn Nebula, NGC 7009
73	6994	Aqr	OC	20 59.0	−12 38	8.9p	2.8	group of four stars only; an "asterism"
15	7078	Peg	GC	21 30.0	+12 10	6.0	12.3	rich, compact globular
30	7099	Cap	GC	21 40.4	−23 11	7.3	11	toughest in one-night Messier marathon
52	7654	Cas	OC	23 24.2	+61 35	6.9	12	young, rich cl.; faint Bubble Neb. nearby
103	581	Cas	OC	1 33.2	+60 42	7.4	6	three NGC open clusters nearby
31	224	And	G-SAb	0 42.7	+41 16	3.4	185 × 75	!! Andromeda Gal.; look for dust lanes
32	221	And	G-E2	0 42.7	+40 52	8.1	9 × 7	closest companion to M31
110	205	And	G-S0/E5 pec	0 40.4	+41 41	8.1	22 × 11	more distant companion to M31
33	598	Tri	G-SAcd	1 33.9	+30 39	5.7	67 × 42	large, diffuse spiral; requires dark sky
74	628	Psc	G-SAc	1 36.7	+15 47	9.4	11 × 11	faint, elusive spiral; tough in small scope
77	1068	Cet	G-SABab	2 42.7	−0 01	8.9	8.2 × 7.3	a Seyfert galaxy; with starlike nucleus
34	1039	Per	OC	2 42.0	+42 47	5.2	35	best at low power
76	650/51	Per	PN	1 42.4	+51 34	10.1	>65″	Little Dumbbell; faint but distinct

THE FINEST NGC OBJECTS
BY ALAN DYER

Those looking for an observing project beyond the Messier Catalogue turn to the New General Catalogue (NGC). The NGC contains 7840 entries and forms the core database of today's computerized backyard telescopes. To match the Messier Catalogue, this list contains 110 of the finest NGC objects visible from midnorthern latitudes. The seasonal order is similar to that used in the Messier list, and there is no overlap. While the brightness of the best NGCs rivals many Messier targets, at least a 200-mm telescope is required to see all 110 objects on this list. Most are easy; a few are challenging.

The NGC was originally published by J.L.E. Dreyer in 1888, a work that expanded upon Sir John Herschel's 1864 "General Catalogue." Supplementary "Index Catalogues" were published by Dreyer in 1895 and 1908. The first IC extends the NGC with another 1529 objects discovered visually between 1888 and 1894. Most are faint, elusive targets. (To provide a flavour of this extension to the NGC, one entry from the first IC is included on this list, IC 289.) The Second Index Catalogue contains 3857 entries, most discovered photographically between 1895 and 1907.

The *Sky Atlas 2000.0*, the sets of index card charts called *AstroCards*, *The Night Sky Observer's Guide Vol. 1 and 2* by Kepple and Sanner, and the *Uranometria 2000.0* star atlas (the latter two published by Willmann-Bell, Inc.) are recommended finder aids. Most planetarium and deep-sky charting computer programs, as well as computerized telescopes, include all the objects on this list and many more.

Notation below is as in the Messier list. Magnitudes (m_v) are visual, with the exception of those marked "p," which are photographic, or blue, magnitudes. Most galaxies appear smaller than the sizes listed. For open clusters, the number of stars (*) is also given. Data are taken from *The Deep Sky Field Guide to Uranometria 2000.0* (see the introduction to the Messier list), with some sizes rounded to two significant figures.

SEASONAL LISTING OF FINEST NGC OBJECTS

#	NGC	Con	Type	RA (2000) Dec		m_v	Size	Remarks
				h m	° '		'	
The Autumn Sky								
1	7009	Aqr	PN	21 04.2	−11 22	8.3p	>25″	!! Saturn Nebula; small bright oval
2	7293	Aqr	PN	22 29.6	−20 48	7.3	>769″	!! Helix Nebula; large, diffuse; use filter
3	7331	Peg	G-SAb	22 37.1	+34 25	9.5	10 × 4	!! large, bright spiral galaxy
4	7635	Cas	EN	23 20.7	+61 12	—	15 × 8	Bubble Neb.; very faint; 0.5° SW of M52
5	7789	Cas	OC	23 57.0	+56 44	6.7	15	!! 300*; faint but very rich cluster
6	185	Cas	G-E3	0 39.0	+48 20	9.2	14 × 12	companion to M31; small and faint
7	281	Cas	EN	0 52.8	+56 37	—	35 × 30	!! large faint nebulosity near η Cas
8	457	Cas	OC	1 19.1	+58 20	6.4	13	80*; rich; one of the best Cas. clusters
9	663	Cas	OC	1 46.0	+61 15	7.1	16	80*; look for NGCs 654 and 659 nearby
10	IC 289	Cas	PN	3 10.3	+61 19	13.3	>34″	dim oval smudge; use nebula filter!
11	7662	And	PN	23 25.9	+42 33	8.3	>12″	!! Blue Snowball; annular at high power
12	891	And	G-SAb	2 22.6	+42 21	9.9	13 × 3	!! faint, classic edge-on with dust lane
13	253	Scl	G-SABc	0 47.6	−25 17	7.6	30 × 7	!! very large and bright but at low altitude
14	772	Ari	G-SAb	1 59.3	+19 01	10.3	7.3 × 4.6	diffuse spiral galaxy
15	246	Cet	PN	0 47.0	−11 53	10.9	225″	large and faint with mottled structure
16	936	Cet	G-SB	2 27.6	−1 09	10.2	5.7 × 4.6	near M77; NGC 941 in the same field

SEASONAL LISTING OF FINEST NGC OBJECTS (continued)

#	NGC	Con	Type	RA (2000) h m	Dec ° '	m_V	Size '	Remarks
Autumn Sky (continued)								
17	869/884	Per	OC	2 21.0	+57 08	≈5	30/30	!! Double Cluster; 315*; use low power
18	1023	Per	G-SB0⁻	2 40.4	+39 04	9.3	8.6 × 4.2	bright lens-shaped galaxy near M34
19	1491	Per	EN	4 03.4	+51 19	—	25 × 25	visually small and faint emission nebula
20	1501	Cam	PN	4 07.0	+60 55	11.5	52″	faint; dark centre; look for NGC 1502
21	1232	Eri	G-SABc	3 09.8	–20 35	10.0	6.8 × 5.6	face-on spiral; look for NGC 1300 nearby
22	1535	Eri	PN	4 14.2	–12 44	9.6p	>18″	bright planetary with blue-grey disk

The Winter Sky

#	NGC	Con	Type	RA (2000) h m	Dec ° '	m_V	Size '	Remarks
23	1514	Tau	PN	4 09.2	+30 47	10.9	>114″	faint glow around 9.4ᵐ central star
24	1931	Aur	E/RN	5 31.4	+34 15	—	4 × 4	haze surrounding four close stars
25	1788	Ori	RN	5 06.9	–3 21	—	5 × 3	fairly bright but diffuse reflection nebula
26	1973+	Ori	E/RN	5 35.1	–4 44	—	≈20 × 10	NGC 1973-5-7 just N. of M42 and M43
27	2022	Ori	PN	5 42.1	+9 05	11.9	>18″	small, faint & distinct with annular form
28	2024	Ori	EN	5 41.9	–1 51	—	30 × 30	bright but masked by glow from ζ Ori
29	2194	Ori	OC	6 13.8	+12 48	8.5	8	80*, fairly rich; look for 2169 nearby
30	2371/2	Gem	PN	7 25.6	+29 29	11.3	>55″	faint double-lobed planetary; use filter
31	2392	Gem	PN	7 29.2	+20 55	9.2	>15″	!! Clown Face or Eskimo Nebula
32	2237+	Mon	EN	6 32.3	+5 03	—	80 × 60	!! Rosette Neb.; very large; use filter
33	2261	Mon	E/RN	6 39.2	+8 44	var	3.5 × 1.5	Hubble's Variable Neb.; comet-shaped
34	2359	CMa	EN	7 18.6	–13 12	—	9 × 6	bright; look for 2360 & 2362 nearby
35	2440	Pup	PN	7 41.9	–18 13	9.4	>14″	almost starlike; irregular at high power
36	2539	Pup	OC	8 10.7	–12 50	6.5	21	50*; rich cluster; near M46 and M47
37	2403	Cam	G-SABc	7 36.9	+65 36	8.5	26 × 13	!! very large & bright; visible in binocs.
38	2655	Cam	G-SAB0	8 55.6	+78 13	10.1	6.0 × 5.3	bright ellipse with starlike nucleus

The Spring Sky

#	NGC	Con	Type	RA (2000) h m	Dec ° '	m_V	Size '	Remarks
39	2683	Lyn	G-SAb	8 52.7	+33 25	9.8	8.4 × 2.4	nearly edge-on spiral; very bright
40	2841	UMa	G-SAb	9 22.0	+50 58	9.2	6.8 × 3.3	!! classic elongated spiral; very bright
41	3079	UMa	G-SBc	10 02.2	+55 41	10.9	8.0 × 1.5	edge-on spiral; NGC 2950 nearby
42	3184	UMa	G-SABc	10 18.3	+41 25	9.8	7.8 × 7.2	large, diffuse face-on spiral
43	3877	UMa	G-SAc	11 46.1	+47 30	11.0	5.1 × 1.1	edge-on; same field as χ UMa
44	3941	UMa	G-SB0°	11 52.9	+36 59	10.3	3.7 × 2.6	small, bright and elliptical
45	4026	UMa	G-S0	11 59.4	+50 58	10.8	4.6 × 1.2	lens-shaped edge-on near γ UMa
46	4088	UMa	G-SABbc	12 05.6	+50 33	10.6	5.4 × 2.1	nearly edge-on; NGC 4085 in same field
47	4157	UMa	G-SABb	12 11.1	+50 29	11.3	7.1 × 1.2	a thin sliver; NGC 4026 and 4088 nearby
48	4605	UMa	G-SBcp	12 40.0	+61 37	10.3	6.4 × 2.3	bright, distinct edge-on spiral
49	3115	Sex	G-S0⁻	10 05.2	–7 43	8.9	8.1 × 2.8	Spindle Galaxy; bright and elongated
50	3242	Hya	PN	10 24.8	–18 38	7.8	>16″	!! Ghost of Jupiter; small but bright
51	3003	LMi	G-Sbc?	9 48.6	+33 25	11.9	5.2 × 1.6	faint elongated streak
52	3344	LMi	G-SABbc	10 43.5	+24 55	9.9	6.9 × 6.4	diffuse face-on barred spiral
53	3432	LMi	G-SBm	10 52.5	+36 37	11.2	6.9 × 1.9	nearly edge-on; faint flat streak
54	2903	Leo	G-SABbc	9 32.2	+21 30	9.0	12 × 6	!! very large, bright elongated spiral
55	3384	Leo	G-SB0⁻	10 48.3	+12 38	9.9	5.5 × 2.9	same field as M105 and NGC 3389
56	3521	Leo	G-SAb	11 05.8	–0 02	9.0	12 × 6	very large, bright spiral
57	3607	Leo	G-SA0°	11 16.9	+18 03	9.9	4.6 × 4.1	NGC 3605 & 3608 in same field
58	3628	Leo	G-Sb pec	11 20.3	+13 36	9.5	14 × 4	large edge-on; same field as M65 & M66
59	4111	CVn	G-SA0⁺	12 07.1	+43 04	10.7	4.4 × 0.9	bright lens-shaped edge-on spiral
60	4214	CVn	G-I AB	12 15.6	+36 20	9.8	10 × 8	large irregular galaxy
61	4244	CVn	G-SAcd	12 17.5	+37 49	10.4	17 × 2	!! large distinct edge-on spiral

SEASONAL LISTING OF FINEST NGC OBJECTS (continued)

#	NGC	Con	Type	RA (2000) h m	Dec ° '	m_v	Size '	Remarks
Spring Sky (continued)								
62	4449	CVn	G-I Bm	12 28.2	+44 06	9.6	5.5 × 4.1	bright with odd rectangular shape
63	4490	CVn	G-SBd p	12 30.6	+41 38	9.8	6.4 × 3.3	Cocoon Gal.; bright spiral; 4485 in field
64	4631	CVn	G-SBd	12 42.1	+32 32	9.2	16 × 3	!! large edge-on; with companion 4627
65	4656/7	CVn	G-SBm p	12 44.0	+32 10	10.5	20 × 3	!! in field with 4631; NE end curves up
66	5005	CVn	G-SABbc	13 10.9	+37 03	9.8	5.8 × 2.8	bright elongated spiral near α CVn
67	5033	CVn	G-SAc	13 13.4	+36 36	10.2	10 × 5	large bright spiral near NGC 5005
68	4274	Com	G-SBab	12 19.8	+29 37	10.4	6.7 × 2.5	NGCs 4278/83/86 in same field
69	4414	Com	G-SAc	12 26.4	+31 13	10.1	4.4 × 3.0	bright spiral with starlike nucleus
70	4494	Com	G-E1-2	12 31.4	+25 47	9.8	4.6 × 4.4	small bright elliptical
71	4559	Com	G-SABc	12 36.0	+27 58	10.0	12 × 5	large spiral with coarse structure
72	4565	Com	G-SAb	12 36.3	+25 59	9.6	14 × 2	!! superb edge-on spiral with dust lane
73	4725	Com	G-SABab	12 50.4	+25 30	9.4	10 × 8	very bright, large spiral
74	4038/9	Crv	G-SB/IB	12 01.9	−18 52	≈10.4	≈5 × 3 ea.	"Antennae" interacting galaxies
75	4361	Crv	PN	12 24.5	−18 48	10.9	>45″	small and bright; with 13ᵐ central star
76	4216	Vir	G-SABb	12 15.9	+13 09	10.0	7.8 × 1.6	nearly edge-on; with NGC 4206 and 4222
77	4388	Vir	G-SAb	12 25.8	+12 40	11.0	5.7 × 1.6	with M84 and M86 in Markarian's Chain
78	4438	Vir	G-SA0/a	12 27.8	+13 01	10.2	8.9 × 3.6	paired w/ NGC 4435 to form the "Eyes"
79	4517	Vir	G-Scd	12 32.8	+00 07	10.4	9.9 × 1.4	faint edge-on spiral
80	4526	Vir	G-SAB0°	12 34.0	+7 42	9.7	7.1 × 2.9	between two 7th mag. stars
81	4535	Vir	G-SABc	12 34.3	+8 12	10.0	7.1 × 6.4	near M49 and 0.75° N of NGC 4526
82	4567/8	Vir	G-SABc	12 36.5	+11 15	≈11	≈3 × 2 ea.	"Siamese Twins" interacting galaxies
83	4699	Vir	G-Sab	12 49.0	−8 40	9.5	4.4 × 3.2	small & bright; look for M4697 3° N
84	4762	Vir	G-SB0°?	12 52.9	+11 14	10.3	9.1 × 2.2	flattest galaxy known; 4754 in same field
85	5746	Vir	G-SA?b	14 44.9	+1 57	10.3	6.8 × 1.0	fine edge-on near 109 Virginis
86	5466	Boo	GC	14 05.5	+28 32	9.0	11	loose class XII; like rich open cl.; faint
87	5907	Dra	G-SAc	15 15.9	+56 20	10.3	12 × 2	!! fine edge-on with dust lane; near 5866
88	6503	Dra	G-SAcd	17 49.4	+70 09	10.2	7.3 × 2.4	bright elongated spiral
89	6543	Dra	PN	17 58.6	+66 38	8.1	>18″	Cat's Eye Nebula; with 10.9ᵐ central star
The Summer Sky								
90	6210	Her	PN	16 44.5	+23 49	8.8	>14″	blue starlike planetary
91	6369	Oph	PN	17 29.3	−23 46	11.4	>30″	"Little Ghost"; look for 6309 nearby
92	6572	Oph	PN	18 12.1	+6 51	8.1	8″	tiny bright blue oval
93	6633	Oph	OC	18 27.7	+6 34	4.6	27	sparse wide field cluster; IC 4756 nearby
94	6712	Sct	GC	18 53.1	−8 42	8.2	7.2	small globular; look for IC 1295 in field
95	6781	Aql	PN	19 18.4	+6 33	11.4	>109″	pale version of the Owl Nebula, M97
96	6819	Cyg	OC	19 41.3	+40 11	7.3	9.5	150*; faint but rich cluster in Milky Way
97	6826	Cyg	PN	19 44.8	+50 31	8.8	>25″	!! Blinking Planetary; 10.6ᵐ central star
98	6888	Cyg	EN	20 12.0	+38 21	—	18 × 13	Crescent Nebula; faint; use nebula filter
99a	6960	Cyg	SNR	20 45.7	+30 43	—	70 × 6	!! Veil Nebula west half; use filter!
99b	6992/5	Cyg	SNR	20 56.4	+31 43	—	72 × 8	!! Veil Nebula east half; use filter!
100	7000	Cyg	EN	20 58.8	+44 20	—	120 × 100	!! North America; use filter & low power
101	7027	Cyg	PN	21 07.1	+42 14	8.5	15″	unusual protoplanetary nebula
102	6445	Sgr	PN	17 49.2	−20 01	11.2	>34″	small, bright and annular; near M23
103	6520	Sgr	OC	18 03.4	−27 54	7.6p	6	60*; small; dark nebula B86 in same field
104	6818	Sgr	PN	19 44.0	−14 09	9.3	>17″	"Little Gem"; annular; NGC 6822 0.75° S
105	6802	Vul	OC	19 30.6	+20 16	8.8	3.2	50*, at east end of Brocchi's Cluster
106	6940	Vul	OC	20 34.6	+28 18	6.3	31	60*; fairly rich cluster in Milky Way
107	6939	Cep	OC	20 31.4	+60 38	7.8	7	80*; very rich; NGC 6946 in same field
108	6946	Cep	G-SABcd	20 34.8	+60 09	8.8	13 × 13	faint, diffuse face-on spiral near 6939
109	7129	Cep	RN	21 42.8	+66 06	—	7 × 7	faint reflection neb. around sparse cluster
110	40	Cep	PN	0 13.0	+72 32	12.4	>37″	unusual red planetary; 11.6ᵐ central star

DAVID LEVY'S DEEP-SKY GEMS
By David H. Levy and Leo Enright[*]

Observers who have completed the Messier Catalogue and the Finest NGC Objects List are fortunate that David Levy is willing to share a list of his favourite deep-sky objects — those that particularly attracted his attention during his 40 years of comet hunting. The objects on this list are numbered as they are in his book, *Deep Sky Objects: The Best and Brightest From Four Decades of Comet Chasing*, (Prometheus Books, New York, 2005, 262 pp.) where approximately 400 objects are numbered chronologically, in the order of their being located in the night sky by the author. Renumbering the objects for this list would have added needless confusion, and would have abandoned the ready reference to the wealth of information in the book. U refers to the chart in *Uranometria 2000.0*. U–DSA refers to the chart in *Uranometria 2000.0 Deep Sky Atlas*. Chart numbers in parentheses indicate that the object is not labelled.

This list has been shortened to 154 objects, to harmonize with conventions of previously published RASC observing lists. Specifically, the following objects have been deleted: all objects south of Dec –30°, objects that appear in the Messier Catalogue, the Finest NGC Objects (L1 being the single exception), and Deep-Sky Challenge Objects lists. In addition, a number of double and variable stars, a few asterisms, a couple of photographic objects, and the gegenschein were deleted, though observing them is strongly encouraged. Refer to the book for information about these additional objects. This list is truly "RASC friendly," with all the objects readily visible from Canada.

Levy 384 deserves special note. Just as the terms "Plaskett's Star" and "Kemble's Cascade" recognize Canadian astronomers of the past, so also the term "Levy 384" is now the recognized name for a previously unnamed asterism.

SEASONAL LISTING OF DAVID LEVY'S DEEP-SKY GEMS

L#	Sky	L#	Sky	L#	Sky	L#	Sky	L#	Sky	L#	Sky	L#	Sky
1	WIN	57	AUT	133	SPR	172	SPR	206	SUM	240	AUT	280	AUT
5	SPR	59	AUT	134	SPR	178	SPR	207	SUM	243	SUM	281	AUT
6	SUM	62	AUT	135	SPR	181	SPR	208	SUM	245	SUM	282	AUT
8	WIN	64	AUT	136	SPR	182	SPR	209	SPR	247	AUT	284	AUT
19	SUM	81	AUT	137	SPR	183	SPR	210	SPR	249	AUT	286	WIN
27	SPR	82	SPR	138	SPR	184	SPR	211	SPR	255	SPR	296	WIN
28	SPR	83	SPR	145	SPR	185	SPR	212	SPR	256	WIN	300	SPR
29	SPR	95	WIN	147	SUM	186	SPR	213	SPR	257	SPR	315	SPR
31	AUT	96	WIN	149	SUM	187	SPR	214	SPR	259	SPR	317	SPR
34	AUT	98	SUM	156	SUM	188	SPR	215	SPR	260	SPR	325	AUT
35	WIN	99	AUT	158	WIN	189	SPR	217	SPR	261	SPR	326	SPR
36	SUM	110	SUM	159	WIN	190	SPR	219	SPR	262	SUM	331	SPR
37	SPR	112	AUT	160	WIN	191	SPR	220	SUM	263	AUT	334	SUM
38	AUT	114	WIN	161	WIN	192	SPR	223	AUT	266	SPR	337	SPR
41	SPR	116	WIN	162	WIN	193	SPR	224	AUT	267	SPR	338	AUT
42	SPR	121	SPR	163	SPR	195	WIN	225	WIN	268	SPR	340	AUT
44	WIN	123	WIN	164	SPR	196	SPR	226	WIN	270	SUM	341	AUT
50	WIN	124	WIN	165	SPR	201	SPR	231	SPR	271	SUM	342	AUT
51	SPR	125	WIN	167	SPR	202	SPR	232	SPR	273	WIN	367	AUT
53	AUT	129	SPR	169	SPR	203	SPR	236	SUM	276	AUT	381	SPR
55	AUT	130	SPR	170	SPR	204	SPR	238	AUT	277	AUT	382	SPR
56	AUT	131	SPR	171	SPR	205	SUM	239	AUT	278	AUT	384	WIN

*Deceased, 2009 Aug. 11.

DAVID LEVY'S DEEP-SKY GEMS

L#	NGC	RA (2000) Dec h m ° '	m_v	Size (')	U	U- DSA	Remarks
The Autumn Sky							
31	514	01 24.1 +12 55	11.7	3.9 × 2.9	173	100	Easily seen galaxy in Pisces
34	488	01 21.8 +05 15	10.3	5.5 × 4.0	217	100	Elongated galaxy in Pisces
38	7753	23 47.1 +29 20	12.0	3.2 × 1.7	89	45	Slightly elongated galaxy in Pegasus
53	752	01 57.8 +37 41	5.7	50	92	61	Very large open cluster in And
55	7664	23 26.6 +25 04	12.7	3.0 × 1.7	169	63	Galaxy in Pegasus
56	270	00 50.6 –08 39	12.1	2.0 × 1.7	262	140	Galaxy in Cetus
57	7723	23 38.8 –12 58	11.2	2.8 × 1.9	304	121	Galaxy in Aquarius
59	524	01 24.8 +09 32	10.2	3.5 × 3.5	173	100	Round galaxy in Pisces
62	898	02 23.3 +41 57	12.9	1.8 × 0.5	91	43	Elongated galaxy in Andromeda
64	404	01 09.4 +35 43	10.3	6.1 × 6.1	91	62	Round galaxy near Beta And
81	147	00 33.2 +48 30	9.5	15.0 × 9.4	60	30	Comet-like galaxy; satellite of M31
99	949	02 30.8 +37 08	11.8	3.3 × 2.1	93	61	Very cometary galaxy in Tri
112	7023	21 00.5 +68 10	7.0	10 × 8	32	9	Unusual-looking nebula in Cepheus
223	150	00 34.3 –27 48	11.3	3.4 × 1.6	306	141	Elongated galaxy in Sculptor
224	IC 1830	02 39.1 –27 27	11.9	1.9 × 1.5	310	157	Galaxy in Fornax
238	578	01 30.5 –22 40	11.0	3.9 × 2.2	308	158	Elongated galaxy in Cetus
239	247	00 47.1 –20 46	9.2	19.0 × 5.5	306	158	Very elongated galaxy in Cetus
240	157	00 34.8 –08 24	10.4	4.0 × 2.4	261	121	Elongated "Amoeba Galaxy" in Cetus
247	7217	22 07.9 +31 22	10.1	3.5 × 3.0	122	46	Round galaxy in Pegasus
249	7457	23 01.0 +30 09	11.2	4.1 × 2.5	124	46	Elongated galaxy in Pegasus
263	7006	21 01.5 +16 11	10.5	2.8	209	83	Globular cluster in Delphinus
276	7814	00 03.3 +16 09	10.6	6.0 × 2.5	170	81	Elongated galaxy in Pegasus
277	7184	22 02.7 –20 49	11.2	6.5 × 1.4	346	142	Very elongated galaxy in Aquarius
278	474	01 20.1 +03 25	11.5	10.0 × 9.2	217	120	Galaxy near NGC 470 in Pisces
280	7721	23 38.8 –06 31	11.6	3.3 × 1.3	304	121	Elongated galaxy in Aquarius
281	7727	23 39.9 –12 18	10.6	5.6 × 4.0	304	121	Round galaxy in Aquarius
282	7314	22 35.8 –26 03	10.9	4.2 × 1.7	347	142	Elongated galaxy in Piscis Austrinus
284	718	01 53.2 +04 12	11.7	2.4 × 2.0	218	119	Round galaxy in Pisces
325	IC 1795	02 26.5 +62 04	—	40 × 15	17	17	Bright nebula in Cassiopeia
338	1042	02 40.4 –08 26	11.0	4.2 × 3.3	215	139	Galaxy in Cetus
340	1134	02 53.6 +13 00	12.1	2.3 × 0.8	175	99	Round galaxy in Aries
341	755	01 56.4 –09 04	12.6	2.8 × 1.1	264	139	Elongated galaxy in Cetus
342	91	00 21.8 +22 25	13.7	2.2 × 0.8	126	63	Galaxy in And, in galaxy cluster
367	613	01 34.3 –29 25	10.0	5.2 × 2.6	352	158	Special galaxy in Sculptor
The Winter Sky							
1	1931	05 31.4 +34 15	13.0	4 × 4	97	59	A "Finest"condensed nebula in Aur
8	1624	04 40.4 +50 27	13.0	5 × 5	40	42	Cluster with nebulosity in Perseus
35	2420	07 38.5 +21 34	8.3	10	139	75	Open cluster in Gemini
44	1333	03 29.2 +31 25	—	6 × 3	94	60	A weird reflection nebula in Perseus
50	1579	04 30.2 +35 16	—	12 × 8	96	60	Reflection nebula in Perseus
95	1999	05 36.5 –06 42	10.0	2 × 2	271	136	Diffuse nebula in Orion
96	2681	08 53.5 +51 19	10.3	5.3 × 3.5	44	39	Galaxy in Ursa Major
114	1637	04 41.5 –02 51	10.8	3.4 × 2.6	224	117	Comet-like round galaxy in Eridanus
116	2158	06 07.5 +24 06	8.6	5	136	76	Compact cluster near M35 in Gemini
123	1600	04 31.7 –05 05	10.9	2.3 × 1.5	223	117	Round, diffuse galaxy in Eridanus
124	2174	06 09.7 +20 30	—	40 × 30	137	76	Large field of dust in Orion
125	2023	05 41.6 –02 14	—	10 × 10	226	116	Nebula near Zeta Orionis
158	IC 2194/6/7	07 33.7 +31 19	(12.5)	—	(100)	57	Three of the Castor Cluster galaxies
159	2264	06 41.1 +09 53	3.9	20	183	95	Christmas Tree Cluster in Mon
160	2254	06 36.6 +07 40	9.1	4	182	95	Open cluster and star chain in Mon
161	2245	06 32.7 +10 10	—	5 × 4	182	95	Comet-like bright nebula in Mon
162	2252	06 35.0 +05 23	7.7	20	227	95	Open cluster; like rope of stars, in Mon
195	2419	07 38.1 +38 53	10.3	4.1	100	95	"Intergalactic Wanderer" in Lynx
225	1187	03 02.6 –22 52	10.7	5.2 × 3.6	311	157	Round galaxy in Eridanus
226	2613	08 33.4 –22 58	10.5	7.6 × 1.9	321	153	Edge-on galaxy in Pyxis
256	IC 2367	08 24.2 –18 46	12.5	2.3 × 0.5	321	153	Galaxy in Puppis

DAVID LEVY'S DEEP-SKY GEMS (continued)

L#	NGC	RA (2000) Dec h m ° '	m_v	Size (')	U	U- DSA	Remarks
The Winter Sky (cont)							
273	1746	05 03.6 +23 49	6.1	42	134	77	Beautiful open cluster in Taurus
286	1360	03 33.3 −25 51	9.4	6.5	312	156	Beautiful planetary nebula in Fornax
296	2362	07 18.8 −24 57	4.1	8	319	153	Open cluster in Canis Major
384	Levy384	08 15.6 −13 58	—	2	(275)	(134)	Compact asterism in Pup (Special!)
The Spring Sky							
5	5676	14 32.8 +49 28	11.2	3.7 × 1.6	77	36	Small elliptical galaxy in Bootes
27	5377	13 56.3 +47 14	11.3	4.1 × 2.3	76	36	Galaxy near Big Dipper's handle
28	5473	14 04.7 +54 54	11.4	2.2 × 1.7	49	23	Comet-like galaxy near M101 in UMa
29	5474	14 05.0 +53 40	10.8	6.0 × 4.9	49	23	Galaxy near M101 in Ursa Major
37	3055	09 55.3 +04 16	12.1	2.0 × 1.1	234	113	Comet-like galaxy in Sextans
41	3810	11 41.0 +11 28	10.8	3.8 × 2.6	192	91	Round galaxy in Leo
42	4340	12 23.0 +16 43	11.2	3.7 × 3.1	193	91	Galaxy near NGC 4350 in Com
51	Arp 321	09 38.9 −04 52	(12.5)	—	(233)	113	"Larry, Moe, & Curly" galaxies in Hya
82	5634	14 29.6 −05 59	9.4	4.9	287	109	Globular cluster in Virgo
83	5638	14 29.7 +03 14	11.2	2.3 × 2.1	242	109	Comet-like galaxy in Virgo
121	5846	15 06.4 +01 36	10.0	3.0 × 3.0	243	108	Galaxy in Virgo
129	U 5373	10 00.0 +05 20	11.3	5.5 × 3.7	234	113	Sextans B galaxy; Local Group member
130	3198	10 19.9 +45 33	10.3	9.2 × 3.5	72	39	Very elongated galaxy in UMa
131	2964	09 42.9 +31 51	11.3	3.2 × 1.8	103	56	Galaxy contains Mrk 404 in Leo
133	3070	09 58.0 +10 22	12.3	1.6 × 1.6	189	93	Round galaxy, near NGC 3069, in Leo
134	4319	12 21.7 +75 19	11.9	2.8 × 2.1	9	5	Galaxy near 4291 & 4386 in Draco
135	4256	12 18.7 +65 54	11.9	4.1 × 0.8	25	13	Edge-on galaxy in Draco
136	3738	11 35.8 +54 31	11.7	3.2 × 2.8	47	24	Galaxy near M97 in Ursa Major
137	3718	11 32.6 +53 04	10.8	10.0x 4.7	47	24	Elongated galaxy in Ursa Major
138	3953	11 53.8 +52 20	10.1	6.0 × 3.2	47	24	Very elongated galaxy in Ursa Major
145	4473	12 29.8 +13 26	10.2	3.7 × 2.4	193	91	Very elongated galaxy in Com
163	2775	09 10.3 +07 02	10.1	4.6 × 3.7	187	93	Round galaxy in Cancer
164	3486	11 00.4 +28 58	10.5	6.6 × 4.7	106	73	Round galaxy in Leo Minor
165	3245	10 27.3 +28 30	10.8	2.9 × 2.0	105	73	Elongated galaxy in Leo Minor
167	3310	10 38.7 +53 30	10.8	3.5 × 3.2	46	25	Round galaxy in Ursa Major
169	2986	09 44.3 −21 17	10.6	4.1 × 3.4	323	152	Round galaxy in Hydra
170	4651	12 43.7 +16 24	10.8	3.5 × 2.3	194	90	Round galaxy in Com
171	4450	12 28.5 +17 05	10.1	5.0 × 3.4	148	72	Elongated galaxy in Com
172	4689	12 47.8 +13 46	10.9	3.7 × 3.2	194	90	Elongated galaxy in Com
178	4596	12 39.9 +10 11	10.4	4.6 × 4.1	194	90	Elongated galaxy in Virgo
181	3887	11 47.1 −16 51	10.6	3.5 × 2.4	292	131	Round galaxy in Crater
182	4636	12 42.8 +02 41	9.5	7.1 × 5.2	239	110	Galaxy with bright core in Virgo
183	4818	12 56.8 −08 31	11.1	3.4 × 1.4	284	130	Very elongated galaxy in Virgo
184	5147	13 26.3 +02 06	11.8	1.6 × 1.5	240	110	Round galaxy in Virgo
185	5248	13 37.5 +08 53	10.3	6.2 × 4.6	196	90	Round galaxy in Bootis
186	5371	13 55.7 +40 28	10.6	4.1 × 3.2	76	36	Round galaxy in Canes Venatici
187	5020	13 12.6 +12 36	11.7	3.0 × 2.6	195	90	Elongated galaxy in Virgo
188	4591	12 39.3 +06 01	13.0	1.6 × 0.8	194	90	Elongated galaxy in Virgo
189	5127	13 23.8 +31 34	11.9	2.3 × 1.7	109	53	Round galaxy in Canes Venatici
190	4956	13 05.1 +35 11	12.4	1.5 × 1.5	109	53	Round galaxy in Canes Venatici
191	4772	12 53.5 +02 10	11.0	2.7 × 1.3	239	110	Galaxy in Virgo
192	4536	12 34.5 +02 11	10.6	6.4 × 2.6	239	110	Very elongated galaxy in Virgo
193	4129	12 08.9 −09 02	12.5	2.3 × 0.7	283	131	Elongated galaxy in Virgo
196	5694	14 39.6 −26 32	9.2	3.6	332	148	Tombaugh's Cluster in Hydra
201	3865	11 44.9 −09 14	12.0	2.0 × 1.6	282	131	Diffuse galaxy in Crater
202	5427	14 03.4 −06 02	11.4	2.6 × 1.8	286	129	Galaxy, interacting with 5426, in Vir
203	5668	14 33.4 +04 27	11.5	3.2 × 2.8	242	109	Comet-like galaxy in Virgo
204	5850	15 07.1 +01 33	10.8	4.6 × 4.1	243	108	Comet-like galaxy in Virgo

DAVID LEVY'S DEEP-SKY GEMS (continued)

L#	NGC	RA (2000) Dec h m ° '	m_v	Size (')	U	U-DSA	Remarks
The Spring Sky (cont)							
209	3049	09 54.8 +09 16	12.1	2.3 × 1.5	188	93	Comet-like galaxy in Leo
210	4685	12 47.1 +19 28	12.6	1.5 × 0.9	149	71	"Winking galaxy" in Com
211	4779	12 53.8 +09 44	12.4	1.9 × 1.7	194	90	Round galaxy in Virgo
212	4795	12 55.0 +08 04	12.1	1.9 × 1.7	194	90	Round galaxy in Virgo
213	4623	12 42.2 +07 41	12.2	2.0 × 0.7	194	90	Very elongated galaxy in Virgo
214	4713	12 50.0 +05 19	11.7	2.9 × 1.8	194	90	Elongated galaxy in Virgo
215	4688	12 47.8 +04 20	11.9	4.0 × 4.0	239	110	Very large galaxy in Virgo
217	3923	11 51.0 −28 48	9.6	6.9 × 4.8	368	150	Elongated galaxy in Hydra
219	3309	10 36.6 −27 31	11.0	4.4 × 3.1	325	151	Hydra I galaxy cluster (five members)
	3311	10 36.7 −27 32	10.9	4.0 × 3.6			
	3312	10 37.0 −27 34	11.8	3.4 × 1.1			
	3314	10 37.4 −27 41	12.8	1.5 × 0.8			(actually two spirals!!)
	3316	10 37.6 −27 36	12.6	1.4 × 1.2			
231	5364	13 56.2 +05 01	10.5	6.6 × 5.1	196	89	Elongated galaxy in Virgo
232	5068	13 18.9 −21 02	9.6	7.1 × 6.6	330	149	Very large galaxy in Virgo
255	5016	13 12.1 +24 06	12.8	1.7 × 1.3	150	71	Round galaxy in Com
257	4866	12 59.5 +14 10	11.2	5.5 × 1.2	194	90	Elongated galaxy in Virgo
259	4722	12 51.5 −13 19	12.9	1.5 × 0.7	284	130	Round galaxy in Corvus
260	4519	12 33.5 +08 39	11.8	3.5 × 2.3	194	90	Galaxy in Virgo
261	5350	13 53.4 +40 22	11.3	3.1 × 2.5	76	36	Galaxy in Canes Venatici
266	5962	15 36.5 +16 37	11.3	2.6 × 1.8	199	88	Round galaxy in Serpens
267	5247	13 38.1 −17 53	10.1	5.2 × 3.2	331	130	Beautiful, diffuse spiral in Virgo
268	5690	14 37.7 +02 17	11.8	3.3 × 1.0	242	109	Very elongated galaxy in Virgo
300	3226	10 23.4 +19 54	11.4	2.5 × 2.2	144	73	Galaxy in Leo
315	5146	13 26.5 −12 19	12.3	1.8 × 1.2	285	130	Round galaxy in Virgo
317	5838	15 05.4 +02 06	10.9	3.5 × 1.6	242	108	Elongated galaxy in Virgo
326	4570	12 36.9 +07 15	10.9	4.3 × 1.3	194	90	Comet-like elongated galaxy in Virgo
331	3319	10 39.2 +41 41	11.1	6.9 × 4.0	72	38	Graceful spiral galaxy in Ursa Major
337	0957− +561A/B	10 01.3 +55 54	15.5	—	45	25	Famous double quasar in Ursa Major (gravitational lens; distinct in 16″ scope)
381	U5470	10 08.5 +12 18	10.2	12.0 × 9.3	189	92	Dwarf elliptical galaxy in Leo
382	U6253	11 13.5 +22 10	12.0	15.0 ×12.5	146	73	Galaxy in Leo
The Summer Sky							
6	6229	16 47.0 +47 32	9.4	4.5	80	34	Compact globular cluster in Hercules
19	6207	16 43.1 +36 50	11.5	3.0 × 1.1	114	50	Spiral galaxy near M13 in Hercules
36	6364	17 24.5 +29 24	12.9	1.5 × 1.2	115	50	Comet-like galaxy in Hercules
98	6709	18 51.5 +10 21	6.7	13	205	85	Open cluster in Aquila
110	6760	19 11.2 +01 02	9.1	6.6	251	105	Globular cluster in Aquila
147	6638	18 30.9 −25 30	9.1	5	340	145	Globular cluster in Sagittarius
149	6553	18 09.3 −25 54	8.1	8.1	339	145	Faint globular cluster in Sagittarius
156	6934	20 34.2 +07 24	8.7	5.9	208	84	Globular cluster in Delphinus
205	6106	16 18.8 +07 25	12.2	2.3 × 1.2	201	87	Galaxy in Hercules
206	6118	16 21.8 −02 17	11.7	4.6 × 1.9	246	107	Galaxy in Serpens
207	6384	17 32.4 +07 04	10.4	6.4 × 4.3	203	86	Galaxy in Ophiuchus
208	6426	17 44.9 +03 00	11.1	3.2	248	106	Globular cluster in Ophiuchus
220	6910	20 23.1 +40 47	7.4	7	84	32	Open cluster in Cygnus
236	6181	16 32.3 +19 50	11.9	2.3 × 0.9	156	69	Galaxy in Hercules
243	6440	17 48.9 −20 22	9.1	5.4	338	146	Globular cluster in Sagittarius
245	6781	19 18.4 +06 33	11.4	>1.8	206	85	Planetary nebula in Aquila
262	6814	19 42.7 −10 19	11.2	3.0 × 3.0	297	125	Round galaxy in Aquila
270	6535	18 03.8 −00 18	10.5	3.6	249	106	Globular cluster in Serpens
271	6287	17 05.2 −22 42	9.3	5.0	337	146	Globular cluster in Ophiuchus
334	6342	17 21.2 −19 35	9.8	3	338	146	Globular cluster near M9 in Oph

DEEP-SKY CHALLENGE OBJECTS
By Alan Dyer and Alister Ling

The beauty of the deep sky extends well past the best and brightest objects. The attraction of observing is not the sight of an object itself but our intellectual contact with what it *is*. A faint, stellar point in Virgo evokes wonder when you try to fathom the depths of this quasar billions of light-years away. The eclectic collection of objects below is designed to introduce some "fringe" catalogues while providing challenging targets for a wide range of apertures. Often more important than sheer aperture are factors such as the quality of sky, quality of the optics, use of an appropriate filter, and the observer's experience. Don't be afraid to tackle some of these with a smaller telescope.

Objects are listed in order of right ascension. Abbreviations are the same as in the Messier and NGC lists, with DN = dark nebula. Three columns have been added: **UI** and **UII** respectively list the charts where you'll find that object in the original edition and the 2001 second edition of *Uranometria 2000.0*; the last column suggests the minimum aperture, in millimetres, needed to see that object. Most data are taken from *Sky Catalogue 2000.0, Vol. 2*. Some visual magnitudes are from other sources.

#	Object	Con	Type	RA (2000) h m	Dec ° '	m_v	Size '	UI	UII	Min. Aper. mm
1	NGC 7822	Cep	E/RN	0 03.6	+68 37	—	60 × 30	15	8	300
	large, faint emission nebula; rated "eeF"; also look for E/R nebula Ced 214 (associated w/ star cluster Berkeley 59) 1° S									
2	IC 59	Cas	E/RN	0 56.7	+61 04	—	10 × 5	36	18	200–250
	faint emission/reflection nebula paired with IC 63 very close to γ Cas.; requires clean optics; rated as "pF"									
3	NGC 609	Cas	OC	1 37.2	+64 33	11.0	3.0	16	17	250–300
	faint patch at low power; high power needed to resolve this rich cluster (also look for Trumpler 1 cluster 3° S)									
4	IC 1795	Cas	EN	2 24.7	+61 54	—	27 × 13	17	29	200
	brightest part of a complex of nebulosity that includes IC 1805 and IC 1848; use a nebula filter									
5	Maffei I	Cas	G-E3	2 36.3	+59 39	≈14	5 × 3	38	29	300
	heavily reddened galaxy; very faint; requires large aperture and black skies; nearby Maffei II for extremists									
6	NGC 1049	For	GC	2 39.7	–34 29	11.0	0.6	354	175	250–300
	Class V globular in dwarf "Fornax System" Local Group galaxy 630 000 ly away; galaxy itself invisible?									
7	Abell 426	Per	Gs	3 19.8	+41 31	12–16	≈30	63	43, A4	200–400
	Perseus galaxy cluster 300 million ly away; mag. 11.6 NGC 1275 Perseus A at centre; see close-up chart A4									
8	NGC 1432/35	Tau	RN	3 46.1	+23 47	—	30 × 30	132	78, A12	100–150
	Pleiades nebulosity (also includes IC 349); brightest around Merope; requires transparent skies and clean optics									
9	IC 342	Cam	G-SBc	3 46.8	+68 06	≈12	17 × 17	18	16	200–300
	large and diffuse face-on spiral; member of UMa–Cam cloud (Kemble's Cascade of stars also on this chart)									
10	NGC 1499	Per	EN	4 00.7	+36 37	—	145 × 40	95	60	80–125 RFT
	California Nebula; very large and faint; use a wide-field telescope or big binoculars plus Hβ filter									
11	IC 405	Aur	E/RN	5 16.2	+34 16	—	30 × 19	97	59	200
	Flaming Star Nebula associated with runaway star AE Aurigae; see Burnham's Handbook p. 285 (also look for IC 410)									
12	HH 1	Ori	E	5 36.3	–06 45	≈14.5	8″	271	136	250
	Herbig-Haro 1; best with no filter at 250× or more; bipolar jets from forming star; not plotted; 2.5′ SW NGC 1999									
13	IC 434 / B 33	Ori	E/DN	5 40.9	–2 28	—	60 × 10	226	116	100–150 in dark sky!
	B 33 is the Horsehead Nebula, a dark nebula superimposed on a very faint emission nebula IC 434; use Hβ filter									
14	Sh 2-276	Ori	EN	5 48	+1 —	—	600 × 30!	226	116	100–150 RFT
	Barnard's Loop; SNR or interstellar bubble? difficult to detect due to size; use filter and sweep with wide field									
15	Abell 12	Ori	PN	6 02.4	+9 39	≈13	37″	181	96	250–300
	plotted on UII as PK 198.6–6.3; on NW edge of μ Orionis; OIII filter required									
16	IC 443	Gem	SNR	6 16.9	+22 47	—	50 × 40	137	76	250–300
	faint supernova remnant very close to η Gem.; use filter (also look for NGC 2174 and Sh 2–247 on this chart)									
17	J 900	Gem	PN	6 25.9	+17 47	12.2	8″	137	76	200
	Jonckheere 900; bright starlike planetary; plotted as PK 194.2+2.5 in UII; use OIII filter & high power									
18	IC 2177	Mon	E/RN	7 05.1	–10 42	—	120 × 40	273	135	200–300
	Seagull Nebula; large, faint; contains bright patches Gum 1 (–10°28′), NGC 2327 (–11°18′) & Ced 90 (–12°20′)									

DEEP-SKY CHALLENGE OBJECTS (continued)

#	Object	Con	Type	RA (2000) Dec h m	° '	m_v	Size '	UI	UII	Min. Aper. mm
19	PK 205 +14.2	Gem	PN	7 29.0	+13 15	≈13	≈700″	184	95	200–250

Medusa Nebula or Abell 21; larger than plotted in UI; impressive in large aperture w/ OIII filter

20	PK 164 +31.1	Lyn	PN	7 57.8	+53 25	≈14	400′	43	26	250

Jones–Emberson 1; faint with two small components; use OIII filter; sometimes confused with nearby NGC 2474–75

21	Leo I	Leo	G-E3	10 08.4	+12 18	9.8	10.7 × 8.3	189	93	300

dwarf elliptical; satellite of Milky Way; very low surface brightness; 0.3° N of Regulus! requires clean optics

22	Abell 1367	Leo	Gs	11 44.0	+19 57	13–16	≈60	147	72, A11	300–400

cluster of some 30 or more galaxies within a 1° field near 93 Leonis; Copeland's Septet nearby

23	NGC 3172	UMi	G-?	11 50.2	+89 07	13.6	0.7 × 0.7	2	1	250

"Polarissima Borealis"—closest galaxy to the north celestial pole; small, faint, and otherwise unremarkable

24	NGC 4236	Dra	G-SBb	12 16.7	+69 28	9.6	18.6 × 6.9	25	13	200–250

very large, dim barred spiral; a diffuse glow (NGC 4395 on UII chart #54 a similar large diffuse face-on)

25	Mrk 205	Dra	Quasar	12 21.6	+75 18	14.5	stellar	9	5	300

Markarian 205; a faint star on SW edge of NGC 4319; centre of redshift controversy

26	3C 273	Vir	Quasar	12 29.1	+2 03	12≈13	stellar	238	111	250–300

at 2–3 billon ly away, one of the most distant objects visible in amateur telescopes; magnitude variable

27	NGC 4676	Com	Gs	12 46.2	+30 44	14.1p	2 × 1	108	53	250

"The Mice" or VV 224—two classic interacting galaxies; very faint double nature detectable at high power

28	Abell 1656	Com	Gs	13 00.1	+27 58	12–16	≈60	149	71, A8	250–300

Coma Berenices galaxy cluster; very rich; 400 million ly away; brightest member NGC 4889; see close-up chart A8

29	NGC 5053	Com	GC	13 16.4	+17 42	9.8	10.5	150	71	100–200

faint and very loose globular 1° SE of M53; requires large aperture to resolve; difficult in hazy skies; class XI

30	NGC 5897	Lib	GC	15 17.4	–21 01	8.6	12.6	334	148	150–200

large and loose; easily hidden in hazy skies at higher latitude; brightest stars mag 13.3, main branch mag 16.3

31	Abell 2065	CrB	Gs	15 22.7	+27 43	≈16	≈30	154	69	500 in superb sky!

Corona Borealis galaxy cluster; perhaps the most difficult object for amateur telescopes; 1.5 billion ly away

32	NGC 6027	Ser	Gs	15 59.2	+20 45	≈15	2 × 1	155	69	400

Seyfert's Sextet (6027 A–F); compact group of 6 small and very faint galaxies; see Burnham's Handbook p. 1793

33	B 72	Oph	DN	17 23.5	–23 38	—	30	338	146	80–125 RFT

Barnard's dark S-Nebula or "The Snake"; opacity of 6/6; 1.5° NNE of θ Ophiuchi; area rich in dark nebulae

34	NGC 6791	Lyr	OC	19 20.7	+37 51	9.5	16	118	48	200–250

large, faint but very rich open cluster with 300 stars; a faint smear in smaller instruments; Type II 3 r

35	PK 64 +5.1	Cyg	PN	19 34.8	+30 31	9.6	8″	118	48	200

Campbell's Hydrogen Star; very bright but very starlike; also catalogued as star BD +30°3639

36	M 1-92	Cyg	RN	19 36.3	+29 33	11.0	12″ × 6″	118	48	250–300

Minkowski 1-92 or Footprint Nebula; bright, starlike reflection nebula; double at high mag.; associated star invisible

37	NGC 6822	Sgr	G-Irr	19 44.9	–14 48	≈11	10.2 × 9.5	297	125	100–150

Barnard's Galaxy; member of the Local Group; large but very low surface brightness; requires transparent skies

38	Palomar 11	Aql	GC	19 45.2	–8 00	9.8	3.2	297	125	200–300

brightest of 15 heavily reddened GCs found on Sky Survey; magnitude is misleading; 11 Terzan GCs more challenging

39	IC 4997	Sge	PN	20 20.2	+16 45	10.9	2″	163	84	200

bright but starlike planetary; the challenge is to see the disk! blink the field with and without a nebula filter

40	IC 1318	Cyg	EN	20 26.2	+40 30	—	large	84	32, A2	80–150 RFT

complex of nebulosity around γ Cygni; multitude of patches in rich starfield; use a very wide field plus filter

41	PK 80 –6.1	Cyg	PN?	21 02.3	+36 42	13.5	16″	121	47	250

the "Egg Nebula"; a very small proto-planetary nebula; can owners of large telescopes detect polarization?

42	IC 1396	Cep	EN	21 39.1	+57 30	—	170 × 140	57	19	100–125 RFT

extremely large and diffuse area of emission nebulosity; use nebula filter and very wide field optics in dark sky

43	IC 5146	Cyg	E/RN	21 53.5	+47 16	—	12 × 12	86	31	200–250

Cocoon Nebula; faint and diffuse; use Hβ filter; at the end of the long filamentary dark nebula Barnard 168

44	NGC 7317–20	Peg	Gs	22 36.1	+33 57	13–14	≈1 ea.	123	46	250–300

Stephan's Quintet; 0.5° SSW of NGC 7331; easy to pick out 3 or 4 (also look for "companions" to 7331)

45	Jones 1	Peg	PN	23 35.9	+30 28	12.1	332″	124	45	250–300

plotted as PK 104.2 –29.6 in UII; large dim glow; OIII filter required

SOUTHERN HEMISPHERE SPLENDOURS
By Alan Whitman

Any serious deep-sky observer yearns to experience the far-southern sky, the home of the finest emission nebula (the Carina Nebula), the most obvious dark nebula (the Coalsack), arguably the best open cluster (NGC 3532), the most impressive globular cluster (47 Tucanae), the biggest and brightest globular cluster (Omega Centauri, although it is likely the core of a small galaxy absorbed by the Milky Way), the galaxy that offers amateur telescopes hundreds of targets within it (the Large Magellanic Cloud), and the closest naked-eye star (Alpha Centauri), just to name a few. Here is a checklist of "must-see" splendours, rated with one to three exclamation marks, plus 17 other significant objects. The author has observed all of these objects under fine, dark skies.

Declination –35 was chosen as the cutoff for this list. However, three slightly more northerly objects that greatly benefit from being viewed higher in the sky were included, notably M83, because it is one of the finest face-on spiral galaxies in the southern sky, but its three spiral arms are not well seen from Canada. Countries like Australia, Chile, and Namibia offer the best views of these magnificent objects. However, most objects on the list can be viewed from the southern Caribbean; many are visible from Hawaii or from the Florida Keys; and some, including Omega Centauri, Centaurus A, and the many glorious clusters in the tail of Scorpius, can be appreciated from the American Southwest. February through April are the preferred months for a southern observing run, since there are no far-southern splendours (those with exclamation marks) located between 20h and 0h of right ascension.

Data for open and globular clusters are from Archinal and Hynes's 2003 reference book *Star Clusters*, with the two noted exceptions. Data for other objects are mostly from Malin and Frew's highly recommended 1995 guidebook *Hartung's Astronomical Objects for Southern Telescopes*, 2nd ed. The dimensions of galaxies and nebulae and a few other numbers are mostly from various lists in the *Observer's Handbook* or from Sinnott's 1988 work, *NGC 2000.0*. Various sources, including private communications, have provided some difficult-to-obtain data.

Notation used below is mostly as defined on p. 307; in addition, * = star or stars, CC = concentration class of a globular cluster (see p. 299), Ast = asterism, and DN = dark nebula. Numbers without a prefix in the **NGC** column are NGC numbers.

#	NGC	Con	Type	RA (2000) Dec h m ° '		m_v	Size '	Remarks
1	55	Scl	G-Sc	0 14.9	–39 11	7.9	32 × 6	! in 100-mm scope: diffuse splinter
2	104	Tuc	GC	0 24.1	–72 05	4.0	50	!!! 47 Tuc; yellow core in 370-mm scope
3	β	Tuc	Dbl*	0 31.5	–62 58	4.4, 4.5	27″	! both blue-white
4	SMC	Tuc	G-Im	0 52.6	–72 48	2.3	3.6°	!!! many NGCs included
5	300	Scl	G-Sc	0 54.9	–37 41	8.1	22 × 16	face-on spiral; low surface brightness
6	362	Tuc	GC	1 03.2	–70 51	6.8	14	! Milky Way GC beside SMC; CC III
7	p	Eri	Dbl*	2 46.3	–30 17	5.8, 5.8	12″	! both yellow-orange dwarfs
8	1097	For	G-SBb	2 46.3	–30 17	9.3	13 × 8	! in 300-mm scope: bar and tough arms
9	θ	Eri	Dbl*	2 58.3	–40 18	3.2, 4.4	8.3″	! both white
10	1313	Ret	G-SBc	3 18.3	–66 30	8.9	9 × 7	in 370-mm scope: bar, one spiral arm
11		For	Gal Cl.	3 22.7	–37 12	—	—	position is for bright 1316, Fornax A
12	1365	For	G-SBc	3 33.6	–36 08	9.5	14 × 10	!! in 300-mm scope: bar with 2 spiral arms
13	f	Eri	Dbl*	3 48.6	–37 37	4.9, 5.4	8.1″	! yellowish stars
14	1566	Dor	G-Sc	4 20.0	–54 56	9.4	13 × 9	! in 250-mm scope: 2 classic spiral arms
15	ι	Pic	Dbl*	4 50.9	–53 28	5.6, 6.5	12.5″	! very nice yellow pair
16	1851	Col	GC	5 14.1	–40 03	7.1	12	! brightest centre of any GC; CC II
17	LMC	Dor	G-SBm	5 23.6	–69 45	0.1	7.2°	!!! many nights' work for large apertures
18	2070	Dor	EN/OC	5 38.7	–69 06	5.4	20	!!! Tarantula Nebula; "spider legs" easy
19	γ	Vol	Dbl*	7 08.7	–70 30	3.9, 5.4	14.1″	! gold and light-green pair

SOUTHERN-HEMISPHERE SPLENDOURS (continued)

#	NGC	Con	Type	RA (2000) h m	Dec ° '	Size m_v	'	Remarks
20	2451	Pup	Ast	7 45.4	–37 57	2.8	50	! not a true OC; nice contrast with 2477
21	2477	Pup	OC	7 52.2	–38 32	5.8	20	! 300*; arcs of 12th -mag.–13th-mag. stars
22	2516	Car	OC	7 58.0	–60 45	3.8	22	!! 100*; resembles the Beehive but richer
23	γ	Vel	Dbl*	8 09.5	–47 20	1.8, 4.3	41"	! 4*; 1.8-mag. star is brightest Wolf-Rayet
24	2547	Vel	OC	8 10.2	–49 14	4.7	25	! The Heart Cluster (description by Dyer)
25	IC 2391	Vel	OC	8 40.3	–52 55	2.6	60	! o Vel Cluster; bright stars; fine in binocs
26	2808	Car	GC	9 12.0	–64 52	6.2	14	! brightest CC I; like a pile of sand
27	3114	Car	OC	10 02.7	–60 06	4.2	35	! 120*; four arcs of stars in binocs
28	3132	Vel	PN	10 07.7	–40 26	9.2	0.8	Eight-Burst Nebula; colourless
29	3199	Car	EN	10 17.1	–57 55	9.0	22	! crescent formed by Wolf-Rayet star
30	3201	Vel	GC	10 17.6	–46 25	6.9	20	star chains right through core; CC X
31	3293	Car	OC	10 35.8	–58 14	4.7	5	!! Gem Cluster; EN/RN/DN involved
32	3324	Car	EN	10 37.3	–58 38	6.7	15	two-lobed nebula
33	IC 2602	Car	OC	10 43.0	–64 24	1.6	100	! θ Car Cl, a.k.a. the Southern Pleiades
34	3372	Car	EN	10 45.1	–59 52	2.5	80	!!! Carina Nebula[A]
35	3532	Car	OC	11 05.5	–58 44	3.0	50	!!! oblate; finest OC?; needs a wide field
36	3699	Cen	PN	11 28.0	–59 57	11.3	1.1	dark rift visible in 200-mm scope
37	3766	Cen	OC	11 36.3	–61 37	5.3	15	! triangular; 60*; λ Cen Nebula nearby
38	3918	Cen	PN	11 50.3	–57 11	8.1	0.2	! the Blue Planetary; round
39	—	Mus	DN	12 25	–72	—	3° × 12'	! the Dark Doodad; near 4372 and γ Mus
40	4372	Mus	GC	12 25.8	–72 39	7.2	19	! CC XII (size is from NGC 2000.0)
41	α	Cru	Dbl*	12 26.6	–63 06	1.3, 1.6	4.0"	! blue-white pair; 3rd star 4.9 mag. at 90"
42	DY	Cru	Red*	12 47.4	–59 42	9v	—	! Ruby Crucis; 3' W of β Cru; B–V is 5.8
43	—	Cru	DN	12 51	–63	—	6°	!!! Coalsack; forms head of the Emu DN
44	4755	Cru	OC	12 53.6	–60 21	4.2	10	! Jewel Box; sparse in small apertures
45	4833	Mus	GC	12 59.6	–70 52	6.9	14	! CC VIII (magnitude is from W.E. Harris)
46	4945	Cen	G-Sc	13 05.1	–49 28	8.4	20 × 4	! in 500-mm scope: dark lane on SW edge
47	5128	Cen	G-S0	13 25.5	–43 01	6.8	26 × 20	!! Cen A; merging spiral and elliptical[B]
48	5139	Cen	GC	13 26.8	–47 29	3.9	55	!!! Omega Cen; huge rich oval; CC VIII
49	5189	Mus	PN	13 33.5	–65 59	9.5	2.6	! the Spiral Planetary; use OIII filter
50	M83	Hya	G-SBc	13 37.0	–29 52	7.6	16 × 13	!! in 200-mm: bar, 1 arm; 370-mm: 3 arms
51	5286	Cen	GC	13 46.4	–51 22	7.4	11	! CC V; bluish PN 5307 nearby
52	5460	Cen	OC	14 07.6	–48 18	5.6	35	25 straggling*; trapezoidal asterism in S
53	α	Cen	Dbl*	14 39.6	–60 50	0.0, 1.3	6.1"	!! rapidly closing yellow pair: 22"-1.7"
54	5822	Lup	OC	15 04.0	–54 20	6.5	35	! triangular; stars are in discrete clumps
55	5927	Lup	GC	15 28.0	–50 40	8.0	6	CC VIII; pair with Nor GC 5946
56	B228	Lup	DN	15 45	–34	—	4° × 20'	! an unknown wonder; opacity 6
57	5986	Lup	GC	15 46.1	–37 47	7.6	10	200-mm resolves large core; CC VII
58	6025	TrA	OC	16 03.6	–60 25	5.1	15	! triangular, in three clumps
59	6067	Nor	OC	16 13.2	–54 13	5.6	15	! 100*; many pairs
60	6087	Nor	OC	16 18.9	–57 54	5.4	15	! 40*; embedded in Norma Star Cloud
61	6124	Sco	OC	16 25.3	–40 40	5.8	40	100*; many trios around circumference
62	6231	Sco	OC	16 54.2	–41 50	2.6	14	!! ζ, 6231, and Tr 24 form the False Comet
63	6242	Sco	OC	16 55.5	–39 28	6.4	9	23*; good for small scopes
64	6259	Sco	OC	17 00.7	–44 39	8.0	15	like a fainter M11; 120*
65	6281	Sco	OC	17 04.8	–37 53	5.4	8	25*; shines in modest scopes
66	6302	Sco	PN	17 13.7	–37 06	9.6	1.5 × 0.5	Bug Nebula; bright core; knots at tips
67	IC 4651	Ara	OC	17 24.7	–49 55	6.9	10	! loops and chains of 70 equal-mag. stars
68	6388	Sco	GC	17 36.3	–44 44	6.8	10	450-mm scope resolves faint stars; CC III
69	6397	Ara	GC	17 40.7	–53 40	5.3	31	!! easily resolved 10th-mag. stars; CC IX
70	6541	CrA	GC	18 08.0	–43 42	6.3	15	! huge outer halo; CC III
71	6723	Sgr	GC	18 59.6	–36 38	6.8	13	! CC VII; part of fine complex below
72	6726–7	CrA	RN	19 01.7	–36 54	—	9 × 7	! 7th-mag. stars involved[C]
73	6752	Pav	GC	19 10.9	–59 59	5.3	29	!! easily resolved 11th-mag. stars; CC VI[D]
74	7582	Gru	G-SBb	23 18.4	–42 22	10.2	4 × 1	brightest member of Grus Quartet

[A] Chevron-shaped dark lane, many other DN involved, including Keyhole Nebula; tiny orange mag. 5 (variable) Homunculus Nebula at centre; four OC involved

[B] Prominent broad dark lane; 370-mm scope reveals thin bright streak within the dark lane

[C] Part of !! complex with GC 6723, DN SL 40+41 (55' long, opacity 6), variable RN 6729 (involved with R CrA), headlight Dbl* Brs 14 (mags. 6.6, 6.8 at 13"), and Dbl* γ CrA (both yellow-white, mags. 4.9, 5.0 at 1.3" and widening)

[D] Curving star chains converge to a tiny central peak; very tight group of four 12th-mag. galaxies 1° SE

DARK NEBULAE
BY PAUL GRAY

Dark nebulae, often appearing as "holes in space," are fascinating to observe. The following is a representative selection of visually observable dark nebulae. The **minimum aperture** in millimetres is what observers have found to be necessary to see each nebula; however, many may be observable with smaller apertures under excellent skies. Quality of optics, the observer's experience, and full dark adaptation are often more important than the size of the aperture. Some objects will also benefit from the use of a filter because they are superimposed upon a bright nebula.

Objects are listed in order of right ascension. The column **UI/II** lists the charts in the *Uranometria 2000.0*, editions 1 and 2, respectively, that contain the object; *italics* indicate that the object is not actually marked in the given chart. The **opacity** is based on a scale of 1 to 6, with 6 being the easiest to observe; no objects of opacity 1 or 2 are listed, since these objects are very difficult to observe visually. Two objects (L 889 and L 896) are from the *Lynds Catalogue*, one (LG 3) is from the *Le Gentil Catalogue*, and one is uncatalogued; all others are from the *Barnard Catalogue*. Showpiece objects are marked "!!". For further information, including finder charts and images, and to view or submit an observation report, visit **www.rasc.ca/handbook/resources.shtml**.

#	B	Con	RA (2000) h m	Dec ° '	UI/II	Size '	Min. Opa- city	Aper. mm	Remarks
1	5	Per	3 48.0	+32 54	95/60	22 × 9	5	200	1° NE of o Per
2	211/3	Tau	4 17.2	+27 48	*133*/78	12 × 110	3	200–250	narrow NW–SE lanes, faint bkgd starfield
3	33	Ori	5 40.9	−2 28	226/116	6 × 4	4	100–150	Horsehead Nebula; use Hβ filter
4	34	Aur	5 43.5	+32 39	98/59	20	4	200	2° W of M37; spider-like appearance
5	35	Ori	5 45.5	+9 03	181/96	20 × 10	5	150–200	near FU Ori and bright nebula Ced 59
6	37	Mon	6 33	+11	*182*/96	3°	5	150 RFT	near NGC 2245, 2247; try binoculars
7	40	Sco	16 14.7	−18 59	335/147	15	3	250	in bright nebula IC 4592; 50' NE of ν Sco
8	44	Oph	16 40.0	−24 04	336/146	35 × 300	6	10 × 70	large dark rift; naked eye in superb sky
9	59	Oph	17 11.4	−27 29	337/146	60	6	10 × 70	3° SW of θ Oph; part of stem of Pipe Nebula
10	64	Oph	17 17.2	−18 32	337/146	20	6	150–200	30' W of M9; causes darkening of M9
11	68	Oph	17 22.6	−23 44	338/146	3	6	200	small; near B72; region rich in dark nebulae
12	70	Oph	17 23.6	−23 58	338/146	4	6	200	small; near B72; region rich in dark nebulae
13	72	Oph	17 23.6	−23 38	338/146	30	6	80–125	!! the Snake; "S" shape; 1.5° N of θ Oph
14	78	Oph	17 33	−26	338/146	3°	6	eye	!! Pipe bowl, "Prancing Horse" hindquarters
15	84A	Sgr	17 57.5	−17 40	339/146	16	5	150–200	1.5° N of M23; try for extensions to S
16	85	Sgr	18 02.6	−23 02	339/145	5	4	100	!! dark lanes inside Trifid Nebula (M20)
17	86	Sgr	18 02.7	−27 50	339/145	4	5	200	!! Ink Spot; nice pair with NGC 6520 5' E
18	87	Sgr	18 04.3	−32 30	377/163	12	4	200	Parrot's Head; 2° S of γ Sgr
19	88	Sgr	18 04.4	−24 07	339/145	2	4	200	on edge of M8; *not* Burnham's "Dark Comet"
20		Sgr	18 04.5	−24 14	*339/145*	2 × 1	4	200	Burnham's "Dark Comet"; use filter
21	303	Sgr	18 09.5	−24 00	339/145	1	5	200–250	inside IC 4685; use filter; challenging
22	92/3	Sgr	18 15.5	−18 11	339/145	12 × 6	6	7 × 50	!! on NW edge of Small Sgr Star Cloud, M24
23	103	Sct	18 39.2	−6 37	295/126	40 × 40	6	10 × 70	on NW side of Scutum star cloud
24	104	Sct	18 47.3	−4 32	250/105	16 × 1	5	150–200	20' N of β Sct; a checkmark shape
25	108	Sct	18 49.6	−6 19	295/125	3	3	200	30' W of M11; rich region
26	112	Sct	18 51.2	−6 40	295/125	20	4	200	30' S of M11; also look for B114, B118
27	133	Aql	19 06.1	−6 50	296/125	10 × 3	6	100	on Scutum star cloud; very dark spot!
28	142/3	Aql	19 40.7	+10 57	207/85	80 × 50	6	10 × 50	!! Barnard's famous "E" cloud
29	145	Cyg	20 02.8	+37 40	*119*/48	6 × 35	4	200	triangular shape
30	L 889	Cyg	20 24.8	+40 10	85/48	100 × 20	–	7 × 50	within γ Cygni Nebula, IC 1318
31	L 896	Cyg	20 37	+42	85/48	6°	–	eye	"Northern Coalsack"
32	150	Cep	20 50.6	+60 18	56/20	60 × 3	5	250	curved filament 1.6° S of η Cep
33	353	Cyg	20 57.1	+45 32	85/32	20 × 10	5	100	in N of North America Nebula; B352 in field
34	LG 3	Cyg	21 00	+53	85/32	12°	–	eye	!! "Funnel Cloud Nebula"; best after Coalsack
35	361	Cep	21 12.9	+47 22	86/32	20	4	100	cluster IC 1369 to N; try for 1°-tendril to W
36	365	Cep	21 34.9	+56 43	57/19	22 × 3	4	200	in IC 1396; indistinct "S" shape; use filter
37	163	Cep	21 42.2	+56 42	57/19	4	4	200	in IC 1396; use filter
38	168	Cyg	21 49.0	+47 29	86/31	100 × 20	5	7 × 50	large E–W lane; Cocoon Nebula at E end

GALAXIES: BRIGHTEST AND NEAREST
BY BARRY F. MADORE

External galaxies are generally of such low surface brightness that they often prove disappointing objects for the amateur observer. However, it must be remembered that many of these galaxies were discovered with very small telescopes and that the enjoyment of their discovery can be recaptured. In addition, the central concentration of light varies from galaxy to galaxy, making a visual classification of the types possible at the telescope. Indeed, the type of galaxy as listed in Table 1 (following) is in part based on the fraction of light coming from the central bulge of the galaxy as compared to the contribution from a disk component. Disk galaxies with dominant bulges are classified as Sa; as the nuclear contribution declines, types of Sb, Sc, and Sd are assigned until the nucleus is absent at type Sm. Often the disks of these galaxies show spiral symmetry, the coherence and strength of which is denoted by Roman numerals I through V, smaller numbers indicating well-formed global spiral patterns. Those spirals with central bars are designated SB, while those with only a hint of a disk embedded in the bulge are called S0. A separate class of galaxies that possess no disk component are called ellipticals and can only be further classified numerically by their apparent flattening, with E0 being apparently round and E7 being the most flattened.

Environment appears to play an important role in determining the types of galaxies we see at the present epoch. Rich clusters of galaxies, such as the system in Coma, are dominated by ellipticals and gas-free S0 galaxies. The less dense clusters and groups tend to be dominated by the spiral, disk galaxies. Remarkably, pairs of galaxies are much more frequently of the same Hubble type than random selection would predict. Encounters between disk galaxies may in some cases result in the instabilities necessary to form the spiral structure we often see. M51 (the Whirlpool) and its companion, NGC 5195, are an often-cited example of this type of interaction. In the past, when the universe was much more densely packed, interactions and collisions may have been sufficiently frequent that entire galaxies merged to form a single large new system; it has been suggested that some elliptical galaxies formed in this way.

Table 1 lists the 40 brightest galaxies taken from the *Revised Shapley-Ames Catalog*. As well as their designations, positions, and types, the table lists the total blue magnitudes, major and minor axis lengths (to the nearest minute of arc), one modern estimate of their distances in 10^6 ly, and their radial velocities corrected for the motion of our Sun about the galactic centre. Although the universe as a whole is in expansion, there are parts that are still bound together (or at the very least, held back in their expansion) by gravity. These groups and clusters are, in essence, representative of the largest material structures in the universe. Recently, large-scale flows of material have been reported, far in excess of the velocities expected due to the perturbing presence of other galaxies and clusters of galaxies. Either there are exceedingly large concentrations of matter yet to be discovered just beyond our limited view of the world, or the universe has had a much more interesting history than our present theories indicate. The brightest and nearest galaxies in Table 1 may be moving not only as a result of the universal expansion, but also through very complex interactions with distant parts as yet only postulated but not seen.

TABLE 1—THE 40 OPTICALLY BRIGHTEST SHAPLEY-AMES GALAXIES

NGC/IC	Other	RA (2000) h	m	Dec °	'	Type	Magnitude B_T	Size '	Distance 10^6 ly	Rad. Vel. km/s
55		0	15.1	−39	13.2	Sc	8.22	32 × 6	10.	+115
205	M110	0	40.4	+41	41.3	S0/E5pec	8.83	22 × 11	2.4	+49
221	M32	0	42.7	+40	51.9	E2	9.01	9 × 7	2.4	+86
224	M31	0	42.8	+41	16.5	Sb I–II	4.38	190 × 60	2.4	−10
247		0	47.2	−20	45.6	Sc III–IV	9.51	21 × 7	10.	+604
253		0	47.6	−25	17.4	Sc	8.13	28 × 7	14.	+504
SMC		0	52.6	−72	48.0	Im IV–V	2.79	320 × 185	0.2	+359
300		0	54.9	−37	41.2	Sc III	8.70	22 × 16	7.8	+625
598	M33	1	33.9	+30	39.2	Sc II–III	6.26	71 × 42	2.2	+506
628	M74	1	36.7	+15	47.2	Sc I	9.77	10 × 10	55.	+507
1068	M77	2	42.7	0	00.9	Sb II	9.55	7 × 6	82.	+510
1291		3	17.3	−41	06.5	SBa	9.42	10 × 8	49.	+512
1313		3	18.3	−66	29.9	SBc III–IV	9.37	9 × 7	17.	+261
1316	Fornax A	3	22.7	−37	12.5	Sa (pec)	9.60	12 × 9	98.	+1713
LMC		5	23.6	−69	45.4	SBm III	0.63	645 × 550	0.2	+34
2403		7	36.9	+65	35.9	Sc III	8.89	22 × 12	12.	+299
2903		9	32.2	+21	29.9	Sc I–III	9.50	13 × 6	31.	+472
3031	M81	9	55.6	+69	04.1	SbI–II	7.86	27 × 14	12.	+124
3034	M82	9	55.9	+69	40.7	Amorphous	9.28	11 × 4	12.	+409
3521		11	05.8	−0	02.0	Sb II–III	9.64	11 × 5	42.	+627
3627	M66	11	20.2	+12	59.1	Sb II	9.74	9 × 4	39.	+593
4258	M106	12	19.0	+47	18.4	Sb II	8.95	19 × 7	33.	+520
4449		12	28.2	+44	05.8	Sm IV	9.85	6 × 4	16.	+250
4472	M49	12	29.8	+7	59.8	E1/S0	9.32	10 × 8	72.	+822
4486	M87	12	30.8	+12	23.6	E0	9.62	8 × 7	72.	+1136
4594	M104	12	40.0	−11	37.4	Sa/b	9.28	9 × 4	55.	+873
4631		12	42.1	+32	32.4	Sc	9.84	16 × 3	39.	+606
4649	M60	12	43.7	+11	33.1	S0	9.83	7 × 6	72.	+1142
4736	M94	12	50.9	+41	07.1	Sab	8.92	11 × 9	23.	+345
4826	M64	12	56.8	+21	41.0	Sab II	9.37	10 × 5	23.	+350
4945		13	05.4	−49	28.0	Sc	9.60	20 × 4	23.	+275
5055	M63	13	15.8	+42	01.7	Sbc II–III	9.33	13 × 7	36.	+550
5128	Cen A	13	25.5	−43	01.0	S0 (pec)	7.89	26 × 20	23.	+251
5194	M51	13	29.9	+47	11.9	Sbc I–II	8.57	11 × 7	36.	+541
5236	M83	13	37.0	−29	52.0	SBc II	8.51	13 × 12	23.	+275
5457	M101	14	03.2	+54	21.0	Sc I	8.18	29 × 27	25.	+372
6744		19	09.8	−63	51.3	Sbc II	9.24	20 × 13	42.	+663
6822		19	45.0	−14	47.7	Im IV–V	9.35	16 × 14	2.2	+15
6946		20	34.8	+60	09.4	Sc II	9.68	12 × 10	22.	+336
7793		23	57.8	−32	35.4	Sd IV	9.65	9 × 6	14.	+241

The nearest galaxies, listed in Table 2, form what is known as the Local Group of Galaxies. Many of the distances are still quite uncertain. However, in the present *Hubble Space Telescope* era, these galaxies are prime targets for a generation of astronomers intent on accurately determining each of their distances to the best possible precision.

TABLE 2—THE NEAREST GALAXIES—OUR LOCAL GROUP

Name	RA (2000.0) h m	Dec ° '	Magnitude B_T	Type	Distance 10^6 ly
Milky Way Galaxy	—	—	—	Sb/c	—
IC 10	0 20.4	+59 17	11.8	IBm	2.6
NGC 147	0 33.2	+48 30	10.36	dE5	2.0
And III	0 35.3	+36 31	13.5	dE	2.4
NGC 185	0 38.9	+48 20	10.13	dE3 pec	2.4
M110 = NGC 205	0 40.4	+41 41	8.83	S0/E5 pec	2.4
M31 = NGC 224	0 42.7	+41 16	4.38	Sb I–II	2.4
M32 = NGC 221	0 42.7	+40 52	9.01	E2	2.4
And I	0 45.7	+38 01	13.5	dE	2.6
SMC	0 52.7	−72 49	2.79	Im IV–V	0.2
Sculptor	1 00.2	−33 42	10.5	dE	0.3
LGS 3	1 03.8	+21 53	18.0	Irr	2.4
IC 1613	1 04.8	+2 07	10.00	Im V	2.4
And II	1 16.5	+33 26	13.5	dE	2.4
M33 = NGC 598	1 33.9	+30 39	6.26	Sc II–III	2.2
Fornax	2 39.9	−34 32	9.1	dE	0.4
LMC	5 23.7	−69 45	0.63	SBm III	0.2
Carina	6 41.6	−50 58	—	dE	0.6
Antlia	10 04.0	−27 20	16.2	dE	4.0
Leo I	10 08.5	+12 19	11.27	dE	0.8
Sextans	10 13.0	−1 36	12.0	dE	0.3
Leo II	11 13.5	+22 09	12.85	dE	0.8
Ursa Minor	15 08.8	+67 12	11.9	dE	0.2
Draco	17 20.1	+57 55	10.9	dE	0.3
Sagittarius	19 00.0	−30 30	15.5	IBm:	0.1
NGC 6822	19 45.0	−14 48	9.35	Im IV–V	1.7

Editor's Notes:

(1) Aside from those famous companions of the Milky Way Galaxy, the Large Magellanic Cloud (LMC) and the Small Magellanic Cloud (SMC), there is only one galaxy beyond our own that is easily visible to unaided human eyes: M31, the Andromeda Galaxy (730 kpc or 2.4 Mly distant). M33, the Triangulum Galaxy, can also be seen, but this is a difficult observation. To locate M31, see the NOVEMBER ALL-SKY MAP on p. 350, where the tiny cluster of six dots above the first "A" of "ANDROMEDA" indicates its location. With modest optical aid (e.g. binoculars) a dozen or more of the galaxies listed in Table 1 can be seen by experienced observers under dark skies. With a 250-mm telescope, the quasar 3C 273, at one thousand times the distance of M31, can elicit a noticeable signal in the visual cortex (see p. 331).

(2) An interesting article by G. Lake entitled "Cosmology of the Local Group" appears in *Sky & Telescope*, December 1992, p. 613.

(3) The National Aeronautics and Space Administration/Infrared Processing and Analysis Center (NASA/IPAC) Extragalactic Database (NED) is a comprehensive compilation of extragalactic data for over 7.6 million distinct extragalactic objects. The database includes most major catalogues and offers references to and abstracts of articles of extragalactic interest that have appeared in most major journals. Also online are over 21 million photometric measurements and over 2 million images. It is possible to search the main NED database for objects selected by catalogue prefix, position, type, or redshift. The database is available at

nedwww.ipac.caltech.edu.

A knowledgebase of review articles and basic information is available at

nedwww.ipac.caltech.edu/level5.

GALAXIES WITH PROPER NAMES
By Barry F. Madore

Below are the catalogue designations and positions of galaxies known to have proper names which usually honour the discoverer (e.g. McLeish's Object), identify the constellation in which the galaxy is found (e.g. Andromeda Galaxy), or describe the galaxy in some easily remembered way (e.g. Whirlpool Galaxy).

Galaxy Name	Other Names / Remarks	RA (2000) h m	Dec ° '
Ambartsumian's Knot	NGC 3561, UGC 06224, ARP 105	11 11.2	+28 42
Andromeda Galaxy	M31, NGC 224, UGC 00454	0 42.7	+41 16
Andromeda I		0 45.7	+38 01
Andromeda II		1 16.5	+33 26
Andromeda III		0 35.3	+36 31
Antennae Galaxy	Ring Tail, NGC 4038/39, ARP 244	12 01.9	−18 52
Antlia Dwarf	AM 1001-270	10 04.0	−27 20
Aquarius Dwarf	DDO 210	20 46.9	−12 51
Arp's Galaxy		11 19.6	+51 30
Atoms For Peace	NGC 7252, ARP 226	22 20.8	−24 41
Baade's Galaxies A & B	MCG+07-02-018/19	0 49.9	+42 35
Barbon's Galaxy	Markarian 328, ZWG 497.042	23 37.7	+30 08
Barnard's Galaxy	NGC 6822, IC 4895, DDO 209	19 44.9	−14 48
Bear's Paw (Claw)	NGC 2537, UGC 04274, ARP 6	8 13.2	+46 00
BL Lacertae		22 02.7	+42 17
Black Eye Galaxy	M64, NGC 4826, UGC 08062	12 56.7	+21 41
Bode's Galaxies	M81/82, NGC 3031/4, UGC 05318/22	9 55.7	+69 23
Burbidge Chain	MCG-04-03-010 to 13	0 47.5	−20 26
BW Tauri	UGC 03087, MCG+01-12-009	4 33.2	+5 21
Carafe Galaxy	Cannon's Carafe, near NGC 1595/98	4 28.0	−47 54
Carina Dwarf		6 41.6	−50 58
Cartwheel Galaxy	Zwicky's Cartwheel, MCG-06-02-022a	0 37.4	−33 44
Centaurus A	NGC 5128, ARP 153	13 25.5	−43 01
Circinus Galaxy		14 13.2	−65 20
Coddington's Nebula	IC 2574, UGC 05666, DDO 81	10 28.4	+68 25
Copeland Septet	MCG+04-28-004/05/07 to 11, UGC 06597, UGC 06602, ARP 320, NGC 3745/46/48/50/51/53/54†	11 37.8	+21 59
Cygnus A	MCG+07-41-003	19 59.4	+40 43
Draco Dwarf	UGC 10822, DDO 208	17 20.2	+57 55
Exclamation Mark Galaxy		0 39.3	−43 06
The Eyes	NGC 4435/8, UGC 07574/5, ARP 120a,b	12 27.7	+13 03
Fath 703	NGC 5892	15 13.7	−15 29
Fornax A	NGC 1316, ARP 154	3 22.7	−37 12
Fornax Dwarf	MCG-06-07-001	2 39.9	−34 32
Fourcade-Figueroa	MCG-07-28-004	13 34.8	−45 33
The Garland	S of NGC 3077 = UGC 05398	10 04.2	+68 40
Grus Quartet	NGC 7552/82/90/99	23 17.8	−42 26
GR 8 (Gibson Reaves)	UGC 08091, DDO 155	12 58.7	+14 13
Hardcastle's Galaxy	MCG-05-31-039	13 13.0	−32 41
Helix Galaxy	NGC 2685, UGC 04666, ARP 336	8 55.6	+58 44
Hercules A	MCG+01-43-006	16 51.2	+4 59
Hoag's Object		15 17.2	+21 35

† Position errors caused these to be historically marked as nonexistent in the NGC and RNGC.

GALAXIES WITH PROPER NAMES (continued)

Galaxy Name	Other Names / Remarks	RA (2000) h m	Dec ° '
Holmberg I	UGC 05139, DDO 63	9 40.5	+71 11
Holmberg II	UGC 04305, DDO 50, ARP 268	8 19.3	+70 43
Holmberg III	UGC 04841	9 14.6	+74 14
Holmberg IV	UGC 08837, DDO 185	13 54.7	+53 54
Holmberg V	UGC 08658	13 40.6	+54 20
Holmberg VI	NGC 1325a	3 24.9	−21 20
Holmberg VII	UGC 07739, DDO 137	12 34.7	+06 17
Holmberg VIII	UGC 08303, DDO 166	13 13.3	+36 12
Holmberg IX	UGC 05336, DDO 66	9 57.6	+69 03
Horologium Dwarf	Schuster's Spiral	3 59.2	−45 52
Hydra A	MCG-02-24-007	9 18.1	−12 06
Integral Sign Galaxy	UGC 03697, MCG+12-07-028	7 11.4	+71 50
Keenan's System	NGC 5216/16a/18, UGC 08528/9, ARP 104	13 32.2	+62 43
Kowal's Object		19 29.9	−17 41
Large Magellanic Cloud	Nubecula Major	5 23.6	−69 45
Leo I	Regulus Dwarf, UGC 05470, DDO 74, Harrington-Wilson #1	10 08.5	+12 18
Leo II	Leo B, UGC 06253, DDO 93, Harrington-Wilson #2	11 13.4	+22 10
Leo III	Leo A, UGC 05364, DDO 69	9 59.3	+30 45
Lindsay-Shapley Ring	Graham A	6 42.8	−74 15
Lost Galaxy	NGC 4535, UGC 07727	12 34.3	+8 11
McLeish's Object		20 09.7	−66 13
Maffei I	UGCA 34	2 36.3	+59 39
Maffei II	UGCA 39	2 42.0	+59 37
Malin 1		12 37.0	+14 20
Mayall's Object	MCG+07-23-019, ARP 148	11 03.9	+40 50
Mice	NGC 4676a/b, UGC 07938/9, IC 819/20, ARP 242	12 46.1	+30 44
Miniature Spiral	NGC 3928, UGC 06834	11 51.8	+48 41
Minkowski's Object	ARP 133 (NE of NGC 541)	1 25.8	−01 21
Pancake	NGC 2685, UGC 04666, ARP 336	8 55.6	+58 44
Papillon	IC 708, UGC 06549	11 33.9	+49 03
Pegasus Dwarf	UGC 12613, DDO 216	23 28.5	+14 44
Perseus A	NGC 1275/6, UGC 02669	3 19.8	+41 31
Phoenix Dwarf Irregular		1 51.1	−44 26
Pinwheel Galaxy	see also Triangulum Galaxy	1 33.9	+30 39
Pinwheel Galaxy	M99, NGC 4254, UGC 07345	12 18.8	+14 25
Pinwheel Galaxy	M101, NGC 5457, UGC 08981, ARP 26	14 03.3	+54 22
Pisces Cloud	NGC 379/80/82-85, UGC 00682/3/6-9, ARP 331	1 07.5	+32 25
Pisces Dwarf	LGS 3	0 03.8	+21 54
Polarissima Australis	NGC 2573	1 42.0‡	−89 20
Polarissima Borealis	NGC 3172, ZWG 370.002	11 50.3‡	+89 07
Reinmuth 80	NGC 4517a, UGC 07685	12 32.5	+0 23
Reticulum Dwarf	Sersic 040.03	4 36.2	−58 50
Sagittarius Dwarf		19 30.0	−17 41
Sculptor Dwarf	MCG-06-03-015	1 00.2	−33 42
Sculptor Dwarf Irregular		0 08.1	−34 34

‡ The high declination of these objects makes the RA particularly uncertain.

GALAXIES WITH PROPER NAMES (continued)

Galaxy Name	Other Names / Remarks	RA (2000) h m	Dec ° '
Seashell Galaxy	Companion to NGC 5291	13 47.4	−30 23
Sextans A	UGCA 205, MCG-01-26-030, DDO 75	10 11.0	−4 41
Sextans B	UGC 05373, DDO 70	10 00.0	+5 19
Sextans C	UGC 05439	10 05.6	+00 04
Sextans Dwarf		10 13.1	−1 37
Seyfert's Sextet	Serpens Sextet, NGC 6027/6027a-e, UGC 10116	15 59.2	+20 46
Shapley-Ames 1		1 05.1	−6 13
Shapley-Ames 2	NGC 4507	12 35.1	−39 55
Shapley-Ames 3	MCG-02-33-015	12 49.4	−10 07
Shapley-Ames 4	UGC 08041	12 55.2	+0 07
Shapley-Ames 5	MCG-07-42-001	20 24.0	−44 00
Shapley-Ames 6		21 23.2	+45 46
Siamese Twins	NGC 4567/4568	12 36.5	+11 15
Silver Coin	Sculptor Galaxy, NGC 253, UGCA 13	0 47.6	−25 18
Small Magellanic Cloud	Nubecula Minor	0 52.7	−72 50
Sombrero Galaxy	M104, NGC 4594	12 39.9	−11 37
Spider	UGC 05829, DDO 84	10 42.6	+34 27
Spindle Galaxy	NGC 3115	10 05.2	−7 42
Stephan's Quintet	NGC 7317-20, UGC 12099-102, ARP 319	22 36.0	+33 58
Sunflower Galaxy	M63, NGC 5055, UGC 08334	13 15.8	+42 02
Triangulum Galaxy	Pinwheel, M33, NGC 598, UGC 01117	1 33.9	+30 39
Ursa Minor Dwarf	UGC 09749, DDO 199	15 08.8	+67 12
Virgo A	M87, NGC 4486, UGC 07654, ARP 152	12 30.8	+12 23
Whirlpool Galaxy	Rosse's Galaxy, Question Mark Galaxy, M51, NGC 5194/5, UGC 08493/4, ARP 85	13 29.9	+47 12
Wild's Triplet	MCG-01-30-032 to 34, ARP 248	11 46.8	−3 49
Wolf-Lundmark-Melotte	MCG-03-01-015, DDO 221	0 02.0	−15 28
Zwicky #2	UGC 06955, DDO 105	11 58.4	+38 03
Zwicky's Triplet	UGC 10586, ARP 103	16 49.5	+45 30

Catalogues:

AM *Catalogue of Southern Peculiar Galaxies and Associations*, by H.C. Arp and B.F. Madore, Cambridge University Press (1987).

ARP *Atlas of Peculiar Galaxies*, H. Arp, *Ap. J. Suppl. 14*, 1 (1966).

DDO *David Dunlap Observatory Publ.*, S. van den Bergh, II, No. 5, 147 (1959).

IC *Index Catalogue*, J.L.E. Dreyer, *Mem. R.A.S.* (1895–1910).

MCG *Morphological Catalogue of Galaxies*, B.A. Vorontsov-Velyaminovet al., Moscow State University, Moscow (1961–1974).

NGC *New General Catalogue of Nebulae and Clusters of Stars*, J.L.E. Dreyer, *Mem. R.A.S.* (1888).

RNGC *The Revised New General Catalogue of Nonstellar Astronomical Objects*, J.W. Sulentic and W.G. Tifft, University of Arizona Press (1973).

UGC *Uppsala General Catalogue of Galaxies*, P. Nilson, *Nova Acta Regiae Societatis Scientiarum Upsaliensis*, Ser. V: A, Vol. 1, Uppsala, Sweden (1973).

UGCA *Catalogue of Selected Non-UGC Galaxies*, P. Nilson, Uppsala Astronomical Observatory (1974).

ZWG *Catalogue of Galaxies and Clusters of Galaxies*, F. Zwicky et al., Vol. 1–6, California Institute of Technology (1961–1968).

RADIO SOURCES
BY KEN TAPPING

There are many types of cosmic radio sources, driven by a wide variety of processes. Some are thermal, that is, producing radio emissions because they have a temperature above absolute zero. Others involve the interaction of high-energy electrons with magnetic fields or complicated interactions of waves with plasmas. There are radio spectral lines from some atoms (such as the 21-cm emission from cosmic hydrogen) and an ever-increasing number of discovered molecular lines originating in cold, dense parts of the interstellar medium.

In this article we list cosmic radio sources that can be observed using small radio telescopes. Flux densities are listed for frequencies of 0.1, 0.5, 1, and 4 GHz (wavelength 3 m, 60 cm, 30 cm, and 7.5 cm respectively). The latter frequency corresponds to highly sensitive and easily available 3.7–4.2 GHz satellite TV receivers for radio astronomy. The unit of flux density used is the Jansky (Jy), where $1 \text{ Jy} = 10^{-26} \text{ W·m}^{-2}\text{Hz}^{-1}$. In the table, m denotes visual magnitude, and z redshift.

The main solar-system radio sources are the Sun, the Moon, and Jupiter. The Sun produces strong thermal emission, with enhanced emission from active regions. Flares produce intense radio bursts of seconds to minutes in duration. The flux densities for the undisturbed (quiet) Sun are 20 000, 250 000, 450 000, and 800 000 Jy. The lunar emission is thermal and equivalent to a mean blackbody temperature of about 225 K. Flux densities are 5, 120, 480, and 8000 Jy. Wavelengths shorter than about 3 cm originate close to the lunar surface and show the temperature variations over the lunar day. Longer wavelengths come from farther down, where the temperature remains more constant. Jupiter is a bright radio source at metre wavelengths, producing strong bursts of emission.

For more information see: *Radio Astronomy*, by J.D. Kraus (Cygnus-Quasar Books, Powell, Ohio, 1986); *Astronomy, 5* (12), 50 (1977); *JRASC, 72*, L5, L22, L38,… (1978); and *Sky & Telescope, 55*, 385 and 475, and *56*, 28 and 114 (1978). Some maps of the radio sky can be found in *Sky & Telescope, 63*, 230 (1982). Some projects to try are described in *Radio Astronomy Projects*, by William Lonc (Radio-Sky Publishing, 1997). Relevant information can be found on the following Web sites: UK Amateur Radio Astronomy Network (**www.ukaranet.org.uk**) and the Society of Amateur Radio Astronomers (**www.qsl.net/SARA**).

Source	RA (2000) Dec h m ° ′	Flux Densities Jy	Remarks
3C10	0 25.3 +64 08	180/85/56/10	remnant of Tycho's Supernova (1572)
W3	2 25.4 +62 06	−/80/150/134	IC 1795; complex, bright HII region; OH emission
3C84	3 25.4 +41 32	40/25/17/47	NGC 1725, Seyfert galaxy; $m = 12.7$, $z = 0.018$
Fornax A	3 20.4 −37 22	900/160/110/40	NGC 1316, galaxy; $m = 10.1$, $z = 0.006$
Pictor A	5 19.9 −45 47	440/140/100/50	galaxy; $m = 15.8$, $z = 0.034$
Taurus A	5 34.5 +22 01	1450/1250/1000/360	Crab Nebula; remnant of 1054 supernova
Orion A	5 35.3 −5 25	90/200/360/330	Orion Neb.; HII star-forming region; OH, IR source
3C157	6 17.6 +22 42	360/195/180/20	IC 443; supernova remnant
Puppis A	8 20.3 −42 48	650/300/100	supernova remnant
Hydra A	9 18.1 −12 05	390/110/65/25	galaxy; $m = 14.8$, $z = 0.052$
3C273	12 29.1 +2 03	150/57/49/30	brightest quasar; $m = 13.0$, $z = 0.158$
Virgo A	12 30.8 +12 23	1950/450/300/170	M87, elliptical galaxy with jet
Centaurus A	13 25.4 −43 02	8500/2500/1400	NGC 5128; galaxy; $m = 7.5$, $z = 0.002$
3C295	14 11.4 +52 12	95/60/28/10	galaxy; $m = 20.5$, $z = 0.461$
Hercules A	16 51.2 +5 01	800/120/65/11	galaxy; $m = 18.5$, $z = 0.154$
Gal. Centre	17 42.0 −28 50	4400/2900/1800	strong, diffuse emission from galactic centre
Sagittarius A	17 42.5 −28 55	100/250/200/336	compact source at gal. cen.; assoc. with black hole?
Cygnus A	19 59.5 +40 44	15500/4000/2100/370	strong radio galaxy
Cygnus X	20 22.6 +40 23	400/150/30/70	complex region
Cassiopeia A	23 23.4 +58 49	25000/4500/2800/806	supernova remnant

2011 OBSERVER'S CHALLENGE
By Lee Johnson and Alister Ling

The Observing Committee of the RASC is pleased to consider your contribution to a future Handbook on any visual phenomenon that will leave sky watchers around the world inspired and hungry for more. What for you might be almost delightfully routine will be new and astounding to many observers. In some cases, a featured event is bound to be something the authors themselves have always wanted to see.

Thought-Problems About Abstract Celestial Coordinates

Stepping away from the Earth with our thoughts allows us to take in the vastness of our reality. We enhance our dynamic sense of where we are in space in relation to the Solar System and ultimately with respect to the Milky Way itself. At first the NCP, NGP and other obscure initials on star-charts can be a source of confusion, but they can serve as guideposts that open up a large-scale appreciation of the entire visible universe. We are able to gain much of this perspective with our naked eyes; a small telescope will take care of finer details as we locate key stars and deep-sky objects that point to the location and crisscrossing of abstract celestial coordinates.

Thought-Problem #1

The North and South Galactic Poles (NGP and SGP) are located, respectively, in Coma Berenices and Sculptor. Within a degree or two of each pole is a spiral galaxy, the striking edge-on NGC 4565 in the north and the huge and nearly edge-on NGC 253 in the south. Late at night in the northern summer when NGC 253 rises, look back under the handle of the Big Dipper to find Coma Berenices in the foreground of NGC 4565, and enjoy the symmetrical placement of these two great galaxies flagging the poles of our own spiral Milky Way. Then, look straight up, exactly midway between them: behold the equator of the Galaxy, running perpendicular from east to west, the stellar stream in which our solar system sails. Go back and forth from the dark rifts and star clouds of the shimmering galactic disc overhead, to the mottled discs or equators of the other two galaxies. Think anew on these characteristics and on the structural reasons that other galaxies are consequently best found away from the obscuring plane of our own. For a different perspective, late on a spring night the NGP lies almost overhead while the equator of our galaxy nearly rings the horizon. Whenever you wander near the NGP and SGP markings, take some moments to regain that memorable, vivid sense of being inside the vast pinwheel structure of the Milky Way.

Thought-Problem #2

The North and South Ecliptic Poles (NEP and SEP), which define the rotational axis of the solar system, take on additional meaning when considered in relation to the North and South Celestial Poles (NCP and SCP), which define Earth's. The North Celestial Pole, next to Polaris, and the South Celestial Pole, near Sigma Octantis, are notable in themselves because the night sky rotates around them. At this epoch in Earth's precessional history, the Cat's Eye planetary NGC 6543 in Draco appears right next to the North Ecliptic Pole. Lying 23.5° away from Polaris, it leads one to picture the "tilt" of Earth's axis in relation to the plane of the solar system. In Dorado, just northeast of the Large Magellanic Cloud (between the stars Epsilon and Eta 1), the South Ecliptic Pole sits at an equivalent distance from the South Celestial Pole. Challenging questions to ask a young observer are "How can deep-sky objects assist us in our comprehension of the geometry of the important angle between Earth's poles and the axis of the ecliptic?" and "How will the objects we select to illustrate this geometry change over the cycle of Earth's precession?"

Thought-Problem #3

The juxtaposition itself of these celestial coordinate systems suggests perhaps their most interesting features. The ecliptic, or plane of the solar system, intersects the galactic plane at two points: roughly 6 and 18 hours right ascension, in Gemini and in Sagittarius, respectively, at just over 23° declination and just under –23° declination. The large open cluster M35 in Gemini is the brightest deep-sky object adjacent to the winter intersection of the ecliptic and the galactic equator, while the great emission nebula M8 (The Lagoon) is next to their summer intersection. In each case, the lines cross at an angle of approximately 60°. Now, keeping this in mind, think back to the Earth, picture its tilt with respect to the plane of the solar system, and superimpose it onto the framework of the Milky Way. By doing this, you will form a precise and dynamic picture of where we are in space as our planet and solar system slowly wheel around our magnificent home galaxy. Descending from this sublime reflection, do not forget the more humble celestial equator of Earth in all this. It intersects the ecliptic around the vernal and autumnal equinoxes and calls attention to key points in the planet's celestial orbit around the Sun. Finally, for those who enjoy the historical development of these coordinate systems, try re-thinking all of the above in relation to the old celestial sphere or globe. Imagine omnisciently looking down upon a mirror-reversed Universe from the outside – and be grateful for our relative humility in the modern world.

The preceding thought-problems are designed as ways of imagining our place in the Universe, but a double-check on the visualization of these problems benefits from sky charts and diagrams. To that end, one may consult sky atlases and computer programs of the night sky; and, as a convenient start on confirming the imagination's adroitness in performing the spatial gymnastics of positional astronomy, there are, just pages away, the all-sky maps in the Appendix of this Handbook (pp. 344-350). For example, in relation to Thought-Problem #1, the July and September charts respectively display the NGP and the SGP, as well as showing the Milky Way high overhead. The invitation to see the NGP near the zenith in the northern springtime and the galactic disc near the horizon is compatible with the May chart. With respect to Thought-Problem #2, these all-sky charts do not label the ecliptic poles; but their positions in the constellations of Draco and Dorado are readily inferred with the assistance of any of the charts for the northern sky plus the chart for "The Southern Sky." Thought-Problem #3 is commensurate with the charts for January and July because they show the angle of intersection of the ecliptic with the galactic plane "at roughly 6 and 18 hours right ascension, in Gemini and in Sagittarius, respectively," as well as showing the positions of M35 and M8, the 2 deep-sky objects highlighted for their proximity to these key points of intersection. Moreover, the intersection points of Earth's celestial equator and the solar system's ecliptic, the equinoxes, are displayed, with labels, on six of the seven all-sky charts. Finally, the text that introduces these charts (with the exception of the locations of the NEP and SEP) refers to the principal celestial coordinates that are inherent in the thought-problems we have been contemplating.

MAPS OF THE NIGHT SKY
By Roy Bishop

The maps on the following seven pages cover the entire sky. Stars are shown down to a magnitude of 4.5 or 5, that is, those that are readily apparent to the unaided eye on a reasonably dark night.

The first six maps are drawn for latitude 45°N but are useful for latitudes several degrees north or south of this. They show the hemisphere of sky visible at various times of year. Because the aspect of the night sky changes continuously with both longitude and time, while time zones change discontinuously with both longitude and time of year, it is not possible to state simply when a particular observer will find that his or her sky fits exactly one of the six maps. The month indicated above each map is the time of year when the map will match the "late evening" sky. On any particular night, successive maps will represent the sky as it appears every four hours later. For example, at 2:00 or 3:00 on a March morning, the May map should be used. Just after mealtime on a January night, the November map will be appropriate. The centre of each map is the *zenith*, the point directly overhead; the circumference is the horizon. To identify the stars, hold the map in front of you so that the part of the horizon you are facing (west, for instance) is downward. (The four letters around the periphery of each map indicate compass directions.)

The southern-sky map is centred on the south celestial pole and extends to 20°S declination at its periphery. Thus there is considerable overlap with the southern areas of the other maps. Note that the orientation of the various names is generally inverted compared to that on the first six maps. This is in recognition that most users of this Handbook will be residents of the Northern Hemisphere and will make use of the southern-sky map when they make trips to the tropics. Thus in "normal" use this map will be read in an area above its centre, unlike the first six maps, which are normally read below their centres. The months indicated around the edge of the map may be used to orient it to each of the preceding six maps and have the same "late evening" significance as explained above. Tick marks around the edge of the map indicate hours of right ascension, with hours 0, 3, 6, etc., labelled. Starting at the centre of the map, the series of small crosses along 0h right ascension indicates southern declinations 90°, 80°, 70°,…, 20°. With the aid of a drawing compass, an observer in the Northern Hemisphere can quickly locate a circle, centred on the south celestial pole, which represents the southern limit of his or her sky.

On all seven maps, stars forming the usual constellation patterns are linked by straight lines, constellation names being given in uppercase letters. Three constellations (Horologium, Mensa, and Microscopium) consist of faint stars; hence no patterns are indicated and the names are placed in parentheses. Small clusters of dots indicate the positions of bright star clusters, nebulae, or galaxies. The pair of wavy dotted lines indicates roughly the borders of the Milky Way. Small asterisks locate the directions of the galactic centre (GC), the north galactic pole (NGP), and the south galactic pole (SGP). LMC, SMC, and CS signify, respectively, the Large Magellanic Cloud, the Small Magellanic Cloud, and the Coal Sack. Two dashed lines appear on each of the first six maps. The one with more dashes is the celestial equator. Tick marks along this indicate hours of right ascension, the odd hours being labelled. The line with fewer dashes is the ecliptic, the apparent annual path of the Sun across the heavens. Letters along this line indicate the approximate position of the Sun at the beginning of each month. Also located along the ecliptic are the Northern Hemisphere vernal equinox (VE), summer solstice (SS), autumnal equinox (AE), and winter solstice (WS).

The epoch of the maps is 1950.0. Because of the small scale of the maps, the effect of precession is not yet significant.

JANUARY ALL-SKY MAP

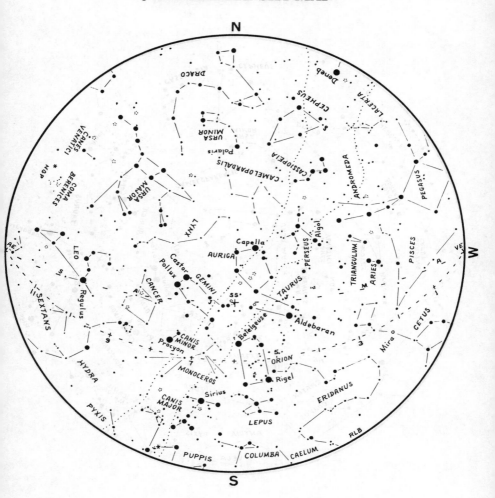

Notes:

MARCH ALL-SKY MAP

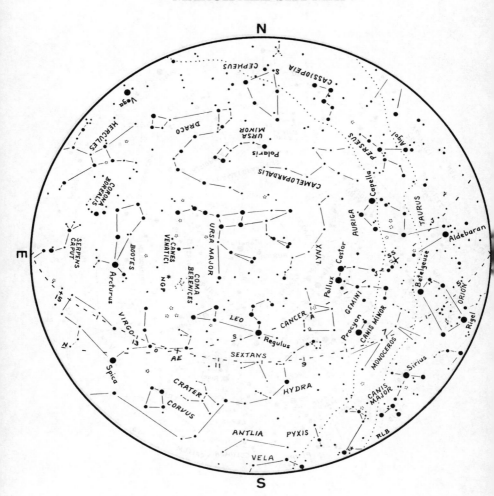

Notes:

MAY ALL-SKY MAP

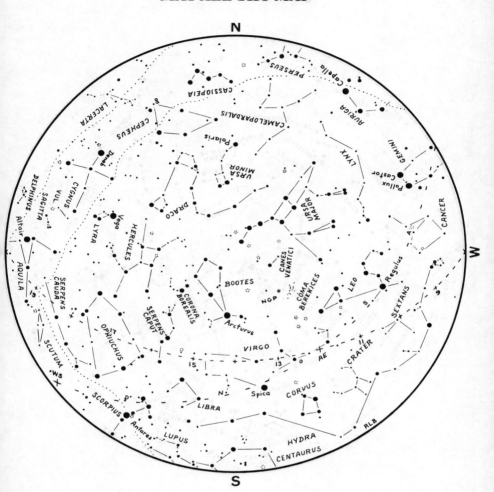

Notes:

JULY ALL-SKY MAP

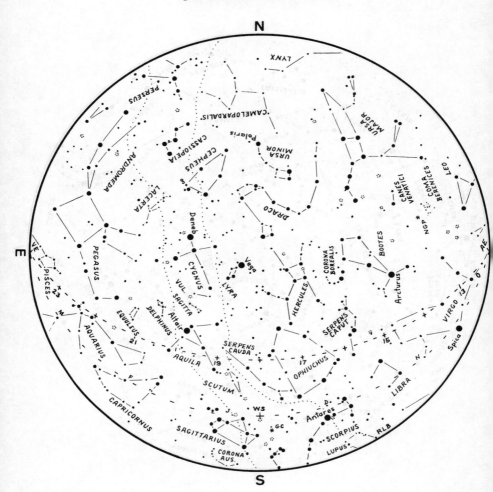

Notes:

SEPTEMBER ALL-SKY MAP

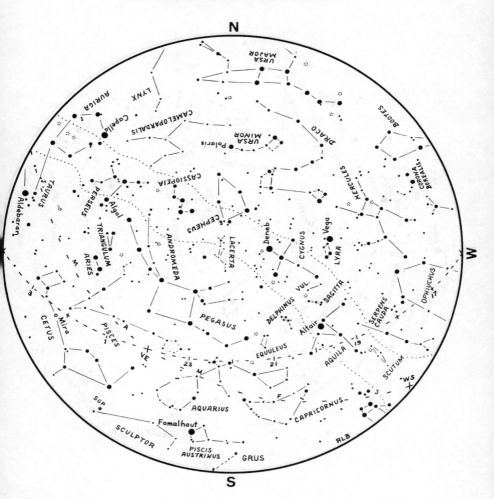

Notes:

NOVEMBER ALL-SKY MAP

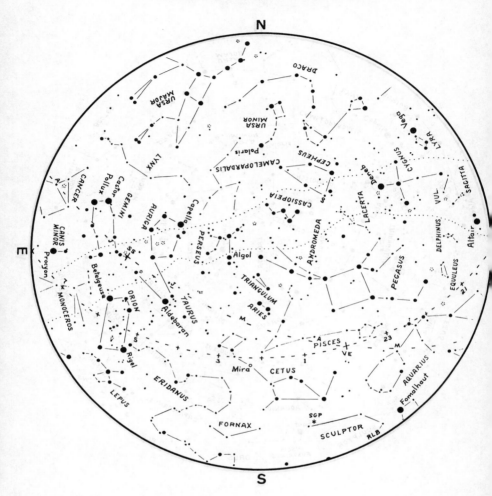

Notes:

THE SOUTHERN SKY

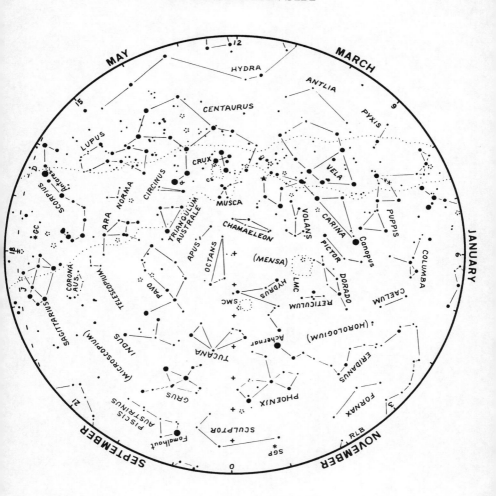

Notes:

OBSERVING NOTES FOR 2011

OBSERVER'S HANDBOOK 2012
ORDER FORM

(The *Observer's Handbook 2012* will be available in autumn 2011.)

MAIL-ORDER PRICE FOR SINGLE COPIES:

Destination	Unit Price	Shipping & Handling	Tax†		Total
Canada	$26.95 Cdn.	+ $5.00 Cdn.			
(Alta., Man., N.W.T., Nun., P.E.I., Qué., Sask., Yuk.)			$1.60	=	$33.55 Cdn.
(British Columbia)			$1.95	=	$33.90 Cdn.
(New Brunswick, Newfoundland & Labrador, Ontario)			$2.00	=	$33.95 Cdn.
(Nova Scotia)			$2.10	=	$34.05 Cdn.
United States	$26.95 U.S.	+ $7.00 U.S.		=	$33.95 U.S.
Elsewhere	$26.95 U.S.	+ $14.00‡ U.S.		=	$40.95 U.S.

† GST registration number 119126282
‡ shipped via airmail
Bulk-order pricing is available upon request. Prices are subject to change without notice.

Name ....

Address ....

....

....

Payment Enclosed $ .... [ ] Cheque [ ] Money Order

[ ] Visa [ ] MasterCard

Number...

Expiry .... Signature...

Name...

Telephone (..........)...

Email...

Order on the Internet using your credit card at **www.store.rasc.ca**

or send this order form to:

Royal Astronomical Society of Canada
203–4920 Dundas Street West
Toronto ON M9A 1B7
Canada

Phone: (416) 924-7973; in Canada only: (888) 924-7272
Fax: (416) 924-2911
Email: **mempub@rasc.ca**

To order any of the other publications of the RASC, please contact the Society or visit **www.rasc.ca**.

GLOSSARY

ablation	erosion of an object (generally a meteorite) by the friction generated when it passes through Earth's atmosphere
achromatic lens	a compound lens whose elements differ in dispersive indices in order to minimize chromatic aberration
albedo (Bond)	the ratio of the amount of light reflected from a surface to the amount of incident light
albedo (geometric)	the reflectivity of the body at zero phase angle to that of a "Lambert sphere", which reflects light according to a $\cos(\theta)$ law, where θ is the angle from the surface normal. Venus approximates a Lambert sphere. Airless satellites with bright icy surfaces can have geometric albedoes greater than 1.0.
altitude	the angular distance of a celestial body above or below the horizon
aperture stop	the physical aperture in an optical instrument that limits the amount of light passing through the instrument
aphelion	for an object orbiting the Sun, the point in its orbit that is farthest from the Sun
appulse	the very near approach of one celestial body to another as seen by an observer
arcminute	one sixtieth of a degree of angular measure
arcsecond	one sixtieth of an arcminute, or 1/3600 of a degree
ascending node	in the orbit of a solar-system body, the point where the body crosses the ecliptic from south to north
asteroid	a small rocky body that orbits a star — in the solar system, most asteroids lie between the orbits of Mars and Jupiter
astigmatism	a defect in a mirror or the eye which results in ligh rays not reaching a common focus and resulting in distarted images
astronomical unit	mean distance between the Earth and the Sun
asynchronous	refers to orbital motion in which the orbital period is not the same as the rotation period of the central body
axis	theoretical straight line through a celestial body, around which it rotates
azimuth	the direction of a celestial body from the north point, measured eastward in the plane of the horizon. Azimuth and altitude, together, specify the position of the body
bandpass filter	a device for suppressing unwanted frequencies without appreciably affecting the desired frequencies
binary star	two stars forming a physically bound pair under their mutual gravitational attraction—the stars move in elliptical orbits about their common centre of mass
black hole	a region of space-time that cannot be seen by distant observers because light is trapped by a strong gravitational field
candela	the SI base unit of luminous intensity
Cassegrain telescope	a reflecting telescope devised by Cassegrain (c. 1672) in which the light from a concave, paraboloidal primary mirror is reflected by a smaller, convex, hyperboloidal secondary mirror to pass through a hole in the centre of the primary to a focus
cataclysmic variable	a star in which the brightness increases suddenly because of an explosive event
celestial equator	projection of the Earth's equator as a line across the sky (for an observer on the equator, such a line would pass through the zenith)
celestial poles	the two points at which the Earth's axis of rotation, if extended, would intersect the celestial sphere
celestial sphere	in astronomy and navigation, the celestial sphere is an imaginary rotating sphere of "gigantic radius," concentric and coaxial with the Earth; all objects in the sky can be thought of as lying upon the sphere
charge	the fundamental property of a subatomic particle that is the source of its electric field and by which the particle is affected by external electric and magnetic fields

chromatic aberration	introduction of spurious colours by a lens, attenuated by the introduction of corrective elements into a compound lens
conjunction	the configuration in which two bodies have the same apparent celestial longitude or right ascension as viewed from a third body
contrast	the difference in visual properties that makes an object distinguishable from other objects and the background
constellation	a group of celestial bodies (usually stars) that appear to form a pattern in the sky or appear visibly related to each other
coordinates	quantities that provide references for locations in space and time
corona	outermost atmosphere of the Sun
cosmic rays	high-speed particles that reach the Earth from outside the solar system
culminate	to reach the highest point above an observer's horizon
declination	angular distance above or below the celestial equator—one of the coordinates, with right ascension, that defines the position of a heavenly body on the celestial sphere
deferent	in the Ptolemaic system, the planets are assumed to move in a small circle, called an epicycle, which in turn moves along a larger circle called a deferent
descending node	in the orbit of a solar-system body, the point where the body crosses the ecliptic from north to south
dichotomy	50 percent illuminated; literally split in two
ecliptic	the apparent path that the Sun traces out in the sky during the year, so named because eclipses occur when the full or new Moon is very close to this path of the Sun
elongation	a planet's elongation is the angle between the Sun and the planet, as viewed from Earth
ephemeris	a table of values that gives the positions of astronomical objects in the sky at a given time or times; plural = ephemerides
epicycle	in the Ptolemaic system, the planets are assumed to move in a small circle, called an epicycle (see deferent)
exit pupil	the image of the aperture stop of an optical instrument as formed by all the optical elements behind it
flux	the surface integral of a vector quantity (such as electric field or magnetic field) that passes through a specified surface area; or the amount of a scalar quantity (such as energy or mass) that flows through a specified surface area per unit time
galaxy	vast system of celestial objects, typically consisting of between 10^6 and 10^{12} stars, plus interstellar gas, dust, and possibly as yet unidentified dark matter
Galilean telescope	a refracting telescope having a single lens as its primary image-forming optical element, and a single, concave (diverging) lens as its eyepiece; it has a very narrow field of view, is somewhat limited by chromatic aberration, was the earliest type of telescope (invented c. 1608, in Holland), and was used by Galileo in his epoch-making discoveries of the heavens.
geocentric	with reference to, or pertaining to, the centre of Earth
geodesic	a path or line of shortest distance joining two points in space (or space-time)
Gregorian calendar	the calendar introduced by Pope Gregory XIII in 1582 to replace the Julian calendar; the calendar now used as the civil calendar in most countries.
heliocentric	a cosmological system in which the Sun is at (or near) the central point
Hertzsprung-Russell diagram	a plot of stellar colour, temperature, or spectral type versus stellar luminosity
illuminance	the luminous flux incident on a surface per unit area; 1 lumen per square metre = 1 lux
inclination	the angle between one plane and another; the (equatorial) inclination of a planet is the angle between the plane of its equator and that of its orbit; the inclination of the orbit of a planet in the solar system other than Earth is the angle between the plane of that orbit and the ecliptic
Lagrangian points	five points in the orbital plane of two massive objects in orbits around a common centre of gravity, where a third body of negligible mass can remain in equilibrium

latitude	angular position of a celestial object on the celestial sphere measured north or south of the ecliptic along the great circle passing through the poles of the ecliptic and the celestial object
light-year	distance travelled at the speed of light during one Earth-year: 9.46 million million km
longitude	angular position of a celestial object on the celestial sphere measured eastward along the ecliptic from the vernal equinox to the great circle passing through the poles of the ecliptic and the celestial object
lumen	the SI unit of luminous flux, equal to the luminous flux emitted by a point source of one candela in a solid angle of one steradian
lunation	the period of time between two successive new Moons
Lyman-alpha line	the characteristic spectral line of atomic hydrogen associated with its two lowest energy states
magnitude	a logarithmic brightness scale for astronomical objects; the measured brightness of a celestial body; dim objects have magnitudes of high numbers, bright objects have magnitudes of low or (sometimes) negative numbers
main sequence	a band that runs from top left to bottom right on the Hertzsprung-Russell diagram representing the majority of stars
Maksutov telescope	similar to a Cassegrain telescope except both the concave primary and convex secondary mirrors have spherical surfaces and are preceded by a deeply-curved meniscus glass lens that corrects the spherical aberration introduced by the two mirrors; invented independently in 1941 by Maksutov in Russia and Bouwers in Holland, and usually limited to apertures of less than 20 cm
metallicity	a term used by astronomers that refers to all chemical elements other than hydrogen and helium
nebula	indistinct, non-terrestrial objects visible in the night sky; "bright" nebulae glow with light emitted by the gas of which they are composed ("emission" nebulae) or by starlight reflected from dust ("reflection" nebulae) or both; "dark" nebulae consist of clouds of gas and dust that are not so illuminated; "planetary" nebulae are shells of gas ejected by stars; spiral nebulae are galaxies
Newtonian telescope	a reflecting telescope devised by Sir Isaac Newton (in 1668) that has a concave, paraboloidal primary mirror as its primary image-forming optical element and a smaller, plane, secondary mirror at 45° to deflect the light from the primary to a focus outside the tube near the top of the telescope
nutation	a small, irregular oscillation in the precessional motion of Earth's rotational axis, caused primarily by lunar perturbations
occultation	the cut-off of the light from a star caused by its passage behind another celestial body; strictly speaking, a solar "eclipse" is a solar occultation
opposition	when Earth comes directly between a planet and the Sun
osculating elements	a set of parameters that specifies the instantaneous position and velocity of a celestial body in its perturbed orbit
parallax (stellar)	half the apparent angular displacement of a star when observed from opposite sides of Earth's orbit
penumbra	the portion of a shadow within which only part of the light from an extended light source can be observed
periastron	the point in the orbit of one component of a binary star system where it is nearest the other component
perihelion	for an object orbiting the Sun, the point in its orbit that is nearest the Sun
precession (of Earth)	the slow (once per 26000 years) conical motion of Earth's rotation axis, caused by gravitational torques exerted by the Moon and Sun on Earth's equatorial bulge
prograde	in a forward direction; in astronomy, an eastward direction
quadrature	elongation of a planet when it makes a 90° angle with the Sun as seen from Earth
quasi-conjunction	said of two planets that, as viewed from Earth, approach near one another but without attaining the same right ascension

radial velocity	velocity along the line of sight toward (negative) or away from (positive) the observer
radiant	the point in the sky from which a meteor shower appears to emanate
redshift	the shift of spectral lines toward longer wavelengths, caused by motion away from the observer, motion transverse to the observer (time dilation), and/or the gravitation field of the source
refracting telescope	a telescope having a lens (usually composed of two or three lens elements) as its primary image-forming optical element and, for visual use, an eyepiece near the focus at its lower end
refraction	the change in direction of travel (bending) of a light ray as it passes obliquely through the atmosphere; in the case of a lens, any ray as it passes obliquely from one medium into another of greater or lesser refractive index
relativity	the theory of how motion and gravity affect the properties of time and space
resonance (orbital)	when two orbiting bodies exert a regular, periodic gravitational influence on each other
retrograde	in a backwards direction; in astronomy, an east-to-west direction
right ascension	angular distance on the celestial sphere measured eastward along the celestial equator from the vernal equinox to the great circle passing through the celestial poles and the object
Ritchey-Chretien telescope	a common form of professional telescope, similar to a Cassegrain telescope except that both the concave primary mirror and the convex secondary mirror have hyperboloidal surfaces resulting in a moderately large field of view free of third-order coma and spherical aberration; invented c. 1912 by George Ritchey and Henri Chrétien
Roche lobe	the Roche lobe is the region of space around a star within which orbiting material is gravitationally bound to that star
Schmidt-Cassegrain telescope	since c. 1970, a common type of telescope used by amateur astronomers, similar to a Cassegrain telescope except that the primary mirror has a spherical surface and is preceded by a thin glass corrector plate (a specialized weak lens) which corrects the spherical aberration that would otherwise be introduced by the primary mirror
Seyfert galaxy	a type of spiral galaxy first discovered by Karl Seyfert in the 1940s; the central region of a Seyfert galaxy is distinguished by powerful radiation, much of it focused into narrow frequencies
SI	abbreviation taken from Système international d'unités—the modern form of the metric system
sidereal	relating to the period of time based on the apparent rotation of the stars, and therefore equivalent to the rotation of the body from which the observation is made
spacetime	the three physical dimensions of space are combined with time, treated as a fourth dimension, to constitute the space-time continuum that is used as the fundamental framework of the theory of relativity
spectrum	the breakdown of light into a rainbow of colours; a good stellar spectrum reveals a star's spectral type, radial velocity (from the spectrum's Doppler shift), and metallicity
steradian	a unit of solid (three-dimensional) angular measure; one steradian is equal to the angle subtended at the centre of a sphere by an area of surface equal to the square of the radius
synchronous orbit	the orbital period of a satellite is the same as that of the rotation period of the central body; for example, ring particles orbiting near the outer edge of Saturn's "B" ring, or stationary satellites orbiting Earth
synchronous rotation	the rotation period of a satellite is the same as its orbital period; for example, Earth's Moon
synodic period	for an Earth-based observer, the time interval for a celestial body to return to its same configuration relative to the Sun; such as between successive oppositions or conjunctions for a planet, or the same phase for the Moon
umbra	the portion of a shadow cone in which none of the light from an extended light source (ignoring refraction) can be observed

INDEX

"MM" denotes the monthly pages of THE SKY MONTH BY MONTH on p. 102.

INDEX (continued)

"MM" denotes the monthly pages of THE SKY MONTH BY MONTH on p. 102.

RASC OBSERVER'S HANDBOOK 2011

INDEX (continued)

"MM" denotes the monthly pages of THE SKY MONTH BY MONTH on p. 102.

INDEX (continued)

"MM" denotes the monthly pages of THE SKY MONTH BY MONTH on p. 102.

INDEX (continued)

"MM" denotes the monthly pages of THE SKY MONTH BY MONTH on p. 102.

2011 HOLIDAYS AND SPECIAL DATES

New Year's Day	Sat.	Jan. 1
Martin Luther King Jr. Day (U.S.)	Mon.	Jan. 17
Chinese New Year	Thu.	Feb. 3
Presidents' Day (U.S.)	Mon.	Feb. 21
Winter Star Party, Florida Keys	Mon.	Feb. 28 – Sun. Mar. 6
Earth Hour 2011 (8–9 p.m. local time)	Sat.	Mar. 26
First Day of Passover	Tue.	Apr. 19
Good Friday	Fri.	Apr. 22
Easter Sunday	Sun.	Apr. 24
International Astronomy Week	Mon.	May 2 – Sun. May 8
International Astronomy Day	Sat.	May 7
Victoria Day (Canada)	Mon.	May 23
RTMC Astronomy Expo (Riverside), California	Wed.	May 25 – Sun. May 29
Texas Star Party, Fort Davis, Texas	Sun.	May 29 – Sun. Jun. 5
Memorial Day (U.S.)	Mon.	May 30
Canada Day	Fri.	Jul. 1
RASC General Assembly, Winnipeg, Manitoba.	Fri.	Jul. 1 – Sun. Jul. 3
Independence Day (U.S.)	Mon.	Jul. 4
Stellafane Convention, Springfield, Vermont	Thu.	Jul. 28 – Sun. Jul. 31
Star-B-Q, Eccles Ranch, Alberta	Sat.	Jul. 30 – Sun. Jul. 31
Mount Kobau Star Party, Osoyoos, B.C.	Sun.	Jul. 31 – Sun. Aug. 7
Civic Holiday (most of Canada)	Mon.	Aug. 1
First day of Ramadân	Mon.	Aug. 1
Saskatchewan Summer Star Party, Cypress Hills, Sask.	Thu.	Aug. 25 – Sun. Aug. 28
Starfest, Mount Forest, Ontario	Thu.	Aug. 25 – Sun. Aug. 28
Nova East, Smileys Provincial Park, N.S.	Fri.	Aug. 26 – Sun. Aug. 28
St. John's Butterpot Star Party, St. John's, Nfld.	Fri.	Sep. 2 – Sun. Sep. 4
Labour Day	Mon.	Sep. 5
Annual Algonquin Adventure, Algonquin Park, Ont.	Fri.	Sep. 23 – Sun. Sep. 25
Alberta Star Party, Starland, Alberta	Sat.	Sep. 24 – Sun. Sep. 25
Northern Prairie Star Party, near Tofield, Alberta.	Tue.	Sep. 27 – Sun. Oct. 2
Rosh Hashanah	Thu.	Sep. 29
Yom Kippur	Sat.	Oct. 8
Thanksgiving Day (Canada)	Mon.	Oct. 10
Columbus Day (U.S.)	Mon.	Oct. 10
Halloween	Mon.	Oct. 31
Remembrance Day (Canada)	Fri.	Nov. 11
Veterans Day (U.S.)	Fri.	Nov. 11
Thanksgiving Day (U.S.)	Thu.	Nov. 24
Islamic New Year	Sun.	Nov. 27
Christmas Day	Sun.	Dec. 25
Boxing Day (Canada)	Mon.	Dec. 26

See pp. 12–14 for Web sites and geographical coordinates of most of the listed *star parties*.

The Royal Astronomical Society of Canada

203-4920 Dundas St West

Toronto, ON M9A 1B7

27807
Alfred H. Johnson
2612 Mireault Crt
Thunder Bay ON   P7C 1P9

2076

2. LA CONFRÉRIE DE LA CLAIRIÈRE

**Catalogage avant publication de Bibliothèque
et Archives nationales du Québec
et Bibliothèque et Archives Canada**

Sydenier, Millie, 1986-
Les sorcières de Salem
Sommaire: t. 2. La Confrérie de la Clairière.
Pour les jeunes de 12 ans et plus.
ISBN 978-2-89585-031-1 (v. 2)
1. Sorcellerie - Massachusetts - Salem - Romans, nouvelles, etc. pour
la jeunesse. 2. Salem (Mass.) - Histoire - ca 1600-1775 (Période coloniale) -
Romans, nouvelles, etc. pour la jeunesse. 3. Procès (Sorcellerie) -
Massachusetts - Salem - Romans, nouvelles, etc. pour la jeunesse. I. Titre.
II. Titre: La Confrérie de la Clairière.
PZ23.S9685So 2009   j843'.92   C2009-941099-0

© 2009 Les Éditeurs réunis (LÉR).

Illustration : Sybiline

Les Éditeurs réunis bénéficient du soutien financier de la SODEC
et du Programme de crédit d'impôt du gouvernement du Québec.

Nous remercions le Conseil des Arts du Canada
de l'aide accordée à notre programme de publication.

Édition :
LES ÉDITEURS RÉUNIS
www.lesediteursreunis.com

Distribution au Canada :
PROLOGUE
www.prologue.ca

Distribution en Europe :
DNM
www.librairieduquebec.fr

Imprimé au Québec (Canada)

Dépôt légal : 2009
Bibliothèque et Archives nationales du Québec
Bibliothèque nationale du Canada

Millie Sydenier

2. La Confrérie de la Clairière

LER
LES ÉDITEURS RÉUNIS

1

— Rentrez vite à la maison ! gronda le révérend. Nous parlerons de cela plus tard.

Les deux jeunes filles ne se firent pas prier et se faufilèrent entre les badauds qui contemplaient le spectacle de la mort de Rebecca Nurse.

— Parris ! hurla l'inquisiteur Patton. Vous savez que ça ne durera pas éternellement ! Vous ne pourrez pas toujours les protéger ! Je n'aime pas que l'on se moque de moi. Vos filles sont souvent au mauvais endroit au mauvais moment. Au début, on parle de coïncidence, mais après… dit-il, menaçant, après il s'agit d'actes délibérément illégaux et perpétrés en toute connaissance de cause.

— Épargnez-moi votre savant discours de justicier, Patton. Tant que je serai vivant, vous ne toucherez pas à un cheveu de mes filles. Et croyez bien que si je me sens menacé de quelque façon que ce soit, je ferai encore tout pour les protéger par-delà ma mort !

Samuel Parris s'éloigna, droit et fier dans son grand manteau aux pans tourbillonnants. Fulminant, il contracta les épaules, prêt à se défendre si quelqu'un tentait de l'arrêter. Au lieu de ça, on le laissa tranquillement continuer son chemin et il se détendit un peu

plus loin. Tout allait de mal en pis ! L'hiver approchait, la famine guettait le village, les inquisiteurs faisaient valoir leurs droits avec trop de zèle. Mais ce qu'il appréhendait le plus était que ses filles tombent entre les mains de l'inquisiteur. Patton avait raison. Il ne pourrait pas toujours les protéger. Et cette accusation publique de sorcellerie ! Et Tituba qui était en prison ! Décidément, trop de choses avaient changé en trop peu de temps. Samuel Parris s'engagea sur le petit sentier qui menait à sa demeure, baissant la tête pour lutter contre les bourrasques glacées qui lui fouettaient le visage. Arrivé à l'entrée de son domaine, il se demandait encore comment son petit village auparavant si tranquille avait pu sombrer dans une telle folie. Alors qu'il poussait la porte, il n'avait toujours pas trouvé de réponse satisfaisante. Miss Salinger l'accueillit, les joues roses et l'air passablement effrayé.

— Je n'ai pas compris. Les petites sont rentrées en courant, excitées et apeurées. Elles m'ont dit que quelqu'un était mort, mais je n'ai pu leur soutirer autre chose. Que s'est-il passé, monsieur ?

— Rebecca Nurse a été jugée et condamnée. Ils viennent de l'exécuter, lui répondit laconiquement le révérend.

Miss Salinger retint un haut-le-cœur de surprise. Samuel Parris passa devant elle et se dirigea vers son bureau. Ne pouvant se retenir plus longtemps, il tonna :

— Amenez-moi les filles !

Miss Salinger s'empressa d'aller les chercher. Elle grimpa dans les étages et entra dans leur chambre.

Abigail et Betty étaient toutes deux pelotonnées sur un lit et pleuraient sans pouvoir s'arrêter. D'une voix douce, la cuisinière leur dit de sécher leurs pleurs et de se rendre immédiatement dans le bureau du révérend. Il voulait les voir.

Lorsqu'elles pénétrèrent dans son bureau, Samuel Parris était assis dans son fauteuil, dos à l'entrée, les yeux perdus dans les champs sans fin qu'il contemplait de la fenêtre. Betty referma la porte sans bruit. Elle et Abigail se tinrent droites, sans oser s'asseoir. Lorsque leur père se retourna, elles se tinrent la main car les yeux hagards du révérend les transperçaient de toute part.

— Je ne vous parlerai pas du discrédit et du déshonneur que vous jetez sur notre famille, commença-t-il d'une voix lourde de menaces, ni de la honte que j'éprouve à vous regarder. Je ne vous dirai pas non plus que votre attitude ne vous apportera que des ennuis, des ennuis tels que vous ne semblez pas les imaginer. J'ai tout fait pour vous protéger jusqu'à maintenant et vous ne m'avez pas écouté.

— Mais… commença Betty.

— Ne m'interromps pas, Elizabeth Parris, gronda le révérend. Je ne tolérerai plus un faux pas à partir de maintenant. Vous n'avez pas l'air de vous rendre compte de ce dont sont capables ces hommes.

— Détrompe-toi, papa. Nous avons très bien vu ce qu'ils peuvent faire et nous comprenons parfaitement que leur pouvoir est sans limites, lança Betty.

— Et comprends-tu aussi qu'après cette accusation publique ils vous chasseront sans répit ? Je ne suis pas éternel, je ne pourrai pas toujours être là. Qu'adviendra-t-il de vous lorsque vous serez seules ?

Les deux jeunes filles baissèrent la tête, contrites. Elles savaient qu'il disait vrai.

— Que s'est-il passé ? Pourquoi Rebecca a-t-elle proféré ce mensonge éhonté ? Lui avez-vous causé du tort de quelque manière que ce soit ?

Abigail regarda Betty puis toutes deux rebaissèrent la tête.

— J'exige une explication ! tonna-t-il.

— Ce n'était pas un mensonge, chuchota Betty.

Abigail la tira violemment par la main pour lui intimer le silence. Betty releva la tête avec défi et soutint le regard de son père qui s'assombrissait.

— Ce n'était pas un mensonge, répéta Betty avec plus de force. Elle a dit vrai.

— Ne te moque pas de moi, Elizabeth !

— Je ne me moque pas de toi, papa. Je ne peux rien te dire de plus que cette vérité. Nous sommes des sorcières.

Samuel Parris s'enfonça la tête dans les mains, conscient que sa fille ne lui mentait pas. Il réfléchissait à toute vitesse à ce que cela impliquait, à leur avenir désormais incertain, à ces chiens d'inquisiteurs qui ne tarderaient plus à découvrir ce terrible secret.

— Papa…

Il leva la main pour la faire taire.

— Sortez. Je ne veux plus en entendre parler.

Elles s'exécutèrent sans un mot.

Le révérend resta longtemps dans son bureau, abattu, anéanti, ne sachant pas quoi faire. Lorsque miss Salinger vint l'appeler pour le souper, il ne releva même pas la tête. Celle-ci sortit pour revenir quelques instants plus tard avec une assiette de soupe fumante et quelques quignons de pain. Au moment où les filles allèrent se coucher, Betty dit à sa cousine de monter et qu'elle la rejoindrait.

— Que vas-tu faire ? Laisse-le. Il en a assez entendu pour aujourd'hui.

— Nous ne pouvons pas laisser Tituba subir le même sort que Rebecca Nurse.

Elle frappa à la porte du bureau de son père. N'entendant pas de permission d'entrer, elle pénétra quand même dans la pièce.

— Tu ne veux sans doute plus nous parler, mais nous avons encore quelque chose à te dire. Tituba s'est trouvée au mauvais endroit au mauvais moment. C'est une fausse accusation. Nous devons la sortir de là. Nous avons besoin d'elle, tu le sais.

Et elle sortit aussitôt sans attendre la réaction de son père. Elle se sentait cuisante de culpabilité. Elle avait délibérément menti à son père. Mais les temps étaient

durs, lui-même l'avait reconnu. Elle retourna dans sa chambre et s'endormit, pleine de honte.

Dès le lendemain, elles apprirent par Cathy que Samuel Parris était allé plaider la cause de Tituba auprès de Patton. Elles se retinrent de sauter de joie car l'une et l'autre savaient pertinemment que le révérend n'était plus dans les bonnes grâces de l'inquisiteur. Lorsqu'il revint dans la matinée, il ne leur adressa pas même un regard. Blessée, Betty accepta en silence le châtiment de leur désinvolture. Mais avides de savoir, Abigail et elle essayèrent d'aller soutirer quelques renseignements auprès de miss Salinger. Celle-ci ne savait rien. Elles remontèrent dans leur chambre pour s'occuper. Elles n'avaient pas osé demander la permission de sortir et le temps ne les autorisait pas de toute façon à aller courir les champs. Une pluie battante obscurcissait le ciel et on n'y voyait pas à quelques pieds. L'eau tombait sans discontinuer depuis le matin et le clapotis incessant des gouttes frappant le toit énervait tout le monde. Miss Salinger ne les voulait plus dans ses jambes dans la cuisine et Cathy avait autre chose à faire que de jouer avec elles. Les autres domestiques couraient dans tous les sens car des fuites s'étaient manifestées dans l'aile ouest de la maison. Un événement joyeux vint quand même briser la monotonie du manoir. Le jardinier, Giles Corey, revint ce jour-là après une visite chez son père. En entendant sa voix dans le corridor, les deux jeunes filles descendirent en trombe l'escalier pieds nus et se jetèrent dans les bras du vieil homme qui les accueillit avec un sourire bienveillant.

— Bonjour, mes jolies! leur dit-il en les serrant contre lui. On m'a dit qu'il y avait du grabuge dans ce village et que deux vilaines petites filles y étaient pour quelque chose.

Abigail et Betty sourirent. Giles Corey n'avait jamais réussi à les gronder véritablement. Ses remontrances n'étaient que des manifestations de tendresse pour les deux enfants qu'il avait vues grandir.

— Comme je suis contente de vous voir, Giles. Comment allez-vous? Votre voyage s'est bien passé? Et comment va votre père?

— Mon pauvre vieux père est mort il y a deux jours. Mais il a eu une bonne vie. À quatre-vingt-huit ans, on en a vu des choses!

— Vous voilà orphelin. Comme moi… lui dit Abigail, sincèrement triste.

— Oui, ma belle. Mais mon fardeau ne sera jamais comparable au tien. Perdre un père à mon âge est une bien moins grande tristesse que la tienne. Mais si je pouvais, j'échangerais ma douleur contre la tienne, mon enfant.

Abigail se serra contre lui avec reconnaissance. Giles avait volontairement omis le fait que lorsqu'il avait perdu sa mère il n'était guère plus âgé qu'Abigail. Miss Salinger vint chasser les filles et entraîna le jardinier dans la cuisine pour qu'il se restaure. Abigail et Betty pouffèrent. Depuis toutes ces années, elles étaient persuadées que le jardinier et la cuisinière étaient amoureux l'un de l'autre. Quand Samuel Parris sortit la tête de son bureau pour comprendre d'où venaient

ces cris, elles s'empressèrent de cacher leur sourire et s'enfuirent dans les étages.

Dans les jours qui suivirent, elles n'entraperçurent plus leur père et celui-ci ne se manifesta pas à elles. Un semblant de soleil revint et elles accompagnèrent chaque jour le vieux jardinier qui inspectait les lieux et déplorait la mort des roses. Celles-ci, battues par une pluie trop puissante pour elles, pendaient lamentablement au bout de leurs tuteurs, leurs pétales éparpillés autour ; les corolles autrefois si belles avaient perdu leur splendeur. Les filles racontèrent à Giles tout ce qui s'était passé au village depuis qu'il était parti. Elles lui confièrent même leur lourd secret et s'enhardirent lorsque le vieil homme ne manifesta pas l'intention de les juger. Il compatit sincèrement à leurs malheurs mais ne dénigra pas son maître qui, leur dit-il, devait aussi sentir peser sur ses épaules un poids qu'il ne pouvait soutenir. Elles lui parlèrent de Tituba, qu'il n'avait pas connue, mais le jardinier comprit tout de suite quel lien les liait. Dans sa tête germait une idée, une idée saugrenue mais qui, jour après jour, s'endurcissait et devenait de plus en plus sensée.

— Mes chères enfants, je dois parler à votre père. Il m'est venu une solution folle pour tirer votre Tituba de ce mauvais pas. Mais je ne vous en parlerai pas car vous ne seriez pas d'accord. Je parlerai au révérend et sitôt qu'il m'aura donné sa bénédiction, je vous dirai de quoi il s'agit. Et vous ne me ferez pas changer d'avis. Sommes-nous d'accord ?

— Oui, mais...

— Ttt, miss Betty, pas de mais. Promettez.

— Très bien, Giles. Nous vous le promettons.

Un sourire malicieux barra le visage ridé du vieil homme. Prenant chacune des filles sous un bras, il les entraîna vers la haie de lauriers au fond du jardin.

— On m'a aussi appris que vous aviez découvert le passage secret !

Surprises, les deux filles le regardèrent, la bouche ouverte. Giles Corey éclata d'un rire caverneux qui se transforma bien vite en toux incontrôlable.

— Mais comment l'avez-vous su ? demanda Abigail.

— J'ai mes sources, mes enfants. Et des sources, ça ne se révèle pas.

— Giles ?

— Oui, Betty ?

— Votre toux ne me paraît pas de bon augure. Est-ce que vous allez bien ?

— Ne t'inquiète pas pour un vieil homme comme moi, ma belle.

Betty haussa les épaules et échangea un regard avec Abigail.

Pendant plusieurs jours, elles ne virent plus non plus Giles Corey. Moroses, elles reprirent leurs déambulations dans toutes les pièces de la maison. L'ennui avait refait surface en même temps que la pluie, qui crevait de nouveau le ciel. En passant devant le bureau du révérend, elles entendaient souvent la voix de leur père et celle, chaude et rocailleuse, du jardinier. Mais dès

15

qu'elles approchaient leurs oreilles de la porte, miss Salinger, Cathy ou un autre domestique venaient les tirer avec véhémence et ne manquaient à aucun moment de les sermonner sur l'impolitesse et la grossièreté de leur action. Elles ne purent surprendre un seul mot, mais tombèrent d'accord sur le fait que la discussion était houleuse et les négociations fermement engagées. Elles surprirent un jour Giles sortant du bureau, furibond. Mais lorsqu'elles se précipitèrent vers lui pour en savoir plus, il les renvoya d'un geste de la main et leur dit :

— Pas encore.

Ce ne fut que le lendemain qu'il leur apparut, souriant et fier. Il avait gagné, leur dit-il.

— Maintenant, dites-nous de quoi il s'agit et nous verrons si nous-mêmes sommes d'accord.

Giles pointa un doigt à peine menaçant devant le nez d'Abigail.

— Vous ne vous souvenez déjà plus de notre accord, miss Abigail ? Nous nous sommes entendus sur le fait que vous n'auriez pas votre mot à dire. Aussi injuste que cela puisse vous paraître, vous m'avez donné votre parole.

Butées, les deux jeunes filles le regardèrent avec un air de défi. Mais sous les yeux rieurs du jardinier elles capitulèrent.

— D'accord, nous acceptons.

— Très bien. J'ai parlé à votre père de la possibilité d'échanger Tituba avec quelqu'un d'autre. Après

maintes discussions, nous sommes finalement tombés d'accord. Ce ne sera sans doute pas facile, mais il y a de fortes chances que cela réussisse.

— Échanger Tituba ? Mais contre qui ?

— Eh bien, contre moi !

Les deux jeunes filles se mirent à hurler d'indignation et à gesticuler. Mais Giles Corey ne bougea pas. Il attendit patiemment qu'elles s'épuisent et manquent de souffle.

— Vous n'avez pas votre mot à dire, je suis désolé. Nous en avons convenu avec votre père et il a finalement cédé.

— Je... je... je vais parler à papa ! annonça Betty.

Avant que Giles ait pu faire un geste, elle était déjà entrée en courant dans le bureau de son père. Celui-ci lui jeta un regard noir, mais il perdit aussitôt contenance quand sa fille, les larmes coulant sur ses joues, le supplia d'interdire à Giles d'aller se livrer aux inquisiteurs.

— Il l'a décidé lui-même. Je ne l'ai pas forcé, bien au contraire. Mais il a des raisons qu'il vous expliquera. Je te prie de sortir maintenant.

Indignée, Betty ouvrit la porte et la laissa frapper le mur derrière avec fracas. Elle se retourna vers son père et lui lança, la voix vibrante de colère :

— Je te déteste.

Et elle sortit sans prendre la peine de fermer la porte. Le révérend ne réagit pas et il se leva pour rabattre

doucement le battant qui vibrait encore. Une larme coula sur sa joue.

Betty retrouva dans le jardin Giles et Abigail qui se tenaient côte à côte sans parler. Elle essuya rageusement les larmes qui roulaient sur ses joues et se planta devant le jardinier.

— Pensez-vous vraiment que Patton vous croira ? Pensez-vous seulement qu'il pensera à la justice et qu'il relâchera Tituba ? Vous serez enfermés tous les deux, c'est aussi simple que ça. Et alors, que deviendrons-nous ?

— Ma chère Betty, je crois revoir ta mère dans ta colère et c'est tout à ton honneur. Elle ne s'encombrait jamais de rages inutiles. Maintenant, j'aimerais que tu te calmes et que vous m'écoutiez. Je ne fais pas ça de gaieté de cœur mais, voyez-vous, je suis vieux et je me sens inutile.

— Vous n'êtes pas inutile pour nous ! s'exclama Abigail.

— Laissez-moi continuer. Je suis malade, je mourrai dans quelques mois tout au plus. Mon père vient de mourir. Je n'ai plus rien qui me rattache à cette terre. Et je connais trop bien la cruauté de la jeunesse face aux anciens. Même si vous démentez, continua-t-il en coupant court à leurs protestations, je sais qu'arrivera un jour où vous serez grandes et prêtes à vous marier. Alors qu'adviendra-t-il du vieux Giles Corey ? Vous rencontrerez bien des gens dans votre vie et alors le souvenir de votre vieux jardinier s'estompera dans votre mémoire. Et c'est bien normal, je ne vous blâme pas

pour cela. Mon action sera le dernier geste utile que je pourrai faire pour vous. Je vous en prie, acceptez-le.

Les deux filles pleuraient maintenant à chaudes larmes, s'accrochant comme deux enfants aux bras du vieil homme. Il les serra contre lui et essuya furtivement la larme qui menaçait de tomber dans les cheveux d'Abigail.

— Vous avez besoin de Tituba.

— Mais de vous aussi ! protestèrent-elles.

— Je suis malade et je ne survivrai pas longtemps. Si vous voyez Tituba mourir sous peu, et moi quelques semaines plus tard, ne pensez-vous pas que cela sera encore plus difficile ? Un de nous deux sera là pour vous protéger, et on m'a dit que cette Tituba avait la poigne qu'il fallait pour vous tenir. Et entre nous, dit-il en souriant, c'est elle qui vous a tout appris, n'est-ce pas ?

Elles hochèrent la tête en riant, la voix mêlée de sanglots.

— Et elle n'a pas terminé. Je laisse ma place et je vous sais entre de bonnes mains. C'est tout ce qui compte.

Elles pleurèrent longtemps ; le soir dans leur lit, des sanglots secouaient encore leur gorge. Leur père s'était montré pour le souper. Il n'avait sans doute aucune intention de parler aux filles et celles-ci, de leur côté, firent comme s'il n'existait pas.

Dès le lendemain, Giles se rendit au bureau des inquisiteurs et il interdit aux deux filles de l'accompagner. Il

n'en menait pas large, il se l'avouait volontiers mais il était prêt à tout pour ces deux enfants. Il se présenta devant celui qui devait être Patton et lui annonça :

— Vous avez fait une erreur dans votre capture, inquisiteur. Il semble que vous avez arrêté une femme du nom de Tituba. Eh bien, je vous demande de la libérer car elle n'est pas responsable. C'est moi qui l'ai entraînée dans ce piège. Elle n'est pas plus sorcière que vous !

Les inquisiteurs fixaient le vieil homme en ricanant, mais Patton le regardait avec attention. Giles soutenait impassiblement son regard, droit et fier.

— Qui me dit que vous ne mentez pas ? demanda Patton. Faites-moi un tour !

Giles Corey trembla d'indignation et cracha :

— Me prendriez-vous pour un sorcier de pacotille, mon cher ? Savez-vous que je pourrais vous tuer, là, d'un seul geste ? Prendriez-vous ce risque ? Je ne suis pas de ces magiciens de rue qui vous font des tours, inquisiteur, je ne ferai pas apparaître un lapin dans mon chapeau. L'honneur a toujours guidé mes pas et je suis là aujourd'hui pour rétablir une accusation injuste. Ni plus ni moins. Libre à vous d'avoir sur votre conscience une âme innocente…

D'un signe de tête imperceptible de Patton, deux inquisiteurs s'emparèrent sans ménagement du pauvre homme qui se concentrait pour ne pas flancher.

— Enfermez-le, dit Patton, en tournant le dos. Nous verrons bien ce qui se passera.

2

Elles étaient sans nouvelles du vieux jardinier. Même dans les cuisines, on ignorait ce qui lui était arrivé. Miss Salinger essayait tant bien que mal de camoufler ses yeux rougis et gonflés. Elle pleurait sans discontinuer depuis le départ de Giles. Abigail et Betty se sentaient responsables du choix du vieil homme et, honteuses, elles ne se rendaient plus aux cuisines que par obligation. Une seconde neige avait déposé son linceul la veille et le temps s'était considérablement rafraîchi. Elles n'avaient pu sortir et erraient comme des âmes en peine dans la maison. Exaspérée de les avoir dans les jambes, Cathy leur demanda d'aller organiser les combles. Peut-être y trouveraient-elles quelque chose pour les occuper. Betty et Abigail s'y rendirent en traînant les pieds. Les marches de l'escalier en colimaçon grinçaient et les cousines se souvenaient parfaitement que, lorsqu'elles étaient plus jeunes, l'endroit les terrifiait. Le grenier était plongé dans une pénombre angoissante propre à ces lieux où l'on se rend rarement. L'étouffante odeur de renfermé les prit à la gorge dès qu'elles passèrent la porte. Betty se précipita vers la lucarne pour l'ouvrir en grand. Un nuage de poussière ponctua l'ouverture de la vitre et Betty toussa en battant l'air.

— Je commence à penser que Cathy veut véritablement se débarrasser de nous !

Abigail éclata de rire en voyant sa cousine, le visage couvert d'une fine pellicule de poussière grasse. Puis elle regarda autour d'elle et soupira bruyamment. Organiser les combles ! Il leur faudrait des années. De vieilles malles mangées par les mites s'entassaient au fond du grenier et recouvraient un mur entier. Des toiles d'araignées maculaient le plafond et même le plancher quand elles ne reliaient pas les deux. Terrifiées mais fascinées, elles observèrent une araignée grosse comme leur poing empêtrer un moustique dans sa toile. D'un commun accord, elles décidèrent de fouiller dans tout ce qui était accessible sans pour autant faire du rangement. La tâche était trop ardue. Elles se promenèrent prudemment aux quatre coins de l'immense grenier sans rien trouver d'intéressant. La plupart des malles étaient fermées par de solides verrous rouillés et qui semblaient avoir été déposées là il y a des siècles. Betty s'impatientait et elle se mit à faire léviter de lourds coffres pour voir ce qu'il y avait en dessous.

— Fais attention, Betty ! Tu ne maîtrises pas encore totalement ce pouvoir. Ces malles sont trop lourdes pour toi ! la mit en garde Abigail.

— Oh voyons, Abi ! Comment pourrai-je m'améliorer si je ne me lance pas quelques défis ? De toute façon, papa est au courant maintenant ! Que veux-tu qu'il m'arrive ?

— Tu te souviens de ce que Tituba nous a dit ? Un trop grand effort quand on ne connaît pas ses limites

peut nous vider de nos forces ! Ça t'est déjà arrivé, Betty !

Exaspérée, Betty soupira et se tourna vers sa cousine pour répliquer.

— Mais je m'ennuie à mourir ici ! Peut-être y a-t-il quelque chose d'intéressant dessous ?

Ce faisant, elle perdit le contrôle du coffre qui s'écroula à quelques pouces des orteils d'Abigail qui hurla.

— Tu vois… tu vois… bégaya cette dernière. Je te l'avais bien dit de faire attention, mais tu ne m'écoutes jamais !

— Mais je ne t'ai pas fait mal ! Je t'ai habilement esquivée !

Abigail n'en croyait pas ses oreilles. Prête à exploser, elle cria :

— Esquivée ? Esquivée ? Mais tu ne regardais même pas ce que tu faisais !

— Bon, ça va ! Ça va ! Miss Abigail Williams a encore raison ! Comme d'habitude !

Chacune tourna le dos à l'autre et partit bouder dans son coin. Elles se lançaient des regards furtifs mais étaient toutes deux trop fières pour demander un cessez-le-feu. Abigail fulminait intérieurement contre la maladresse et la nonchalance de sa cousine. Elle tourna les yeux vers la malle qui avait failli l'écraser. Celle-ci s'était ouverte sous le choc. Un livre en sortait et elle n'en voyait que les coins racornis, comme brûlés

par le feu. Curieuse, elle s'en approcha et le tira de sous le couvercle de la malle. Le livre était très large avec une épaisse couverture de cuir noir à la reliure d'argent. Elle le souleva avec peine et retourna s'asseoir sur une pile de couvertures mangées par les mites. Abigail ne jeta même pas un regard à Betty qui lorgnait le livre avec avidité. Il n'y avait rien d'écrit sur la couverture, aussi Abigail l'ouvrit-elle pour découvrir le titre. À l'intérieur, sur la première page en parchemin, était écrit en belles lettres argentées *De l'Ombre surgira*. Tout en bas de cette même page, il y avait de minuscules lettres qui semblaient avoir été effacées par le temps. Abigail se pencha plus en avant pour les déchiffrer et ne put retenir un cri de surprise. N'y tenant plus, Betty la rejoignit en courant.

— Qu'est-ce que c'est ? demanda-t-elle. Montre-moi !

Abigail oublia instantanément sa querelle avec sa cousine et lui montra l'ouvrage qu'elle tenait sur ses genoux.

— *De l'Ombre surgira*… Qu'est-ce que ça veut dire ?

— C'est le titre. Mais regarde au-dessous.

— C'est trop petit, je n'arrive pas à lire.

— C'est un grimoire, dit Abigail sans parvenir à cacher son excitation. Un vrai grimoire de sorcières qui dormait au-dessus de nous depuis peut-être une éternité !

Betty était sans voix. Un grimoire ! Abigail tourna la première page et réprima un nouveau cri. Cette fois, Betty l'avait lu en même temps qu'elle. En haut à

droite était écrit en lettres déliées et gracieuses *Rose Parris*.

— Ma mère? s'étonna Betty. C'est impossible! Elle n'était pas une sorcière!

— Peut-être est-elle tombée sur ce livre comme nous. Ça ne fait pas d'elle une sorcière. Quoique cela expliquerait d'où viennent tes pouvoirs!

— J'ai fouillé des centaines de fois le grenier, bien que cela fasse longtemps que je n'y étais pas venue. Je n'ai jamais vu ce livre!

— Il était enfermé dans une malle, et tu n'en as jamais ouvert aucune!

— Mais…

— Ta mère est morte quand tu es née, elle t'en aurait sans doute parlé si elle avait vécu. En attendant, c'est un signe qu'elle nous envoie. Ce grimoire peut nous servir. Ouvrons-le.

Joignant le geste à la parole, Abigail tourna la première page. Mais au même moment, au rez-de-chaussée, la voix stridente de Cathy retentit.

— Miss Betty, miss Abigail, descendez! C'est l'heure du repas!

Encore abasourdie, Betty emboîta le pas à Abigail qui camoufla l'épais volume sous sa robe. Prudemment, elles descendirent les escaliers et se rendirent à la cuisine. Le lourd silence qui y régnait les dissuada bien vite de parler de leur découverte. Le temps était toujours aux larmes. Miss Salinger servit une assiette

25

de soupe chaude à chacune et en renversa la moitié à côté. Ses yeux étaient rouges et des larmes s'en écoulaient encore. Betty et Abigail baissèrent toutes deux la tête dans leur assiette fumante. Cathy leur jetait des regards sévères et outrés, comme si elles étaient seules responsables de ce qui se passait dans le village.

— Le révérend vous fait savoir que vous pourrez aller rendre visite à Tituba demain, leur dit miss Salinger, de gros sanglots roulant dans sa voix.

Elles sourirent mais se reprirent aussitôt. Si elles pouvaient voir Tituba, c'est que Giles Corey était en bonne voie de réussir.

— Quant à mon pauvre Giles, continua miss Salinger, pleurant maintenant à chaudes larmes, Dieu seul sait ce qu'on lui a fait !

Cathy essaya de la réconforter, mais la grosse cuisinière se dégagea de ses bras pour s'enfuir vers un bol empli de blancs d'œufs qu'elle se mit à battre avec fureur. Abigail et Betty engloutirent leur soupe et sortirent précipitamment sous le regard accusateur de Cathy.

Dans la montée d'escaliers, Abigail dit à Betty :

— Il faut montrer le grimoire à Tituba dès demain !

— Tu es folle ! Nous n'allons pas faire entrer la preuve de ce que nous sommes dans cet endroit ! Ce serait signer notre arrêt de mort.

— Allons, Betty ! Tu es capable de plier quelqu'un à ta volonté. Tu l'as déjà fait, souviens-t'en !

— Mais je l'ai fait sans le savoir. Je n'ai jamais recommencé.

— Alors demain sera le jour où tu te découvriras un nouveau pouvoir performant et particulièrement utile.

— Et si ça ne marche pas ?

— Alors nous prierons ! Mais nous sommes des sorcières, et nos pouvoirs grandissent rapidement. Les inquisiteurs ne nous garderaient pas longtemps dans leurs cages.

Betty n'en revenait pas. Sa cousine qui auparavant ne voulait plus utiliser ses pouvoirs semblait habitée d'une force nouvelle. Elles ne parlèrent pas davantage et s'endormirent tout de suite, pleines d'appréhension pour le lendemain.

Au matin, Cathy vint les réveiller comme d'habitude. Mais depuis l'arrestation de Tituba, elle était de plus en plus froide avec les deux filles. Sans ménagement, elle arracha de leur lit les draps chauds et leur intima l'ordre de se lever rapidement.

— Le révérend ne vous accompagnera pas voir Tituba et je le comprends. Quel déshonneur pour vous que d'aller rendre visite à cette… cette sorcière ! cracha-t-elle.

— Comment irons-nous alors ? demanda Betty, furieuse.

— Je vous y emmènerai mais je ne rentrerai pour rien au monde dans cet endroit.

— Et on ne te l'a pas demandé, lui lança Abigail.

— Vous avez tellement changé, mes enfants. Et pas en bien avec cela !

— Et toi, tu es devenue méchante, Cathy ! Cela te rendra cruelle et vieille avant l'âge !

— Comment oses-tu ? J'en parlerai à ton père, Elizabeth Parris.

— Fais ! lui dit Betty, les yeux pleins de colère, de fureur et de défi.

Elles s'habillèrent en silence et sortirent sans prendre la peine de manger. Assises sur les marches du perron, elles attendirent que Cathy daigne sortir. Le chemin jusqu'au village se fit sans bruit et la tension entre les trois était palpable. Abigail et Betty marchaient loin devant Cathy qui s'efforçait de les suivre sans donner l'impression de courir. Elles arrivèrent sur la place où subsistaient encore des restes du bûcher de Rebecca Nurse ; sans y prêter attention, elles continuèrent leur chemin en direction de la prison. Cathy ne se donna même pas la peine de les prévenir et, lorsque les deux filles se retournèrent pour lui faire comprendre qu'à partir de là elles se débrouilleraient, elles la virent qui s'éloignait précipitamment. En haussant les épaules, Abigail respira un grand coup et poussa la lourde porte cloutée de la prison. Elles pénétrèrent dans l'antre de Patton. Betty se demanda subrepticement si son père ne les avait pas envoyées là pour les livrer. Les inquisiteurs levèrent la tête à leur entrée et ne dissimulèrent pas leur surprise en voyant deux jeunes filles marcher la tête haute. Tout au bout du couloir, une porte était entrouverte et, derrière le bureau, on pouvait voir Patton qui les regardait, un sourire carnassier aux lèvres. Ce fut à ce moment-là

que toutes deux commencèrent à avoir peur. Betty serrait contre elle le grimoire protégé par un petit sac de toile. Dans sa tête tournoyaient des milliers d'idées pour arriver à le faire entrer dans les cellules sans passer par la magie. Elle n'en trouva aucune qui pourrait marcher. Résignée, elle avança la tête basse et rassembla tout son courage.

— Mesdemoiselles, que puis-je faire pour vous ? leur demanda Patton, mielleux. Êtes-vous venues visiter vos prochains appartements ? ricana-t-il.

— Nous sommes venues voir Tituba car on nous en a donné l'autorisation. Veuillez nous y conduire, je vous prie, lui répondit Abigail, la voix tremblotante.

— Nous devons d'abord procéder à quelques mesures de sécurité, leur dit-il, doucereux. Veuillez poser sur le bureau tout ce que vous portez sur vous… Je ne parle pas des habits, évidemment, ajouta-t-il, salace.

Tremblantes, elles déposèrent devant elles tout ce qu'elles trouvèrent dans leurs poches et leurs sacs. Un bric-à-brac s'éparpilla sur le secrétaire. Une brosse à cheveux, des crayons, quelques bouts de papier froissés et le livre qui avait l'apparence d'un innocent ouvrage de contes pour enfants.

— À quoi vous attendiez-vous ? osa Betty, courageuse. Des baguettes magiques ? dit-elle ironiquement.

Patton lui lança un regard qui en aurait fait rentrer plus d'un sous terre, mais Betty leva la tête fièrement.

— Ne vous avancez pas trop, miss Parris, dit-il, menaçant, je trouverai tôt ou tard quelque chose pour

vous inculper. Je ne me fais aucun souci pour cela. Surveillez vos paroles car je pourrais oublier jusqu'à la notion de justice et de miséricorde et vous envoyer dans la plus profonde de mes geôles d'où vous ne sortiriez que pour mourir. Avouez que ce serait fâcheux pour vous et votre famille. Votre cher papa se dresserait sans doute pour vous défendre. Dans le but d'exercer MA justice, je serais dans l'obligation de le tuer pour entrave au bon fonctionnement de l'ordre.

— Connaissez-vous vraiment le sens du mot «miséricorde»? demanda Betty sans se démonter tandis qu'Abigail tirait sur sa manche pour l'enjoindre à se calmer.

Un sourire cruel apparut sur les minces lèvres de l'inquisiteur, dévoilant des dents jaunâtres et légèrement effilées. Ses yeux s'étaient fixés sur Betty et un éclat malfaisant y luisait. Il détourna soudainement le regard et, posant un doigt négligent sur le livre, il demanda ce que c'était.

— C'est un livre de contes, *monsieur* l'inquisiteur, répondit Betty dont la voix laissait encore apparaître le mépris. Il me semble que c'est écrit dessus.

— Pourquoi l'apportez-vous pour voir la sorcière?

— Nous nous sommes dit que cela pourrait lui faire plaisir d'entendre de jolies histoires, dit précipitamment Abigail avant que Betty ne lui sorte de nouveau une réplique bien sentie.

— Vous le laisserez ici, annonça simplement Patton en faisant un geste pour ouvrir le livre. Peut-être le récupérerez-vous à votre sortie.

Betty avait pris de l'ampleur et du charisme. Une aura sombre flottait autour d'elle et elle donnait l'impression de dominer la scène bien qu'elle n'ait pas grandi. L'air tressautait à son contact. Lorsque sa cousine ouvrit la bouche, Abigail ne reconnut pas sa voix. Un ton grave en sortit, chaud et glacé en même temps, un son étrange les enveloppant de sa puissance. Les mots qu'elle prononça résonnèrent longtemps aux oreilles d'Abigail. Patton ne détachait plus ses yeux de la jeune fille qui se tenait en face de lui.

— Vous nous laisserez entrer avec ce livre, inquisiteur. Suis-je bien claire ? Il n'est nulle part stipulé qu'il est interdit d'apporter de la distraction aux prisonniers. Vous nous laisserez entrer avec ce livre !

Aussi soudainement que l'atmosphère avait changé, tout redevint normal. Betty reprit une attitude normale. Sans un regard pour Patton, elle s'empara de ses effets et se dirigea vers la porte des cachots. Abigail, sur ses talons, exultait. L'inquisiteur ne les retint pas et, d'un regard particulièrement absent, il les observa s'engouffrer dans l'escalier tortueux qui descendait aux cellules. L'humidité qui régnait dans ces lieux était étouffante et les odeurs putrides de moisi et de corps décomposés les prenaient à la gorge.

— Je n'arrive pas à croire que tu aies si bien réussi, Betty ! C'était... magistral ! souffla Abigail, sincèrement impressionnée. Même moi je me suis sentie étrange. Tu aurais pu me dire de faire n'importe quoi et je l'aurais fait sans hésiter un instant ! C'est un sacré pouvoir que tu as là !

Betty ne répondit pas, mais un petit sourire de contentement s'afficha sur son visage. Très vite, elles

se serrèrent l'une contre l'autre tandis que des bras décharnés apparaissaient entre les barreaux des geôles et que des voix les suppliaient de leur donner quelque chose à manger, de les sortir de là. La puanteur était suffocante, les odeurs d'urine et d'excréments leur donnaient la nausée. Betty et Abigail furent horrifiées de la condition des prisonnières. Certaines étaient nues, la peau couverte de plaques noirâtres qui devaient être les conséquences des sévices qu'on leur infligeait. La crasse, les rats et la moiteur se disputaient les malheureuses. Se demandant dans quel était elles allaient retrouver Tituba, elles avançaient prudemment pour éviter les flaques d'eau saumâtre et les mains squelettiques qui essayaient de les toucher. Dans la dernière cellule, et sans aucun doute la plus petite, se trouvait leur servante. Elle avait l'air moins abattue que les autres prisonnières mais s'était considérablement amaigrie. Tituba releva doucement la tête lorsque le bruit des pas s'arrêta devant ses barreaux. Si elle fut surprise de découvrir les deux filles, elle n'en laissa rien voir. Pas plus qu'elle ne montra sa joie de les retrouver. Abigail mit cet accueil froid sur le compte de l'épuisement, mais le ton bourru de Tituba la détrompa.

— Qu'est-ce que vous faites là ? Les petites princesses ont daigné descendre dans le cloaque de la sorcellerie ?

Betty fut choquée de l'entendre parler ainsi. Mais Abigail s'accroupit sans prendre garde où trempait sa robe et tendit une main vers Tituba.

— Nous sommes venues voir comment vous alliez, murmura-t-elle. Jusqu'à maintenant, nous n'en avions

pas le droit, mais hier soir on nous a dit que nous y étions autorisées. Souffrez-vous beaucoup?

Tituba la regarda d'un œil méfiant, puis elle sembla s'adoucir. Elle lui effleura le bout des doigts.

— Ce n'est pas tant la souffrance que l'humiliation de rester enfermée, répondit-elle.

— Ne pouvez-vous pas vous enfuir? demanda Betty.

— Hélas! Je suis affaiblie car nous sommes moins nourries que les chiens. Et quand ils nous donnent à manger, ils cachent dans la nourriture une drogue ou une potion qui nous rendent somnolentes et incapables du moindre geste.

— Mais là, s'exclama Abigail, vous parlez et vous bougez!

— Je suis encore trop faible. J'ai bu cette infâme mixture il y a plus d'une journée. Les effets commencent seulement à s'estomper.

— Profitez-en alors! cria Betty.

— Betty, la coupa Abigail, cela signifie aussi qu'elle n'a rien avalé depuis plus d'un jour. Elle n'aurait pas la force.

— Nous n'avons pas pensé à vous apporter à manger. Je ne croyais pas qu'ils traitaient les prisonnières aussi mal!

— Ce n'est pas grave, mes petites! Ils ne laissent entrer personne avec de la nourriture. Je compte sortir bientôt. On m'a dit qu'un brave homme s'était dénoncé pour me libérer. Que Dieu le bénisse!

Betty et Abigail se regardèrent, gênées. Si Giles Corey était enfermé à la place de Tituba, il ne survivrait pas plus de quelques jours. Mais elles n'en dirent rien. Betty tira de son sac le grimoire et le tendit à Tituba. Elle se pencha vers la servante pour lui chuchoter à l'oreille.

— Nous avons trouvé ça dans le grenier, Tituba. Un véritable grimoire de sorcellerie, dit-elle, la voix frémissante d'excitation. Et ce n'est pas tout ! Il y a le nom de ma mère inscrit dedans.

Tituba feuilleta le livre sans paraître le moins du monde impressionnée. Betty se vexa un peu de ce manque d'intérêt.

— Comment avez-vous fait pour apporter ce livre jusqu'ici ?

— Betty a été très persuasive, lui dit Abigail, souriant.

— Peu importe, coupa brusquement Tituba. Rapportez-le chez vous. Ce ne sont que des sornettes, de faux sortilèges sans aucun doute. Les véritables grimoires de sorcellerie sont extrêmement rares, on dit même que tous ont disparu de la terre. Amusez-vous avec ça, ce sont sûrement des jeux d'enfants.

Brusquement, elle se retourna, leur signifiant que l'entretien était terminé. Abigail était déçue et Betty vibrait de rage. Elles ressortirent précipitamment des cachots et traversèrent le bureau de Patton sans que celui-ci lève la tête.

— Quelle vieille harpie! s'exclama Betty une fois dehors. Nous venons la voir en risquant notre vie et elle… elle… ah!

Abigail préféra ne rien dire mais elle comprenait sa cousine. Au détour d'une rue, alors qu'elles couraient presque pour rentrer chez elles, Ann Putnam manqua de leur rentrer dedans.

— Faites attention où vous allez! cria-t-elle, mimant la colère. Enfin!

Betty la toisa haineusement et Ann frémit sous son regard. Elle passa son chemin mais Betty se retourna et Abigail la vit murmurer quelque chose. Avant qu'elle ait pu l'arrêter, elle aperçut du coin de l'œil Ann se soulever de terre et planer quelques instants au-dessus du sol. Terrifiée, Ann en oublia de crier, mais quand Betty la fit virevolter dans tous les sens, elle hurla à se déchirer la gorge. Abigail repensa à Rebecca Nurse sur son bûcher et, attrapant Betty par le bras, elle l'entraîna en courant avant que les cris d'Ann n'attirent tout le village. Elles marchèrent un instant en silence puis Betty coula un regard à sa cousine. Celle-ci s'efforçait d'avoir l'air sévère mais, au bout d'un moment, toutes deux éclatèrent de rire. Et c'est toujours en riant qu'elles entrèrent chez elles, tombant nez à nez avec Samuel Parris.

3

Le second jugement de Tituba eut lieu le lendemain, mais il fut interdit à Betty et à Abigail d'y assister. Le révérend s'y rendit tôt le matin sans prêter la moindre attention aux récriminations des filles. Il n'avait cure de leurs jérémiades, et il savait pertinemment qu'il ne pourrait rien changer à ce qu'avait déjà décidé Patton. Le jugement n'était qu'une façade pour montrer aux citoyens un semblant de justice, mais tout était faussé. Les inquisiteurs faisaient eux-mêmes leur loi. Aussi, quand il entendit ses filles lui faire promettre de tout faire pour sauver Tituba, il ne les écouta pas, ne fit pas attention à leurs sanglots étouffés et à leurs peurs enfantines. Elles étaient encore trop jeunes pour comprendre les rouages de la fourberie et il ne voulait pas les en informer tout de suite.

Betty ressentait désormais pour son père une rancœur sincère qui lui ôtait tout jugement. Pas une fois elle put se dire que le révérend ne souhaitait que les protéger, sa cousine et elle. La jeune fille pensait au contraire qu'il voulait leur faire du mal, les faire souffrir. Elle ne voyait là qu'un sévère châtiment à leur conduite irraisonnée. Faisant les cent pas dans la maison en attendant le retour de Samuel Parris, Abigail et Betty fulminaient, l'une contre son père, l'autre contre les inquisiteurs. Dans la cuisine, miss

Salinger pleurait toutes les larmes de son corps mais continuait courageusement à remuer ses casseroles. Elle serrait convulsivement les petites dans ses bras dès que l'une d'elles passait à proximité. La tension était palpable dans l'air et les domestiques, affairés, s'exaspéraient rapidement à la vue des deux filles qui se mettaient dans leurs jambes.

— Si on montait dans notre chambre pour lire un peu le grimoire? On va finir par se faire punir si on reste là. Cathy cherche une raison de nous faire exécuter ses corvées depuis tout à l'heure. Ne la vois-tu pas rôder autour de nous? Disparaissons et allons nous occuper!

Betty acquiesça de mauvaise grâce. Elle craignait que son père ne rentre et n'aille s'enfermer directement dans son bureau sans donner de nouvelles du procès. Elle grimpa à la suite de sa cousine, traînant à chaque marche, jetant un coup d'œil dans son dos dès qu'une porte claquait. Finalement, elle alla s'affaler sur son lit à côté d'Abigail qui tirait déjà de sous le matelas l'épais et sombre grimoire. Celle-ci l'ouvrit religieusement à la première page et toutes deux se penchèrent sur l'écriture déliée qui s'étalait comme une immense toile d'araignée. Les mots penchés étaient difficiles à lire et elles se rendirent vite compte qu'elles avaient sous les yeux une œuvre originale où tout avait été écrit et dessiné à la main, des sortilèges aux illustrations. Les enluminures étaient splendides et témoignaient d'un passé riche et studieux. Sur cette première page, elles lurent: *Prends garde car cette œuvre n'est pas comme les autres. Néophyte, ne tourne pas ces pages au hasard. L'impudence qui te trahira sera cause de ta perte. Une âme vit en ce grimoire, une âme qui fut enfermée et torturée. Dans les*

obscurs tréfonds de la magie, elle fut tordue, séparée et vouée à une éternelle vie au travers de ces pages. Souvent, la nuit, tu l'entendras respirer. Peut-être même hurler. Sois effrayé car tu ne peux même imaginer de quoi est capable une âme entachée et souillée. Frémissantes d'excitation, elles se regardèrent et Abigail tourna fébrilement la seconde page. Le titre annonçait *Sortilèges simples au service des débutants.* Elles lurent une sorte de sommaire qui semblait avoir été écrit de la main de l'ancien possesseur. Ébahies, elles découvrirent toutes sortes d'enchantements qu'elles n'avaient même pas imaginés. Certains leur permettraient de faire apparaître de la nourriture, d'autres de coudre les lèvres des bavards ou encore d'assourdir les curieux en repliant leurs oreilles. Mais un sortilège attira particulièrement leur attention. Abigail trouva d'ailleurs étrange que ce sort soit placé dans la section pour débutants alors qu'à côté figurait une mise en garde : *À n'utiliser qu'en dernier recours.* L'incantation seule était inscrite : *Meortusita.*

— Je serais tentée d'essayer ce dernier sort sur Cathy. Ça lui apprendrait à nous traiter de la sorte, s'exclama Betty, irritée. Allons voir ce qu'elle fabrique et nous lui jetterons ce charme dès qu'elle aura le dos tourné.

— Voyons, Betty, lui dit Abigail, glacée d'effroi, tu n'as pas vu ce qui est écrit juste à côté ?

— Bien sûr que si. Mais il me semble que nous en sommes au dernier recours, non ?

— Je ne pense pas qu'infliger un sort, dont nous ne connaissons pas les effets, à Cathy parce qu'elle nous a énervées soit un dernier recours, Betty. Allons, ne rentrons pas dans son jeu ! Laisse-la donc parler, la pauvre s'ennuie à mourir.

Betty se renfrogna. Abigail était toujours si sage, si raisonnable que c'en était agaçant parfois. Que n'aurait-elle donné pour agir sur un coup de tête et prendre Cathy comme exutoire à sa colère? Et par la même occasion lui donner une bonne leçon! Elle n'avait pas fini avec ses pensées qu'elle entendit la porte de l'entrée s'ouvrir. Le révérend avait à peine eu le temps de la refermer qu'elles descendaient toutes les deux l'escalier à grand fracas. Betty sauta la dernière marche et atterrit presque sur les pieds de son père qui lui jeta un regard sévère. Abigail, emportée par son élan, percuta sa cousine qui tomba finalement dans les bras de son père.

— Ne vous tiendrez-vous jamais convenablement? gronda-t-il.

— Papa, dis-nous! Comment s'est passé le jugement? Que va-t-il arriver à Tituba?

— Et à Giles Corey, ajouta Abigail en baissant la voix et en jetant un regard furtif vers les portes de la cuisine.

Le révérend fit mine de ne pas avoir entendu leurs questions et se dirigea à grands pas vers son bureau, les pans de sa cape noire et luisante de pluie virevoltant autour de lui. Des dizaines de gouttes s'en échappaient et glissaient vers le sol pour y former de minuscules flaques qui seraient bientôt essuyées par les domestiques.

— PÈRE! hurla Betty, ulcérée par la façon dont il les ignorait.

Celui-ci, surpris, se retourna, incrédule. Ce son tonitruant était-il sorti de la bouche si fine de sa petite fille ?

— Je me moque éperdument du temps que vous allez nous ignorer, mais la réponse que je vous demande nous est essentielle. Tituba a joué pour nous le rôle de mère, c'est bien cela que vous souhaitiez, n'est-ce pas ? Seriez-vous assez cruel pour enlever une nouvelle fois à deux jeunes filles la chance d'avoir une mère ?

Samuel Parris se ressaisit bien vite même si l'étrange vouvoiement de sa fille le bouscula.

— Tituba ne sera pas graciée tant que les aveux de Giles Corey ne seront pas vérifiés.

— Comment le seront-ils ? demanda timidement Abigail qui n'avait pas osé se mêler du conflit.

— Il sera torturé jusqu'à ce que mort s'ensuive. Patton croit que l'agonie fera avouer à Giles son mensonge. Je pense même que son supplice a commencé sur la place publique. Souhaitez-vous lui rendre une ultime visite ?

Sur ces mots, il disparut dans son bureau, dont il claqua violemment la porte, laissant ses filles atterrées sur le seuil. De la cuisine retentirent des sanglots déchirants qui firent venir aux yeux d'Abigail des larmes de honte.

— Torturé jusqu'à ce que mort s'ensuive, répéta Betty, pétrifiée. Torturé jusqu'à ce que mort s'ensuive…

Elle répétait inlassablement ces quelques mots tandis qu'Abigail, le corps secoué de pleurs, se tordait les mains de désespoir.

— Il faut aller le voir, déclara stoïquement Betty. Nous devons aller le voir et le supplier de changer d'avis.

— Mais Tituba ? Que lui arrivera-t-il ? demanda Abigail, déchirée.

— C'est une sorcière, non ? Et nous aussi ? Nous la sortirons de là !

Abigail ne paraissait pas aussi sûre que sa cousine si bien que celle-ci, exaspérée, lui lança un regard méprisant et lui dit :

— Sèche tes larmes ! Elles ne servent à rien. Habillons-nous et allons voir Giles. S'il y en a un qui a le droit de pleurer aujourd'hui, il s'agit sans aucun doute de lui.

Sans laisser le temps à Abigail de s'offusquer, Betty monta quatre à quatre l'escalier, attrapa un chaud manteau dans sa chambre et redescendit précipitamment. Abigail ne s'activa que lorsque Betty disparut par la porte et sauta les marches du perron. Elle courut chercher une veste et suivit sa cousine sous la faible et désagréable bruine annonciatrice de l'orage. Toutes deux avaient relevé leur capuchon mais, en quelques instants, elles eurent le visage ruisselant d'eau. Des mèches de cheveux se collaient sur leurs joues et leur donnaient un aspect maladif. Elles se rendirent au village sans échanger un mot. Abigail ne cessait de se demander ce que l'on avait bien pu infliger au vieil

homme et elle essayait tant bien que mal de se rassurer en se disant que même des brutes comme les inquisiteurs devaient respecter l'âge des personnes. Giles Corey devait sans doute avoir été humilié en public pour faire bonne mesure, mais elle était sûre que personne n'aurait osé le faire souffrir. Elle ressassait ces maigres pensées rassurantes sans en faire part à Betty qui devait partager les mêmes. Lorsqu'elles arrivèrent en vue de la place, Abigail avait repris espoir et elle avait hâte de convaincre le vieux jardinier de renoncer à cette sinistre manigance. Son inquiétude réapparut quand elle vit l'attroupement. Les deux filles entendirent des cris et des pleurs qui résonnèrent à leurs oreilles comme annonciateurs de mauvaises nouvelles. Abigail s'accrocha au bras de Betty qui ne fit rien pour s'en défaire. Approchant doucement, elles se frayèrent un chemin au milieu des villageois en jouant des coudes. Personne ne fit attention à elles et elles réussirent à se faufiler jusqu'au premier rang. Betty stoppa si violemment qu'Abigail la percuta. Se penchant par-dessus l'épaule de Betty, elle regarda ce qui avait freiné cette dernière. Le spectacle qui s'étendait sous ses yeux lui arracha un gémissement d'angoisse, de désolation et d'incompréhension. Le monde sembla tourner autour d'elle et elle se sentit devenir légère, si légère qu'elle tomba comme une plume. Des bras vigoureux la rattrapèrent avant qu'elle ne percute le sol et une gifle de sa cousine acheva de lui faire reprendre ses esprits. Giles Corey était étendu sur un épais banc de bois. Les bras et les jambes attachés sur les côtés donnaient à son corps une étrange forme de marionnette désarticulée. Il avait été ligoté avec si peu de soin que les liens avaient déjà entamé sa peau diaphane, laissant un sillon sanguinolent. Mais le pire

résidait dans cette immense dalle de pierre large de dix pouces qu'on avait étalé sur sa poitrine, enfonçant ainsi sa cage thoracique, rendant plus ardue la respiration. Le vieil homme souffrait déjà et ses ahanements saccadés brisèrent le cœur des deux filles. Elles se précipitèrent à ses côtés et pleurèrent en l'implorant de renoncer. Giles Corey leur demanda d'être fortes.

— J'en ai vu d'autres, vous savez !

— Mais cette pierre ! Elle vous tuera ! Oh, je vous en prie, Giles ! Nous trouverons une autre solution pour Tituba.

— Malheureusement, ma chère enfant, si je reviens sur mes dires, je serai aussitôt exécuté pour trahison et mensonges. Quant à Tituba, cela reviendrait à leur dire qu'elle est véritablement coupable. Je ne mourrais donc pas seul.

Ces quelques phrases arrachèrent un soupir de douleur au vieil homme et il passa plusieurs minutes à respirer doucement.

— Souffrez-vous beaucoup ? demanda Abigail, larmoyante.

— Oui, mais la justice passe avant tout. Mes enfants, ne soyez pas tristes. J'ai eu une belle vie.

— Combien de temps vont-ils vous laisser ainsi ?

— Malheureusement, jusqu'à ce que mon pauvre vieux corps n'en puisse plus de souffrir. Ils empileront sur moi une nouvelle pierre chaque matin. Je ne tiendrai pas longtemps, ainsi de nombreux jours de souffrance

me seront épargnés. Et j'aurai sauvé celle à qui vous tenez tant. Je ne pouvais rêver plus belle mort.

Abigail et Betty restèrent longtemps à pleurer sur le corps de leur vieil ami. Celui-ci, par la fatigue et la souffrance, restait silencieux, leur chuchotant de tendres mots lorsque son souffle redevenait normal. Il ne leur dit pas que plusieurs de ses côtes s'étaient brisées sous le poids de la roche, ni que celles-ci avaient sans doute commencé à perforer ses organes vitaux. Il avait promis de toujours les protéger. Et il l'avait fait promettre à Tituba lors d'une brève entrevue. Il mourrait l'esprit en paix. Au bout d'un moment, Giles leur demanda de rentrer chez elles. Elles n'avaient pas à endurer ce spectacle plus longtemps. Et il préférait qu'elles gardent un beau souvenir de lui plutôt que ce visage violacé et ces yeux fous de douleur. Elles s'en allèrent en lui promettant néanmoins de revenir et, le corps lourd, les épaules tendues, elles marchèrent en silence, la tristesse et le désespoir marquant leurs traits épuisés. Aussitôt arrivée à la maison, Abigail se précipita sur le grimoire caché sous sa couche. Sa cousine et elle dévorèrent le livre en long, en large et en travers sans trouver le moindre sort, le moindre charme qui aurait pu les aider à tirer des griffes des inquisiteurs le vieux jardinier. S'arrachant les cheveux de désolation, Abigail continuait fébrilement à tourner les pages, espérant découvrir à chaque ligne que suivait son doigt un sortilège qui résoudrait tout.

— Arrête, lui intima Betty. Ça ne sert à rien. Cela fait quatre fois que tu lis ce livre. S'il y avait eu quelque chose dedans, nous l'aurions déjà vu.

Pleurnichant, Abigail referma le grimoire et s'allongea sur son lit pour pleurer tout son soûl. Elle se releva tout aussi brusquement.

— Tu sais faire léviter des objets, Betty! s'exclama-t-elle, pleine d'espoir. Tu peux soulever cette pierre!

— J'y ai déjà pensé, bien sûr, répondit-elle, lasse. Mais cette dalle est beaucoup trop lourde pour moi, je n'ai jamais fait voler d'objets aussi volumineux. La malle du grenier était plus petite, et tu as vu le résultat.

— Tu n'as même pas essayé! fulmina Abigail. On dirait que tu ne veux rien faire pour sauver Giles!

— Que crois-tu que je faisais pendant que tu étais lamentablement penchée sur son corps, déversant toutes ces larmes inutiles? Oui, j'ai essayé de soulever la pierre. Crois-tu que je doive t'attendre pour avoir des idées? Ma pauvre Abigail, le chagrin te rend stupide, semble-t-il.

Abigail ne répondit pas, honteuse.

— Je ne peux non plus plier les inquisiteurs à ma volonté. Ils sont beaucoup trop nombreux. Et cela attirerait les soupçons sur notre famille. Je regrette, mais je pense qu'il n'y a pas de solutions. Giles nous l'a dit lui-même.

À ce moment, Abigail cessa de pleurer sur le sort du jardinier en présence de sa cousine. Celle-ci, malgré toute la cruauté dont elle avait fait preuve envers Abigail, avait raison. Les larmes étaient bien inutiles en pareille circonstance.

Chaque matin, elles se rendaient sur la place où Giles demeurait sous la pluie froide. Les membres raidis par l'humidité, ses souffrances s'étaient décuplées depuis le premier jour. Il paraissait ridiculement fin, les lourdes pierres, au nombre de trois maintenant, aplatissant sa poitrine autrefois vigoureuse. Sa respiration était de plus en plus aiguë et ses yeux, désormais révulsés, ne semblaient aspirer qu'à la délivrance. Il supportait cependant son mal sans qu'aucune plainte ne franchisse ses lèvres sèches. Les deux filles s'agenouillaient à ses côtés et lui racontaient la vie au manoir. Elles ne lui contaient pas les plaintes déchirantes qui tourmentaient leurs nuits et qui parvenaient sans nul doute des quartiers de miss Salinger. Elles ne lui parlaient même pas de l'indifférence glacée du révérend à leurs égards. Betty avait déclaré que la vie de Giles Corey devait s'éteindre avec de bons souvenirs, des paroles chaudes et des histoires réconfortantes. Les villageois, pudiques, s'éloignaient bien vite lorsqu'ils voyaient ces deux enfants s'asseoir près de ce vieil homme qu'on suppliciait au nom d'une justice inexistante. On jetait des coups d'œil émus et larmoyants devant cette amitié indéfectible, mais tout un chacun savait que cela ne durerait plus très longtemps. Le vieil homme approchait de la fin, tous étaient même étonnés de l'avoir vu survivre jusque-là. Les inquisiteurs partageaient cet étonnement.

Ce fut au matin du quatrième jour que Giles Corey expira. Les deux jeunes filles, sentant la fin proche, avaient hâté leur visite du matin et elles arrivèrent en même temps que trois inquisiteurs goguenards portant la quatrième pierre. Betty s'était élancée, les yeux flamboyants, prête à en découdre avec ces hommes sans scrupules. Mais dans un effort prodigieux, Giles

avait tourné la tête vers la jeune fille vengeresse, lui intimant de son regard scrutateur le silence. Betty en avait été stoppée net. Lorsque la dalle se posa sur les autres, Abigail et sa cousine se précipitèrent car elles entendirent distinctement craquer définitivement la cage thoracique du vieil homme.

— Approchez, leur dit-il, lamentable.

Se penchant sur la bouche du jardinier, Abigail essaya tant bien que mal de retenir les larmes qui inondaient déjà ses joues. Elle se laissa aller quand elle sentit sur son poignet des pleurs qui n'étaient pas les siens.

— Je suis fier de vous, mes filles, souffla le vieux jardinier, exténué. Je suis fier et vos mères le seraient aussi car vous êtes devenues ce qu'elles souhaitaient pour vous.

Égarées d'entendre parler de leurs mères en cet instant, Abigail ne trouva aucun mot pour apaiser les souffrances de Giles.

— Devenir quoi ? chuchota Betty.

Mais le dernier souffle venait de quitter le vieux corps brisé de Giles Corey. Elles pleurèrent longtemps sur ces pierres froides qui avaient été le dernier contact avec la vie du jardinier. Lorsque les inquisiteurs, ricanant, vinrent chercher le corps, Betty se dressa et leur demanda, avec toute la force qui pouvait transparaître dans sa voix tremblotante, de bien vouloir leur remettre le corps du jardinier pour que ses amis lui offrent une sépulture décente. Ils lui répondirent qu'ils devaient d'abord en parler à Patton.

— Ce chien a bien mérité ça ! cracha l'un des deux.

Abigail retint Betty qui levait déjà le bras. Elles rentrèrent en courant, étouffées de larmes et de sanglots. Miss Salinger, qui les guettait discrètement à chaque retour, hurla de détresse lorsqu'elle aperçut sur les joues salies des deux filles les sillons luisants que les larmes avaient creusés. Elle hurla et hurla jusqu'à ce qu'elle tombe évanouie. Ces cris inhumains stoppèrent Abigail et Betty devant la porte d'entrée. Refusant de rentrer et de lire sur le visage de miss Salinger toute la culpabilité qu'elles avaient refusée jusque-là, elles s'assirent sur les marches du perron, frissonnant dans l'air froid matinal. Leur souffle saccadé de hoquets laissait échapper de petits nuages de condensation, et l'une et l'autre se perdirent dans la contemplation de ces émanations blanches et duveteuses. Lorsque la porte s'ouvrit derrière elles, elles ne se retournèrent pas mais toutes deux sentirent sur leurs épaules un lourd manteau jeté pour les réchauffer. Puis, sans dire un mot, leur mystérieux bienfaiteur retourna dans l'antre chaud de la maison. Elles restèrent dehors jusqu'à ce que le soleil soit au zénith dans le ciel brumeux. Et même si la faim les tiraillait, elles se résolurent à ne pas manger. La fin de la journée s'étira considérablement et quand elles se couchèrent, le soir, elles avaient l'impression que leur langue était sèche et n'articulerait plus jamais un mot.

Lorsqu'elles apprirent le lendemain matin que Tituba avait été libérée, elles ne sautèrent pas de joie. Seul un mince sourire montra qu'elles avaient bien entendu la nouvelle. Quand la servante arriva à la maison, elle serra longuement les filles dans ses bras. Et celles-ci pleurèrent encore longtemps.

Au fur et à mesure que la douleur s'adoucissait, la vie reprenait son cours dans le manoir des Parris. Tituba était faible et sortait peu de sa chambre. Abigail et Betty lui montaient ses repas à tour de rôle, mais aucune n'avait envie de passer du temps dans sa chambre. Tituba, d'ailleurs, ne les pressait pas de rester. Patton lui avait intimé de quitter Salem aussitôt qu'elle serait rétablie, et de ne jamais y revenir. Tituba avait promis et les filles vivaient dans l'appréhension d'une nouvelle déchirure sans penser que la servante barbadienne avait d'autres projets.

4

Les derniers événements avaient presque fait oublier aux filles Parris l'épidémie de choléra qui sévissait depuis plusieurs semaines déjà dans le village. La maladie, qui n'avait jusque-là touché que le bétail, s'en prenait maintenant aux habitants. En quelques jours à peine, plusieurs familles furent décimées, celles qui comptaient parmi les plus pauvres de la ville. Chaque jour l'église était bondée. Des dizaines de fidèles venaient supplier Dieu de les aider à surmonter cette catastrophe. Le révérend restait impuissant face aux plaintes de ses ouailles et son inefficacité à soulager le chagrin de tous ces gens le rendait fou. Il partait très tôt le matin pour visiter les familles touchées par la maladie, bénir les mourants ; il pratiqua l'extrême-onction bien plus souvent que dans toute sa vie vouée aux ordres. Malheureusement, les prières ne servaient à rien contre l'épidémie qui semblait se répandre toujours plus vite. Il y eut bientôt trop de corps à ensevelir pour le petit cimetière du village et on les entassa, comme les carcasses de vaches, loin des habitations pour les brûler. L'immense charnier charriait des odeurs putrides qui exhalaient la mort et les habitants ne pouvaient s'empêcher de regarder leurs proches partir en fumée. Certains avaient pleuré lorsque le révérend leur avait expliqué que leur famille

ne pourrait avoir une sépulture décente car il avait peur que les corps malades empoisonnent la terre. Mais ses paroissiens abdiquèrent finalement. Des veuves aux joues creusées par les larmes et la maladie qui se terraient en elles serraient dans leurs bras des enfants désormais sans père et proches d'être orphelins. Des mères à genoux hurlaient au ciel contre ce malheur qui leur avait pris leurs enfants, et des pères impuissants les serraient contre eux, brûlants de fièvre les uns et les autres, près de trépasser et de rejoindre le charnier. Samuel Parris s'arrachait les cheveux de désespoir ; il lui semblait trahir ses engagements envers Dieu, envers sa paroisse. Il avait l'impression d'abandonner ses ouailles à un triste coup du sort. Une idée germait dans sa tête mais il s'efforçait de la repousser. Il ressassait les mêmes pensées.

« Elles ont soi-disant sauvé des bêtes, peut-être pourraient-elles sauver des hommes ? Mais ce serait contre la religion. Je ne peux m'allier à ces femmes qui ont le diable en elles. Seigneur, que dois-je faire ? Je pourrais sans doute épargner la vie de nombre de mes paroissiens. Et si cela était une épreuve pour prouver ma bonne foi envers toi et tes brebis ? Que dois-je faire ? Ce sont mes filles, après tout, elles sont bonnes. Mais ce qui couve en elles est monstrueux… »

Les heures défilaient ainsi, et Samuel Parris ne parvenait pas à prendre une décision. Les habitants le pressaient de questions. Pourquoi Dieu leur infligeait-il cela ? Pourquoi reprenait-il des enfants qui n'avaient même pas atteint l'âge d'homme et de femme ? Pourquoi enlevait-il des femmes belles et jeunes et des hommes vigoureux ? Le révérend ne savait que leur répondre. Il se contentait de hocher la tête d'un air

grave qui se voulait rassurant en leur répétant que les voies du ciel étaient impénétrables, mais que seule une bonne raison poussait Dieu à faire subir cette maladie à ses hommes. De jour en jour, il perdait l'appui de ses fidèles et lui-même se sentait honteux. Alors il se décida.

Un soir, alors qu'il faisait déjà nuit depuis plusieurs heures, il entra dans la chambre de ses filles endormies. Se penchant sur l'oreille de Betty, sa fille, il lui chuchota de se réveiller. La jeune fille sursauta et se redressa sur son séant, pensant à une intrusion. Lorsqu'elle vit son père debout dans la chambre, une chandelle à la main, elle fut surprise. Celui-ci ne venait jamais dans cette pièce.

— Va réveiller Abigail, lui dit-il dans un souffle. Mais ne fais pas de bruit.

Betty sortit de son lit douillet. Lorsque ses pieds nus touchèrent le plancher froid, elle frissonna et se dépêcha d'entrer dans la pièce adjacente. Quelques instants plus tard, elle revint accompagnée d'Abigail, les yeux encore brouillés de sommeil.

— Habillez-vous chaudement, le vent est froid cette nuit. Cachez vos cheveux sous vos bonnets de laine, je ne veux pas que l'on vous reconnaisse. Je vous ai apporté des pantalons des domestiques. Ils seront bien trop grands pour vous, mais je préfère que vous soyez méconnaissables.

Sans discuter, les deux filles se déguisèrent puis suivirent leur père dans les couloirs noirs et glacés. Le révérend ouvrit la porte d'entrée délicatement et, regardant par-dessus son épaule, il leur fit signe de

sortir. L'air glacial les surprit. Elles avaient fait à peine quelques pas dehors qu'elles se retrouvèrent transies de froid. Samuel Parris les fit accélérer.

— Où allons-nous, papa ? demanda Betty. Il fait un froid mordant et nous sommes en pleine nuit. Que se passe-t-il ?

Il ne leur répondit pas tout de suite. Cela faisait plusieurs jours qu'il ne leur avait pas parlé. Et la raison pour laquelle il sortait de son mutisme lui paraissait révoltante. Il continua à marcher à grands pas sans attendre les deux filles qui couraient presque dans son sillage.

— Je veux que vous soigniez tous ces gens qui tombent malades. Vous avez réussi à le faire avec du bétail, vous y parviendrez sûrement avec des hommes. C'est un véritable massacre, je veux que vous arrêtiez cela.

Il avait tout dit d'une traite comme s'il voulait se débarrasser de cette idée impure. Betty et Abigail s'arrêtèrent brusquement.

— Tu as besoin de nous maintenant… chuchota Betty. Tu ne voulais plus nous parler parce que nous t'avons avoué que nous étions des sorcières mais maintenant, tu as besoin de nous, ajouta-t-elle plus fort. Eh bien, je ne t'aiderai pas ! hurla-t-elle.

Et elle tourna les talons, pressant le pas, la démarche fière, l'air blessé. Abigail lui courut après.

— Attends !

— Non ! Il se sert de nous pour se faire bien voir de ses fidèles. Aussitôt que nous aurons soigné ces malheureux, il nous méprisera de nouveau ! Peut-être même nous livrera-t-il lui-même aux inquisiteurs pour laver la honte dont nous avons souillé la famille ! cria-t-elle en direction de son père.

Celui-ci devint rouge et ses yeux flamboyèrent. Il s'approcha rapidement de sa fille et colla son visage à quelques pouces du sien. Betty sursauta tant la colère de son père était manifeste.

— Elizabeth Parris, n'accuse plus jamais ton père de vouloir trahir son propre sang ! gronda-t-il entre ses dents. Comment oses-tu ? Crois-tu que je me serais embarrassé d'une enfant si je ne t'avais aimée ? Crois-tu que j'aurais promis à ta mère sur son lit de mort de te protéger toujours et qu'aujourd'hui je renierais mon serment ? Crois-tu que j'aurais recueilli ma nièce si je ne l'avais aimée aussi et si je n'avais su que ta vie serait plus légère avec une sœur ? Crois-tu que j'aurais supporté les médisances des commères du village qui pensaient qu'un père veuf ne pourrait élever seul une fille ? Ne t'avise plus de me parler comme cela ! Ma patience a des limites, jeune fille ! Et ne pas tenir la promesse faite à une défunte serait pour moi l'ultime trahison qui me ferait mériter l'enfer ! Tu ne sais rien des choix que j'ai dû faire dans ma vie, en vous gardant toujours en première place, en pensant toujours à vous avant les autres. J'ai sacrifié un ami de longue date pour votre bonheur et il l'a fait de bon cœur car il vous aimait comme un père. Giles travaillait déjà pour mon père, il a connu vos mères et m'a aidé dans bien des épreuves, notamment la mort de Rose ! C'était un être que je chérissais beaucoup car c'était un homme bon et

le dernier lien que j'avais avec mes propres parents ! Ne pense pas que tu es seule contre tous, ma chère fille, car c'est bien l'inverse.

Il s'éloigna rapidement et Betty en profita pour essuyer les quelques larmes qui avaient perlé. La tête basse, elle se laissa entraîner par sa cousine qui n'avait dit mot. Tous trois arrivèrent bientôt devant une vieille masure délabrée par les âges. Elle semblait bancale et tordue, et sa cheminée sinuait vers le ciel, la gueule béante à cause de l'éboulement de plusieurs pierres. Le révérend frappa rapidement et poussa aussitôt la porte. Une vieille dame recroquevillée et vêtue de haillons vint à leur rencontre. L'intérieur de la maison, malgré la pauvreté manifeste de la famille, était convivial. La chaleur bienvenue réchauffait les membres gourds des visiteurs, et même s'il était flagrant que la table et les chaises servaient désormais de bois de chauffage, subsistait près du foyer un confortable fauteuil aux tissus rougis. La vieille dame se précipita pour débarrasser le révérend de sa cape. Celui-ci la remercia d'un sourire. Il poussa ses filles en avant vers l'homme allongé dans une cache de la pièce. Abigail recula à la vue du malheureux qui respirait avec difficulté. Il ne lui restait sur les os qu'une peau parcheminée qui menaçait de se déchirer au moindre contact. La sueur dégoulinait sur son corps et laissait des traces usées sur ses membres frêles. Elles reconnurent Oliver Saglord, le palefrenier du village. Ses muscles avaient fondu, son large cou était maintenant plus fin que celui de sa femme. Et ses épaules si larges, ses bras musculeux qui venaient habituellement à bout des chevaux les plus fous ne luttaient même plus pour la vie. Une odeur nauséabonde montant de la couche dissuadait les filles de s'en approcher.

— Margaret, la prévint le révérend. Ce que mes filles vont faire maintenant doit rester dans cette maison. N'en parlez à personne! Si cela marche, et j'ai bon espoir, ajouta-t-il à l'intention de ses enfants, vous direz autour de vous que votre mari est fort et vigoureux, que son corps s'est remis seul. Vous m'avez compris?

La petite dame hocha la tête en tremblant, jetant aux filles un regard terrorisé. Samuel Parris prit chacune d'elles par les épaules et, après les avoir pressées doucement en signe d'encouragement, il les poussa vers le renfoncement. Abigail et Betty furent prises d'une terreur indicible lorsque le rideau se ferma derrière elles, les enfermant dans la pièce putride en compagnie d'un moribond. Betty reprit ses esprits en premier. Elle s'agenouilla près de la couche et tendit les mains au-dessus du malheureux.

— Que fais-tu? demanda Abigail, tremblotante.

— Je ne sais pas vraiment. J'essaie de faire comme Tituba nous a appris. Viens m'aider. Nous ne serons pas trop de deux!

Abigail s'assit à ses côtés et toutes deux restèrent longtemps à marmonner dans leur tête des incantations qu'elles n'avaient jamais utilisées. Jusqu'à maintenant, elles avaient jeté des sorts de guérison sans réfléchir, mais leur inconscient leur disait que soigner une bête et un homme n'était pas pareil. Elles se laissèrent emporter par le doux flot de paroles qui entravaient leur esprit à toute autre chose.

Derrière le rideau, la vieille femme et le révérend se tenaient côte à côte, silencieux. Il leur semblait que cela durait depuis des heures déjà, mais ni l'un ni

l'autre ne voulait déranger les filles. Quand enfin elles sortirent, leur père poussa un soupir de soulagement tandis que Margaret Saglord se précipitait au chevet de son époux. Celui-ci avait toujours son air décharné, mais sa respiration était souple et il paraissait dormir paisiblement.

— Je pense que ça ira, dit dans un souffle Betty. Mais nous n'en sommes pas sûres du tout.

Le révérend serra brièvement contre lui Betty et Abigail, tandis que Mrs. Saglord se répandait en remerciements, les appelant ses sauveurs.

— Reposez-vous et occupez-vous bien de votre mari. Et n'oubliez pas : pas un mot de ce qui s'est passé cette nuit !

La vieille femme acquiesça, les yeux larmoyants, et retourna précipitamment veiller son mari. Les visiteurs sortirent discrètement et, après avoir jeté un coup d'œil des deux côtés, Samuel Parris poussa les deux filles dehors. Le retour se fit en silence, mais le ressentiment et la colère l'avaient déserté. Betty et Abigail rayonnaient, espérant à tout le moins avoir abrégé les souffrances du malheureux si elles ne l'avaient pas sauvé. Mais au fond d'elles-mêmes, elles savaient qu'il guérirait rapidement. Avant de monter dans sa chambre, Betty se retourna vers son père.

— Continuerons-nous la nuit prochaine ?

Il ne lui répondit pas, mais il lui sourit si tendrement qu'elle en fut satisfaite.

Les nuits suivantes, elles s'en allèrent toujours avec le révérend dans le froid et déguisées en hommes. Elles

soignèrent plusieurs personnes et abrégèrent la vie d'autres devenue trop douloureuse. Souvent, les larmes les prenaient au retour, mais le révérend les consolait en leur disant qu'il était fier de ce qu'elles faisaient et que tous ces gens leur en étaient reconnaissants. Lui-même frissonnait à l'idée que ses ouailles, emportées par l'allégresse, se mettent à discourir des soins que les filles Parris donnaient une fois la nuit venue, de ces étranges pouvoirs qui leur permettaient d'aller contre la volonté de Dieu et de soigner les mourants. Mais les jours se suivirent et aucun incident n'eut lieu. Les filles avaient demandé à Tituba de les accompagner, mais celle-ci arguait que cela ne pouvait que leur porter préjudice. Le révérend ne l'accepterait sans doute pas et son état était encore trop faible. Patton était en outre persuadé que Tituba avait définitivement quitté Salem et la servante n'avait pas encore recouvré son pouvoir d'invisibilité.

Un matin, Abigail et Betty virent les inquisiteurs s'affoler. Craignant une nouvelle rafle, elles retournèrent immédiatement chez elles. Lorsqu'elles en parlèrent à leur père, celui-ci se précipita au village pour voir ce qui s'y passait. Patton était tombé malade et on craignait que le choléra ne l'ait atteint. Samuel Parris ne partagea ni l'allégresse de ses paroissiens ni le désespoir des hommes de l'inquisiteur. Il rentra chez lui, le pas tranquille, la face détendue. Abigail et Betty, après avoir entendu l'histoire, demandèrent avec appréhension à leur père s'il fallait qu'elles aillent le soigner.

— Mes chères filles, je sais que Patton est une brebis du Seigneur comme nous tous mais les mauvaises choses qu'il a accomplies dans sa vie ne le mettent pas

à l'abri du châtiment divin. Il semblerait que ce jour soit arrivé. Je ne veux pas que vous alliez le soigner. Cet homme, cracha-t-il, se montrera doucereux avec vous, mais dès que vous l'aurez soigné, il s'empressera de vous faire enfermer. Allons, mes enfants, la mort de ce triste sire ne me chagrinera pas et vous non plus, n'est-ce pas ?

Les filles acquiescèrent, soulagées.

Le jeune homme n'en pouvait plus de cette route de graviers qui lui tordaient les chevilles et rentraient dans ses chaussures. Sans cesse, il s'arrêtait, enlevait ses souliers et les vidait des cailloux qui s'y étaient immiscés. Il avait tellement marché depuis Boston que ses semelles étaient trouées. Il aspirait désormais à un repos bien mérité, à un lit moelleux et à un repas chaud. Il savait qu'au bout de cette route se tenait sa récompense. Il avait quitté Boston deux semaines plus tôt sans rien dire à ses quelques amis qui ne devaient de toute façon pas être très inquiets. Les derniers temps, ils le craignaient beaucoup, lui et ses accès de colère et de violence. Réunissant ses maigres économies et prenant son courage à deux mains, il était parti sur les routes, jetant ce qui le rattachait à sa vie d'avant, ses tissus, ses balles, ses anneaux et ses torches. Sur la route, des gens attentionnés rencontrés au hasard lui avaient fait faire un bout de chemin avec eux dans leur voiture, mais jamais plus de quelques milles. Ils n'allaient pas dans la même direction et le jeune homme s'ennuyait souvent avec ces vieux couples riches qui faisaient semblant de s'intéresser à sa vie. Au fur et à mesure des différentes voitures, il

s'était inventé des personnalités. Tantôt il devenait un médecin qui courait la campagne à la recherche d'un endroit où s'établir, tantôt il devenait un poète qui cherchait l'inspiration dans la nature. Il poussa même l'audace jusqu'à prendre le nom de ce juge connu de tout Boston. Le conducteur tiqua lorsqu'il lui dit son nom, mais lorsque la femme s'extasia en disant qu'elle était effectivement sûre de l'avoir déjà vu à Boston, le jeune homme se détendit. Il leur expliqua qu'il avait eu envie de faire un bout de chemin à pied avant d'aller voir des connaissances au village de Salem. Mais le chemin avait été long et plein d'embûches. Il avait failli se faire détrousser de ses quelques affaires par des brigands au détour d'un sentier. Par chance, un honnête homme qui passait par là l'avait aidé à mettre les gredins en déroute. Tous deux avaient fait un bout de chemin ensemble puis le bienfaiteur lui avait dit qu'il se rendait à Marblehead. Ils s'étaient donc séparés. Le jeune homme regretta un temps son compagnon de route mais, bien vite, il prit goût aux merveilles que lui offrait la nature. Il prit conscience que le silence lui permettait d'avancer plus vite et plus longtemps sans s'épuiser alors que les incessantes palabres de cet inconnu le fatiguaient autant qu'elles le charmaient. Il allongea le pas quand les prémices de l'hiver se firent sentir. Le soir, il se couchait à l'abri d'un bosquet, enroulé dans une grosse couverture, grignotant la miche de pain qu'il avait achetée dans le dernier village. Au matin, il se mettait en marche dès l'aube. Il ne voulait pas se faire prendre par les premières neiges, et ses provisions s'amenuisaient dangereusement. Des rumeurs avaient couru jusqu'à Boston. On avait besoin d'inquisiteurs dans le village de Salem. Il ne savait pas vraiment ce qu'était un

inquisiteur mais aux airs horrifiés des gens qui en parlaient, il s'était dit qu'il aurait sans doute un certain pouvoir. Il se voyait déjà dans un bel uniforme qui inspirerait la crainte et le respect des villageois. Peut-être serait-il nourri et logé, et pourquoi pas payé aussi ! Cela lui servirait bien pour ce qu'il avait à faire. Il continua à marcher un temps en rêvassant à un intérieur chaud et douillet, un verre d'alcool et sa femme qui lui préparerait un délicieux repas chaud. Si elle se pliait à ses volontés… Il rit un peu au souvenir de ce qu'il avait fait à Boston. Sa dernière action avant de prendre la route. Comme elle avait crié cette femme ! Et son mari, impuissant à la protéger ! Il les avait torturés jusqu'à ce qu'ils lui disent ce qu'il voulait entendre. Et jusqu'à ce qu'ils rendent l'âme aussi. Après tout, ce qu'il avait demandé n'était pas si dur, et si ces gens avaient accueilli ces deux filles pendant quelques jours, ils savaient bien où elles habitaient. Au souvenir des yeux larmoyants de l'homme lorsqu'il avait, devant lui, coupé la gorge de sa femme, Anton s'esclaffa.

Plusieurs jours s'écoulèrent pendant lesquels on ne vit plus les inquisiteurs persécuter les villageois. On aurait dit qu'ils ne savaient plus quoi faire depuis que leur chef était malade et alité. Et quand les inquisiteurs s'étaient mis à hurler sur la place publique qu'il leur fallait un médecin, un villageois leur avait tranquillement répondu qu'ils n'étaient pas les seuls et qu'il trouvait fort mal à propos de rappeler son chagrin à la jeune veuve du seul médecin du village. Penauds, les inquisiteurs s'étaient terrés dans leur quartier. Un vague espoir courait dans les rues. Tous pensaient que si l'inquisiteur

en chef mourait, les autres partiraient. Et même si le révérend Parris était sceptique quant à cette éventualité, il se gardait bien de le dire. Toutes les nuits, il continuait avec ses filles à sauver ses ouailles de la maladie, et malgré son épuisement, il rassurait, priait et bénissait à tour de bras sans jamais se reposer.

Les inquisiteurs le pressaient de venir au chevet de leur chef. Ils l'invectivaient, le menaçaient mais toujours le révérend prétextait un enfant à accompagner vers la mort, un corps à enterrer. Et lorsque les hommes en noir l'avertissaient, il se contentait de leur répondre que s'il ne répondait pas au dessein de Dieu tous seraient perdus. Ces grands hommes en noir qui maltraitaient et torturaient des innocents prirent peur et cessèrent de le presser. Ainsi, Samuel Parris ne se rendit jamais au chevet de Patton, priant en son for intérieur et suppliant le Seigneur de lui pardonner cela, qu'il ne recouvre pas la santé. Malheureusement, au bout de quelques jours, des villageois virent Patton debout sur le seuil de sa prison, l'air frais, le teint un peu pâle mais guéri. La nouvelle circula dans le village et arriva aux oreilles du révérend qui ne put laisser échapper un soupir de désespoir. Ainsi, tout recommençait. Le même jour, Anton pénétra dans le village de Salem, sale, affaibli mais porté par sa vengeance.

5

Ezra respira à pleins poumons l'air glacial du début de l'hiver. Il inspira jusqu'à ce que ses poumons crient grâce. Après toutes ces semaines passées enfermé dans l'air putride et rance des cachots, ce grand bol d'air arrivait comme une bénédiction. Il prit conscience de sa peau nue au contact du froid et se frotta vigoureusement les bras pour se réchauffer. Patton était venu le voir quelques minutes plus tôt pour lui dire qu'il n'avait plus rien à faire en prison, que sa peine était purgée. Ezra comprit qu'il avait besoin de place pour les femmes qu'il se faisait un plaisir d'enfermer. Pendant ces semaines, Ezra avait sans cesse ressassé l'histoire qui l'avait fait emprisonner et sa colère s'était peu à peu éteinte jusqu'à ce qu'il croit lui-même qu'il avait menti. Mais à l'air libre, au contact de l'horizon, sa rancœur remontait peu à peu. Tout ce temps perdu, et sa vie qui allait être plus difficile maintenant. Il haussa les épaules et s'en alla d'un pas traînant dans les rues du village, redécouvrant Salem. L'automne avait fait place à l'hiver sans qu'il puisse se repaître de ses couleurs enflammées, mais l'air froid et sec lui plaisait aussi. Le ciel était d'une clarté évanescente et à perte de vue, il admirait la brume opaline qui rendait la lumière si éblouissante. Les arbres frissonnaient et perdaient leurs dernières feuilles et la terre sèche craquait sous ses pas.

Il avait dû geler cette nuit. Par habitude, Ezra se dirigea vers la maison de Hank puis se ravisa. Celui-ci n'aurait sans doute aucune envie de le voir. Il se promit pourtant de retourner lui demander un emploi. En sillonnant les rues, il fut surpris de ne croiser personne. Les ruelles désertes étaient silencieuses et les joies intestines, si bruyantes habituellement, brillaient par leur absence. Le jeune homme eut l'impression de se promener dans un village fantôme. Tout à son bonheur d'être libre, il savoura aussi le plaisir d'être seul. Il n'avait pas encore le courage d'affronter les mines déconfites de ceux qui auraient voulu le voir captif plus longtemps, et encore moins les figures empreintes de pitié des autres. Finalement, il décida de se diriger vers ses anciens terrains de jeux pour accroître encore ses chances de ne croiser personne. Il hésita un instant entre le bois de Kyron et la forêt de Belwack puis choisit le premier. Le bois était éloigné de toute habitation et c'était exactement ce dont avait besoin Ezra. Lorsqu'il aperçut au coin d'une rue un homme de son âge qui arrivait dans sa direction, il chercha une échappatoire. N'en trouvant aucune, il se résolut à baisser la tête. Mais quand le piéton le frôla, il ne put s'empêcher de jeter un regard furtif sur son visage. Ezra ne le reconnut pas. Le visage froid et fin ne lui disait rien mais, après tout, il y avait tellement de nouvelles têtes au village avec les inquisiteurs qu'il faisait sûrement partie de ceux-ci. L'autre homme ne lui prêta pas attention. Manifestement, il ne savait pas qui il était. Ezra en fut soulagé et un instant il caressa l'idée de tout recommencer dans un autre village, où personne ne le connaîtrait. On lui avait parlé de Manchester, un village de pêcheurs plus au nord. Ezra avait souvent rêvé à la vie de la mer. Mais ce fut une suggestion

fugace car il ne se voyait pas quitter Salem malgré tout ce qu'il allait encore devoir y endurer.

Samuel Parris se réveilla la tête lourde et les membres gourds comme s'il avait dormi dans une mauvaise position et au froid. Pourtant, sa chambre était parfaitement chauffée et il ne ressentait pas de frissons. Il se leva, ne prêtant pas attention aux signaux de fatigue que son corps lui envoyait encore, et s'habilla prestement. Il avait encore passé la nuit avec ses filles à veiller les mourants et à soigner ceux qui avaient une chance de s'en sortir. Ne rentrant qu'à l'aube, il s'était octroyé deux heures de sommeil avant de repartir en pèlerinage contre la maladie. La lassitude avait profondément marqué ses traits et en quelques jours il semblait avoir pris plusieurs années. Ses cheveux grisonnaient et une barbe de plusieurs jours salissait son visage tandis que les cernes noirs qui entouraient ses yeux achevaient de lui donner cet air maladif qui le faisait frémir chaque fois qu'il apercevait son reflet. Sa peur était aussi attribuable aux bubons noirâtres qui étaient apparus sur sa peau aux articulations. Il ne ressentait encore aucune douleur ni symptôme du choléra mais il savait qu'il l'avait contracté. Chaque nuit, en revenant de leurs pérégrinations, il voulait demander à ses filles de le soigner aussi, mais devant leur mine épuisée, il remettait sans cesse sa requête au lendemain. Jamais il n'aurait accepté de se faire guérir avant ses paroissiens. Si bien qu'il cachait courageusement sa maladie et sa fatigue la journée pour s'affaler sur son lit à l'aube et dormir d'un sommeil fiévreux. Après s'être aspergé le visage de l'eau glacée du broc, il faisait un pas vers la porte de

sa chambre quand une douleur fulgurante le terrassa. Il sentit entre ses jambes couler un liquide chaud et nauséabond sans pouvoir se retenir, et avant que sa tête ne heurte le sol, il sut que c'était la fin.

Il fallut plusieurs heures aux membres de la maison des Parris pour découvrir le corps sans vie du maître des lieux. Ses filles pensaient qu'épuisé il avait oublié de se réveiller et elles décidèrent de le laisser se reposer. Les domestiques se firent la même réflexion et ce ne fut qu'aux alentours de midi, lorsque le repas fut sonné, qu'on décida d'aller réveiller le révérend. Howard, le majordome, déclara qu'il s'en occupait, connaissant bien le rituel du lever de son maître. Il monta donc et son hurlement ne tarda pas à retentir. Betty et Abigail frissonnèrent et montèrent quatre à quatre l'escalier. Dans la chambre de leur père s'étaient déjà réunis tous les domestiques de la maisonnée et on leur bloqua l'entrée. Betty fulminait, déclarant qu'elle voulait voir son père. Mordant et griffant, elle gesticulait comme une diablesse, mais Abigail se tenait coite. Elle avait, entre les jambes d'Howard, entraperçu le corps affaissé de Samuel Parris gisant dans ses déjections. Il n'y avait aucun doute sur la cause de sa mort. Une grosse larme coula sur sa joue tandis que les domestiques essayaient de retenir Betty. L'air tremblotait autour de cette dernière, mais personne ne semblait s'en rendre compte et ses yeux rougeoyants ne firent frémir qu'Abigail. Soudain, elle s'affaissa dans les bras qui tentaient de la retenir et les pleurs brouillèrent vite ses traits. Cathy la prit dans ses bras et la tira hors de la chambre, entraînant aussi Abigail. Tituba, qui s'était approchée pour voir quelle était la

cause de tout ce tapage, fut surprise lorsque Betty s'agenouilla devant elle, prenant l'ourlet de sa robe entre ses mains tremblantes.

— Faites quelque chose, Tituba, je vous en supplie !

Cathy agita la tête en direction de la Barbadienne comme pour signifier que Betty n'avait pas toute sa tête puis elle articula silencieusement entre ses dents : « Le révérend est mort. » Tituba sursauta et se précipita dans la chambre de Samuel Parris pour constater qu'il n'y avait plus rien à faire. Betty pleura tout le jour de n'avoir pu parler une dernière fois à son père, de n'être pas allée plus tôt dans sa chambre, de toutes ces choses méchantes qu'elle lui avait dites, de se savoir orpheline. Abigail pleura parce que pour la deuxième fois de sa vie elle perdait un père. La maison endeuillée était d'un silence glaçant. Les domestiques marchaient sur la pointe des pieds pour ne pas déranger le chagrin des héritières tandis que dans la cuisine miss Salinger s'appliquait à ne pas faire tinter ses casseroles tout en pleurant à chaudes larmes dans la soupe. Cathy apporta le repas des filles dans leur chambre mais toutes deux refusèrent d'y toucher. Des hommes vinrent chercher le corps du révérend, sommairement nettoyé et chastement enroulé dans une couverture qui cachait ses traits déformés par la douleur de sa mort. Même s'il était le révérend du village, il n'eut pas droit à une sépulture décente, l'ayant stipulé dans son testament. Cela le rapprocha encore des villageois qui s'amassèrent autour du charnier pour rendre un dernier hommage au corps supplicié de leur révérend qui les avait si bien aidés, au détriment de sa santé. Les filles Parris ne s'y rendirent pas, ne voulant pas voir le corps de leur père disparaître en fumée vers le ciel, sa

demeure éternelle. Betty resta à faire les cent pas dans la chambre, envoyant valser les objets aux quatre coins de la pièce, faisant apparaître des papillons par centaines qui voletaient et se cognaient partout. Elle fit même jaillir un tel geyser d'eau qu'Abigail dut intervenir pour stopper l'inondation. De sa main, elle fit sortir une petite flamme avec laquelle elle sécha en douceur le tapis détrempé. Betty ne se contrôlait plus et, à chaque pas, elle devenait invisible pour réapparaître quelques pieds plus loin. Abigail tentait de la calmer, mais sa cousine ne l'écoutait pas et, bientôt, elle abandonna.

Ezra s'énervait de plus en plus et l'amertume de son séjour en prison remontait à ses lèvres comme une bile écœurante. Il n'avait pu trouver de baies ou de champignons dans le bois de Kyron, le froid était bien trop installé ; alors, après quelques promenades, il s'était décidé à retourner au village demander la charité d'un commerçant. Il savait que cela n'allait pas être simple, mais il ne se serait pas douté que tous les magasins étaient fermés, de la taverne à la mercerie. Des planches de bois clôturaient les entrées et les vitrines, et des lettres malhabiles avaient été tracées dessus : CHOLÉRA. Furieux, Ezra avait erré dans le village à la recherche d'une bonne âme qui aurait pu lui donner un bol de soupe et un morceau de pain. Cependant, personne ne sortait et l'on se méfiait de lui lorsqu'il frappait à une porte. Tout en donnant des coups de pied rageurs dans les pierres qui parsemaient le chemin, ses jambes le menèrent inconsciemment devant le manoir des Parris. Il regarda longuement cette haute bâtisse de pierre aux lierres grimpants

couvrant toute sa surface. La grille était béante et le chemin de graviers menant jusqu'au perron lui apparaissait comme un élément familier dans toute sa mauvaise fortune. Les fenêtres étaient toutes fermées par les lourds rideaux qu'il avait déjà aperçus et il se prit au jeu d'essayer de deviner ce qui se passait derrière. Ezra connaissait parfaitement le chemin qui menait aux cuisines à l'arrière du manoir, mais il se demandait comment il allait être reçu.. Même s'il ignorait qu'un drame venait d'avoir lieu, il trouvait l'endroit oppressant et moribond. Le manoir n'avait plus sa beauté d'autrefois. Lorsqu'un rideau bougea au premier étage, là où se trouvaient les chambres des filles, Ezra s'aplatit sur le sol glacé derrière un bosquet famélique où ne subsistaient que quelques feuilles marron et sèches. Le visage d'Abigail apparut derrière les carreaux et, bien qu'il ne distinguât pas bien sa figure, il crut y lire des traces de tristesse. Le rideau s'abaissa de nouveau, et au lieu de ressentir de la tendresse ou de l'amour pour cette fille qui avait été sa plus proche amie, il sentit poindre en lui la colère, et le goût de la vengeance envahit sa bouche avide. Comment pouvait-elle vivre dans le faste alors que lui avait toujours lutté pour subsister? Comment pouvait-elle vivre alors que par sa faute il avait failli mourir dans les cachots humides de l'inquisition? Il tremblait de rage et d'impuissance, de froid et de faim. Son esprit brouillé par tous ces sentiments ne le prévint pas que quelqu'un s'était approché discrètement derrière lui et avait, comme Ezra, observé le visage derrière la fenêtre pour repartir, l'air triomphant. Les poings serrés, Ezra gardait en mémoire le beau visage blanc d'Abigail pour entretenir sa fureur et son impatience.

Anton s'éloigna en se frottant les mains. Il l'avait retrouvée. Ces deux vieux bourgeois ne lui avaient donc pas menti. Un rictus cruel barra son visage. Tout avait été si facile depuis qu'il était arrivé. Patton l'avait reçu comme un prince lorsqu'il lui avait dit son désir de devenir inquisiteur. L'homme s'était étalé sur tout ce que requérait ce métier et Anton l'avait vite rassuré. Un uniforme lui avait été confié aussitôt ainsi qu'un quartier qui ne correspondait pas à ses rêves mais qui lui conviendrait très bien. Il bénéficiait maintenant d'une petite chambre avec un lit confortable et un bureau, et il aurait droit à trois repas chauds par jour. Il ne pouvait rêver mieux, lui qui, il y a quelques jours encore, n'était qu'un vagabond sur les routes. Et cette fille qui avait peuplé ses pensées depuis qu'il l'avait vue à Boston, depuis qu'elle s'était moquée de lui avec l'autre petite garce… Il l'avait enfin retrouvée.

Le lendemain matin, après avoir dormi au creux d'un arbre de la forêt de Belwack, Ezra retourna au manoir. Il ne savait pas ce qui le poussait à revenir en ce lieu mais cette fois, au lieu d'aller s'installer à l'endroit d'où il pouvait espionner sans être vu, il alla frapper à la lourde porte de l'entrée. Ses gestes étaient mécaniques et il agissait inconsciemment. Il ne savait même pas ce qu'il allait dire au révérend. La porte s'ouvrit sur la servante barbadienne. Tituba le reconnut aussitôt et son pâle sourire de circonstance se transforma aussitôt en un rictus de colère.

— Qu'est-ce que tu viens faire ici ? gronda-t-elle.

— Je dois parler aux filles Parris, déclara Ezra, la voix claire et haute.

— Pour leur dire quoi ?

— Mais ça ne vous regarde pas !

— Je lis en toi, mon ami ! Et ce que j'y vois ne me plaît guère !

— Je dois comprendre et savoir. Je veux comprendre pourquoi elles m'ont laissé me faire enfermer alors que nous étions amis.

— Parce que tu as menti, bien sûr. Pour quelle autre raison crois-tu ?

Ezra frémit de fureur devant l'attitude parfaitement calme et froide de Tituba. Il leva le poing vers la servante.

— Je les retrouverai un jour ou l'autre et vous ne serez pas là pour les protéger. Elles ne s'en tireront pas comme ça. Elles ont mis ma vie en l'air ! Je les retrouverai et…

— Et que feras-tu, misérable pourceau ? gronda Tituba, effrayante. Ne t'avise pas de proférer des menaces contre ces filles, tu ne sais pas de quoi je suis capable. Je pourrais en un clin d'œil t'expédier à l'autre bout de la terre, te faire dévorer par des insectes ou t'enterrer vivant. Que crois-tu que tu ferais après ça ? Je te conseille de partir d'ici et d'aller tenter ta chance ailleurs. Cette maison est en deuil de son maître et tu lui manques beaucoup de respect. Pars si tu tiens à ta vie !

Ezra frissonna car les yeux glacés de la servante semblaient lui transpercer le corps. Ses menaces ne lui faisaient pas vraiment peur puisqu'il n'y croyait pas, mais il avait entendu dire que Tituba avait été accusée

73

de sorcellerie puis relâchée. Peut-être les inquisiteurs s'étaient-ils trompés. Il s'éloigna sous le regard furibond de la Barbadienne et leva les yeux vers les fenêtres. Le visage d'Abigail était apparu à nouveau derrière la fenêtre et il se sentit bouillonner. Ainsi, le révérend était mort. Ce n'était qu'un juste retour des choses. Ne voulant pas encore dormir dehors car le froid mordant l'avait tourmenté pendant la nuit précédente, il se rendit chez Hank, prêt à le supplier de le reprendre. Arrivé devant la boucherie, il sentit son cœur se serrer à la vue de la devanture placardée. Cela n'annonçait rien de bon. Il espéra que Hank était toujours en vie. Ezra cogna plusieurs fois à la porte et il faillit bondir de joie lorsqu'il vit le gros homme rougeaud aux cheveux roux hirsutes venir lui ouvrir. Hank avait l'air hagard et fatigué et il jeta un regard morne sur son visiteur. Ezra souriait à pleines dents, certain que son ancien maître, dès qu'il l'aurait reconnu, le serrerait comme un fils dans ses bras. Mais Hank garda sa mine renfrognée et grogna :

— Que viens-tu faire ici ?

Douché par cet accueil peu enthousiaste, Ezra ne perdit pas son sourire.

— Te voir et te demander de reprendre ma place auprès de toi.

— Voyons, Ezra, qui voudrait te reprendre ? On t'a traité de menteur et te voilà ancien prisonnier. Personne ne te fait plus confiance, et je dois t'avouer que moi non plus. Et tu as bien vu que j'ai fermé mon commerce. Plus personne n'achète de viande maintenant. La maladie est partout, les gens restent cloîtrés chez eux de peur de respirer le même air que les autres.

Les affaires ne marchent plus comme avant, alors je n'ai pas besoin d'un employé.

— Mais, commença timidement Ezra, pourrais-je au moins prendre mon ancienne chambre, Hank ? Il commence à faire froid, je ne peux plus dormir dehors. Je pourrais faire n'importe quoi comme travaux en échange. Le ménage de ta maison, ou te préparer tes repas. Je ne te dérangerais pas et…

— Non, Ezra, je ne veux pas de toi chez moi.

Et Hank lui ferma la porte au nez. Ezra resta un moment interdit, espérant une farce de son ami, mais celui-ci ne revint pas ouvrir la porte. Le jeune homme repartit en traînant les pieds. Si Hank ne voulait pas le reprendre, personne ne le voudrait. D'ailleurs, le boucher le lui avait bien fait comprendre. Il se résigna une nuit de plus à aller dormir dans la forêt ; il chercherait une autre solution demain. En attendant la tombée de la nuit et pour tromper sa faim, il se promena à travers le village, vola une pomme qui ne lui remplit pas le ventre puis se décida à aller traîner vers la rivière. Il quitta le village par un petit sentier de terre qui n'était jamais emprunté.

Au même moment, Abigail pénétrait dans Salem. Miss Salinger lui avait demandé d'aller voir au village si elle ne pourrait pas trouver un morceau de pain. La soupe était claire car les légumes venaient aussi à manquer et elle voulait l'enrichir d'une miche. Betty n'avait pas voulu l'accompagner, restant prostrée sur son lit. Mais Abigail n'en pouvait plus de l'atmosphère viciée de la chambre et elle avait accepté cette

promenade avec reconnaissance. Le village était désert. Arrivée sur la place, elle se retint de jeter un œil sur le charnier qui, telle une petite colline, surplombait le village au loin. Devant la boulangerie, elle soupira. La devanture barrée de planches ne laissait aucun doute. Il n'y avait plus de pain ou la fille de Rebecca Nurse, qui l'avait aussitôt remplacée, était malade. La nuit dernière, Abigail avait tenté de convaincre Betty de continuer d'aller soigner les gens, mais sa cousine n'avait rien voulu entendre et Abigail ne s'était pas décidée à y aller seule. Les inquisiteurs la terrorisaient. Elle se résigna à rentrer en flânant un peu au hasard des rues, profitant de cette belle journée froide. Ezra était venu à la maison tout à l'heure, elle l'avait vu, et Tituba n'avait sans doute pas été tendre avec lui. Son regard glacé lui avait brisé le cœur. Elle aurait tant voulu descendre et courir après lui, tout lui expliquer mais elle n'en avait pas eu le courage et, de toute manière, Tituba l'en aurait empêchée. Alors, elle espérait le rencontrer maintenant même si elle ne savait pas s'il était encore dans le village. À chaque coin de rue, elle se disait qu'il était juste derrière, prêt à lui rentrer dedans. Mais c'est une tout autre personne qu'elle percuta. L'homme en noir se répandit en blasphèmes et épousseta son habit sans prendre la peine d'aider la malheureuse enfant étendue sur le sol. Abigail regarda le jeune homme en uniforme. Un inquisiteur! Elle manquait cruellement de chance. Comment se sortir de ce mauvais pas? Son visage lui disait vaguement quelque chose, mais elle se dit que c'était parce qu'elle l'avait vu dans le village ces derniers jours. Celui-ci releva les yeux vers elle, prêt à l'insulter mais sa langue se colla à son palais. «Ça alors! se dit Anton. Quelle chance!» Il prit un ton

doucereux pour s'adresser à la frêle demoiselle tout en savourant la peur que lui inspirait son habit.

— Eh bien, miss, il faut faire attention où vous allez.

Abigail perçut tout de suite le ton menaçant de l'inquisiteur et elle paniqua. Elle se retourna et voulut partir en courant, mais une main puissante l'attrapa par le bras et la secoua sans ménagement. Elle voulut crier ; une autre main la bâillonna bien vite. « Oh mon Dieu, pensa-t-elle, sortez-moi de là ! »

— Me reconnaissez-vous, miss Abigail ?

Elle sursauta en entendant son nom. Comment la connaissait-il ? Elle secoua la tête en signe de dénégation et le sourire de l'homme se fit encore plus large et plus cruel.

— Non ? demanda-t-il, feignant la surprise. Vous êtes sûre ? Nous nous sommes déjà rencontrés pourtant.

Abigail secoua de nouveau la tête. La main sur sa bouche l'empêchait de respirer suffisamment et le gant de cuir était froid sur sa peau tandis que l'étau de l'autre main de l'inquisiteur lui faisait mal au bras. Il l'avait ceinturée et elle ne pouvait même pas esquisser un mouvement.

— Vous souvenez-vous d'un jeune jongleur à la sortie d'un théâtre ? Un jeune jongleur dont vous auriez ri, vous et votre stupide cousine ?

Abasourdie, Abigail resta immobile.

— Vous vous êtes moquée de moi et de mon amour pour vous devant mes amis dont j'ai été la risée

pendant des semaines. À cause de vous, j'ai dû tuer tous les malheureux que vous avez approchés pour savoir où vous retrouver. Et me voilà, continua-t-il sans prendre attention aux grosses larmes qui coulaient sur sa main. Je suis venu pour redemander votre main et, dans le cas où vous n'accepteriez pas, pour vous tuer aussi.

Il éclata d'un rire si violent qu'il relâcha sa prise un instant. Abigail parvint à se libérer, mais la puissante main la tenait toujours par le bras. Une secousse partit de son ventre et sembla se diffuser partout dans son corps. La main qui l'empoignait devint soudain flasque et, en levant les yeux vers son agresseur, elle le découvrit raide et les yeux laiteux. Elle dégagea son bras et recula. Le corps du jeune homme s'affaissa sur lui-même, évanoui. Abigail s'enfuit aussi vite qu'elle le put.

6

Abigail n'avait parlé de sa mésaventure qu'à Betty. Elle n'osa en toucher un mot à Tituba. Ses excursions au village se raréfièrent et elle ne se déplaçait plus seule. Betty avait retrouvé un regain d'énergie lorsque sa cousine lui avait conté comment elle s'était débarrassée de l'importun. Un tel pouvoir, disait-elle, pourrait lui sauver la vie dans de mauvaises circonstances. Mais Abigail n'avait pas été capable de le reproduire.

— Je pense qu'il faut te trouver dans une situation fâcheuse pour qu'il se déclare, la rassurait Betty.

Celle-ci sortait à nouveau de sa chambre et accompagnait Abigail dans ses promenades. Elles évitaient toutes deux le village. Le sujet de prédilection était le retour d'Ezra.

— Crois-tu qu'il voudrait nous faire du mal? demanda Abigail, anxieuse. Ses yeux étaient si froids lorsqu'il m'a vue.

— Ezra n'est pas un mauvais bougre, dit Betty, rêveuse. Cependant, son séjour dans les cachots des inquisiteurs a dû le perturber un peu. Je ne sais pas s'il chercherait à nous faire du mal, mais restons sur nos gardes. De toute façon, Tituba est là. Mais j'aimerais

quand même lui parler. Après tout, nous avons été amis. Il doit bien s'en souvenir.

Abigail acquiesça distraitement.

— Si nous le voyons, reprit Betty avec véhémence, nous lui expliquerons ce qui s'est véritablement passé. Il comprendra sûrement.

Abigail n'osa pas la contredire, mais Ezra avait justement très bien compris ce qu'il avait vu et c'était pour cela qu'il les avait dénoncées.

— Où peut-il être ? demanda Abigail. Il commence à faire tellement froid qu'il ne pourra bientôt plus dormir dehors. J'espère que Hank l'a repris avec lui.

— J'ai entendu dire que Hank avait fermé la boucherie depuis bien longtemps. Ses affaires ne marchent plus. Il n'a sans doute pas pu offrir une place à Ezra.

— Il risque de mourir de froid et de faim, s'indigna Abigail.

— Je ne me fais pas de souci pour lui, s'exclama sa cousine. Ezra est débrouillard. Il trouvera de quoi se nourrir dans la forêt. Quant au froid, il lui reste un peu de temps avant les premières neiges pour se construire un nid douillet.

Le ton enjoué de Betty était forcé et Abigail ne s'y trompa pas. Les jours suivants, elle s'éclipsa de la maison, les poches pleines de pommes, de pain et de fromage qu'elle alla déposer aux orées de Belwack et de Kyron. Elle se rendit même jusqu'au bord de la rivière. Après avoir trouvé une cache dans un bosquet,

elle y posa son butin en espérant qu'Ezra était bien passé par là et non un animal.

Chaque soir, Betty s'endormait avec la même question sur les lèvres.

— Comment va-t-on faire sans papa?

Mais Abigail se savait protégée par Cathy, miss Salinger et Tituba. Cela durerait-il? Elle appréhendait le moment où il allait falloir se lever contre la menace des inquisiteurs. Plus les jours passaient et plus elle sentait ce jour proche. Elle aurait aimé qu'Ezra soit à ses côtés.

Un après-midi, on frappa à la porte. Abigail, qui se trouvait à côté de l'entrée, alla ouvrir. Les jumelles Mary et Alice Parker étaient devant elle. Abigail sautilla de joie et poussa des hurlements d'allégresse qui attirèrent Betty et Tituba. Les retrouvailles furent chaleureuses car même Tituba se montra plus exubérante que d'ordinaire. Elle fit entrer les visiteuses au salon et ordonna à Cathy d'apporter le thé. Celle-ci obéit de mauvaise grâce. Tituba avait pris l'ascendant sur les employés de la maison sans rencontrer d'obstacles, mais Cathy montrait de plus en plus de signes de sédition. La présence de deux filles rousses passablement identiques n'arrangeait en rien son malaise. Tituba, Betty, Abigail et les invitées s'installèrent en cercle autour d'une petite table ronde. Le visage grave, Tituba demanda aux sœurs Parker où elles étaient passées.

— Nous nous sommes réfugiées dans une grotte loin derrière le bois de Kyron. Pas par peur! dit Alice, défiant du regard la Barbadienne. Mais si nous nous

étions fait prendre, comment aurait-on pu entreprendre une grande révolte ?

Tituba tiqua à ce mot.

— Une révolution ? interrogea Betty, avide. Mais comment ?

— Nous sommes revenues pour vous proposer de nous aider. Le dessein des sorcières est de se débarrasser de ces fils de chiens qui nous insultent, nous maltraitent et nous torturent. Il faut que nous regroupions toutes les sorcières du village. Car il y en a beaucoup qui sont nées avec des pouvoirs. J'en suis certaine.

— Mais comment les reconnaîtrez-vous ? interrogea Tituba.

— Eh bien, lui dit Mary, mal à l'aise, nous pensions que vous en seriez capable.

— Navrée, ma chère Mary, mais je viens juste de recouvrer toute l'étendue de mes pouvoirs et je n'ai jamais entendu parler d'un sortilège permettant de sonder les gens. Nous ne pourrions nous fier qu'à notre instinct et cela me paraît dangereux.

Elle tourna brusquement la tête vers la porte close du salon et sa voix tonitrua :

— Cathy, je sais que vous êtes derrière cette porte, vos oreilles malingres étant à la recherche de quelques détails croustillants. Je vous serais gré de venir déposer le plateau et de vous en retourner à vos minables corvées avant que je vous fasse regretter d'être née.

La porte s'ouvrit brusquement et la pauvre Cathy, le visage rouge, entra précipitamment et déposa le plateau sur la table avec une telle violence que la théière se renversa sur le tapis.

— Ma pauvre enfant, vous n'êtes même pas capable de porter un plat ! Ne vous avisez pas de répéter à qui que ce soit ce que vous avez entendu car alors mon esprit viendra hanter toutes vos nuits jusqu'à la fin de vos jours. Vous n'aimeriez pas ça, n'est-ce pas ?

Cathy hocha la tête frénétiquement et sortit en vitesse. D'un geste négligent, Tituba pointa sa main vers la théière brisée qui se reforma aussitôt et s'envola pour servir toutes les tasses posées avant d'atterrir délicatement sur la table. Abigail et Betty apprécièrent grandement cette manifestation de magie.

— Je ne pense pas que votre idée de révolution soit une bonne chose, mes amies, continua Tituba comme si rien ne s'était passé. Nous prendrions trop de risques à aborder des femmes qui nous trahiraient peut-être par la suite. Restons terrées jusqu'à ce que les choses se calment.

— Mais rien ne se calmera. Les mêmes événements ont lieu à Andover, à Salisbury, à Marblehead et aussi à Charlestown, à Billerica, à Woburn, à Ipswich et j'en passe. Toutes les communautés alentour sont touchées par le même mal. Cela s'est étendu jusqu'à Boston.

Tituba ne leur demanda pas comment elles avaient eu vent de tout ça. Elle semblait réfléchir intensément. Si les inquisiteurs sévissaient partout, Salem n'était plus un incident isolé. L'idée du combat ne la séduisait pas vraiment, mais peut-être était-ce la seule solution.

Abigail eut une illumination. Elle sauta sur ses jambes et sortit de la pièce en courant.

— Où vas-tu ? lui cria Betty.

— J'ai une idée !

Dans la chambre, Abigail arracha les couvertures de son lit et renversa son matelas tant son excitation grandissait. Elle redescendit avec le grimoire qu'elle tenait serré contre elle. Tituba soupira en la voyant réapparaître avec le livre.

— Ce n'est pas l'heure des enfantillages, miss Abigail ! Ce livre n'est rien d'autre qu'une vaste supercherie pour les enfants naïfs ! Allez me ranger ça !

— Mais Tituba, j'ai le souvenir d'avoir vu dedans un sortilège qui pourrait peut-être nous aider. Laissez-moi au moins voir !

Tituba haussa les épaules et laissa la jeune fille tourner fébrilement les pages de son grimoire. Abigail poussa un cri de triomphe qui fit sursauter les jumelles. Elles essayaient d'entendre les pensées de Betty qui s'amusait à les en empêcher.

— J'ai trouvé ! cria Abigail, extatique. Écoutez ça. *Si de l'âme d'untel vous voulez être sûr, prononcez sans frayeur ces quelques mots impurs. Sans torture vous saurez de l'âme sondée si sorcière elle naquit ou bien femme ne vit.* Et il est expliqué en dessous que lorsque l'on dit le sortilège *Intentiona Reveledad,* une aura noire rayonnera autour d'une personne sans pouvoirs. Au contraire, s'il s'agit d'une sorcière, une lumière argentée l'entourera. Essayons ! s'exclama la jeune fille.

Abigail s'éclaircit la gorge et prononça les mots magiques, les yeux rivés sur sa cousine, et attendit. Déçue, elle fut vite forcée d'admettre que rien ne s'était produit.

— Mais je ne suis encore qu'une novice en matière de sorcellerie. Peut-être devriez-vous essayer, Tituba.

— Je refuse de me prêter à de facétieux tours de magie. C'est une affaire sérieuse dont nous parlons là !

— Oh, s'il vous plaît, Tituba, s'exclamèrent en chœur les jumelles et les filles Parris.

— Essayez et si cela ne marche pas, ajouta Betty, nous ne vous embêterons plus avec ce grimoire.

La grosse Barbadienne esquissa un sourire devant l'air suppliant des quatre filles et flancha en soupirant. Elle prononça les deux mots en regardant Abigail et, à son air choqué, celle-ci sut que ça avait marché.

— Qu'avez-vous vu, Tituba ? la pressa-t-elle. Une aura argentée ? Je savais que ce grimoire n'était pas une imposture ! Il nous faut nous entraîner toutes pour pouvoir identifier celles qui rejoindront nos rangs.

Toutes l'approuvèrent, même Tituba qui avait paru si sceptique.

Le village s'enfonçait de jour en jour dans une atmosphère moribonde qui glaçait Ezra. Ses chances de trouver un refuge avant les neiges s'amenuisaient. Le froid gardait les gens chez eux et le garçon devait se donner beaucoup de mal pour dénicher des victuailles.

Une âme charitable déposait souvent de la nourriture aux endroits où il passait et silencieusement, tandis qu'il dévorait pommes, pain et fromage, il remerciait son mystérieux bienfaiteur. Le jour où il trouva les provisions enroulées dans une épaisse couverture de laine, il faillit pleurer de bonheur. Mais maintenant la couverture ne suffisait plus à le réchauffer. Un vent glacial s'infiltrait dans son abri et gelait ses membres. Il avait essayé de retourner plaider sa cause auprès du boucher mais celui-ci ne lui avait même pas ouvert. Ezra déambulait comme un fantôme dans les rues du village, la faim au ventre. Les lieux étaient déserts et les seuls bruits trahissant le peu de vie qui restait étaient les pleurs et les cris des enfants, des hommes et des femmes venant de perdre un proche. Il avait vu ce que le choléra infligeait aux corps. La putréfaction était rapide et les odeurs si fortes que les familles, désireuses de veiller leurs morts, se résignaient à aller les mettre sur le charnier. Pris d'une curiosité morbide, Ezra s'était aventuré proche de la nécropole, une main solidement plaquée sur son nez pour s'empêcher d'inhaler les relents putrides. Il avait reconnu nombre des villageois et même certains des garçons avec qui il courait la campagne avant de rencontrer les filles Parris. Étrangement, il n'éprouva aucune tristesse envers eux non plus que de la haine. Les gémissements des agonisants étaient, à ses oreilles, plus tragiques que les pleurs des autres et ces râles le hantaient des heures entières même lorsqu'il s'était éloigné du village pour chercher le calme de la forêt.

Ce jour-là, après avoir traîné dans les rues pendant plusieurs heures sans trouver autre chose qu'une carotte moisie, il s'en alla à nouveau pour retrouver le couvert des arbres. Ezra respira attentivement l'air

ambiant et avec frayeur il sentit la neige. Frissonnant, il essaya de s'imaginer dormir dehors tandis que la neige tombait. Il allait mourir de froid. À peine quelques minutes après ce constat, de gros flocons moelleux et cotonneux commencèrent à voleter dans les airs. Avec appréhension, Ezra se rendit compte qu'ils ne fondaient pas aussitôt qu'ils avaient touché le sol. Tendant sa main nue, il attrapa un flocon et l'observa. Ces cristaux si fins lui avaient toujours paru comme une merveille du ciel mais aujourd'hui, il voyait dans leurs fines ramures un instrument de mort. D'ici quelques heures, une épaisse couche recouvrerait la terre et s'il ne mourait pas cette nuit, ce serait pour la prochaine. Ses doigts et ses pieds s'engourdissaient déjà ; la température avait chuté brusquement et le ciel s'obscurcissait. Prenant son courage à deux mains, il se dirigea vers le manoir des Parris. Une idée avait germé dans son esprit au cours de la nuit et elle ne lui paraissait plus si absurde que ça. Il cogna bruyamment à la porte et souffla sur ses doigts gelés en attendant qu'on lui ouvre. Comme il l'espérait, ce fut Tituba qui vint. Elle le regarda, soupçonneuse.

— Que veux-tu encore ?

— Je ne veux pas faire de mal aux filles, mais je ne veux pas non plus mourir de froid. La neige s'est mise à tomber et ma cache dans la forêt ne suffira pas à me garder en vie. Je suis venu vous demander de m'aider. Offrez-moi un endroit où dormir, où je ne souffrirai pas trop du froid et je vous laisserai en paix.

— Pourquoi t'aiderais-je ?

— Je… je… balbutia Ezra. Je veux devenir un sorcier, chuchota-t-il. Plus personne ne veut de moi. Il

me faudra donc me débrouiller seul. Apprenez-moi ce que vous pouvez et je disparaîtrai.

Tituba le jaugea un instant. Elle ferma la porte et laissa Ezra sur le seuil. Celui-ci, interdit, décida d'attendre. En effet, quelques instants plus tard, la servante revint en portant dans ses bras une grande cape doublée qu'elle lui donna.

— Traverse le bois de Kyron jusqu'aux collines. Là, tu trouveras une grotte. Passes-y la nuit, tu auras chaud. Et reviens me voir demain. Je dois réfléchir.

Ezra la remercia chaudement et partit, le cœur plus léger.

Abigail avait essayé d'entendre la discussion de Tituba avec Ezra, mais un bourdonnement agaçant envahissait ses oreilles dès qu'elle écoutait. Craignant pour sa santé, elle se dit bien vite que Tituba avait dû jeter un sort qui assourdirait quiconque tenterait de surprendre ce qu'ils se disaient. Mais elle fut rassurée lorsqu'elle aperçut Ezra quitter la maison, le sourire aux lèvres.

Les cinq sorcières s'étaient décidées à se rendre dès maintenant au village pour essayer de sonder les gens. Abigail avait rétorqué que plus personne ne se promenait comme avant, mais Tituba lui avait dit que le sortilège leur permettrait de voir les auras à travers les murs. Betty s'extasiait devant cette magie et elle ne tarissait plus d'éloges au sujet du grimoire de sa mère. Toutes s'habillèrent chaudement. La vue des flocons ne

faisait gronder que Tituba, qui avait toujours vécu dans les mers chaudes, mais les jumelles Parker, Abigail et Betty gémissaient de bonheur. Ces deux dernières sortirent en courant, visage levé vers le ciel, tandis que Tituba les suivait avec circonspection. Au village, elles se séparèrent toutes avec pour obligation de se retrouver dix minutes plus tard derrière la scierie. Tituba et Betty se rendirent invisibles et chacune partit dans une direction.

Abigail fut la première à arriver à la scierie. Quelques instants plus tard, Betty apparut à côté d'elle, la faisant sursauter. Puis Tituba et les jumelles arrivèrent. Mary trépignait.

— C'est incroyable toutes ces personnes pourvues de dons ! J'en ai vu au moins une dizaine.

— Et moi aussi ! renchérit Betty.

— J'ai vu des familles entières ! lança Abigail.

— Je sais, répondit calmement Tituba. Je ne pensais pas trouver autant de possibles alliés. Je ne comprends même pas comment il se fait qu'autant de magie se soit regroupée en ce lieu. Mais n'oublions pas que nous ne pourrons convaincre tout le monde. Choisissons quelques personnes parmi celles que nous avons trouvées et essayons de les amener à notre cause. Qui irez-vous voir ?

— J'irai chez les Proctor, déclara Betty. John Proctor et sa femme rayonnaient fortement. Et nous le connaissons assez pour savoir qu'il sera sans doute heureux de se dresser avec nous face aux inquisiteurs.

— Les Bishop nous accueilleront sans doute, ajoutè-rent les jumelles.

— Abigail, toi et moi irons voir Dorcas Hoar, dit Tituba. Ce vieux bougre serait capable d'ameuter tous les environs si j'y allais seule.

Elles se rendirent donc chez les familles. Betty fut accueillie avec bonté chez les Proctor. Elizabeth lui offrit une tasse de thé et compatit aux malheurs de la jeune fille.

— Mrs. Proctor, commença prudemment Betty, sauriez-vous par hasard faire des choses étranges ? Je veux dire, ajouta-t-elle devant l'air effrayé d'Elizabeth, je ne suis pas venue pour vous dénoncer, je cherche des gens... comme vous et votre mari. Je sais que vous avez des pouvoirs, continua-t-elle en se tournant vers John Proctor qui la regardait, l'air sévère. Je ne peux pas vous dire comment je l'ai su, mais je le sais. Je sais aussi que vous ne portez pas dans votre cœur les inquisiteurs...

— Qui le pourrait ? gronda John Proctor.

L'homme aux cheveux hirsutes mais à l'élégance racée était impressionnant. Ses yeux bleus dardaient sur Betty un mélange de crainte et de sévérité qui faisait frémir la jeune fille. Les Proctor étaient très respectés dans le village malgré les lubies du mari qui s'entêtait à labourer ses champs le dimanche, loupant ainsi l'office.

— Que veux-tu, Betty Parris ? demanda-t-il d'une voix douce. Si tu es venue pour nous livrer, je crois malheureusement que ce sera la dernière des choses que tu feras sur cette terre.

— Non ! s'empressa de dire Betty. Je suis venue vous rallier à notre cause.

— Quelle cause ? Et quelles sont les personnes qui y sont engagées ?

— Nous sommes plusieurs pour le moment. Je ne vous en dirai pas les noms avant que vous n'acceptiez de vous rallier également. Nous souhaitons libérer le village de l'emprise des inquisiteurs et permettre aux gens comme… nous, risqua-t-elle, de vivre librement sans cacher ces dons que le Seigneur nous a donnés.

— Mais Betty, ces dons, comme tu les appelles, comment peux-tu être sûre que ce soit Dieu qui nous en ait fait cadeau ?

— Mrs. Proctor, si cela avait été un présent du diable, ma cousine et moi ne serions jamais allées sauver tous ces malheureux du choléra.

Les Proctor restèrent silencieux. Puis John s'approcha d'elle et la raccompagna dehors.

— Nous y réfléchirons, miss Parris. En attendant, je te serais gré de nous laisser en paix. Lorsque le temps sera venu, nous viendrons à vous.

Betty respecta le choix de John Proctor et partit.

Les jumelles Parker avaient eu les mêmes problèmes avec les époux Bishop. Ils avaient même pensé qu'elles étaient à la solde des inquisiteurs. Mais ils leur avaient finalement dit qu'ils y penseraient. Seules Abigail et Tituba s'étaient mises en danger. À peine arrivées devant la maison de Dorcas Hoar, Abigail avait supplié Tituba de rester près d'elle mais

de devenir invisible. Tituba avait finalement plié et grand bien lui en fit, car à peine Abigail avait-elle frappé à la porte que le vieil homme s'était précipité sur elle, un couteau à la main. Il l'avait prise pour un inquisiteur. Pensant trouver en cet homme un valeureux allié, Abigail avait parlementé.

— Maître Hoar, aimeriez-vous que les inquisiteurs quittent le village ? avait-elle demandé.

— Pour sûr, miss Parris, avait beuglé le vieil homme. Un bon coup de pied au... Pardonnez ma franchise, mais ces chiens ne méritent pas mieux.

— Je... des amies et moi travaillons à ce dessein, voyez-vous, et vous nous feriez honneur si vous joigniez notre cause.

Hoar, dès lors, avait paru soupçonneux.

— Dans quoi essayez-vous de m'embarquer ?

Abigail avait paniqué, car Dorcas haussait la voix et elle avait peur de voir arriver des gens. Un violent coup de Tituba la fit chanceler et Hoar se tourna vers l'endroit où se tenait Tituba.

— Qui est-là ? hurla-t-il. Montrez-vous ! Je vais appeler les inquisiteurs et nous verrons bien si ces « fantômeries » vous feront autant rire !

— Non, maître Hoar, je vous en prie. Écoutez-moi. Tituba, apparaissez.

Devant les yeux terrifiés du vieil original, la servante noire brisa brusquement le vide. Portant les mains à son cœur, il recula dans sa maison.

— Sorcellerie ! cria-t-il. Sorcellerie ! Sorcières ! Sorcières !

Abigail avait essayé de le faire taire, mais Hoar ne se laissait pas approcher. La jeune fille avait eu beau lui dire qu'elle savait que lui aussi avait des pouvoirs, le pauvre homme ne se contrôlait plus. D'un geste, Tituba avait stoppé le cœur du vieillard qui s'était écroulé à leurs pieds. Étrangement, Abigail n'avait rien ressenti. Elle savait désormais que leur cause en sacrifierait plus d'un et que ce serait le prix à payer pour vivre.

7

Les cinq sorcières avaient donné rendez-vous à la clairière aux gens qu'elles essayaient de recruter. Ne pouvant se fier entièrement aux villageois, elles s'y rendaient chaque jour, invisibles et silencieuses. Le temps passa, et personne ne vint. Les jumelles commençaient à désespérer.

— Si personne ne joint nos rangs déjà maigres, comment allons-nous combattre les inquisiteurs? déploraient-elles.

— Avant toute chose, il ne s'agit pas de combattre, leur dit Tituba. Vous êtes encore en apprentissage et ceux qui viendront à nous auront besoin qu'on leur enseigne le minimum. Le combat sera pour plus tard. Beaucoup plus tard.

La perspective d'une guerre proche épouvantait les filles Parris, mais il fallait se rendre à l'évidence. Elles ne pouvaient passer toute leur vie ainsi, chassées, torturées, exécutées. Bien sûr l'idée d'avoir à maltraiter et à tuer des gens dans leur combat les terrorisait, mais il s'agissait d'une bonne cause. Tituba les empêchait de trop réfléchir à leur avenir en leur imposant un rythme d'entraînement acharné. Et pour leur permettre de se concentrer pleinement sur autre chose que garder leur

invisibilité, elle plaça autour d'elles une frontière protectrice et invisible. Ceux qui s'approchaient de cette barrière ne voyaient ni n'entendaient ce qui se passait derrière. Ils continuaient leur chemin comme si de rien n'était. Seules les personnes pourvues de pouvoirs pourraient la traverser. Tituba espérait qu'aucune de celles à qui elles avaient parlé n'aurait la mauvaise idée de mener les inquisiteurs jusqu'à leur repaire. Elle restait constamment vigilante, laissant les quatre jeunes filles se provoquer en duel et aiguiser leurs pouvoirs.

Dès le lendemain de leur visite aux villageois, Tituba était allée chercher Ezra dans sa tanière. Lorsqu'il l'avait vue arriver dans l'entrée de la grotte étroite, masquant les rayons de soleil, Ezra avait paniqué, croyant qu'elle venait l'abattre. Mais la servante s'était tranquillement installée sur le sol froid, les mains posées sur les pierres et elle lui avait souri. D'abord sceptique, Ezra avait finalement consenti à s'approcher d'elle tout en gardant une distance de sécurité. Il n'aimait pas l'idée de lui demander quelque chose et celle de lui être redevable le répugnait. Mais il n'avait pas le choix. La grotte ne lui offrait qu'un abri sommaire et le vent hurlant qui s'y engouffrait en pleine nuit, le gelant jusqu'aux os, avait eu raison de ses derniers soupçons.

— Mon ami, lui dit-elle, doucereuse, je ne viens pas de gaieté de cœur ici. Je sais que tu laisses traîner tes oreilles partout. Tu es donc au courant qu'un rassemblement s'engage et qu'un combat approche.

— J'ai cru l'entendre dire, oui, avoua-t-il.

— Nous arrivons à un moment où les vieilles querelles doivent être oubliées, ainsi que les trahisons, susurra-t-elle en insistant sur ce dernier mot. Je ne te cacherai pas que nous sommes faibles et qu'un nouvel allié serait plus que bénéfique pour le moral de nos troupes, si j'ose dire.

— Je combattrai avec plaisir à vos côtés ! s'exclama Ezra.

— Oui. Je vois cela. Il me faut cependant éclaircir un point avec toi, mon jeune ami, murmura Tituba, menaçante.

Avant qu'Ezra ne puisse faire un geste, elle se jeta sur lui à une vitesse prodigieuse et le plaqua au sol, sa large main calleuse enfonçant la gorge du garçon. La poigne de fer de la servante le maintenait avec tant de force par terre qu'il ne pouvait même plus bouger la tête. Le jeune homme sentit rapidement le sang lui monter à la tête et l'air commença à lui manquer.

— Je veux être sûre que tu ne chercheras pas à nuire aux filles Parris. Promets-moi que cette histoire est terminée !

Haletant, Ezra essaya de parler, mais il ne produisit qu'un borborygme lamentable. Tituba desserra un peu sa prise et il avala avidement une goulée d'air.

— Je vous promets, crachota-t-il.

Elle le relâcha et se rassit, satisfaite.

— Mais ne me demandez pas de leur pardonner. J'aurai besoin de temps.

— Il ne m'en fallait pas plus, assura-t-elle avant de se passer la langue sur les lèvres.

Tituba se leva et fit mine de sortir de la grotte.

— Où vous trouverai-je? demanda Ezra, se massant le cou.

— Nous trouver?

— Oui, pour commencer mon apprentissage.

— Je viendrai te voir tous les jours. Mais tu ne t'approcheras pas de notre repaire avant que je l'aie décidé.

Tituba tint parole et revint le lendemain alors qu'Ezra se réveillait tout juste. Elle lui jeta un bout de pain qu'il dévora avec gratitude puis alluma un feu à l'entrée de la caverne. Ezra l'observa préparer une potion, mais il se garda bien de lui demander quoi que ce soit. Il avait encore sur la gorge l'empreinte des doigts de la servante. Lorsqu'elle eut terminé, elle remplit un gobelet de la mixture qui exhalait des effluves nauséabonds et le lui tendit.

— Bois, lui ordonna-t-elle.

Docile, Ezra prit le verre et le porta à sa bouche, faisant mine de ne pas sentir la puanteur qui en sortait.

Il se réveilla quelques heures plus tard, perclus de courbatures sur le sol froid. Tituba avait disparu et la nuit était tombée depuis longtemps. Maudissant la servante qui avait éteint le feu avant de partir, il s'enroula dans sa couverture rongée, le ventre vide et la tête lourde. Une idée lui traversa l'esprit. Elle lui parut

aussitôt stupide. Pourtant, il se leva, s'approcha des cendres et tendit une main au-dessus d'elles. Ezra attendit un moment qu'un miracle se produisît. Puis riant de sa propre stupidité, il abattit ses mains dans les débris calcinés. Une puissante flamme le rejeta en arrière et sa tête alla heurter une aspérité dans le sol. Un moment assommé, il se releva et hurla de joie à la vue du bon feu qui crépitait désormais. Rapprochant sa couverture, il se lova près des flammes et s'endormit rapidement, bercé par la chaleur bienfaisante. Un nouveau monde s'ouvrait à lui.

Les sorcières de la clairière avaient cessé de guetter l'arrivée de possibles alliés. Le découragement leur avait fait regarder les choses en face. Les gens avaient peur, certains pensaient à s'enfuir. Personne ne voulait combattre les inquisiteurs. Alors, elles s'entraînaient. Alice et Mary Parker pouvaient se multiplier à l'infini et entendre les pensées sur plusieurs lieues. Betty rendait invisible quiconque se trouvait dans un rayon de trente pieds et Abigail s'envolait maintenant aisément pour aller se percher sur les plus hautes branches de la forêt. Même Betty, pourtant aussi agile qu'un singe, ne pouvait la suivre. Leurs pouvoirs s'étaient décuplés et elles pouvaient toutes faire ce que bon leur semblait. Il n'était pas rare, pendant une séance d'entraînement, qu'un arbre pousse inopinément au centre de la clairière, ni que des nuées de papillons volettent par centaines aux alentours. Des flammes géantes jaillissaient des paumes d'Abigail tandis que les geysers d'eau de Betty les contraient vaillamment. Les jumelles restaient ébahies devant ces prodiges. Leurs pouvoirs paraissaient si faibles en

comparaison. Betty s'amusait souvent à soulever Alice et Mary et à les faire virevolter dans les airs jusqu'à ce que leurs fous rires aient raison de sa volonté. Tituba rattrapait toujours les jumelles avant qu'elles ne touchent le sol car Betty n'était plus en mesure de s'en occuper. La Barbadienne soupirait avec ostentation devant ces jeux puérils, mais aucune ne lui prêtait attention. Il était si bon de s'amuser un peu en ces temps obscurs.

Tituba se surprenait à prendre plaisir à aller voir Ezra. Celui-ci était bien plus sérieux que les filles et elle était sincèrement impressionnée par ses progrès. Il travaillait dur et ne se disait jamais que ce n'était qu'un jeu. Au bout d'à peine quelques semaines, il avait développé des pouvoirs que Tituba elle-même n'avait pas. Ezra arrivait à créer des vagues de terre hautes de vingt à trente pieds. La première fois qu'il montra ce prodige à Tituba, celle-ci fut terrorisée quand ce raz-de-marée de terre fondit sur elle. Elle s'attendait à être écrasée sous des tonnes de limon. Mais lorsque la vague se referma sur la servante recroquevillée, elle disparut. Ezra, tout fier, regardait Tituba, les poings sur les hanches.

— Pas mal, hein ? s'exclama-t-il, bravache.

Tituba tendit la main vers lui. Un puissant vent le projeta en arrière et l'envoya s'affaisser contre la paroi de la grotte. Le souffle coupé, Ezra se releva difficilement.

— Ne me menace plus jamais, lui intima Tituba.

Ezra continua donc à lui montrer l'étendue de ses pouvoirs mais avec prudence. À l'instar d'Abigail qui produisait des bulles d'air, Ezra créait des balles d'eau tournoyantes et impressionnantes. Ces hectolitres menaçants pouvaient devenir une arme essentielle. Mais ce que préférait le jeune homme était sa faculté à parler aux arbres et à les diriger. Alors qu'elle venait pour sa leçon quotidienne, Tituba l'avait surpris en train de mener une ronde de buissons. Ceux-ci, dociles, tournaient autour du jeune homme qui, extatique, ne les quittait pas des yeux. Aussitôt que Tituba avait manifesté sa présence, les arbustes s'étaient immobilisés et étaient redevenus de simples plantes.

— Ce pouvoir est une bénédiction, dit Tituba qui n'arrivait pas à cacher son admiration. Si tu t'entraînes, tu arriveras sans doute à diriger les plus gros arbres de cette forêt.

Au même instant, dans la clairière, Tituba disputait Betty.

— Mais qu'avez-vous dans la tête, ma pauvre Betty ?

— Je… je… Ce n'est pas ma faute, balbutia-t-elle.

Les jumelles Parker étaient allongées sur les feuilles mortes, grimaçant de douleur. Abigail, à leur côté, soignait leurs diverses fractures.

— Betty, je vous avais pourtant prévenue de ne pas vous amuser à ce jeu stupide ! Voyez le résultat !

— Abigail les soigne.

— Oui, tonna Tituba, Abigail les soigne ! Mais que faites-vous de l'énergie que cela demande à votre cousine ? Que faites-vous de la souffrance et de la douleur que vous avez causées à ces malheureuses pour le simple plaisir de montrer encore une fois combien vous êtes puérile ?

Penaude, Betty baissa la tête. Ne résistant pas à faire léviter les jumelles, elles-mêmes friandes de ce jeu, elle les avait fait tournoyer plus longtemps que de coutume, se vidant ainsi de toute son énergie. Les jumelles riaient tellement qu'elle n'avait pas eu le cœur à arrêter. Abigail l'avait pourtant mise en garde. Tituba s'occupait des mesures de protection autour de la clairière, elle n'avait pas fait attention à ce qui se passait. Lorsque Betty s'était sentie faible, sa concentration s'était relâchée et les jumelles avaient fait une chute de presque dix pieds, se brisant un poignet, une jambe ou un bras. Tituba était furieuse et vitupérait sans s'arrêter contre la pauvre Betty.

— Comment pouvez-vous être si stupide ? Je me demande vraiment si c'était une bonne chose que de vous livrer les secrets de cette magie !

— Allons, Tituba, ne soyez pas trop dure ! Regardez le bon côté des choses, intervint Abigail. Je ne m'étais jamais entraînée à soigner des fractures. Il semble que j'y arrive parfaitement.

Alice et Mary reprenaient des couleurs au fur et à mesure des soins de la jeune fille. Lorsqu'elles purent parler, après qu'Abigail eut soigné leur mâchoire, elles défendirent avec véhémence Betty. Tituba flancha et, furieuse, elle s'éloigna.

— Allez chercher du bois pour le feu, cracha-t-elle à Betty.

— Mais Abigail peut l'allumer avec ses…

— DU BOIS ! tonna Tituba.

Toute la clairière résonna et trembla de cette voix caverneuse. Les oiseaux s'envolèrent en pépiant et Betty ne songea même pas à désobéir. Elle s'enfuit dans la forêt.

— Personne ne se demande où vous êtes lorsque vous venez me voir ? interrogea Ezra.

— Non, car je suis aussi là-bas en ce moment, lui répondit Tituba en souriant. Betty n'en fait qu'à sa tête. C'est malheureux ! Cette petite est douée mais elle ne pense qu'à jouer.

— Vous êtes dans la clairière en ce moment même ? demanda le jeune homme, ébahi. Vous vous dédoublez ? Comment appelle-t-on ce don ?

— L'ubiquité, mon jeune ami.

— Pourriez-vous me l'enseigner ?

— Je ne crois pas. Man Yaya m'a légué ce pouvoir alors que je n'étais qu'une petite fille. Ce n'est pas un art qui s'apprend. Malheureusement, je n'ai pas encore découvert comment le donner à quelqu'un qui s'en montrerait digne.

Devant l'air étonné d'Ezra, elle s'esclaffa de son rire rauque et dérangeant.

— Je ne suis pas omnisciente, jeune homme. Personne ne découvrira jamais tous les secrets que recèle la sorcellerie.

Ezra continuait à voir ses pouvoirs grandir et il ne se lassait jamais des exercices que lui imposait Tituba. Il commençait à se rendre compte qu'au fur et à mesure de son apprentissage ses sens s'aiguisaient. Il entendait la servante plusieurs minutes avant qu'elle n'apparaisse à l'entrée de la grotte. Et lorsqu'il grimpait au-dessus de la colline où il vivait, il pouvait voir, loin derrière le bois de Kyron, le village de Salem. Sa vue s'était tant affûtée qu'il apercevait les moindres mouvements des habitants. Il se nourrissait seul désormais et ne dépendait plus de ce que Tituba lui apportait. La vitesse de ses mouvements s'était accrue et il parvenait à chasser des biches et des cerfs. Cela serait plus dur lorsque l'hiver serait bien installé; il trouverait alors un autre moyen de se sustenter.

— Tituba, comment se fait-il que j'arrive à faire de grandes choses alors que je ne suis pas capable de trouver de l'eau ou de faire apparaître de la nourriture? demanda Ezra. Même allumer un feu me demande plus d'énergie que de chasser.

— De tout temps, les sorciers et les sorcières n'ont jamais eu les mêmes pouvoirs. Ils se manifestent différemment. Un sortilège des plus simples pour ton amie Abigail t'est impossible à reproduire. Je ne peux pas t'expliquer pourquoi. C'est comme ça. À l'inverse, Abigail n'égalera jamais ta puissance dans certains de tes sorts.

— Alors... est-ce que cela veut dire qu'à nous deux nous pourrions devenir invincibles?

Tituba marqua un temps, observant intensément le jeune homme.

— Dans mon pays, on dit que l'union d'un sorcier et d'une sorcière donnerait naissance à un être terrible. Puissant, certes, mais capable de choses terrifiantes. C'est pourquoi nous évitons de nous marier avec nos semblables. Il n'y a pas eu d'héritier depuis des siècles.

— Que s'est-il passé la dernière fois qu'un enfant est né de parents sorciers ?

— Il s'est échiné à faire disparaître tous ceux qui avaient des pouvoirs. Bajano, c'est son nom, les a traqués pendant des années. Et plus il en éliminait, plus il devenait puissant. Les dons de ses victimes lui appartenaient. On a cru qu'il arriverait à ses fins ; cela aurait été la fin de la magie sur terre. Mais quelqu'un l'a tué.

— Comment ?

— Un homme s'est sacrifié. Il s'appelait Tayam. C'était un grand sage, dont le pouvoir était la connaissance. Mais depuis quelques années, Tayam ne supportait plus le poids du savoir et d'atroces migraines commençaient à le rendre fou. Alors, il s'est dévoilé au grand mage qui avait juré la perte de tous les sorciers. Bajano, avide, accourut au chevet du mourant. Il prit son pouvoir et trépassa aussitôt.

— Mais pourquoi ?

— Tayam vivait depuis des siècles et il avait emmagasiné bien plus de connaissances que tu ne pourrais jamais imaginer. Celui qui lui a pris ce pouvoir était à peine plus âgé que toi. Cela, ajouté à tous les

dons qu'il avait volés, fut trop pour lui. Dès lors, les mariages entre sorciers furent condamnés, et même sans cette interdiction, personne n'aurait été assez sot pour tenter le diable. La noirceur de ces temps reste encore bien ancrée dans notre mémoire, même pour moi qui n'étais pas là.

— Alors… commença Ezra.

— Tu ferais bien d'oublier tout de suite miss Parris ! lui dit Tituba, glaciale à nouveau.

— Je n'y pensais pas du tout ! protesta le jeune homme, rougissant.

— Je te préviens, le menaça-t-elle, ses yeux froids dardés sur Ezra. Ne t'avise même pas d'y rêver. Je le saurai et alors…

Ezra haussa les épaules et retourna en maugréant au fond de la grotte. Tituba le regarda s'éloigner, un sourire carnassier aux lèvres. L'éclat glacé de ses yeux luisait dans la pénombre de la caverne, et sa peau sombre dans la lumière déclinante rendait ses traits évanescents. Ezra ne vit pas le tableau terrifiant que représentait cette femme.

Dans le village retentirent les cris de Patton. Exaspéré par les habitants qui lui juraient que leur rétablissement était un don du ciel et non pas un quelconque acte de sorcellerie, il n'avait pu mettre la main sur les coupables. Il savait pertinemment que la magie avait cours dans les maisons et il aurait mis sa main au feu que les filles Parris avaient quelque chose à y voir. Dès la mort du révérend, il s'était frotté les

106

mains à l'idée de les jeter au cachot. Malheureuse-ment, son supérieur hiérarchique à Boston, Craig Dorson, avait reçu une lettre d'un ami de Samuel Parris lui donnant l'ordre de s'occuper des filles. Patton avait fulminé, mais son patron lui avait fait comprendre que ce ne serait que temporaire. Samuel Parris avait eu des amis influents à Boston et faire disparaître l'un d'entre eux n'était pas une mince affaire. Dorson avait mis quelqu'un sur l'affaire et il avait demandé à Patton d'être patient. Pourtant, aujourd'hui, l'inquisiteur n'en pouvait plus d'attendre. Il entrait régulièrement dans des crises de rage qui terrifiaient ses acolytes. Ceux-ci battaient précipitamment en retraite car la folie passa-gère de Patton était d'une violence inouïe. Ce jour-là, sa démence atteignit son paroxysme et les hommes présents dans le bureau le regardèrent avec appréhen-sion faire les cent pas et fulminer.

— Combien de temps allons-nous devoir attendre encore ? Ces femmes se rient de nous. Elles exercent leurs maléfiques pouvoirs à notre nez et à notre barbe ! Et nous devrions rester les bras croisés ? Nous sommes la risée du village. Plus personne n'est effrayé par nous ! Il faut que ça cesse.

Il sortit en courant, suivi par les autres inquisiteurs. Marchant à grands pas, il se rendit sur la place du village et regarda autour de lui. Un sourire vicieux apparut sur son visage lorsqu'il trouva ce qu'il voulait.

— Toi, amène-moi cette femme ! ordonna-t-il à un de ses hommes de main.

Soucieux de ne pas le contredire, l'homme se dépêcha d'obéir. Il attrapa la jeune femme qui se rendait à l'église par le bras et la tira avec lui sans se préoccuper

de ses cris. Patton l'empoigna par les cheveux et la fit mettre à genoux.

— JE VEUX QUE TOUT LE MONDE VIENNE SUR LA PLACE PUBLIQUE! MAINTENANT! hurla-t-il.

En quelques minutes, toute la population du village s'était regroupée. La jeune femme aux pieds de Patton roulaient des yeux horrifiés et suppliants. L'inquisiteur en chef ne lui lâchait pas les cheveux et la secouait sans arrêt.

— Que tout le monde prête attention! s'exclama-t-il.

Il sortit un poignard de sa poche et trancha la gorge de la malheureuse sans même lui accorder un regard. Dans la foule, on entendit des cris épouvantés, de véhémentes protestations, des imprécations et des menaces. Patton n'en avait cure. Il attendit que le calme revienne et lâcha les cheveux de la jeune femme qui s'effondra dans la flaque de sang qui ne cessait de croître.

— Ceci est un avertissement. Je sais que des choses se passent dans ce village. Je sais que la nuit des femmes viennent vous soigner, vous, vos enfants, vos femmes et vos maris. À partir de maintenant, tout rassemblement sera considéré comme suspect et chaque personne arrêtée sera tuée sans autre forme de procès. Chaque villageois qui tentera de protéger un membre de sa famille ou un ami soupçonné sera exécuté aussi. Si l'un de vous sait quoi que ce soit qui pourrait nous aider dans cette chasse à la sorcière, je le prie de venir me voir dans mon bureau. Il sera récompensé pour son aide précieuse, ajouta-t-il d'une voix doucereuse.

Puis il partit, suivi de ses hommes, sans jeter un regard en arrière. Son sourire ne laissait aucun doute quant à ce qu'il venait de faire. La fourberie des habitants le gratifierait bientôt. Tous savaient que les inquisiteurs vivaient dans le luxe et le faste en cette période de famine. Tôt ou tard, quelqu'un l'aiderait dans son dessein.

8

— Ne faites pas de bruit, chuchota Tituba. Nous ne savons pas si elles viennent avec de bonnes intentions.

— Voyons, Tituba, elles ont l'air apeurées.

— C'est peut-être un piège, miss Alice, vous le savez aussi bien que moi. Comment savoir si elles n'ont pas avec elles plusieurs inquisiteurs ? Attendons.

— Mais combien de temps ? protesta Betty.

— Ne faites pas l'enfant, miss Parris, grogna Tituba.

Tituba, Abigail, Betty et les jumelles Parker étaient debout au milieu de la clairière, immobiles. Malgré les protections que Tituba installait chaque fois qu'elles venaient ici, elles restaient silencieuses. Plusieurs femmes se trouvaient à quelques pieds des cinq sorcières. On aurait pu croire à une simple promenade entre amies s'il n'y avait eu ces regards inquiets et ces brusques sursauts au moindre craquement. Toutes se tenaient l'une contre l'autre, en proie à un véritable effroi. S'en fût assez pour Abigail qui marcha rapidement jusqu'à la barrière invisible. Tituba n'eut pas le temps de la retenir que les femmes se mirent à hurler. Abigail était apparue d'un coup devant elles. Furieuse,

la Barbadienne sortit à sa suite et provoqua un nouveau concert de cris.

— Taisez-vous toutes ! Et suivez-moi ! gronda l'imposante servante.

Abigail poussa devant elle celles qui n'étaient plus sûres d'avoir envie de venir. Lorsqu'elles s'aperçurent qu'il y avait d'autres personnes encore, certaines hoquetèrent bruyamment. L'une d'elles manqua de s'évanouir ; Betty se précipita pour la rattraper.

— Que faites-vous ici ? pesta Tituba. Et aussi nombreuses ?

Une femme s'avança avec courage et parla au nom de ses camarades.

— Le bruit court que les sorcières se rassemblent au cœur de la forêt pour stopper la menace des inquisiteurs. Nous sommes venues vous aider.

— Mettez-vous en ligne, leur intima Tituba. Abigail, Alice, sondez-les.

Celles-ci obéirent. Au bout de quelques minutes, elles hochèrent la tête.

— Toutes ont des pouvoirs, commença Abigail.

— Et aucune n'est venue dans le dessein de nous dénoncer.

— Parfait, s'adoucit la servante. Bienvenue parmi nous.

Soulagées, les effusions commencèrent. Abigail et Betty furent surprises de trouver Candy parmi les femmes du village.

— Comment êtes-vous sortie de votre cachot ? demanda Abigail, surprise.

— Je ne sais pas vraiment, lui répondit Candy. Je crois que... je pense que je suis passée à travers les murs de la prison.

La jeune esclave était nerveuse. Nul doute qu'elle avait été maltraitée dans les geôles. Elle agrippait fréquemment le bord de sa tunique et la pressait entre ses mains tordues. Betty comprit avec horreur qu'on lui avait cassé tous les doigts. Elle les montra à Abigail qui hocha la tête et prit entre ses paumes les mains suppliciées. La jeune fille ferma les yeux tandis que Candy la regardait sans comprendre. Une douce chaleur irradia soudain jusque dans ses bras et elle regarda ses mains. Les doigts avaient repris leur forme normale et elle pouvait les agiter sans souffrir.

— Vous êtes une passe-muraille, Candy ? lui demanda Tituba.

— Je n'ai jamais réessayé depuis.

— C'est le moment.

D'un geste négligent, Tituba fit apparaître devant elle un épais mur de pierres. Toutes les femmes présentes se turent pour admirer le prodige.

— Allez-y !

Candy, mal à l'aise, regarda tour à tour Tituba, le mur et ses compagnes qui la dévisageaient.

— Mais... je ne sais pas si ça va marcher... Peut-être suis-je sortie d'une autre façon ?

— Si vous voulez rester ici, Candy, si vous voulez notre protection et notre enseignement, il vous faut faire vos preuves. Cela est valable pour vous toutes, ajouta-t-elle, le doigt pointé sur les nouvelles arrivantes. Ne vous inquiétez pas, continua-t-elle à l'adresse de Candy, si cela ne marche pas, mes filles connaissent de très bons sorts de guérison, comme vous avez pu le constater.

Abigail ressentit encore une fois l'envie malsaine de Tituba de faire du mal à autrui. Candy dut le percevoir aussi car elle tressaillit. Respirant un grand coup, elle ferma les yeux et marcha d'un pas décidé vers le mur en pierre. Betty et les jumelles retinrent leur souffle, attendant l'impact. Le visage de Candy se contractait à mesure qu'elle sentait approcher l'obstacle. Mais elle le traversa comme s'il ne s'était agi que d'un vulgaire rideau. Les explosions de joie lui firent ouvrir les yeux et elle constata avec fierté qu'elle possédait le don de passer à travers les murs. Chacune à leur tour, les dix femmes présentes montrèrent ce qu'elles savaient faire. Susannah Post faisait pousser des fruits à n'importe quelle saison. Un don qui s'avérait fort utile en cette période. Abigail, Betty et les jumelles continuèrent de regarder le spectacle en dévorant les bleuets qui étaient apparus dans les buissons environnants. Rebecca Eames parvenait à créer de petites tornades et des nappes de brume tandis que Mary Black se métamorphosait en d'autres personnes. Les sœurs Hobbs se complétaient puisque l'une obligeait quiconque à danser jusqu'à épuisement alors que l'autre condamnait à la pétrification. Toutes s'extasièrent devant Lila Mantion qui rapetissa jusqu'à disparaître de leur vue ; Ann Dolliver les effraya lorsqu'elle laissa des empreintes brûlées sur le tronc d'un arbre. Le pouvoir

de Sarah Bassett intéressa grandement Tituba lorsqu'elle montra la lame qu'elle avait façonnée dans la pierre. Le spectacle se conclut sur un grand éclat de rire. Martha Carrier, très fière de son don, s'installa face à toutes les sorcières et se mit à parler. Ses lèvres ne remuaient pas et, bien vite, les sorcières comprirent que les sons provenaient de son ventre. Tituba argua qu'un tel pouvoir serait inutile dans un combat mais Martha continua à discourir, à la grande joie de son public.

— Comment se fait-il que nous soyons toutes capables de jeter un seul sort alors que vous-mêmes en avez plusieurs dans vos poches ? demanda Lila Mantion.

— Il y a une différence entre don et sortilège, répondit Tituba. Ce que vous savez faire fait partie de vous, et c'est là votre don le plus puissant. D'autres arriveront, mais il faudra les amadouer pour qu'ils sortent. Je vous enseignerai certains sortilèges. Vous devrez toutes apprendre des sorts de guérison, et nous nous pencherons plus tard sur ceux qui donnent la mort.

— La mort ? s'indigna Abigail. Mais…

— Il faudra les apprendre tôt ou tard, miss Abigail. Inutile de vous demander de ne parler de ces réunions à personne, continua Tituba. Je propose que nous signions ce parchemin pour nous assurer de la bonne volonté de chacune.

— Que dit-il ? s'informa Betty.

— *Quiconque bravera ma loi et laissera sa langue pendre,*
Aussitôt dans les tourments sombrera et périra dans les cendres.

> *Si dans votre cœur la trahison, perfide ennemie de la*
>   *loyauté,*
> *Prend le pas sur vous et rompt ce contrat dûment signé*
> *À tout jamais les nuits d'enfer vous poursuivront et de*
>   *leurs fouets*
> *Zébreront votre peau claire de la marque honteuse des*
>   *déshonorés.*

— Mourrons-nous vraiment si ce contrat est rompu ? Ou n'est-ce qu'une mise en garde ? demanda Alice en signant le parchemin.

— Souhaitez-vous essayer, miss Parker ? susurra Tituba.

Toutes apposèrent leur nom sur le papier que la servante enroula prestement et rangea dans une de ses larges manches.

— Vous ne le signez pas, Tituba ? demanda timidement Betty.

— Allons, j'ai créé moi-même ce parchemin. Cela ne vous suffit-il pas comme preuve de confiance ? répondit-elle, glaciale. Il est évident que si l'une d'entre nous se fait prendre, les autres devront l'abandonner, quitte à la libérer plus tard. Tout le monde est d'accord ?

Un regain de joie semblait parcourir l'assemblée malgré les paroles de Tituba. La frénésie des femmes était palpable dans l'air et toutes attendaient la suite avec impatience.

— Si nous nous donnions un nom ? proposa Martha Carrier.

— Nous nous préparons à survivre, non pas à donner un spectacle, répliqua Tituba, méprisante. La sorcellerie est un art noble. Il n'est pas dans nos projets de faire des tours de passe-passe sur la place publique.

— Je suis d'accord avec Martha, déclara Abigail. Cela donne du courage à une armée que d'avoir un nom.

— Je propose les Sorcières de Salem, dit Mary Black.

— La Vengeance des Sorcières.

— Sorcières contre Inquisiteurs.

— La Menace gronde.

Toutes éclatèrent de rire à cette suggestion d'Abigail Hobbs.

— Pourquoi pas la Confrérie de la Clairière? demanda Abigail Parris. Cela ne parle pas de nos activités et le lieu reste vague. Si l'une de nous laisse échapper ce nom, personne ne se doutera de quoi que ce soit.

Le nom fut accepté et c'est ainsi que naquit la Confrérie de la Clairière.

— La Confrérie de la Clairière, soupira Tituba.

— Pardon? lui demanda Ezra.

— Nous sommes plus nombreuses désormais et nous voilà avec un nom.

— C'est une bonne idée, je trouve. Cela donne du courage aux troupes…

— Mon cher Ezra, tu répètes exactement ce qu'a dit ta précieuse Abigail. Je me demande si c'est une bonne chose de vous revoir.

— Nous avons bien le temps. Et elle ne m'est pas précieuse.

Les pouvoirs d'Ezra s'étaient encore améliorés. Lorsque Tituba était apparue au pied de la colline, il s'était empressé de faire apparaître un épais mur de glace à l'entrée de la grotte. Arrivée devant, Tituba n'avait eu d'autre solution que de faire fondre une petite ouverture.

— Qu'as-tu appris d'autre, mon garçon ?

Il tendit les mains au-dessus du sol et ferma les yeux. Son esprit se vida et il créa dans ses pensées un lieu inconnu. Il songea à une plage de galets, à des falaises coupantes et à une mer déchaînée. Lorsqu'il rouvrit les yeux, il fut satisfait de constater que cela avait marché. Tituba et lui se trouvaient désormais dans le paysage qu'il avait vu. Véritablement impressionnée par l'étendue des pouvoirs d'Ezra et parce qu'elle ne savait pas que de telles choses pouvaient exister, Tituba le félicita chaudement.

— Je peux aussi stopper le temps. Quelques instants seulement. Accrochez-vous à mon épaule, sinon vous ne pourrez pas vous en rendre compte.

Tituba obéit et, aussitôt, le temps se figea. Dehors, le vent ne soufflait plus et les feuilles avaient cessé de frissonner. Les nuages eux-mêmes s'étaient arrêtés dans leur course.

— C'est sans doute plus impressionnant lorsqu'il y a du monde, lui dit Ezra, mais je n'ai pas eu l'occasion de voir d'autres personnes que vous ces derniers temps.

Le choléra continuait de sévir. Jusqu'alors, il n'avait touché que les habitants, mais aussitôt qu'un inquisiteur le contracta, plusieurs autres en furent victimes. Au bout de quelques jours, Patton ne se retrouva plus qu'avec une poignée d'hommes à sa botte. Une vingtaine d'hommes avaient péri dans d'atroces conditions. L'inquisiteur avait réitéré ses menaces. Il avait même offert la place de ses hommes aux gens du village. Tous avaient refusé. Sous le coup de la colère, Patton en avait fait emprisonner plus d'un et deux femmes avaient été tuées. Mais les villageois persistaient à garder le silence sur les bienfaitrices qui les avaient soignés. Les hommes sentaient en eux le souffle de la liberté et de la révolte, et les sorcières de la clairière qui, chaque soir, revenaient dans leur maison vibraient de vengeance. Tituba les enjoignit de ne rien faire. Toute action justicière entraînerait des représailles. Il leur fallait construire patiemment leur défense pour être prêtes lorsque le jour viendrait. Certaines des sorcières n'aimaient pas les méthodes passives de Tituba et de violents affrontements avaient lieu dans la clairière. La Barbadienne leur interdisait d'aller délivrer ceux qu'on avait enfermés ; elle refusait aussi que les femmes parlent à leurs maris de leurs agissements. Le temps viendrait, ne cessait-elle de répéter. Abigail et Betty lui faisaient aveuglément confiance mais elles partageaient aussi les désirs de leurs complices. La seule action probante qu'elles pouvaient faire pour manifester leur désaccord était de

ne pas aller soigner les inquisiteurs. Aucune d'entre elles n'en avait eu l'intention. Quelques jours plus tard, Lila Mantion revint avec une nouvelle déconcertante. Ann Putnam avait été accusée de sorcellerie. Patton s'était rendu lui-même chez les Putnam pour emprisonner la jeune fille. Il y avait été accueilli par la famille au grand complet, les parents et les dix enfants.

— Votre fille va être conduite dans mes geôles, Astor, déclara Patton. Elle a été accusée de magie noire. C'est bien triste ! Une famille aussi honnête et noble que la vôtre.

— De magie noire ? Mais voyons, inquisiteur Patton, c'est impossible. Ann est une jeune fille exemplaire. Elle prie et se confesse chaque soir. Elle n'a jamais manqué une messe.

— C'est une amie des filles Parris. Elle n'est donc pas si irréprochable.

— Pourquoi n'allez-vous pas les arrêter, elles, s'énerva Astor Putnam, au lieu d'emprisonner les honnêtes gens ?

— Allons, allons, Astor. Un aussi grand homme que vous ne peut raisonnablement préférer la mort de deux jeunes filles contre le déshonneur de sa propre progéniture. Il y a déjà plusieurs jours, deux de mes hommes ont trouvé votre enfant tournoyant dans les airs et hurlant à la mort. Elle nous a assurés que c'était là un fait de miss Elizabeth Parris. Or, nous n'avons trouvé aucune trace de la présence de cette dernière à proximité. Et votre fille était, pardonnez-moi, hagarde et hallucinée. Nous avons fait preuve de commisération en ne l'arrêtant pas tout de suite.

— Vous voulez faire des exemples, Patton, je le vois bien ! Ma fille n'en sera pas un !

— Je vous conseille de ne pas vous opposer à mes ordres, Putnam, ou vous irez rejoindre votre fille au fond d'un trou.

— N'y a-t-il pas moyen de s'arranger ? demanda lamentablement le père d'Ann. Je... je possède une fortune considérable et...

— Seriez-vous en train de m'acheter ? Est-ce là ce que vous faites ? Souhaitez-vous payer mon silence et celui de mes hommes ?

— Oh non ! Bien sûr que non, inquisiteur Patton. Je me disais juste qu'une agréable compensation pourrait vous faire oublier cette fâcheuse histoire. Disons, soixante dollars par mois...

Patton sursauta au montant. Soixante dollars par mois pour ne pas emprisonner une pauvre fille dont il ne connaissait rien. À vrai dire, lorsqu'il s'était rendu chez les Putnam, il était en proie à une avidité de violence intarissable. Le goût d'enfermer quelqu'un pour le simple plaisir l'avait fait sortir de son bureau. Mais l'appât du gain était plus fort. Il fit mine d'hésiter. Après tout, il n'avait que faire de cette gamine et ce petit pécule servirait grandement à lui et à ses hommes. S'il décidait de le partager...

— Très bien, Astor. Je prends cette ridicule somme. Mais attention ! Ne croyez-pas que je vous oublierai ! Votre fille est dans notre collimateur et je compte bien que justice soit rendue. Tôt ou tard. D'ici là, n'oubliez

jamais de me payer ou les conséquences seraient terribles.

Il fit signe à ses hommes de sortir. Sur le pas de la porte, il se retourna.

— Qu'elle reste chez vous, enfermée. Je ne veux pas la voir au village. Sinon, il vous en cuira, mon ami. Une bonne journée à vous, Mrs. Putnam, ajouta-t-il, doucereux.

Abigail n'arrivait pas à le croire. Ann Putnam, accusée d'être une sorcière ! Son père avait raison. Patton était en train de faire des exemples. Il n'en devenait que plus dangereux. D'après ce que Lila Mantion leur avait raconté, la mère d'Ann s'était confiée à elle, la jeune fille était restée prostrée dans sa chambre depuis la visite de l'inquisiteur, refusant de manger, de boire ou de dormir. Ses parents s'inquiétaient pour sa santé mentale mais en aucun cas ils n'auraient désobéi aux ordres de Patton. Betty ne semblait pas éprouver de remords après ce qu'elle avait entendu.

— Oh Abi, lui dit-elle, exaspérée, je n'y peux rien. Toi aussi, tu as trouvé ça très drôle.

— Sur le moment, oui ! Mais je ne pensais pas aux conséquences. Et toi non plus. Pauvre Ann !

— Pauvre Ann ? Je ne compatirai pas car je me souviens de toutes les méchancetés qu'elle nous a faites ou dites. Cette fille ne mérite pas que l'on se soucie d'elle. De toute façon, son père la protège, non ? Il paie sa liberté. Alors, occupons-nous plutôt de notre avenir.

Abigail soupira. Elle savait que sa cousine avait raison et se doutait bien que leur impunité ne durerait pas longtemps. Bien qu'elle ignorât le marché passé entre Patton et Craig Dorson, son supérieur, elle sentait que ce n'était plus qu'une question de temps avant qu'elles n'élisent domicile dans la clairière. Elles rentrèrent au manoir avec Tituba alors que d'épais flocons se posaient en douceur. À peine eurent-elles franchi la porte que miss Salinger les accueillait avec une tasse de thé et Cathy avec sa maussaderie habituelle. Les deux femmes de la maison ne leur posèrent aucune question quant à leurs activités mais Tituba sentait que Cathy brûlait de savoir. La servante avait entendu dire que Patton avait promis une récompense à ceux qui seraient délateurs et elle décida de tenir à l'œil Cathy.

9

Ezra s'était découvert un nouveau pouvoir qui l'étonnait. Sans savoir pourquoi, il avait invoqué de sauvages destriers. Lorsqu'il avait ouvert les yeux, il avait devant lui une horde de puissants chevaux translucides. Ils étaient effrayants. Leurs yeux pâles reflétaient la clarté de la lune opalescente et de légères fumerolles s'échappaient de leurs naseaux. Leur chef était sans conteste l'étalon le plus fier. Le poitrail droit et robuste, la crinière luisante et les muscles tendus, il semblait invincible. Ses congénères piaffaient à ses côtés et Ezra se demandait ce qu'ils attendaient. En pensée, il leur dit de filer au galop, le plus vite possible, et de s'envoler bien loin derrière les collines. Aussitôt, les splendides chevaux obéirent et disparurent à l'horizon sous les yeux éblouis du jeune homme. Ezra avait aussi compris que sa force résidait dans les éléments de la nature. Il pouvait à sa guise faire apparaître une muraille d'eau, de terre, de feu ou de vent. Même la glace se modelait sous ses mains. Respirer sous l'eau et marcher dans les airs n'avaient plus de secret pour lui et il ne s'étonnait plus des flammes qu'il parvenait à faire jaillir de ses paumes. Le jeune homme ne se reposait presque plus, ses forces grandissaient tant que la forêt, le ciel, l'eau et la terre lui transmettaient leur puissance. Ses traits s'étaient affinés et ses sens

devenaient surhumains. À l'aube, il aperçut Tituba avant même qu'elle ne pénètre dans le bois de Kyron de sa démarche lourde. Quelques instants plus tard, elle se tenait devant lui. La servante avait attendu d'être sous le couvert de la sylve pour s'épargner la longue marche.

— Je suis venue te proposer de te joindre à nous, lui déclara-t-elle avant même qu'il puisse dire un mot. Je crois qu'il est temps pour toi de sortir de ta retraite et de te mêler aux sorcières. Nous sommes encore plus nombreuses, de nouvelles recrues ont rallié nos forces.

— Je ne pense pas en avoir très envie. Il me reste encore beaucoup de choses à apprendre et ici j'ai le calme et la tranquillité qu'il me faut pour m'améliorer.

— Ezra, il ne te reste plus rien à apprendre. Du moins, je n'en suis plus capable. Tes pouvoirs ont largement dépassé les miens. Si tu nous rejoins, tu pourras en tout temps t'exercer. J'aimerais que tu m'aides à former certaines d'entre nous ; leurs pouvoirs sont trop faibles et elles auraient besoin d'un bon enseignement. Tu es capable de leur fournir cela. Mais c'est à toi de décider. Nous y serons toute la journée.

Elle s'éloigna tranquillement, laissant Ezra à ses pensées. Le jeune homme pesait le pour et le contre. Sa solitude lui pesait parfois mais, grâce à elle, il avait évolué rapidement en peu de temps. L'éventualité de retrouver des gens l'effrayait un peu. Il avait peur d'être devenu trop sauvage pour apprécier le contact humain. Mais l'envie de revoir Abigail lui tordait les entrailles depuis longtemps, il ne pouvait l'ignorer. Peut-être que Tituba avait raison. Ses pouvoirs pouvaient être utiles à d'autres que lui. Et la perspective d'enseigner le gonflait

d'orgueil et de fierté. « Mais je ne sais même pas où elles sont, pensa-t-il en sursautant. Je ne les trouverai pas tout seul. » Il entendit résonner dans son crâne une voix orageuse, grave et sourde, la voix râpeuse de Tituba. « La clairière de la forêt de Belwack, mon jeune ami. Bienvenue parmi nous. » Ezra tressaillit violemment. Tituba entendait les pensées et pouvait même communiquer avec lui. Ses pouvoirs semblaient sans limites et cela l'effrayait un peu. Il n'accordait pas une pleine et entière confiance à l'imposante Barbadienne et l'idée qu'elle avait accès à ses pensées le mit en colère. Désormais, il apprendrait à s'en protéger. Un instant, Ezra pensa à reprendre toutes ses affaires et à quitter définitivement son refuge. Il se reprit bien vite. Maintenant qu'il maîtrisait pleinement ses pouvoirs, il n'avait plus à souffrir du froid ou de la faim et sa grotte était devenue chaleureuse et accueillante. Il décida de tout y laisser, il reviendrait dormir là. Ezra entama la descente de la colline avec agilité, roulant avec adresse sur les pierres et sautant de racine en racine. Sa légèreté l'empêchait de vaciller et, en quelques secondes, il se retrouva au pied du coteau. Laissant ses pouvoirs de côté, il se rendit tranquillement à pied à la clairière.

Sur le chemin, Ezra se dit qu'il pardonnerait tout à Abigail et à Betty, mais que leur complicité à tous les trois aurait besoin de temps pour redevenir comme avant. Il ne souhaitait pas précipiter les choses. Après tout, s'il les voyait sous le bon angle, c'était grâce à elles qu'il était devenu un grand sorcier. Mais peut-être que s'il n'était pas allé en prison, les filles Parris auraient partagé leur secret avec lui. Ezra chassa ses mauvaises pensées et se concentra sur ce qui l'attendait. La vie dans la nature l'avait durci et lorsqu'il voyait son reflet dans l'eau il ne se reconnaissait plus.

Les cheveux hirsutes, le regard dur, les muscles apparents, le large cou et la barbe qui ombrageait ses traits : tout cela lui avait enlevé les dernières formes d'enfant de son corps. Il paraissait plus vieux, plus sage. Cela ne lui déplaisait pas mais il devait s'attendre à la stupéfaction de ceux qui l'avait connu.

— Anton, c'est ça ? demanda Patton. C'est bien ton nom ?

— Oui, murmura le jeune homme.

Il avait été convoqué dans le bureau de l'inquisiteur le matin même et s'attendait à une réprimande en règle. Ses camarades avaient compati et lui avaient prodigué toutes sortes de mots de réconfort. Il ne faisait pas bon se faire mander par Patton aussi tôt.

— Je crois savoir que tu viens de Boston. Pourquoi cette envie de t'installer à Salem ?

— Je souhaite me rendre utile, sir Patton, répondit-il prudemment.

— N'y a-t-il que le service ? N'avais-tu pas un autre dessein en tête ? Tu peux tout me dire, je ne te blâmerai pas.

Enhardi par le ton paternel de l'inquisiteur et sûr de lui, Anton lui répondit sincèrement.

— Vous avez raison, sir Patton. Une autre intention m'a conduit ici, outre la convoitise et l'ambition. Je suis venu pour me venger d'un affront.

Patton se frotta les mains, satisfait. Ainsi, il avait vu juste.

— Quel affront, mon ami ? Et de qui veux-tu te venger ?

— Miss Abigail Parris, sir. Celle-ci m'a humilié lors de son voyage à Boston où nous nous sommes rencontrés. Je n'ai eu de cesse, dès lors, de la traquer et de demander réparation.

— Tu es donc l'homme qu'il me faut, Anton. Je me réjouis déjà de notre collaboration.

— Qu'attendez-vous de moi, sir Patton ?

— Je veux que tu deviennes mon homme de main, mon bras droit, si tu veux. Tu seras mon plus fidèle complice. Tu auras le champ libre, je fermerai les yeux sur toutes tes exactions, tes folies et tes désirs.

— Que me demandez-vous en échange ?

— Des sorcières ont pris ce village en otage et je veux que tu les trouves. Elles se réunissent sûrement en un endroit qu'elles seules connaissent. Je veux des noms, des visages, des coupables et des aveux. Peu importe le moyen que tu utiliseras pour cela, je n'en ai cure. La menace, la violence, la torture… ajouta-t-il, cruel, fais ce que bon te semble. Bien entendu, tu seras récompensé pour tes bons et loyaux services. Car c'est bien de cela que nous parlons, n'est-ce pas ? Des services ? Maintenant, file. J'attends des résultats rapidement.

Anton ne se fit pas prier et s'empressa d'aller rejoindre ses camarades qui l'attendaient avec inquiétude. Devant sa mine réjouie, ils le pressèrent de tout leur

raconter. Fier de l'admiration que ses acolytes lui portaient, Anton s'interrogea sur la meilleure façon d'entreprendre ses recherches. Certes, être dans les petits papiers de Patton était un honneur, encore fallait-il être digne de s'y tenir. Or, Anton n'avait pas la moindre idée de comment procéder. Si une vingtaine d'inquisiteurs à l'affût n'avaient pu trouver le moindre indice, comment y parviendrait-il, seul ? Il réfléchit d'abord aux endroits où plusieurs personnes pouvaient se regrouper sans attirer l'attention. Pas dans le village, c'était sûr. Aux alentours, il y avait des bois mais Anton ne s'y était jamais aventuré.

Ezra se retrouva dans la clairière rapidement et aperçut une troupe de jeunes femmes se lançant mutuellement des sorts. Il se cacha derrière un tronc pour observer à son aise. Surpris, il vit Abigail s'envoler à une vitesse vertigineuse tandis que Betty bondissait de branche en branche à ses côtés. Celle-ci sauta sur sa cousine en plein vol et toutes deux tombèrent comme des pierres. Ezra retint son souffle ; à quelques pouces du sol, Abigail parvint à les maintenir en l'air et elles atterrirent sans difficulté. Une femme qu'il ne connaissait pas s'amusait à s'entourer de nappes de brouillard bien maigres par rapport à celles qu'il était capable de faire apparaître. Et les sœurs Hobbs, qu'il reconnut pour les avoir souvent servies à la boucherie, jouaient avec une troisième femme qui n'en pouvait plus de rire. Tour à tour, elle exécutait des pas de danse complexes et qui avaient l'air épuisants avant d'être pétrifiée dans des positions grotesques. Ezra comprit ce que voulait dire Tituba. Ces femmes ne donnaient pas l'impression de prendre leur travail au sérieux. Cependant, cette

manifestation puérile de magie était sans doute un exutoire aux malheurs qui couraient dans le village. Ezra décida de se montrer et il s'approcha des sorcières. Plusieurs hurlèrent à sa vue et Tituba, lorsqu'elle se tourna pour connaître la raison de cette agitation, lui adressa un sourire carnassier qu'elle aurait sûrement voulu chaleureux.

— Comment as-tu fait pour percer les sortilèges de protection ? lui demanda une femme.

— Je ne les ai pas vus, répondit sincèrement Ezra.

Tituba eut un sourire en coin que personne ne remarqua.

— Bonjour, Ezra, susurra-t-elle. Mes amies, je vous présente votre nouvel allié et celui qui vous aidera à développer vos pouvoirs.

Abigail et Betty, qui étaient encore en plein affrontement, cessèrent leurs hostilités et s'approchèrent de l'attroupement, curieuses. Lorsqu'elles aperçurent Ezra, elles ne purent dire un mot. Tituba s'approcha d'elles et leur murmura :

— Je m'attends à ce que vos vieilles querelles ne viennent pas troubler le bon ordre de nos réunions. Je me suis déjà entretenue avec Ezra à ce sujet. Ne l'approchez pas tant qu'il ne le voudra pas ou je vous le ferai payer, mes chères enfants.

— En quoi va-t-il nous aider ? demanda Betty.

Tituba parut surprise par la question.

— C'est un sorcier, miss Betty. Et un très bon sorcier ! Il aura de quoi vous apprendre !

— Un sorcier ? s'exclama Abigail. Mais comment...

— Je l'ai formé moi-même et je dois dire que je suis époustouflée par ses vifs progrès. C'est une bénédiction de l'avoir parmi nous !

Soufflées, Betty et Abigail tentèrent de s'approcher d'Ezra pour lui dire quelques mots. Mais à leur vue, le jeune homme fit mine de discuter avec plus d'entrain avec une sorcière qui l'entraîna bien vite à sa suite. Ann Dolliver lui demanda comment développer ses pouvoirs et Ezra le lui expliqua en prenant son rôle très au sérieux.

— C'est bien qu'il soit avec nous, non ? dit Betty à Abigail.

— Il n'est pas vraiment avec nous, soupira-t-elle.

— En tout cas, il n'est pas contre nous.

— Un sorcier !

— J'ai tellement de mal à le croire.

— Penses-tu qu'il va nous faire une petite démonstration ?

À peine avait-elle prononcé ces mots que sa cousine et elle entendirent des exclamations d'émerveillement. Ezra faisait tournoyer dans les airs une immense bulle d'air qui se transforma en eau puis en feu avant de devenir cette monstrueuse vague de terre qui avait effrayé Tituba. Lorsqu'elle s'écrasa sur le sol, la poussière qui en émana se métamorphosa en bancs de

brouillard épais. Abigail pencha la tête et se rendit compte qu'elle ne voyait plus ses pieds, ni même Betty qui était pourtant accrochée à son bras. Les femmes se mirent à hurler lorsque cette brume se mua en ténèbres implacables. Abigail et Betty croyaient être devenues aveugles ; quand la noirceur se dissipa, elles retinrent un soupir de soulagement. Toutes les sorcières étaient hagardes et impressionnées. Tituba ne manifestait aucune émotion, elle avait déjà tout vu. Ezra se retrouva au milieu d'une foule de femmes qui se pressaient pour le féliciter et l'implorer de leur apprendre tout ce qu'il savait.

— Impressionnant, n'est-ce pas ? souffla Tituba. Moi-même, je n'en reviens pas.

Bouche bée, aucune des deux filles ne lui répondit.

Anton s'était d'abord rendu au bois de Kyron. Éloigné du village, il offrait une cachette parfaite, propice aux rendez-vous secrets. Mais il n'avait pas eu le courage de continuer loin dans le sous-bois. Les arbres grinçaient à son approche et les croassements lugubres des corbeaux ne le rassuraient pas. La forêt de Belwack semblait être un environnement plus joyeux, aussi s'y rendit-il en se promettant de retourner à Kyron s'il ne trouvait rien de concluant. À son arrivée à la forêt, il remarqua aussitôt que plusieurs personnes avaient piétiné au même endroit. Même s'il avait toujours vécu en ville, il savait reconnaître une piste lorsqu'il en voyait une. Et ce qu'il avait à ses pieds en avait tout l'air. Une tranchée, peu profonde mais visible, s'enfonçait dans la futaie. Heureusement, la neige fraîchement tombée n'avait pas recouvert cet

indice. Les hautes cimes avaient si bien freiné sa chute que seules quelques traînées parsemaient le sol. Anton s'employa à suivre le sillon, mais il le perdit lorsqu'il déboucha dans une clairière. Confus, il revint sur ses pas et, le nez au ras du sol, reprit sa route. La trace s'arrêtait net à l'entrée de cette clairière. Le jeune homme regarda autour de lui, s'attendant à voir une nuée de femmes prises sur le fait. Il guetta le moindre son suspect, un pied écrasant une branche ou des cris d'effroi. Rien. Haussant les épaules, il rebroussa chemin et se rendit au village, perplexe quant à ce qu'il allait dire à Patton. « Après tout, ce n'est que mon premier jour », se rassura-t-il.

Ezra et les sorcières avaient retenu leur souffle en voyant un inconnu déboucher dans la clairière avec l'air de chercher quelque chose de précis. Tituba s'était figée et avait levé une main impérieuse pour réclamer un silence complet. Personne ne s'était fait prier. Seule Abigail semblait plus effrayée que les autres. Elle avait maladroitement agrippée le bras d'Ezra qui se trouvait à portée et l'avait serré si fort qu'il en portait encore les marques. Abigail ne donnait pas l'impression de s'être rendu compte de ce qu'elle faisait. Il comprit néanmoins que cet homme la terrorisait. Lorsque l'inquisiteur avait disparu sous les arbres, toutes avaient poussé un soupir de soulagement. Mais leur joie avait été de courte durée.

— Si cet homme est là, c'est que nous n'avons pas été assez prudentes. Il a réussi à suivre notre trace. Il ne faudra pas longtemps aux inquisiteurs pour comprendre que c'est ici que nous nous cachons.

— Doit-on changer de lieu ? avait demandé une femme.

— Non, ce serait encore plus dangereux. Nous sommes trop nombreuses pour nous déplacer toutes ensemble. Et cette clairière est un endroit parfait.

— Que pouvons-nous faire ?

— Celles qui sont capables de se rendre invisibles iront chercher celles qui ne peuvent se déplacer sans être vues. Nous ne nous réunirons que la nuit, désormais, cela me paraît moins risqué.

Les sorcières approuvèrent les mesures de Tituba. Celle-ci, Betty, Ezra et une autre femme du nom de Margaret Scott furent chargés d'escorter leurs comparses.

Penaud, Anton sortit du bureau de Patton. Celui-ci lui avait hurlé dessus pendant ce qui lui avait semblé des heures. L'inquisiteur en chef n'avait pas cherché à comprendre, il lui avait donné l'ordre de continuer encore et encore. Il se fichait que ce soit son premier, quinzième ou dernier jour, il voulait des résultats et il les voulait tout de suite.

— Que ce soit bien clair entre nous, Anton. Si je t'ai pris avec moi, c'est parce que je pense que tu es capable de réussir. Mais si tu ne m'apportes pas rapidement de probantes preuves de ce que j'avance, il se peut que je sois beaucoup moins gentil. Tu n'aimerais pas que je devienne un problème pour toi, n'est-ce-pas ?

Honteux, Anton avait hoché la tête.

— Nous sommes d'accord. Ce ne sont pas des vacances que je t'ai offertes. Reste debout toutes les nuits s'il le faut, mais ne reviens pas me voir sans une réponse !

Patton l'avait congédié et, dès que le jeune homme était sorti, il était entré dans une phase de violence. Après avoir balayé le dessus de son bureau, il l'avait renversé entièrement. Sa chaise n'était plus bonne qu'à servir de bois de chauffage et lui-même, avec les cheveux hérissés et les yeux fous, faisait peur à voir.

La nuit même, Anton obéit scrupuleusement aux ordres de Patton et s'installa sur la place du village. Caché au coin d'un mur, il avait une vision parfaite de presque toutes les rues. Les sorcières n'allaient pas pouvoir lui échapper. Les heures passaient, et la nuit était noire. Le froid glacé le maintenait éveillé mais il aurait suffi que le vent forcisse pour qu'un engourdissement mortel le prenne. Lorsque la lune arriva à son zénith, Anton somnolait. Il essayait tant bien que mal de garder ses paupières ouvertes en se racontant des histoires, mais elles étaient si lourdes… Même la pensée d'un joli pécule en récompense de tous ses efforts ne l'excitait plus. Il n'entendit pas les chuchotements étouffés tout près de lui car le sommeil l'avait vaincu. Invisibles, Betty, Tituba, Ezra, Margaret et Abigail, qui avait tenu à se faire dissimuler, frôlèrent le jeune homme.

— Jouons-lui un bon tour, proposa Betty.

— Bien sûr, miss Parris, persifla Tituba. Et pourquoi ne pas nous montrer et le laisser nous attraper ? Décidément, vous êtes incorrigible.

Betty bougonna et continua son chemin. Ezra s'attarda un peu.

— Avez-vous besoin de moi, Tituba. Je… je voudrais faire quelque chose avant de vous rejoindre.

Suspicieuse, Tituba lui jeta un regard qui le fit frissonner. Il sentit soudain quelque chose tenter de pénétrer son esprit. Mobilisant toutes ses forces, il repoussa l'intrus.

— Je vois que tu as développé un nouveau pouvoir et que tu n'as pas jugé utile de m'en parler.

— Je lis aussi dans les pensées et je vois que vous ne me faites pas confiance.

— Très bien ! Va faire ce que tu veux ! Mais si tu nous attires des ennuis…

Ezra avait déjà filé. Il attendit que ses compagnes aient disparu pour retourner auprès du jeune inquisiteur. Il sonda les pensées de celui-ci et chercha sa peur la plus profonde. Anton était effrayé par la solitude. Riant sous cape, Ezra ferma les yeux et imagina un paysage désertique. Personne à des lieues à la ronde. Rien que des rochers, du sable et le soleil desséchant. Il constata que cela avait marché à merveille. Se penchant à l'oreille d'Anton, il murmura son nom, d'abord doucement puis de plus en plus fort. Le jeune homme se réveilla en sursaut. La première chose qu'il sentit fut la sueur qui dégoulinait le long de son visage. Or, on était en plein hiver. Ezra se délecta de l'expression de terreur qui apparaissait sur son visage au fur et à mesure qu'Anton regardait autour de lui. Lorsque l'inquisiteur se mit à hurler, Ezra eut peur qu'il n'attire tous les autres ; il l'assomma d'un bon coup de poing sur le nez. Il dissipa aussitôt le mirage et s'enfuit dans l'ombre en direction de la forêt.

Quelques minutes plus tard, lorsqu'il reprit conscience, Anton crut avoir rêvé. Une douleur lancinante le convainquit du contraire. Les alentours étaient sombres et il ne distinguait rien dans l'obscurité. Une peur atroce l'empoigna et il se précipita vers le bureau de Patton. Ses poings martelèrent follement la porte de bois jusqu'à ce que l'inquisiteur en chef, fulminant, l'attrape par le collet.

— Pour qui te prends-tu, maudit avorton ?

— Je... je les ai vues... bégaya le pauvre Anton.

— Vues ? répéta Patton, soudain intéressé.

— Enfin, pas vraiment. Mais elles étaient là, c'est sûr !

— Ne me prends pas pour un imbécile. Les as-tu vues, oui ou non ? tonna l'inquisiteur.

— Je me suis réveillé et j'étais dans un autre endroit, un désert. C'était terrifiant. Et soudain, quelqu'un m'a donné un coup, expliqua-t-il en montrant son nez en sang et son œil qui devenait noir. C'était de la magie, sir.

Patton le regarda, perplexe. Un autre inquisiteur avait fait irruption pendant leur conversation, alerté par le tapage.

— Devine, dit Patton à l'intention de l'arrivant. Ce pourceau a fait un mauvais rêve et il est venu me le raconter en pleine nuit !

Il éclata d'un rire qui n'avait rien de joyeux et qui glaça Anton.

— Occupe-toi de lui, lâcha-t-il à l'intention de l'autre homme.

10

Les réunions qui avaient désormais lieu toutes les nuits étaient très satisfaisantes pour tout le monde. Chacune sentait ses pouvoirs se développer. Ainsi, Candy pouvait désormais passer à travers toutes sortes de murs, et elle était même capable de voir à travers. Ann Dolliver brûlait ou glaçait grâce à ses fameuses mains. Les tornades de Rebecca Eames étaient à présent terrifiantes et balayaient tout sur leur passage. L'une des sorcières les plus dangereuses était Sarah Osborne qui contrôlait les pensées et les émotions. Ce pouvoir était effrayant et personne ne voulait l'aider à s'entraîner. Si bien qu'elles établirent un tour de rôle. Mais chaque sorcière qui sortait d'un affrontement avec elle était bouleversée. Sarah Osborne parvenait à faire inspirer la peur, la tristesse ou la solitude à des degrés si forts que des esprits instables pouvaient y perdre toute raison. Ezra se mesurait souvent à elle car il parvenait sans effort à contrer ses sorts, mais Sarah devait développer son don qui était un des plus importants de la Confrérie. Une nouvelle arrivante, Mary English, parvenait, pour sa part, à faire vieillir ou rajeunir ses adversaires. Le spectacle d'une sorcière devenant tour à tour un nouveau-né vagissant puis un vieillard tremblant de tous ses membres était grandiose. La clairière était devenue un lieu hautement magique et l'ambiance

électrique qui y régnait chaque nuit regorgeait de bonheur et de vaillance.

Vers minuit, Betty aperçut Abigail qui revenait d'entre les arbres. Elle était partie se promener pour échapper au bruit incessant des luttes intestines. La jeune fille devina que sa cousine n'était pas seule. Elle se précipita à sa rencontre. Une enfant de sept ou huit ans, maculée de crasse et les cheveux emmêlés, l'accompagnait.

— Qui est-elle? demanda Betty.

— Je ne sais pas. Elle ne m'a pas dit son nom. Je l'ai trouvée seule dans les bois. Elle a un pouvoir, chuchota-t-elle.

— Amenons-la à Tituba.

Abigail acquiesça et entraîna avec elle la petite qui n'avait pas lâché sa main. À la clairière, toutes saluèrent le retour d'Abigail et se rapprochèrent lorsqu'elles découvrirent l'enfant. Tituba s'avança et s'accroupit aux pieds de la petite fille.

— Quel est ton nom? demanda-t-elle d'une voix qu'elle essaya de rendre douce.

L'enfant tressaillit et s'agrippa aux jambes d'Abigail.

— Ma maman est morte et mon papa pleure.

— C'est la seule phrase qu'elle dit, expliqua Abigail.

— Nous ne pouvons pas garder une enfant, trancha Tituba. Il faut la ramener au village.

— Qui s'en occupera là-bas ? Les inquisiteurs ? Tituba ! Elle est capable de diriger les animaux. Lorsque je l'ai trouvée, elle faisait marcher au pas des centaines de fourmis.

— À quoi nous servirait une armée de fourmis ?

— Si elle reste avec nous, nous pourrons l'aider à progresser. C'est un atout inestimable.

— C'est une petite fille. Et elle n'a pas sa place dans une guerre.

— Nous ne sommes pas encore en guerre, protesta Abigail. Et sa place est parmi nous où elle sera mieux avec ses semblables qu'au village où ils la tueront dès qu'ils sauront ce qu'elle sait faire. Gardons-la avec nous et aidons-la à s'améliorer. Si un combat point à l'horizon, ce sera peut-être dans plusieurs mois.

— Ou demain !

— Nous n'en savons rien, cria la jeune fille.

— Très bien, faites ce que bon vous semble, capitula Tituba. Vous en serez responsable, miss Parris. Vous et vous seule. Nourrissez-la, occupez-vous-en. Si quelque chose lui arrive, vous serez seule à avoir ce remords sur la conscience.

Farouche, Abigail prit l'enfant dans ses bras et s'éloigna rapidement. Elle l'installa sur un tapis de feuilles mortes et fit jaillir de l'eau avec laquelle elle lui nettoya sommairement le visage. Sortant de sous sa robe le grimoire qui ne la quittait jamais, elle le feuilleta jusqu'à trouver ce qu'elle cherchait.

— *Ageris assovio*, murmura-t-elle.

Un pain apparut aussitôt entre ses mains. La miche était dure mais Abigail ne doutait pas qu'avec un peu d'entraînement elle parviendrait à faire apparaître de bons petits plats. La petite dévora le quignon qu'elle lui tendit. Abigail aurait pu demander à Susannah Post de faire pousser quelques baies pour la fillette. La sorcière aurait accepté de bon cœur, mais Tituba avait bien dit que c'était là sa seule responsabilité. Elle soupira en regardant sa cousine enchaîner tous ses pouvoirs le plus vite possible. Celle-ci fit jaillir de l'eau de la terre qu'elle fit ensuite léviter dans les airs comme des bulles de savon. Les gouttes d'eau se mirent à briller avec une telle force qu'elles éblouirent les femmes autour. D'un geste négligent, Betty fit disparaître l'eau et devint aussitôt invisible. Abigail étouffa un cri de surprise quand toutes les personnes présentes dans la clairière disparurent. Rendre indétectables une vingtaine de personnes ne semblait plus être un problème pour Betty. Impressionnée, Abigail chercha sa cousine des yeux lorsque tout le monde eut réapparu.

— Hou! hou! Je suis là-haut! cria une voix perçante.

Betty était perchée sur une haute branche et, hilare, regardait Abigail qui essayait de déterminer d'où venait la voix.

— C'est incroyable, Betty! s'exclama Abigail. Tu es devenue vraiment très bonne!

— Merci! Mais il reste encore tellement de choses à apprendre.

Ezra, qui écoutait leur conversation, détourna les yeux dès qu'Abigail le regarda.

La nuit suivante, alors qu'une épaisse couche de neige s'était déposée dans la forêt, très peu de sorcières se retrouvèrent dans la clairière. Frissonnantes, malgré les efforts de Tituba pour rendre le sol sec, elles se serraient les unes contre les autres et attendaient impatiemment leurs amies pour commencer. Plusieurs heures passèrent, Betty et Margaret Scott, qui étaient chargées de ramener leurs alliées, ne revenaient pas. La tension était palpable et Abigail, inquiète pour sa cousine, faisait les cent pas. Des scénarios tous plus tragiques les uns que les autres se bousculaient dans sa tête. Betty était morte, Betty était enfermée, prisonnière, torturée, battue. Les inquisiteurs avaient mis la main sur elle et la maltraitaient jusqu'à ce qu'elle flanche et dise où se trouvait leur repaire. Incapable d'attendre plus longtemps, elle se précipita dans l'obscurité.

Tituba la rattrapa aussitôt.

— Où allez-vous ?

— Je dois savoir ce qui leur est arrivé.

— C'est trop risqué.

— C'est ma cousine, ma sœur, la seule famille qu'il me reste ! hurla Abigail.

— Souvenez-vous que le pacte que nous avons signé stipule que si l'une de nous est prise, nous l'abandonnons. Nous sommes en territoire hostile, miss Parris, les inquisiteurs ont déployé de grands moyens pour

nous attraper. Ils savent désormais annihiler nos pouvoirs rapidement. Si Betty a été attrapée, nous ne pouvons rien pour elle, ce soir.

— Je ne la laisserai pas.

— Votre grand cœur vous perdra !

— Et le vôtre est de pierre !

Tituba découvrit ses dents en un rictus menaçant. Abigail soutint son regard. La servante lui agrippa violemment le bras et la tira vers leur cachette. La jeune fille avait beau se débattre, la poigne de la Barbadienne était de fer et Abigail se retrouva, traînant dans la neige, emmenée vers le sol sec comme si elle n'avait pas pesé plus lourd qu'une plume. Tituba la laissa tomber sans douceur et se pencha sur elle.

— Ne vous avisez pas de nous mettre en danger par vos caprices sentimentaux, miss Parris. Je ne serai pas toujours là pour vous protéger. Vous ne valez, à mes yeux, pas plus qu'une autre, et si je vous prends encore à risquer notre vie, je vous tuerai.

Des larmes de rage dans les yeux, Abigail baissa la tête pour que la servante ne les voie pas. Ezra et les quelques femmes qui avaient observé l'affrontement ne dirent mot. Le jeune homme voulut s'approcher d'Abigail, mais un regard de celle-ci dissuada quiconque de lui venir en aide. Elle resta longtemps prostrée dans le noir. Un vent froid faisait voleter ses cheveux mais, pour le reste, elle était immobile, plongée dans d'âpres pensées. La forêt, étrangement silencieuse, faisait peser sur tous une angoisse indicible. Le grincement des branches achevait de donner

une ambiance lugubre à l'endroit. Les cimes des hauts sapins empêchaient la lueur des étoiles de pénétrer dans la futaie et l'obscurité semblait insondable. Quand le frisson d'un buisson fit sursauter les jumelles, elles le regardèrent avec appréhension.

— Êtes-vous obligée de vous comporter comme un tyran ? demanda Ezra à Tituba, frémissant de colère. Comment voulez-vous qu'on vous fasse confiance si vous nous traitez comme ça ? Vous effrayez la moitié des personnes présentes et l'autre moitié ne sait pas si elle doit vous aimer ou vous détester !

— Ne commence pas.

— Vous n'avez jamais appris à parler calmement ? Vous m'avez menacé de représailles si je levais la main sur les sœurs Parris, mais vous-même, vous les traitez comme vos domestiques ! Avez-vous déjà aimé, Tituba ? Peut-être est-ce cela qui vous manque. Vous n'auriez sans doute pas réagi comme ça si vous saviez ce que c'est que de trembler pour un proche.

— Mon ami, dois-je te rappeler que la dernière fois que tu as toi-même tremblé pour celle que tu aimais les geôles de Patton t'ont ouvert leurs portes ?

Ezra ne répondit pas car il surprit un mouvement du coin de l'œil. Abigail se précipitait vers Betty et Margaret Scott qui venaient d'apparaître sous les arbres, à la limite de la clairière.

— J'ai eu si peur ! s'exclama Abigail en serrant violemment sa cousine contre elle.

— Abi, tu m'étouffes !

— Que vous est-il arrivé ? Pourquoi êtes-vous seules ? Où sont les autres ?

— Nous les avons attendues longtemps. Ne les voyant pas arriver, Margaret et moi sommes allées voir à la prison.

— Elles ont été arrêtées, dit dans un souffle Margaret Scott.

— Qui ? demanda Rebecca Eames.

— Les sœurs Hobbs, Mary English, Sarah Bassett, Abigail Faulkner, Sarah Bishop, Sarah Wildes et Lila Mantion.

Des exclamations horrifiées retentirent dans la foule. Huit sorcières en moins. Elles n'avaient même pas commencé à riposter. C'était un coup dur pour la Confrérie de la Clairière.

— Comment ont-ils fait pour les attraper ?

— D'après ce que nous avons entendu des inquisiteurs, toutes s'étaient regroupées en pleine journée pour discuter. Elles ont très vite attiré l'attention et une vingtaine d'hommes sont venus les cueillir.

— Quelle négligence ! s'exclama Tituba, dédaigneuse.

Tout le monde ignora sa remarque acerbe et continua d'interroger Betty et Margaret.

— Pourquoi n'ont-elles pas usé de leur pouvoir pour s'échapper ? demanda Mary Parker.

— J'ai entendu Patton parler d'une nouvelle arme, répondit Betty. Une sorte de soufflet qui exhale des

vapeurs d'opium si puissantes qu'elles assomment tout de suite, inhibant aussitôt toute magie. Elles n'ont pas eu de chance. La prison aura raison de leurs dernières forces.

— Lila Mantion s'en est sortie, dit-on, coupa Margaret. Un des inquisiteurs a dit l'avoir attrapée mais qu'elle a aussitôt disparu entre ses bras.

— Elle a rapetissé ! s'exclama Abigail, triomphante. Elle va sûrement nous rejoindre.

Le reste de la nuit se passa en silence. Personne n'avait le cœur à engager des duels. Assises autour d'un grand feu qu'Abigail avait allumé, les sorcières se racontaient des histoires banales pour tromper leur inquiétude. La petite fille qu'Abigail avait recueillie était pelotonnée contre ses jambes et regardait avec de grands yeux les immenses flammes qui projetaient mille étincelles incandescentes, luisantes comme des lucioles dans le ciel obscur. Ezra restait silencieux, un peu en retrait, scrutant les profondeurs du bois, les yeux plissés par la concentration. Une volonté farouche s'était emparée de lui. Il aurait souhaité, dès ce soir, organiser une action vengeresse et courir délivrer les sorcières emprisonnées. Il fallait attendre que les autres soient assez fortes. Une action solitaire pourrait lui être fatale.

Au-delà de la bulle protectrice, la neige s'était remise à tomber, étouffant les bruits, et la vision des flocons cotonneux tourbillonnant dans les rafales de vent avait quelque chose de magique derrière cette barrière rassurante. Les yeux fixés sur les ténèbres, toutes essayaient de repérer un mouvement, la preuve de la présence d'une survivante. Mais Lila Mantion ne réapparut pas,

ni cette nuit ni les suivantes. Personne ne sut ce qu'elle devint et la perte de huit de leurs amies se fit plus poignante. Cette arrestation massive avait entamé leur moral car jusqu'à maintenant la perspective de vaincre grâce à leurs pouvoirs était encourageante. Tous avaient pensé que le combat serait inégal et pencherait facilement en leur faveur mais les hommes de Patton rivalisaient d'ingéniosité. Celle nouvelle arme, les vapeurs d'opium, pouvait leur être fatale. Sans leurs pouvoirs, elles ne vaudraient rien contre les inquisiteurs. Ezra quitta avant l'aube, retournant dans sa tanière, et les sorcières se séparèrent sur cette dernière pensée. Sur le chemin du retour au manoir, Betty et Abigail, qui tenait la petite fille par la main, ruminaient. Tout était perdu. La victoire semblait désormais impossible.

— Je sais ce qui vous tracasse, mes enfants, leur dit Tituba. Mais cela ne fait que commencer. Ne baissons pas les bras tout de suite.

— On ne pourra pas lutter contre eux. Nos armes sont inégales.

— Je ne vous le fais pas dire, miss Betty. Nous possédons de puissants pouvoirs et eux, non. Une vulgaire fumée narcotique ne viendra pas à bout de nos capacités.

— Alors pourquoi se sont-elles fait prendre? demanda Abigail, acerbe.

— Elles n'ont sans doute pas assez réfléchi.

— Si vous êtes si intelligente, dites-nous comment faire alors!

— Je ne le sais pas encore, miss Abigail, mais je compte bien y réfléchir sérieusement.

Tituba les laissa à l'entrée du manoir pour se rendre à la cuisine. Betty se tourna vers sa cousine.

— Pourquoi lui as-tu parlé comme ça ?

— Je ne lui fais pas confiance, répondit Abigail.

— Quoi ?

— Je ne lui fais pas confiance, répéta la jeune fille. C'est tout.

Elle s'adoucit devant le regard interrogateur de Betty.

— J'ai eu si peur pour toi ce soir. Qu'est-ce que je deviendrais s'il t'arrivait quelque chose ?

— Comme tu l'as dit, je suis impressionnante, se rengorgea Betty. Je peux me débrouiller, ne t'inquiète pas. Et si nous dormions dans le même lit, ce soir, comme avant ? proposa-t-elle.

Abigail acquiesça de bon cœur et elles montèrent dans la chambre. Aussitôt endormies, chacune se perdit dans les rêves. Le sommeil agité d'Abigail, qui voyait dans ses songes Tituba la dominant de toute sa hauteur et lui jeter un éclair d'argent qui la tuait sur le coup, ne gêna pas celui de Betty. Elle-même se voyait sauver toute la Confrérie des griffes de Patton.

— Pourquoi n'ai-je pas reçu la rançon de votre fille, Putnam ? demanda Patton, patibulaire. Nous étions convenus qu'au début de chaque mois vous viendriez

déposer à mon bureau les soixante dollars que vous
m'aviez promis. Or, nous sommes le 6 février. J'ai fait
preuve d'une bonté sans bornes en vous accordant ces
quelques jours de délai. Maintenant, je veux savoir où
est mon argent.

Astor Putnam, tremblotant, lançait des regards
apeurés aux inquisiteurs qui avaient fait irruption dans
sa maison en plein cœur de la nuit. Les hommes de
main de Patton ricanaient, l'air sournois.

— Mais… je vous ai payé il y a deux semaines à
peine et je pensais que…

— Bien sûr, mais c'était pour le mois de janvier,
n'est-ce pas ? Nous voilà en février, et je veux mon dû.

— Je n'ai plus beaucoup d'argent, sir Patton. Veuillez
pardonner mon retard, mais les temps sont si durs ; la
chair est bien maigre en ce moment et j'ai ma famille à
nourrir.

— Et moi mes hommes, pour vous garder en
sécurité. N'est-ce pas plus important ? Ou votre
égoïsme aurait-il atteint des sommets vertigineux ?

— Oh non ! Bien sûr que non ! Mais…

— Si vous ne pouvez pas me payer, j'envoie tout de
suite un de mes hommes chercher votre fille là-haut.
Cela vous fera une bouche de moins à nourrir. Avouez
que ce n'est pas négligeable.

— Non ! cria Putnam. Ce ne sera pas nécessaire ! Je…
je vais trouver une solution. Attendez-moi !

S'empêtrant dans ses pieds, il prit sur le buffet un vase dans lequel il plongea le bras. Il en extirpa les dernières pièces de sa fortune et les fourra dans la main tendue de l'inquisiteur en chef. Celui-ci, sceptique, compta l'argent qu'il tenait. Paraissant satisfait, il pointa un index sous le nez de Putnam et lui murmura d'une voix méchante :

— Ne vous avisez plus de me payer en retard !

Tous sortirent. Astor Putnam resta un moment derrière la fenêtre à guetter. Dès que les inquisiteurs eurent disparu au loin, il monta en courant dans les étages et réveilla sa femme.

— Lève les enfants ! Nous partons ! Habille-les chaudement.

Mrs. Putnam ne demanda pas d'explications et elle passa de chambre en chambre pour réveiller son monde. Quelques minutes plus tard, les dix enfants aux yeux ensuqués et aux traits brouillés par le sommeil étaient réunis en bas. Astor prit une torche, jeta sur son épaule un gros sac dans lequel se trouvait de la nourriture et fit sortir tout le monde. Sans un regard en arrière, il claqua la porte de sa maison et tous partirent dans l'obscurité. Mrs. Putnam tenait la main d'Ann qui ne cessait de faire des mouvements brusques. Les yeux de la jeune fille n'avaient plus rien de séduisant et il semblait que quelque chose s'était brisé dans son esprit.

Ils traversèrent précipitamment la clairière de la forêt Belwack sans même se rendre compte qu'un large cercle au centre était dépourvu de neige.

11

Abigail était assise sur le lit de sa cousine qui dormait profondément. Après sa promenade nocturne dans la neige autour de la prison, Betty était tombée malade. Un léger rhume qui l'empêchait quand même de sortir. Abigail était donc restée près d'elle tandis que Tituba continuait à se rendre aux réunions. La jeune fille n'était toujours pas apaisée et elle avait fait en sorte de croiser le moins possible la Barbadienne. La neige tombait sans discontinuer depuis deux jours et un épais manteau recouvrait désormais le sol. Il perdurerait jusqu'au printemps. L'étrange silence qui régnait avait permis à Betty de se reposer. Abigail feuilletait le grimoire, cornant les pages qui l'intéressaient, essayant certains sortilèges. Ses journées se résumaient à cela. Elle montait régulièrement un bol de soupe à Betty qui, la gorge enflée, ne pouvait rien avaler d'autre, elle la distrayait lorsque cette dernière ne dormait pas et elle lisait attentivement le grimoire. Contrairement à ce qu'elle pensait, le livre ne renfermait pas des centaines de sorts. Il donnait plutôt une histoire de la magie ponctuée de quelques formules magiques. Mais il n'en était que plus captivant. Ainsi, Abigail apprit que la magie avait fait son apparition dans le monde plusieurs siècles avant Jésus-Christ, quelque part dans les îles du sud de l'océan Pacifique, les îles Samoa. Et

non pas à la Barbade comme l'avait dit Tituba. Là-bas, un enfant était né et, le jour même, ses parents étaient morts. Or, personne ne voulut s'occuper du petit garçon. On l'abandonna dans la maison impure de sa famille, croyant qu'il mourrait rapidement. Contre toute attente, l'enfant survécut. Au bout de quelques jours, les Samoans virent sortir de la hutte un jeune garçon de quelques années. Surpris, ils l'interrogèrent, pensant qu'il venait d'un autre village. L'enfant leur répondit :

— Mes parents sont morts il y a quatre jours et vous n'avez pas voulu vous occuper de moi. Je me suis donc débrouillé seul. Maintenant, je ne vous importunerai plus car je m'en vais.

Et le garçon s'éloigna, suivi par tout le village. Il disparut dans les forêts luxuriantes de l'île et on ne le revit pas. Les villageois eurent tôt fait d'oublier l'enfant, parlant d'un rêve collectif. Mais à peine quelques jours plus tard, un cyclone vint dévaster leurs récoltes. Ce genre de phénomène atmosphérique était très courant pour la région ; toutefois, le mode de vie des Samoans étant réglé sur les saisons, ce phénomène n'aurait pas dû survenir à cette période de l'année. Les habitants de l'île furent catégoriques : on les punissait. Ils repensèrent à cet enfant qui avait grandi de plusieurs années en quelques jours. Les familles prirent peur et, à l'entrée du village, on établit un autel où, chaque jour, elles venaient déposer des offrandes. Leurs récoltes, ravagées par le cyclone, repoussèrent en un jour tandis que les cadeaux déposés disparaissaient pendant la nuit. Et la magie naquit. Au fil des ans, les Samoans préférèrent penser à la naissance d'un dieu qu'ils vénérèrent encore longtemps.

Abigail releva les yeux, rêvant de cette île perdue d'où un enfant avait répandu la magie dans le monde et dans le temps, jusqu'à elle. Elle sursauta quand Betty agrippa son bras.

— Est-ce que je peux avoir un verre d'eau? demanda-t-elle d'une voix enrouée.

Abigail sauta du lit et descendit en courant. Elle remonta rapidement avec un verre et un broc rempli d'eau fraîche. Betty but puis se recoucha.

— On dirait que tu as moins de mal à avaler!

— Ça commence à aller mieux. Je pense que demain soir nous pourrons retourner dans la clairière. Les réunions me manquent, pas toi?

— Si, un peu, répondit Abigail, évasive. Mais tu t'habilleras chaudement. Inutile de retomber malade.

Betty redevint silencieuse et regarda la neige tomber par la fenêtre. Abigail se replongea dans le grimoire. Elle venait de terminer l'histoire de la naissance de la magie et entrait dans un chapitre intitulé *Les créatures magiques*. Avec intérêt, elle dévora les premières pages qui parlaient de licornes, de lutins, de phénix et de dragons. Tous ces êtres possédaient une forme de magie élevée. Abigail savait pertinemment que ce n'était que des contes pour enfants mais une partie d'elle croyait à l'existence de ces créatures et rêvait de les voir un jour. Au milieu de sa lecture, elle trouva une formule permettant de faire apparaître des fées, comme Betty qui donnait naissance à des papillons. Abigail se leva et se plaça au milieu de la chambre, le livre dans la main. Sa cousine la regarda attentivement.

— *Nymphea Apparitia* ! s'exclama-t-elle.

Aussitôt, des dizaines de minuscules êtres lumineux apparurent. Les fées voltigeaient dans la chambre et leurs pépiements aigus allaient alarmer toute la maison.

— Fais-les taire ! s'exclama Betty.

— Comment ?

— Ordonne-leur ! C'est comme ça que je dirige mes papillons.

Abigail obéit. Aussitôt, les fées se regroupèrent au niveau de son visage et attendirent patiemment un autre ordre. Les deux jeunes filles les observèrent avec curiosité. Dépourvues d'ailes, les fées n'étaient pas plus grosses qu'une aiguille mais leurs traits fins leur conféraient une grande beauté. Toutes étaient identiques, vêtues d'une longue tunique beige et de pantalons de la même couleur. Leurs longs cheveux roux luisaient dans la faible lumière du soleil ; leurs yeux, vifs et noirs, leur donnaient un air intelligent et malin.

— Incroyable, murmura Abigail. Elles sont si belles.

— Oui. Il ne faudrait pas qu'elles soient plus grandes car tous les hommes de la terre deviendraient fous.

Elles pouffèrent sous les yeux introspectifs des fées.

— Je les ai juste fait venir pour voir si j'y arriverais. Comment fais-tu pour faire disparaître tes papillons ?

— Je leur dit que je n'ai pas besoin d'eux tout de suite. Tu peux le faire dans ta tête, ajouta Betty préci-

pitamment en voyant sa cousine ouvrir la bouche. Normalement, elles entendront.

Effectivement, aussitôt qu'Abigail leur dit de partir en pensée, toutes disparurent. Absorbées dans la contemplation des fées, ni l'une ni l'autre n'avait vu que Cathy était entrée dans la chambre, attirée par le bruit. Quand Abigail releva la tête, elle l'aperçut, la bouche bée et les yeux exorbités. Sursautant, Abigail lui dit :

— Oh Cathy ! Nous n'avions pas vu que tu étais là. Tu…

Mais la pauvre Cathy était déjà partie en courant. Betty haussa les épaules.

— Elle est si timorée.

— Nous avons réagi comme elle la première fois que nous avons vu Tituba jeter un sort, souviens-toi, lui répondit Abigail, inquiète.

La porte du bas claqua et la jeune fille se précipita à la fenêtre pour voir le jardin. Bousculant Betty qui protesta, elle poussa un cri.

— Cathy s'en va. Elle se dirige vers le village.

— Elle va sans doute faire quelques courses, supposa Betty.

— Il faut en parler à Tituba.

— Je croyais que tu la détestais.

— Et alors ? Il s'agit de notre sécurité à toutes les trois, non ?

Abigail sortit de la chambre et alla jusqu'à celle de Tituba. La servante était là, en train de plier du linge. Abigail s'étonnait toujours de voir Tituba persévérer à accomplir les tâches les plus simples sans recourir à la magie.

— Tituba... risqua-t-elle.

— Entrez, miss Parris. Que puis-je pour vous ?

— Eh bien, je jouais dans la chambre et j'ai utilisé un sortilège du grimoire.

Tituba retint un soupir de dédain.

— Je n'ai pas vu que Cathy était entrée et elle a tout vu. Je crois qu'elle a pris peur.

— Cela ne m'étonne pas d'elle.

— Mais Cathy est partie. Elle se rendait au village et j'ai pensé qu'il valait mieux vous prévenir.

La servante arrêta de ranger les vêtements et la regarda attentivement.

— C'est très fâcheux. Les inquisiteurs promettent nombre de récompenses à ceux qui dénoncent. Je savais que ce n'était qu'une question de jours avant que Cathy ne flanche.

— Qu'allons-nous faire ?

— Nous retournerons à la clairière ce soir et...

— Mais Betty est encore malade.

— Nous la soignerons là-bas. Miss Abigail, vous rendez-vous compte que cela signifie que les inquisi-

teurs vont venir vous chercher, nous chercher devrais-je dire, aujourd'hui ? Sans doute cette nuit puisque nous dormirons.

— Je comprends.

— Comprenez-vous aussi que vous ne reviendrez plus jamais dans cette maison ?

Abigail essuya rageusement une larme sur sa joue. À cause de sa négligence, elles perdaient un refuge.

— Allez préparer quelques affaires chaudes à apporter dans les bois. Ce sera notre demeure désormais. Et aidez votre cousine à faire de même. Je viendrai vous chercher.

La jeune fille retourna dans la chambre et commença à rassembler des habits sous l'œil interrogateur de Betty.

— Que se passe-t-il ? Tituba t'a renvoyée de la maison ? gloussa-t-elle.

— Nous partons.

— Comment ça, nous partons ? Où ça ? Et pourquoi ?

— Tituba pense que Cathy est allée alerter les inquisiteurs. Nous allons nous installer dans la forêt.

— Quoi ? Mais je suis malade et nous sommes en plein hiver. Nous allons mourir de froid dans les bois !

Abigail haussa les épaules en signe d'impuissance.

Tituba vint les chercher quelques minutes plus tard, un ridicule bonnet de laine tenant difficilement sur sa

>LES SORCIÈRES DE SALEM

tête aux cheveux crépus. Mais dès que les deux filles mirent le pied dehors, elles regrettèrent amèrement de ne pas porter de coiffe. Le vent soufflait fort et les tourbillons de neige leur glaçaient le visage. Des larmes ruisselaient déjà de leurs yeux et gelaient instantanément sur leurs joues. Leurs capes doublées battaient sur les côtés et le froid s'insinuait partout sous leurs habits. Tituba ne semblait pas ressentir la morsure glacée du vent et elle marchait d'un pas alerte vers la forêt comme si de rien n'était. Le soleil avait commencé sa longue course vers l'autre bout de la terre, et les ombres s'allongeaient sur le sol blanc. Dans quelques heures, il ferait nuit. La peur étreignit Abigail à l'idée de passer une nuit complète dans la forêt. Certes, elles s'y rendaient toutes les nuits mais y retrouvaient une vingtaine d'amis. La clairière résonnait de bruits joyeux et de vie, et lorsque tout le monde était fatigué, chacun rentrait chez soi. Or, ce soir, elles seraient seules dans les profondeurs des bois, cernées uniquement par les arbres, l'obscurité et le silence.

Patton se frottait les mains. Cette jeune gourde qui avait fait irruption dans son bureau quelques instants plus tôt venait de lui servir sur un plateau d'argent le prétexte dont il avait besoin pour s'occuper des filles Parris. Souvent, Patton s'étonnait de la haine féroce qu'il portait à ces deux jeunes filles. Mais bien vite, il se raisonnait en se disant que tout était leur faute.

Il avait reçu hier une missive de Craig Dorson, de Boston, lui donnant le champ libre. Et aujourd'hui, il pouvait agir. Patton avait à peine écouté les propos abracadabrants de la jeune servante qui parlait de fées

et de lumière, à moins que ce ne soit d'insectes volants. Il n'avait pas détourné les yeux du visage apeuré de Cathy mais son esprit était parti loin. Enfin, vengeance serait faite. Le village avait été mis à feu et à sang à cause de ces deux gamines, elles allaient payer. Il crut entendre dans les paroles décousues de Cathy un troisième nom qu'il ne connaissait pas, mais il le rangea au fond de ses pensées. Battant des mains, il coupa court au discours de la jeune fille.

— Merci beaucoup, miss. Je vous suis très reconnaissant. N'ayez crainte, tout sera réglé ce soir ! Vous pouvez rentrer chez vous. Faites comme si de rien n'était, nous viendrons cette nuit. Je vous serais gré de laisser la porte ouverte pour que les filles ne soient pas réveillées par les bruits.

— Et qu'allez-vous faire de la Barbadienne ?

— Oui, oui, répondit Patton, évasif, nous nous en occuperons aussi.

— Elle est dangereuse et…

— Ne vous inquiétez pas, trancha Patton.

Et il fit signe à un de ses hommes qui empoigna Cathy et la fit sortir.

— Et ma récompense ? demanda celle-ci.

Patton se retourna vers elle. Il n'avait plus rien de l'homme chaleureux et compréhensif.

— Elle arrivera, susurra-t-il.

Effrayée par ce changement, Cathy sortit précipitamment et trébucha sur la première marche. L'homme

161

qui l'avait accompagnée dehors éclata d'un rire peu charitable. Elle le regarda froidement et s'éloigna dignement.

Dans la clairière, Betty et Abigail furent surprises de voir que nombre de leurs comparses étaient déjà là, discutant tranquillement autour d'un feu ou engageant d'anodins duels. Ezra fit aussi son apparition à peine quelques minutes après leur arrivée. Il ne leur dit pas un mot et un bref hochement de tête à leur endroit fut le seul signe montrant qu'il les avait vues. Après cette course dans la neige froide et humide, Abigail et Betty se réfugièrent près du feu et se pelotonnèrent l'une contre l'autre.

— Que faites-vous là aussi tôt, mes enfants ? leur demanda Ann Dolliver. On ne vous attendait pas avant cette nuit !

— Notre femme de chambre est allée nous dénoncer aux inquisiteurs, d'après Tituba, répondit Betty. Alors nous voilà sans toit au-dessus de notre tête, condamnées à vivre dans le froid et les bois, comme de vulgaires animaux.

— Allons, allons, tempéra Ann. Je ne doute pas que Tituba fera tout ce qu'elle peut pour que vous soyez confortablement installées ici.

— Ça n'a pas l'air de vous contrarier !

— Non, car voyez-vous, mes enfants, il ne reste que peu de temps avant que nous soyons toutes obligées de faire comme vous. Le rapt de huit de nos amies en est la preuve. Patton ne s'arrêtera pas là.

Betty continua à grommeler et ne fit pas attention à Abigail qui s'écartait des autres et se mettait à couvert. Là, elle s'envola et, silencieusement, elle s'enfonça entre les arbres. Du coin de l'œil, pendant que Betty et Ann parlaient, elle avait vu Ezra repartir. Ces derniers temps, il était de plus en plus taciturne et Tituba leur avait dit qu'il recherchait plus souvent la solitude. Abigail ne cherchait pas à lui parler, il reviendrait vers elles lorsqu'il s'en sentirait capable. Elle attendrait le temps qu'il faudrait. Mais d'ici là, elle n'avait pu s'empêcher de savoir ce qu'il allait faire. Ezra marchait tranquillement, slalomant entre les troncs. Il s'arrêta brusquement et déterra de sous la neige un grand rocher plat sur lequel il s'installa, croisant les jambes. Le jeune homme ferma les yeux et Abigail faillit tomber de son perchoir lorsqu'elle vit un cheval translucide arriver au grand galop, aussi silencieux que la brise. Ezra sourit.

— Bonjour, Ulsam.

Le destrier, pensa Abigail, semblait lui répondre. À l'entente de son nom, il avait noblement abaissé son encolure jusqu'au niveau de la tête d'Ezra.

— Je me sens si seul, Ulsam. Et si vieux, déjà. Je les vois toutes, heureuses de se retrouver, riant, jouant. Et je suis incapable de me mêler à elles. C'est comme si j'étais en avance sur elles de plusieurs décennies. Comme si je savais tellement de choses que cela me séparait de toutes les sorcières.

L'étalon s'approcha et resta immobile face à Ezra. Celui-ci le regardait, concentré. En un instant, Abigail comprit. Il lui parlait. Ulsam était en train de répondre à Ezra. Impressionnée, elle continua à les observer.

— Non, elle, c'est différent. Tu as raison. Mais je ne sais plus sur quel pied danser. Grâce à elle, j'ai cette vie-là... Ou est-ce à cause d'elle...? De grandes choses ? continua Ezra après qu'Ulsam lui eut parlé. Je ne sais pas de quoi tu parles. Je me sens parfaitement inutile, pour l'instant.

Abigail était tellement concentrée qu'elle crut entendre, comme une voix lointaine, quelqu'un dire : «Le temps viendra.» Sans doute abusée par ce qu'avait dit Ezra, elle n'y prêta pas attention. Celui-ci se leva au bout de quelques instants, et le fier coursier repartit d'où il était venu. La jeune fille manqua de tomber de sa branche lorsque la monture tourna la tête vers elle et la fixa de ses yeux vides. Elle rentra vite à la clairière où elle retrouva Betty se disputant avec Tituba.

— Je suis sûre qu'ils ne viendront pas ! protestait la jeune fille.

— Allez le vérifier par vous-même, miss Parris, et cessez de m'embêter avec vos questions. Faites en sorte de ne pas vous faire voir, car des mirages de vous-même déambulent en ce moment même dans la maison. Et je ne viendrai pas vous chercher en prison. Bon débarras !

Vexée, Betty se dirigea droit vers Abigail et lui dit :

— Elle a raison. On y va. Je nous rends invisibles et nous allons voir à la maison.

Abigail n'eut pas le temps de répondre. Betty la traînait déjà à sa suite.

La nuit était profonde. Patton et huit de ses hommes marchaient dans la neige, pestant contre les flocons glacés qui glissaient dans leur cou. Le manoir se dessinait au fond, masqué de temps en temps par des volutes de neige. Son imposante et sombre stature était effrayante dans cette nuit sans étoiles et les inquisiteurs se sentaient moins en verve que lorsqu'ils avaient quitté le village. Ils serraient compulsivement dans leurs mains les soufflets qui rendraient les sorcières inoffensives. Arrivés sur le perron, l'un d'eux éternua bruyamment. Patton lui mit une claque qui fit presque autant de bruit. Cathy les attendait. Elle les fit entrer et leur indiqua le chemin. Silencieusement, tels des loups, les neuf hommes montèrent dans les étages et disparurent dans le noir. Angoissée, Cathy attendait, les mains tordues. Patton fit signe à ses hommes de faire attention au plancher qui craquait sûrement. Il poussa doucement la première porte à sa gauche et entra, suivi de tous. La vue d'un seul lit dans la pièce lui fit immédiatement comprendre qu'il leur fallait se séparer. Il envoya cinq de ses hommes dans la chambre attenante et, sur la pointe des pieds, s'approcha du grand lit duquel sortait une tête sombre, profondément enfoncée dans les draps. Un sourire cruel étira ses lèvres. Les quatre hommes se mirent autour du lit, nouèrent un foulard couvrant leur bouche et leur nez et levèrent leurs soufflets. Tous ensemble, ils appuyèrent, libérant des nuages d'opium. Ils attendirent que la fumée s'évapore et Patton tendit les mains, prêt à attraper la gamine si elle se débattait. Au lieu de ça, il découvrit qu'elle n'avait pas bougé d'un pouce. Il voulut l'attraper mais hurla de terreur lorsque sa main traversa la tête. Quand Patton arracha les draps, le mirage se dissipa

aussitôt. De l'autre côté de la chambre, il entendit les mêmes cris. Furieux, il redescendit quatre à quatre l'escalier et donna un violent coup à Cathy qui attendait en bas. Il sortit sans voir Betty et Abigail qui se tenaient derrière le portail, observant les événements. La fureur de Patton était bien visible, même dans ce noir d'encre, et elles reculèrent pour être à l'abri. Tonitruant, l'inquisiteur retourna au village. Les filles restèrent immobiles le temps que tous aient quitté les lieux, de peur que leurs traces de pas dans la neige fraîche ne trahissent leur présence.

De retour à la clairière, elles ne dirent pas un mot à Tituba qui s'affairait à rendre les lieux plus accueillants.

12

De nombreuses sorcières avaient renoncé à retourner au village. Elles avaient, la nuit dernière, fait un ultime aller et retour pour rapporter des affaires et quelques vivres. Mais la majorité de la Confrérie refusait encore de se terrer dans les bois. La plupart avaient une famille, des enfants dont elles devaient s'occuper. Tituba les enjoignait de venir se réfugier dans la clairière, et d'y emmener par la même occasion tous leurs proches. Mais elles n'étaient pas encore prêtes à abandonner leur demeure, leur quotidien. Plus les jours passaient, plus la Barbadienne craignait que leur cache soit découverte à cause de toutes ces femmes qui disparaissaient du village la nuit pour n'y revenir qu'à l'aube. Pourtant, rien ne vint troubler leur quiétude en ces lieux. La bulle de protection de Tituba, outre le fait qu'elle rendait invisible, chauffait l'atmosphère glaciale de cet hiver de neige. Elle avait mis Abigail et Betty dans le creux d'un arbre tricentenaire. Après s'être assurées qu'aucune bête ne s'y terrait, les deux jeunes filles s'y installèrent confortablement. Chaque nuit, les femmes revenaient du village avec des nouvelles. Patton n'avait pas encore tué toutes les sorcières emprisonnées mais ça ne tarderait pas. Sa colère grandissait chaque jour et il devenait de plus en plus difficile de passer entre les griffes des inquisiteurs.

— Abigail! tonna Tituba. Où sont vos fées? Je croyais vous avoir dit que je les voulais sans arrêt aux alentours de la clairière!

— Ce grimoire vous arrange bien, lorsque vous le voulez, marmonna la jeune fille entre ses dents.

Tituba lui lança un regard haineux qu'Abigail essaya tant bien que mal de soutenir. Puis haussant les épaules, l'imposante servante s'éloigna. D'un geste terriblement enfantin, Abigail lui tira la langue, puis rougit immédiatement, surprise par sa cousine. Elle s'empressa d'invoquer ses fées gardiennes et les fit se disposer à quelques pieds de la clairière, sous le couvert des arbres. Les fées voletaient dans tous les sens et, dans l'obscurité de la forêt, on apercevait des éclairs de lumière argentée. Abigail espéra que personne ne les remarquerait. Puis elle retourna près de Betty. Là-bas, elle avait une vue imprenable sur Ezra et observait à la dérobée ses moindres faits et gestes sans que le jeune homme s'en doute. Elle repensait à sa rencontre dans la forêt avec ce superbe destrier fantôme. Ezra était puissant, mieux valait l'avoir dans son camp. Il avait changé, remarqua-t-elle. Plus grand, plus ténébreux aussi, il faisait plus homme et elle ne l'en aimait que plus encore.

— Allons, la secoua Betty. Arrête de le regarder comme ça, tu vas l'user!

Abigail pouffa de rire et se tourna vers Betty qui, assise sur le sol sec, en tailleur, feuilletait l'épais grimoire. Les cheveux en bataille d'avoir dormi dans des feuilles, les traits de Betty s'étaient encore affinés. Qu'elle est belle! pensa Abigail.

— Dis-moi, Abi, penses-tu que ma mère était une sorcière ?

— Peut-être. Mais nous ne le saurons sans doute jamais.

— Je me dis que si elle avait vraiment été une sorcière, elle n'aurait pas pu mourir à ma naissance.

Abigail posa une main réconfortante sur le bras de sa cousine. Pour elle aussi, le deuil de sa famille était lourd à porter et la mort encore récente du révérend les emplissait l'une et l'autre de crainte et de tristesse. Abigail savait qu'elle ne pourrait plus se laisser éduquer par Tituba, celle-ci étant trop ombrageuse pour être digne de confiance. Mais Betty ne partageait pas encore son point de vue. Et Abigail n'avait pas le cœur de lui faire perdre une fois de plus quelqu'un à qui elle tenait. De toute façon, elles vivaient désormais dans la forêt, et Tituba ne les quittait pas. L'heure viendrait où elle lui en parlerait.

— Regarde, Abi !

La voix excitée de Betty la sortit de ses pensées.

— Regarde ce sort ! Là ! ajouta-t-elle en pointant son index sur la page.

— Enlève ta main ! Je ne vois rien !

Betty obtempéra et Abigail put lire : *De ce sort complexe ne sort jamais rien de bon. Seuls les avertis doivent s'en servir et jamais pour leur propre compte. Prenez garde à ces bâtons car le maniement n'en est pas aisé et le novice aura vite fait de se trancher un pied.*

169

— Je ne vois pas en quoi se trancher un pied est une bonne chose, lui dit Abigail.

— Mais non ! Regarde ça ! Cela peut nous procurer ce que nous n'avons pas. Des armes !

— Pourquoi aurions-nous besoin d'armes ?

— Pour nous battre, voyons ! Notre retraite ne sera pas indéfiniment sûre. Le temps est compté avant que les inquisiteurs nous trouvent. Et alors que ferons-nous ? Nous devrons résister et nous battre. Cette formule tombe à pic ! Je vais l'essayer.

— Le livre dit que c'est un sort réservé à ceux qui ont de l'expérience. Or, nous…

— Nous en avons bien assez, coupa Betty.

Elle courut hors de la bulle de protection avant que sa cousine n'ait pu faire un geste et s'enfonça sous les arbres. Se mordant les lèvres d'appréhension, comme chaque fois que quelqu'un ne se trouvait pas dans la clairière, Abigail attendit que Betty revienne. Celle-ci ne tarda pas, réapparaissant les bras chargés de longues branches droites qu'elle déposa aux pieds d'Abigail. Tituba les observait du coin de l'œil, prête à intervenir si l'une des deux faisait encore quelque chose d'irresponsable.

— Tiens-moi le livre, Abigail, que je puisse voir quelle est la formule !

Abigail ramassa le grimoire et retrouva la page voulue. Betty se pencha, l'air concentré, sa petite langue pointue sortant de ses lèvres roses et fines. Les pommettes rougies par le froid et l'excitation, Betty

ramassa une branche et la tint à bout de bras. Elle plaça son autre main sur le bois et prononça la formule *Gentlam Statuo*. Rien ne se passa. De dépit, Betty jeta le rameau par terre. Abigail la regarda, ébahie.

— Et c'est tout ?

— Tu vois bien que ça ne marche pas !

— Tu n'as essayé qu'une fois ! protesta sa cousine. Tu abandonnes déjà ?

Betty grommela quelques imprécations à l'endroit d'Abigail et reprit sa branche. Elle la tint fermement et répéta la formule. Quelque chose changea. La branche devint d'une droiture impeccable, au polissage parfait et d'une couleur argentée luminescente. Abigail s'exclama de surprise devant ce prodige. Plus aucune imperfection du bois n'était apparente. Le bâton était désormais lisse et ses bouts, arrondis. Betty regardait son œuvre en se demandant si ce n'était que cela.

— Comment un bâton aussi lisse et aussi rond peut-il trancher quoi que ce soit ?

Elle envoya la perche au loin qui alla frapper une haute et épaisse branche. Betty et Abigail s'attendaient à la voir se casser sous le choc. Elles hurlèrent de stupeur lorsque l'arbre se trouva soudain départi de son plus gros rameau qui s'effondra dans la neige, envoyant des volutes de flocons, et faisant trembler la terre. Remise de sa surprise, Betty se précipita à l'endroit où elle avait jeté le bâton et le rapporta en le regardant avec déférence. Tituba s'était approchée d'elle et considérait l'arme que Betty tenait dans ses mains avec froideur.

— Qu'est-ce que cette nouvelle lubie, miss Parris ? demanda-t-elle, glaciale.

— La solution à tous nos problèmes, Tituba. Regardez !

Elle s'empara de toutes les branches qui attendaient à ses pieds, vulgaires bouts de bois, et les transforma. Intéressées, nombre de sorcières se penchèrent pour en attraper une. Abigail leur murmurait du bout des lèvres de faire attention.

— En quoi cela peut-il nous servir ? continua Tituba.

— Je vais vous montrer ! Mary ! cria-t-elle. Venez ! Vous vous régénérez, n'est-ce pas ?

— Oui, mais... commença l'intéressée, sceptique.

— Cela vous fait-il mal ?

— Non, c'est à peine plus désagréable qu'une piqûre.

Satisfaite, Betty se tourna vers Tituba comme si leur bref échange allait changer leurs vies à toutes.

— Tendez le bras ! ordonna Betty à Mary.

Celle-ci, visiblement peu encline à obéir, jeta un regard interrogateur à Tituba qui haussa les épaules. Mary offrit donc sa main à Betty qui leva le bâton argenté au-dessus de sa tête et l'abattit avec force sur le bras de Mary. Au début, toutes crurent qu'il ne s'était rien passé mais lorsque la main sectionnée de la pauvre femme tomba à ses pieds, plusieurs se mirent à hurler. Mary regardait le moignon de son bras avec intérêt. Betty faisait preuve d'une satisfaction que personne ne partageait. Tituba calma tout le monde dès que la main de Mary eut repoussé.

— Alors? s'exclama Betty, avide. Qu'en pensez-vous? Je n'ai jamais vu quelque chose d'aussi incroyable! Grâce à ces bâtons d'argent, nous serons victorieuses!

— Il est hors de question que nous nous servions de ces armes, miss Parris.

— Quoi? s'étrangla Betty. Mais pourquoi?

— Nous ne sommes pas des tueuses, gronda Tituba.

Abigail ne ressentit pas la sincérité de Tituba.

— Mais les inquisiteurs nous déciment! Nous sommes moins que des bêtes à leurs yeux! Ils nous détruiront toutes si nous ne faisons rien! Tôt ou tard.

— Eh bien, ce sera tard, beaucoup plus tard. Le temps n'est pas à la vengeance, ma fille. Ne soyons pas aussi sottes qu'eux. Prouvons-leur que nous valons plus que ce qu'ils croient.

— Ces bâtons magiques sont notre gage de victoire. Finissons-en avec l'oppression. Et retournons toutes vivre chez nous!

— Non! tempêta Tituba. Il ne sortira rien de bon de ces armes. Rangez-les, cachez-les, détruisez-les. Faites ce que bon vous semble avec, mais je vous interdis de les utiliser.

— Pourquoi vous obéirais-je? gronda Betty, méconnaissable.

Tituba s'avança vers elle, menaçante. Elle dominait la jeune fille d'à peine une tête mais une grande

puissance émanait de la servante. Betty soutint son regard, les lèvres pincées de colère pour ne pas rugir.

— Si vous êtes contre moi, miss Parris, vous êtes contre nous toutes, dit-elle en accompagnant ses paroles d'un large geste du bras qui engloba toutes les sorcières regardant l'affrontement.

— Pourquoi ne serait-ce pas l'inverse, Tituba ? lui répondit Betty d'une voix forte et claire.

Abigail aperçut les poings de sa cousine si serrés que ses jointures avaient considérablement blanchi. Avec stupeur, elle se rendit compte que des gouttes de sang perlaient entre ses doigts. Betty s'enfonçait les ongles dans la peau.

— Demandons donc l'avis des concernées ! Qui veut garder ces armes ?

Tituba promena un regard si froid et si sombre sur chacune des sorcières que toutes baissèrent la tête sans rien dire.

— Nous avons donc notre réponse. Jetez-moi ça ! lança la Barbadienne.

Et elle s'éloigna sans rien ajouter. Betty fulminait et tremblait de rage et d'impuissance. Abigail se jeta sur elle et lui ouvrit les mains. Ses paumes étaient rouges et le sang avait coulé dans les sillons tendres de sa peau. Sur chaque main se trouvaient cinq entailles. Elle soigna rapidement sa cousine et voulut l'entraîner à sa suite. Mais Betty se raidit et ouvrit la bouche.

— Vous êtes… mauvaise ! hurla-t-elle à Tituba.

— Vraiment ? répondit celle-ci, l'air ironique. Le suis-je plus que Patton et vous-même, prêts l'un et l'autre à tuer sans concession ?

Betty s'affaissa soudainement et Abigail la soutint, aidée d'Ezra qui venait d'apparaître à leurs côtés. Abigail lui lança un regard de remerciement, mais le jeune homme ne tourna même pas la tête vers elle. Betty marmonnait et se laissa transporter vers le creux de l'arbre. Ezra s'éloigna avant de se retrouver en tête-à-tête avec Abigail. Il ressassait dans sa tête l'échange entre Betty et Tituba. Il n'arrivait pas à comprendre ce qui s'était passé. Tituba semait le doute dans leur esprit mais elle n'était pas une mauvaise personne. Elle ne souhaitait simplement pas qu'ils deviennent des tueurs. Il chassa la Barbadienne de ses pensées sans prêter attention à l'amertume qu'il avait ressentie quelques instants plus tôt. L'heure était venue de retourner dans son abri. Décidément, soupira-t-il, les femmes sont bien compliquées.

— Nous organiserons des battues jusqu'à ce que nous les trouvions ! hurla Patton, fou de rage. Elles ne peuvent pas disparaître ! Elles sont là, quelque part !

— Mais, sir Patton, osa intervenir un jeune inquisiteur, et si elles étaient invisibles ? Ce sont des sorcières après tout et…

Il se tut devant le regard glacial de Patton. Celui-ci s'approcha de lui.

— Te voilà bien renseigné ! murmura-t-il, menaçant. Saurais-tu quelque chose que nous ignorons ?

— Je... non... balbutia le malheureux.

— Alors, cesse de dire des âneries pareilles ! Nous avons autre chose à faire qu'écouter tes élucubrations !

Le jeune inquisiteur hocha frénétiquement la tête, tremblant, et ne dit plus un mot.

— Anton, susurra Patton, doucereux. Nous allons dans la forêt parce que tu penses qu'elles sont là-bas. Tu n'ignores pas ce que je te ferai subir si cela s'avère faux... Bien sûr, je te rassure, tu auras quelques jours de délai avant que je ne te punisse. La persévérance, mon ami ! Je ne suis pas homme à abandonner dès le premier jour !

Anton trembla involontairement, réveillant la douleur dans ses côtes. Le visage bouffi, le contour des yeux violacés et le nez se parant d'un éventail de couleurs moribondes, Anton n'osa rien dire de peur de déchaîner une nouvelle fois la colère de l'inquisiteur en chef. Il se souvint de sa séance de matraquage. Le plus humiliant avait été de remercier Patton, à la fin, de lui avoir laissé l'usage de ses jambes. Son visage et son torse n'étaient plus que douleur et la vengeance faisait palpiter ses veines. Il n'aurait su dire s'il en voulait plus à Abigail Parris ou à Patton. Mais le jeune inquisiteur avait raison. Elles étaient sans doute invisibles. Cela n'allait pas leur faciliter la tâche.

Patton les répartit en groupes de cinq, ce qu'Anton trouva bien inutile puisqu'ils avancèrent tous côte à côte dès qu'ils pénétrèrent dans la forêt de Belwack. Il se garda bien de le dire. Le froid le transperçait de toute part mais calmait aussi la lancinante douleur qui parcourait son corps. Anton n'avait pas le souvenir

d'avoir déjà été aussi battu. Sa famille avait été aimante à son égard. Quand il s'était enfui à dix-sept ans, épris de liberté, il avait reçu quelques corrections dans son apprentissage de la rue, mais rien n'égalait la fureur avec laquelle Patton et son homme de main l'avaient frappé. Il en frissonna encore, songeant à ce que ce dernier ferait aux femmes qui tomberaient sous sa main. Anton se redressa, décidé à remonter dans l'estime de son maître. Coûte que coûte, il retrouverait ces sorcières.

Ils étaient entrés dans la forêt par le côté ouest et ratissaient une large bande sur toute la largeur des bois. Les hommes pestaient contre la neige qui tombait des branches et s'insinuaient dans leur cou en coulées glaciales. Tous étaient peu vêtus. Leurs capes n'offraient aucun obstacle au vent furieux qui sinuait entre les arbres pour se perdre en sifflant dans les profondeurs du bois. Et la neige dans laquelle ils s'enfonçaient était si profonde qu'ils eurent tôt fait d'avoir les pieds glacés et trempés. Patton ne semblait pas se plaindre des conditions ; aussi, aucun de ses hommes n'eut le courage de lui demander de rebrousser chemin pour mieux se vêtir. Quand l'un d'eux trébucha et tomba tête la première dans une congère, ses compagnons étouffèrent des rires vite réprimés par le regard méprisant de Patton. Pendant des heures, ils déambulèrent dans les bois, ombres nocturnes et vengeresses. Anton se prenait pour un chasseur et, bien qu'il ne connût rien au langage de la nature, il ne pouvait s'empêcher de voir dans chaque trace au sol un indice de leur bon cheminement. Quand Patton s'arrêta, Anton crut qu'il avait perdu patience. Il se recroquevilla et se cacha derrière les autres inquisiteurs.

— Vous cacheriez-vous en plein bois si vous étiez elles ? demanda soudainement Patton.

Personne n'osa répondre. Patton se tourna vers eux.

— Eh bien ! tonna-t-il. À leur place, useriez-vous de la protection des arbres pour dissimuler vos réunions secrètes ?

— Oui, sir Patton, répondit l'un des hommes.

— Elles sont sans doute plus de dix mais moins de trente, réfléchit tout haut Patton. Trouvez-vous que la pleine forêt soit très pratique lorsque vous êtes nombreux ? Regardez-nous, enfoncés dans la neige jusqu'aux genoux, obligés de contourner chaque arbre, trébuchant sur chaque racine !

N'obtenant aucune réponse, Patton hurla.

— Mais réfléchissez, bougres d'imbéciles ! Quel endroit serait plus approprié pour un rassemblement ?

— Un pré ? proposa quelqu'un.

— Un champ ?

— Abrutis ! Idiots ! Comment ai-je pu vous prendre avec moi si vous n'êtes même pas capables de faire marcher vos minuscules cervelles ! vociféra Patton, hors de lui.

Il gesticulait dans tous les sens, envoyait des claques aux têtes les plus proches de lui, donnait des coups de pied dans la neige qui allait s'écraser contre les inquisiteurs qui n'osaient bouger.

— La clairière, sir Patton, osa dire Anton.

— Évidemment, répliqua l'inquisiteur, froidement, sans accorder un regard au jeune homme.

Ils se dirigèrent donc tous vers la grande clairière de la forêt. Aucun d'eux n'aperçut les petites fées qui s'empressèrent de disparaître pour aller prévenir leur maîtresse. Ils déboulèrent, hagards et sûrs de leur coup, dans la clairière… déserte. Patton devint rouge et fit le tour de la trouée à grands pas, pestant et fulminant, agitant les bras devant lui comme pour saisir une menace invisible. Il tourna et tourna, sous le regard effaré de ses hommes. De long en large, le nez à hauteur de ses bottes, Patton reniflait comme un chien de chasse. Il sentit monter en lui sa coutumière violence lorsqu'il était désappointé. Sortant un couteau de sa cape, il sectionna la gorge d'un de ses hommes sans même prendre la peine de le regarder. Le malheureux tomba à genoux, des flots bouillonnants sortant de son cou ouvert. Ses compagnons le regardaient, figés et incrédules. Le pauvre homme tomba la tête la première dans la neige immaculée et, dans un dernier soubresaut, rendit l'âme. Patton n'entendit pas les sanglots qui retentirent dans l'air froid et obscur. Mais derrière la bulle de protection, toutes les sorcières se serraient les unes contre les autres, témoins de la cruauté de Patton. Abigail regardait la neige autour du sacrifié s'imbiber d'un rouge vermeil si brillant dans cette nuit sans lune. Betty serrait ses mâchoires à se rompre, immobile et souveraine dans le temps figé. Les petites fées elles-mêmes avaient cessé de gigoter et respectaient un calme empreint de tristesse. Tituba ne semblait pas ressentir autre chose qu'une terrible indifférence. Lorsqu'Abigail tourna la tête vers elle, elle aurait juré l'avoir vu sourire.

— Pourquoi ne nous voient-il pas? demanda l'une des femmes.

— Nous sommes entourées de sorts complexes de protection qu'Ezra et moi avons jetés. Ils ne peuvent ni nous voir, ni nous sentir, ni nous entendre.

— Mais nous prenons toute la clairière, Tituba! s'exclama Betty. Ils doivent bien se rendre compte que quelque chose ne va pas. Il y a un grand cercle miraculeusement dépourvu de neige.

— Lorsqu'ils pénètrent dans la clairière, ils la voient telle qu'elle est normalement. Ils ont l'impression de la parcourir en long et en large mais ce n'est qu'une vision, un mirage.

Abigail se rendit soudain compte que toutes ignoraient l'étendue des pouvoirs de Tituba. Rien ne semblait l'arrêter. La jeune fille frissonna à nouveau et tourna la tête vers l'homme que ses compagnons avaient laissé dans la neige sur l'ordre de Patton. «Qu'il pourrisse ici!» avait hurlé l'inquisiteur.

— Donnons-lui une sépulture! s'exclama Abigail.

— À notre pire ennemi? s'étonna Tituba.

— Ce n'est plus qu'un homme mort maintenant.

— Réfléchissez, miss Parris. Qu'adviendra-t-il si les hommes de Patton reviennent et qu'ils ne trouvent plus le cadavre de cet inquisiteur? Nous leur donnerons alors la preuve que nous sommes là! Laissons le corps aux bêtes de la forêt. Ils s'en repaîtront sur place et laisseront ainsi des traces.

— Mais…

— Nous sommes toujours en guerre, miss Parris, aboya Tituba. Une guerre où nous ne nous battons pas mais une guerre où nous devons jouer de prudence! Cet homme restera là.

Abigail reconnut finalement que Tituba n'avait pas tort et, à peine quelques instants plus tard, un ours sortit du couvert des arbres et se mit à dévorer avec application l'homme à terre. Betty et Abigail se bouchèrent les oreilles de leurs mains plaquées pour ne pas entendre les atroces bruits de la chair déchirée. Elles tournèrent le dos au triste spectacle tandis que toutes reprenaient leurs activités, le cœur lourd, la peur au ventre.

13

Aussitôt qu'il fut de retour au village, Patton lança des ordres à tous ses hommes qui se dispersèrent dans les rues sombres. Levant la tête vers le ciel, il chercha en vain la lune, mais la profonde obscurité qui baignait les lieux ne laissait aucun doute quant à son absence. Apaisé par ce qu'il venait de mettre en branle et oublieux de sa cuisante défaite, Patton se rendit d'un pas léger vers ses quartiers pour attendre ses hommes et leur butin. Un sourire sans joie étirait ses lèvres minces et jaunies, et c'est en sifflotant qu'il poussa la porte de son bureau. Il allait les pousser à commettre des erreurs. Ainsi, il leur tomberait dessus. Tirant sa chaise, il s'affaissa dessus et se balança pour poser ses bottes mouillées sur le bureau. Les mains croisées derrière la tête, il se perdit dans la contemplation du plafond. Il étouffa un bâillement et regarda par la fenêtre la neige qui s'était remise à tomber à gros flocons. L'air dégoûté, il plissa ses petits yeux sournois et cracha à terre. «Maudite neige! proféra-t-il. On a bien assez de problèmes sans elle!» Un bruit de pas étouffé le fit se redresser. Il attendit le cœur battant que la porte s'ouvre, se pourléchant les lèvres comme quelqu'un devant un repas particulièrement succulent. Cinq de ses hommes firent leur apparition, couverts de neige, les

cheveux hirsutes et gelés, traînant derrière eux huit enfants blêmes aux traits encore endormis. Quatre inquisiteurs suivirent, tenant cinq enfants qu'ils avaient attachés ensemble.

— Bien, bien, bien! s'exclama Patton, se frottant les mains. Quelle bonne fortune, mes amis!

Les enfants, terrifiés, se taisaient. L'un d'entre eux, plus grand que les autres, leva la tête et regarda Patton droit dans les yeux.

— Qu'est-ce que vous voulez? demanda-t-il en essayant de maîtriser sa voix qui tremblait.

Patton le jaugea, ses yeux dardant sur lui une cruauté qui fit frissonner le garçon. Un bref signe de tête à l'homme qui tenait l'enfant et celui-ci reçut un coup de pied à l'intérieur des genoux. Le garçon tomba à terre en rugissant et, aussitôt, une avalanche de coups lui grêla dessus. Horrifiés, certains enfants se précipitèrent à son secours, mais les inquisiteurs les attrapèrent vigoureusement par les cheveux pour les maintenir à distance. D'un autre signe de tête, Patton ordonna à ses hommes d'arrêter. Le pauvre garçon était en boule à terre, du sang maculant son visage et le bras tordu en un angle étrange.

— Relève-toi, mon garçon, ou ce que tu viens de prendre ne sera rien en comparaison de ce que je te réserve.

L'enfant se redressa tant bien que mal, une lueur farouche transparaissant entre ses larmes de douleur.

— Vous êtes ici car vos mères, tantes, sœurs ou amies ont fait de très grosses bêtises, commença

Patton, onctueux. Et comme je n'arrive pas à les trouver, vous paierez pour elles jusqu'à ce qu'elles se décident à se rendre.

— Elles ne le feront jamais! s'exclama le garçon, crachant du sang.

— Tais-toi, jeune sot! Elles le feront car sinon vous mourrez tous. Que ne ferait une mère pour sa progéniture? demanda-t-il en ricanant. Je ferai une annonce demain matin. En attendant, vous croupirez en prison, tous. Les nourrissons aussi. Ceux dont la mère se rendra seront libérés, mais je ne garantis pas qu'ils la reverront! ajouta-t-il. Emmenez-les!

Ses hommes obéirent et traînèrent tant bien que mal tous les enfants qui se serraient les uns contre les autres. Le nombre de cellules n'étant pas suffisant, ils les entassèrent à plusieurs dans les trous infâmes souillés d'eau croupie et de déjections.

Le lendemain matin, Patton fit son annonce sur la place du village. Les pères des enfants enlevés avaient le visage tuméfié pour les plus chanceux, certains ne s'étaient pas relevés. Mais à la Confrérie de la Clairière, toutes les sorcières étaient déjà au courant. Candy était retournée dans la maison de sa maîtresse, Sarah Bishop, et elle y était arrivée en même temps que des inquisiteurs furieux qui emmenaient avec eux une horde de gamins terrorisés. Elle était passée à travers plusieurs murs pour rester invisible et dès que le danger avait été écarté elle s'était précipitée à la clairière pour annoncer à tout le monde ce qui se passait au village. La folie et la peur s'étaient emparées des femmes et certaines avaient voulu partir de ce pas au village pour libérer leurs enfants.

Tituba les avait calmées en tonitruant dans le silence nocturne des bois. Toutes s'étaient figées.

— C'est exactement ce qu'il cherche ! s'exclama-t-elle.

— Nous n'allons pas laisser nos fils et nos filles entre ses mains. Dieu sait ce qu'il leur fera !

— Nous trouverons une solution. En attendant, tout le monde reste ici.

Et elle avait rendu la bulle de protection impossible à traverser. Certaines femmes s'étaient dressées contre elle, mais Tituba ne s'en était pas occupée. Tant qu'elle veillerait, aucune ne sortirait de la clairière. Seule Mary Black comprit cela. Elle pouvait désormais se transformer en ce qu'elle voulait, que ce soit animal ou végétal. Usant de messes basses avec ses amies pour les avertir de ce qu'elle allait faire, toutes se regroupèrent et s'allongèrent sur les nattes installées à même le sol en tant que couchettes. Tituba les vit se calmer et ne se douta pas de ce qu'elles tramaient. Abigail et Betty, qui avaient rejoint le creux de leur arbre, ne virent rien non plus. Mary se fit cacher par d'autres femmes et se métamorphosa doucement en fleurs de Baïan, une plante courante dans les environs par ces temps froids.

— Comment vas-tu faire pour te rapprocher d'elle sans qu'elle te voie ? chuchota Ann Dolliver.

— Elle ne remarquera pas une plante. Et les fleurs de Baïan sont aussi bien connues pour leur puissant somnifère que pour leur don de caméléon. Elle ne verra rien.

Les sorcières n'arrivaient toujours pas à s'accoutumer aux métamorphoses de Mary. Voir un animal ou une plante leur parler les effrayait encore.

— Maintenant, couchez-vous. Faites comme si vous capituliez !

Elles obéirent et s'allongèrent sagement sur leurs nattes, frémissantes d'excitation et de colère. À cette heure-là, on s'en prenait sans doute à leurs enfants. L'aube pointait au loin, le soleil se lèverait bientôt. Mary, transformée en une longue tige verte aux belles corolles blanches, avançait doucement en direction de Tituba. Du point de vue de la plante, la distance était longue et ses maigres racines ne lui permettaient pas de parcourir de grandes distances. Elle ondulait dans la légère brise et souvent un coup de vent plus fort que les autres la faisait se courber, ses fleurs caressant le sol. Une heure s'était écoulée et Mary s'épuisait. Elle n'avait pas pensé que ce serait si dur, mais les fleurs de Baïan, dépourvues d'eau et de terre, perdaient leur énergie progressivement et la traversée de la clairière était de plus en plus ardue. Elle sentait la tension sourde de ses amies qui s'impatientaient.

Enfin, elle atteignit Tituba. Elle voyait son large dos droit, ses épaules raides. Assise sur un large rocher plat, Tituba n'avait pas bougé d'un sourcil depuis qu'elle avait annoncé que personne ne partirait. Mary se demanda d'ailleurs si la Barbadienne ne dormait pas les yeux ouverts. Tituba se retourna brusquement au bruissement que la plante fit en s'enfonçant dans un tas de feuilles mortes. La servante ne vit rien d'autre qu'une souple tige aux fleurs blanches. Mary en profita pour libérer de ses étamines son puissant

sédatif à peine plus gros que de la poussière. Il s'envola directement autour de Tituba qui le respira bien malgré elle. Mary attendit, le cœur battant. La Barbadienne s'affaissa doucement et se mit à ronfler légèrement. Soupirant d'aise, la jeune femme retrouva sa forme normale et alla rejoindre ses amies qui s'étaient déjà levées, prêtes à partir.

— Combien d'entres vous partent ? demanda-t-elle.

— Nous sommes quatre, répondit Martha Carrier.

— Que Dieu vous protège ! Nous viendrons vous chercher !

— Que faites-vous ? s'exclama Betty qui s'était approchée en silence.

— Elles vont se rendre, Betty, lui dit Mary Black.

— Mais Tituba...

— Ce sont nos enfants, trancha Sarah Osborne. Je pars avec Rebecca, Susannah et Martha.

— Nous viendrons vous délivrer ! cria Betty.

Elle les regarda s'enfuir sous la neige et pria pour leurs âmes. Les forces de la confrérie se trouvaient considérablement amoindries. Elles n'étaient plus que dix avec Ezra. Tituba allait être furieuse.

Au village, Patton avait à peine eu le temps de terminer son discours qu'il vit arriver quatre femmes sales et hirsutes. Il sut alors qu'il avait vu juste. Un

négligent geste de la main jeta sur elles huit inquisiteurs qui les ficelèrent et les emmenèrent à la prison.

— Nos enfants ! hurla Rebecca. Relâchez-les !

— Nous verrons, susurra Patton.

Il les suivit jusqu'à ses quartiers et pénétra à leur suite.

— Quatre sorcières, murmura l'homme, les yeux brillants et malsains, luisants de contentement. Mais où sont les autres ?

— Il n'y a que nous, brava Susannah.

Patton se tourna vers elle, l'air furibond, et lui mit une claque si forte qu'une dent se brisa.

— Ne me mentez pas, infâme vermine. Je sais que vous êtes nombreuses. Mais j'attendrai ! Je ne suis pas pressé. D'ici là, vous croupirez avec vos enfants.

Les inquisiteurs les emmenèrent vers la porte du fond qui conduisait aux geôles.

— Attendez ! Mettez-leur un bandeau sur les yeux, je ne veux pas qu'elles les voient.

Et il se mit à rire sous les imprécations furieuses des mères.

— Comment ça, elles sont parties ? tonna Tituba, hors d'elle. Imbéciles ! Qui leur a permis de sortir ?

— Vous vous êtes endormie et… commença Mary.

— Je le sais bien, triple ânesse! J'aimerais savoir comment!

— Si vous les aviez aidées dès le début, elles ne se seraient pas enfuies! cria Abigail.

— Vous ne comprendrez jamais rien, miss Parris, hurla Tituba, les yeux révulsés d'une rage incontrôlable. Toutes! Vous ne comprendrez jamais qu'agir à chaud est le meilleur moyen de faire des erreurs qui peuvent nous coûter tout ce qu'on a! Croyez-vous vraiment que j'allais laisser ce Patton décimer nos rangs sans rien faire?

— Vous nous avez interdit de nous battre, avança Betty.

— Car ça ne nous mènerait à rien, pour l'instant. Nos meilleurs alliés sont l'invisibilité, la nuit et le silence.

— Que voulez-vous dire?

— J'avais prévu aller délivrer tout le monde une nuit prochaine. Candy nous aurait fait passer à travers les murs, je pouvais m'occuper de tous les liens qui les retiendraient, et nous sommes plusieurs à maîtriser l'invisibilité.

Bouche bée, Abigail et Betty n'en croyaient pas leurs oreilles. Mary Black rougit violemment. Les jumelles Parker, qui étaient réapparues il y a peu, gardaient le silence. Elles venaient juste d'être mises au courant des événements de la nuit.

— Vous vouliez les aider? demanda Abigail, incrédule.

— Pour qui me prenez-vous, miss Parris ?

— Vous êtes toujours si froide, si distante…

— Ce n'est pas seulement votre combat ! lui dit Tituba, glaciale.

— Mais c'est toujours possible, n'est-ce pas ? l'interrogea Betty.

— Oui. Ce sera juste plus compliqué.

Mary Black cacha son visage empreint de honte derrière ses mains qu'elle fit mine de réchauffer. Elle espéra que les inquisiteurs n'avaient pas fait de mal à ses amies.

— Quand agirons-nous, Tituba ?

— Ce soir. Nous n'avons plus le choix maintenant !

Tituba fit aussitôt apparaître un épais mur de pierres et demanda à Candy de s'entraîner à les faire passer une par une puis plusieurs à la fois au travers. La jeune esclave ne mit pas longtemps à maîtriser parfaitement ce pouvoir. Tituba se désintéressa des autres. Abigail et Betty la regardèrent s'éloigner.

— Peut-être sommes-nous trop dures avec elle, commença Betty. Après tout, elle veut bien faire, comme nous toutes. Nous sommes juste trop empressées.

Abigail marmonna une réponse inaudible, mais elle était d'accord avec sa cousine. Tituba avait l'air sincèrement abattue par la perte de ses alliées. Betty s'entraîna mollement à les rendre toutes invisibles, mais elle s'en lassa bien vite. Tituba, Ezra et Margaret Scott partageaient le même pouvoir qu'elle. C'était

largement suffisant. Abigail chercha Ezra des yeux mais ne le trouva pas. Il avait encore disparu.

La nuit tomba tôt et un froid implacable l'accompagna. Frissonnantes, au centre de la clairière, les sorcières écoutaient les instructions de Tituba.

— Nous partirons en groupe pour nous retrouver devant les murs de la prison. Chaque groupe prendra un chemin différent. Là, Candy, vous nous ferez entrer dans les cachots deux par deux. Les premiers entrés s'occuperont de calmer les effusions. Je ne veux pas entendre un bruit. Si les inquisiteurs suspectent quoi que ce soit, c'en est fini ! Ezra et moi, nous détruirons les liens et autres chaînes qui les retiennent. Puis Candy nous fera sortir, Margaret, Ezra, Betty et moi. Ensuite, ce sera le tour des prisonniers. Vous devrez faire preuve de beaucoup de force, ajouta-t-elle à l'intention des trois intéressés. Il y aura de nombreuses personnes et la quantité d'énergie à déployer sera sans doute bien plus intense que vous ne pensez. Candy, vous ferez l'aller-retour entre les murs jusqu'à ce qu'il n'y ait plus personne. Nous nous séparerons à nouveau pour nous retrouver ici. Tout le monde a bien compris ?

Tous approuvèrent, l'air apeuré. Même Betty, qui n'avait cessé de rêver d'action, tremblait comme une feuille.

— Betty, vous emmènerez les jumelles avec vous, continua Tituba. Margaret, vous prendrez Ann et Candy ; Ezra ira avec Abigail, et Mary, vous viendrez avec moi.

Mary Black réprima un soupir de déception. Elle n'aimait pas l'idée d'être seule avec Tituba. Betty, espiègle, mit un coup de coude dans les côtes de sa cousine qui rougit violemment. Elle tourna la tête vers Ezra, espérant qu'il n'avait rien vu. Le jeune homme s'était perdu dans la contemplation d'une feuille rouge vif sur le sol et il semblait bien loin des préoccupations des femmes.

Lorsque vint l'heure du départ, Tituba leur dit les dernières recommandations puis elle fit partir les petits groupes. Margaret, Candy et Ann partirent les premières. Elles avaient le chemin le plus long à parcourir puisqu'elles passeraient par-derrière le manoir des Parris. Puis ce fut le tour de Betty et des jumelles qui sortirent par le sentier habituel. Mary, armée d'une branche de sapin, effaçait tant bien que mal leurs traces dans la neige. Ezra et Abigail s'éloignèrent par l'endroit d'où étaient venus les inquisiteurs. Tituba se tourna vers Mary.

— Nous voilà seules ! chuchota-t-elle.

Mary frémit.

— Je sais que c'est vous qui m'avez endormie et avez permis à vos amies de s'évader. Je n'aime pas que l'on s'attaque à moi, surtout dans mon dos, continuat-elle, menaçante. Mais l'heure n'est pas aux règlements de compte et nous sommes, vous et moi, dans le même camp, n'est-ce pas ?

— Oui, bien sûr.

— Alors, c'est oublié.

Mais Mary eut l'impression que ce n'était pas le cas. Elles s'enfoncèrent dans l'obscurité en silence.

Sur le chemin, Abigail perdit patience. L'oppressant silence la rendait folle et l'action désespérée qu'elle et les autres allaient accomplir la transperçait d'effroi.

— Vas-tu me battre froid encore longtemps ? demanda-t-elle brusquement à Ezra.

Celui-ci tourna la tête vers elle, les yeux vagues, comme s'il ne la voyait pas. Il ne lui répondit pas. Soufflant d'un air excédé, elle continua :

— Je sais que je t'ai fait souffrir, je sais que je t'ai menti, je sais que je t'ai trahi. Mais comprends-moi ! Je n'avais pas d'autre choix ! Les choses ne se seraient pas passées comme ça si nous avions avoué. Tituba serait restée en prison, le choléra aurait détruit tout le village et tu ne serais pas devenu ce grand sorcier !

— C'est lâche de se cacher derrière le destin.

Les premiers mots d'Ezra à son égard n'étaient pas sympathiques mais cela l'encouragea. Cela faisait si longtemps qu'il ne lui avait pas adressé la parole.

— Je ne me cache pas derrière le destin. Je ne cherche pas d'excuses. Tout ce que je peux te dire, c'est que c'est comme ça que ça s'est passé. Et nous en sommes là aujourd'hui. Nous ne pouvons pas retourner en arrière. Et même si c'était possible, je crois que je referais la même chose. Il me semble que tout est de la faute de Tituba, c'est elle qui a regroupé toutes ces sorcières, les exposant à la colère des inqui-siteurs. Mais personne n'a été forcé. Nous ne

méritons pas cette oppression, et nous allons le prouver. Tituba nous a libérés, tout simplement.

— Tu as changé.

Le jeune homme ne dit plus un mot après cela et Abigail choisit de prendre ça pour un compliment.

Tous se retrouvèrent devant la prison et Candy commença ses nombreux allers et retours. Tituba avait raison. À l'intérieur des murs, une joie bruyante explosa qu'Ezra eut tôt fait d'anéantir. Tous les prisonniers se retrouvèrent muets. Ezra les rassura. Les effets ne dureraient pas longtemps. Tituba et lui s'acharnèrent sur les chaînes rouillées qui liaient les pieds et les poings des captifs.

— Candy, murmura Tituba, il reste encore beaucoup de prisonniers. Cela fait trop longtemps que nous sommes là. Fais passer Betty et Margaret, elles commenceront à ramener les autres. Dis-leur de se rendre à la clairière et de revenir. Qu'elles fassent vite !

Candy hocha la tête et fit ce que lui demandait Tituba. Lorsque les trois jeunes femmes furent dehors et invisibles, elles découvrirent avec stupeur un rang d'inquisiteurs autour des murs de la prison. Ils ne semblaient pas les avoir vues ou entendues, ils faisaient une ronde nocturne. Patton craignait sans doute une évasion massive. Et il parait à toute éventualité. Candy traversa immédiatement.

— Tituba, tous les inquisiteurs sont dehors. On ne peut pas passer.

La servante jura entre ses dents et ordonna à Candy de l'emmener dehors. Elles revinrent aussitôt, s'arrachant les cheveux et blasphémant tout bas.

— Qu'allons-nous faire ? demanda Betty.

Les prisonniers les regardaient, effrayés à l'idée de ne pouvoir sortir. Tituba releva la tête.

— Vous deux, gronda-t-elle à l'adresse d'Abigail et d'Ezra, vous savez voler ! Ces chiens sont si serrés qu'on ne peut passer à travers leur barrière sans qu'ils nous sentent. Vous emmènerez les prisonniers et les mettrez à l'abri plus loin dans le village. Abigail ! tonna-t-elle. Vous prendrez avec vous Betty pour chaque voyage. Ainsi que quelques prisonniers. Restez invisibles !

— Mais… je ne peux pas porter plusieurs personnes. Déjà que Betty sera lourde !

L'intéressée grogna.

— Je peux tous les rendre légers ! Mais vous n'en porterez pas plus de deux ou trois. Ezra ! cria la Barbadienne.

Le jeune homme hocha la tête et se rendit invisible. Il attrapa plusieurs prisonniers qui s'accrochèrent à lui. Candy les fit passer au-dehors avec Tituba qui observa avec appréhension si tout marchait. Elles attendirent, invisibles. Lorsqu'Ezra revint, Abigail faillit sauter de joie.

— Je les ai laissés sur le sentier qui mène à la rivière. On ne les trouvera pas. Mais il faut faire vite.

Abigail et lui commencèrent les voyages. Si les inquisiteurs avaient pu les voir, ils auraient été impressionnés d'apercevoir dans les airs, au-dessus de leurs têtes, une jeune fille et un jeune homme flanqués de corps sales et martyrisés s'envoler avec grâce dans le ciel nuageux.

Lorsque minuit sonna, tous s'étaient retrouvés dans la clairière. Épuisée, Tituba regarda autour d'elle. Il y avait là les douze sorcières qui avaient été arrêtées dernièrement, des hommes efflanqués retrouvant leurs femmes après leur longue et épuisante captivité, et des enfants accrochés aux jupes de leurs mères ou de leurs sœurs. La Confrérie de la Clairière venait de grossir d'une trentaine de membres. Tituba soupira et, aidée d'Ezra, elle construisit des cloisons sommaires pour séparer les familles. Le reste attendrait demain. Ezra monta les protections tout autour. Tous se couchèrent, exténués. Abigail pensa en frissonnant à la réaction de Patton qui découvrirait ses geôles vides le matin. Les choses n'allaient pas s'arrêter là.

14

Au matin, quelle ne fut pas la surprise des sorcières de voir arriver en convoi la plus grosse partie du village. Une famille arriva même avec une charrette tirée par un cheval. Tituba pesta haut et fort. Mais le contenu de la charrette la calma rapidement. Des couvertures, des chaussettes et des bonnets de laine, des serviettes et des brocs, des couverts, des assiettes et des verres, de la corde et des scies. Et même plusieurs miches de pain et des lambeaux de viande séchée. John et Elizabeth Proctor n'étaient pas arrivés les mains vides. Ils furent acclamés, embrassés et serrés. Même Tituba se dérida. Abigail et Betty, accompagnées des jumelles Parker, prirent les choses en main. Elles s'enfoncèrent dans les bois et revinrent les bras chargés de branches et de rameaux de sapins. S'installant confortablement sur une couverture moelleuse, elles s'emparèrent chacune d'une pelote de corde et commencèrent à nouer ensemble les longues branches. La petite fille qu'Abigail avait recueillie et qui n'avait pas encore dit son nom s'approcha d'elle. Elle la suivait partout désormais et dormait entre les deux cousines, bien au chaud. Abigail lui avait donné le nom d'Emma.

— Approche, Emma, viens nous aider. Tiens, regarde. Prends ces branches comme ça et noue-les ainsi. Nous construisons des paravents pour séparer les familles, comme ça chacune aura son intimité. Après, nous nouerons dessus les rameaux de sapins pour qu'on ne voit pas à travers et pour que le vent ait du mal à passer.

La petite imita les gestes de son aînée et, bientôt, elle devint aussi rapide que les autres. Certaines femmes se joignirent à elles et les constructions sommaires se multiplièrent. D'autres personnes venaient les récupérer et allaient les installer. La clairière se transforma en un immense meuble truffé de compartiments. Les hommes s'occupaient de rendre le sol confortable tandis que les femmes couraient à droite et à gauche derrière les enfants. Des feux s'allumèrent ici et là, rendant l'ambiance plus chaleureuse encore. Des marmites se mirent à bouillir ; des racines, de maigres légumes et de l'eau claire crépitèrent joyeusement. La chère était maigre, mais la compagnie agréable. Une soixantaine de personnes vivaient désormais dans la clairière que Tituba avait dû agrandir. Les espaces pour les familles entouraient toujours le grand cercle où elles s'entraîneraient. Nombre des villageois n'avaient aucun pouvoir, mais la constante oppression du village les avait fait fuir. Le repas se fit dans le plus grand bruit, à l'immense joie des enfants qui s'égaillaient alentour. Emma esquissa même un sourire et se mit aussi à courir après un jeune garçon de son âge. Abigail avait espéré que le père de la petite se trouverait parmi les nouveaux arrivants, mais ce n'était pas le cas. Malgré la joie et le bonheur des retrouvailles, la tension restait palpable. Les sorcières de la Confrérie savaient que lorsque Patton se rendrait compte que sa prison avait été vidée sous son nez et qu'en plus la moitié du

village avait déserté, sa colère ne connaîtrait aucun exutoire. Et elles étaient maintenant responsables de tant de gens ! Rien qu'à penser au combat qui s'ensuivrait forcément, Abigail tremblait. Elle se demandait continuellement si c'était une bonne chose et ressassait ce qu'elle avait dit à Ezra. Elle n'était plus aussi sûre qu'elle aurait refait la même chose si le retour en arrière avait été possible. En soupirant, elle alla chercher Emma. Betty et elle s'occupaient beaucoup de la petite, dont les pouvoirs s'étaient développés. L'enfant pouvait désormais diriger les oiseaux. Ces petits animaux se révélaient redoutables lorsqu'ils plongeaient tous griffes et bec dehors.

— Betty ! Abigail ! hurlèrent des voix.

Abigail se retourna pour voir d'où provenaient les cris. Les jumelles sortaient du couvert des arbres, gesticulant dans tous les sens, le visage rouge. Elles s'égosillaient et semblaient en proie à une furieuse excitation. Alice et Mary stoppèrent leur course au centre de la clairière et se tournèrent de tous les côtés pour trouver les filles Parris. Curieuses, Betty et Abigail s'approchèrent. Un attroupement se forma autour des quatre jeunes filles.

— Que se passe-t-il ? demanda Betty en riant. On dirait que vous avez vu le diable en personne !

— Du feu… détruit… le manoir… peut rien faire, balbutièrent les deux sœurs, essayant de reprendre leur souffle.

— Je ne comprends pas, commença Abigail qui pensait le contraire.

— Ils brûlent le manoir.

Le choc de la nouvelle propulsa les deux jeunes filles coude à coude dans la neige. Elles avancèrent de front, sans se préoccuper des branches qui leur cinglaient les joues. Du sang ruissela sur la robe de Betty, mais elle n'y prit pas garde. Comme deux furies, elles débouchèrent dans le champ et suivirent le chemin qu'elles avaient emprunté tant de fois.

— Rends-nous invisibles, chuinta Abigail, essoufflée par un point.

Betty ne tourna même pas la tête vers elle et sans ralentir elle les fit disparaître. Dès qu'elles furent en vue du manoir, elles comprirent que les jumelles ne leur avaient pas menti. Un attroupement d'hommes en noir et une épaisse fumée grise qui s'envolait en volutes malmenées par le vent le prouvaient. Et il y avait aussi ces grandes langues rouge et orange qui léchaient avidement la moindre parcelle de la maison. Abigail tomba à genoux, des larmes ruisselant déjà sur ses joues raidies par le froid. Betty regardait le spectacle en silence. Tous leurs souvenirs, toutes ces belles années, leurs joies, leurs tristesses, leurs colères, leurs bêtises, leurs rires, le révérend, miss Salinger, leur enfance… Tout s'envolait en fumée qui sinuait vers le ciel où elle se disperserait et ferait oublier jusqu'à l'existence de cette maison qui les avait abrités elles et leurs ancêtres depuis des décennies. Abigail sanglotait maintenant. Elle hurla toute sa souffrance et son déchirement tandis que Betty restait de marbre. Les poings serrés, elle tremblait mais ses yeux restaient secs. Abigail n'y parvenait pas. La douleur était trop rude. Elle se rappela leurs courses dans les couloirs, les

glissades le long de la rampe du grand escalier, les nuits où elles avaient peur des craquements de la maison, les biscuits au gingembre de miss Salinger, les fauteuils confortables du salon, la grande table de la salle à manger et les icônes qui les mettaient mal à l'aise. Et les livres, les centaines de livres qui trônaient dans le bureau de Samuel Parris. Tout disparaissait. Abigail se remémorait tous ses souvenirs. Elle voulait y entrer, se perdre en eux, ne plus jamais s'en séparer. Son retour à la réalité se fit par le contact d'une peau qui lui rappela d'autres choses. Elle tourna la tête, misérable, et découvrit à ses côtés Ezra, le regard fixé sur les flammes, serrant si fort sa main qu'elle sentait ses jointures se cogner. Elle n'était plus seule devant le spectacle de l'embrasement de sa vie. Ezra l'accompagnait. Betty ne bougea pas tout le temps que dura l'incendie. Et le jeune homme ne lâcha pas la main d'Abigail jusqu'à ce que le dernier mur du manoir ne s'affaisse. Lorsque tout fut fini, la nuit était tombée et Ezra disparut sans un mot. Betty et Abigail retournèrent à la clairière, encore sous le choc. Elles refusèrent toutes les attentions qu'on leur portait. Elles se recroquevillèrent dans le creux de leur arbre, firent une place entre elles à Emma qui les avait rejointes et restèrent allongées en silence. De ses petits poings, Emma effaçait les traces de larmes du visage d'Abigail. Ce fut à ce moment-là que Betty commença à pleurer. De longs sanglots déchirants d'une bête blessée et abandonnée. Ils peuplèrent les ténèbres jusque tard dans la nuit.

Le lendemain, elles ne demandèrent même pas à retourner sur les lieux pour voir si elles pouvaient récupérer quelque chose. Elles savaient ce que Tituba leur aurait dit : les inquisiteurs n'attendaient que ça.

Abigail et Betty vaquèrent donc à leurs occupations en observant un silence poignant. Comme avec toutes les personnes qui vivaient un deuil, on les approchait doucement, on leur parlait en chuchotant, comme si un mot trop fort pouvait les briser. Abigail n'avait pas revu Ezra.

Anton n'avait pas reçu la correction promise par Patton. Celui-ci était devenu fou en voyant ses cages vidées de ses prisonniers. Il avait retourné les bureaux. Tous les papiers jonchaient le sol et les chaises n'étaient plus que des tas de bois. Une tornade semblait être passée par là.

— Comment ont-elles fait ? aboya-t-il. Et vous, bande d'incapables, ajouta-t-il en distribuant à la volée des paires de claques, je vous avais ordonné de rester aux alentours de la prison, toute la nuit. En rangs serrés pour que personne ne s'échappe ou ne rentre. Plus de vingt prisonniers disparus ! Envolés ! Partis en fumée !

Penauds, les inquisiteurs baissaient la tête, attendant que la fureur de leur maître se dissipe. L'exutoire de Patton avait été le manoir des Parris. Il s'était fait une joie d'y mettre le feu et de le regarder disparaître. Anton entendait encore son rire dément, la gorge offerte au ciel, ses dents crissant désagréablement quand il reprenait son souffle. L'angoisse avait étreint le jeune homme. Une fois que l'incendie du manoir serait loin derrière eux et qu'aucune arrestation notoire n'aurait eu lieu, Patton se souviendrait sans doute d'Anton. Il devait trouver les sorcières. Anton s'arrêta, les poings bien serrés au fond de ses poches, pour réfléchir. Cette

clairière, à Belwack ! Il était sûr que c'était le point de départ. Mais comment les surprendre ? Il décida d'attendre la nuit. Là, il s'habillerait de noir et se couvrirait le visage de charbon. Il saurait être aussi silencieux qu'un chat. En attendant, il alla se promener dans les environs. Les rives de la rivière débordaient d'une douce neige, et l'eau qui était directement en contact avec la terre avait gelé. Il s'avança prudemment et posa doucement le pied sur la glace. Elle se brisa sous son poids. Prudent, il recula et continua ses pérégrinations. Anton ne pensait plus qu'à son plan et, lorsque la nuit tomba, il avala un léger repas et fut le premier à aller se coucher. Ses compagnons en furent très étonnés. Anton était d'habitude le premier à lancer un jeu de cartes et à boire jusqu'à tard dans la nuit. Sous ses couvertures, tout habillé, Anton suait à grosses gouttes. Mais il attendit patiemment que toute la maisonnée soit endormie. Dès qu'il n'y eut plus un bruit, il sortit avec précaution de son lit, prit dans la cheminée quelques cendres dont il se barbouilla le visage, puis sortit silencieusement. Aussi discret qu'une ombre, Anton se mit à courir. Il ne ralentit que lorsque la forêt de Belwack lui apparut. La neige crissait bruyamment sous ses pas, lui donnant l'impression d'être le seul être vivant alentour. Décidé à les débusquer ce soir, il ne voulait pas être découvert. Alors, un pied après l'autre, il glissa, s'enfonçant largement dans les congères, mais ne produisant qu'un maigre chuintement qui pourrait s'apparenter aux bruissements des branches. Anton s'enfonça alors dans la forêt. Le hululement lugubre d'un hibou le fit sursauter et il se rendit compte que son cœur battait la chamade. « L'entendraient-elles ? » se demanda-t-il. Étouffant un rire nerveux, il reprit sa marche. La

clairière lui apparut soudain. Les éclairs d'argent qui, il en était sûr, avaient averti de la présence des inquisiteurs il y a deux jours, n'étaient pas là.

— Une chance pour moi ! s'exclama-t-il, se plaquant aussitôt une main sur la bouche.

Il regarda partout pour se dénicher un endroit où il pourrait observer et attendre. Anton choisit le tronc épais d'un vieux sapin bleu. Il dégagea un peu la neige qui s'était amoncelée sur les racines, en découvrit une et s'y installa confortablement. Et l'attente commença. Il se demanda s'il ne commettait pas une erreur. Peut-être étaient-elles nombreuses, là-bas. Chassant ses mauvaises pensées et se concentrant sur les récompenses que Patton lui donnerait, il évita de penser au froid et au noir qui l'étreignaient.

Alors qu'il se sentait somnoler, un mouvement le réveilla. Il avait vu quelque chose bouger dans la clairière. D'où il était, il n'aurait su dire s'il s'agissait d'un homme ou d'un animal, mais l'adrénaline qui courait dans ses veines le fit se redresser et regarder avec attention les environs. Rien. Il soupira et reprit sa position.

— Crois-tu que c'est une bonne idée ? chuchota une voix.

Anton manqua de hurler de joie et d'excitation.

— Ils ne nous attendrons pas en pleine nuit, lui répondit une autre. Et même s'ils sont là, je nous rendrai invisibles. Je veux voir s'il reste des choses que nous pourrons emporter.

Le jeune homme se déplaça silencieusement autour du tronc. Les deux voix se dirigeaient vers lui. Il allait leur sauter dessus. Il entrevit deux silhouettes s'approcher, discutant tranquillement entre elles. Dès qu'elles dépassèrent le tronc, Anton se dressa sur ses jambes, prit appui sur les racines et se détendit. Il leur tomba dessus sans prendre garde à leurs hurlements. Il saisit un bras dans chaque main et essaya tant bien que mal de se redresser. Mais les deux furies sous lui ne cessaient de gesticuler et de hurler. Comment allait-il les ramener au village ? Un rayon de lune éclaira la scène. « Les filles Parris ! » se dit-il sans parvenir à croire à sa bonne fortune.

— Levez-vous ! leur ordonna-t-il.

Il les tenait fermement. Elles grimaçaient sous sa poigne. Anton exultait.

— Comme on se retrouve, dit-il à Abigail qui ne leva pas les yeux vers lui. Je vous emmène avec moi. Patton sera content. Mais avant…

Anton se pencha vers le visage d'Abigail et chercha ses lèvres. Celle-ci hurla de terreur et fit un mouvement brusque qui la fit tomber. Elle entraîna avec elle Betty et Anton. Celui-ci jura et se releva précipitamment.

— Petite garce ! Je n'en ai pas fini avec toi !

Betty se mit à ruer dans tous les sens, si violemment qu'Anton peinait à la tenir. Abigail se mit à faire de même et le jeune homme eut soudain peur de les perdre toutes les deux. Il s'accrocha à leurs bras et les maintint si serrés qu'il sentit ses doigts s'enfoncer dans leur chair. Betty et sa cousine se remirent debout et

toutes deux gesticulèrent, gigotèrent en reculant vers la clairière. Anton ne se rendait pas compte de la direction qu'elles lui faisaient prendre. Il ne pensait qu'à ne pas les lâcher. S'enhardissant, les deux jeunes filles continuèrent de le mener où elles voulaient. Lorsqu'elles furent au centre de la clairière, elles s'arrêtèrent brusquement. Anton souffla. Elles s'étaient enfin épuisées. Puis il se rendit compte que le décor avait changé. Le sol était sec et couvert de feuilles mortes, sans une trace de neige. Un grand feu flambait, autour duquel se tenaient nombre de villageois qui le regardaient, ébahis. Autour de lui se tenaient les sorcières, en un cercle parfait. Ne pensant même pas au danger, Anton jubilait. Il les avait trouvées et il allait les servir à Patton sur un plateau d'argent. Nul doute que sa récompense serait plus que méritoire.

— Vous êtes toutes en état d'arrestation ! clama-t-il. Je vais aller chercher les inquisiteurs, et dès ce soir, vous serez toutes en prison.

Confiant, il marcha d'un pas impérial jusqu'à la bulle de protection qu'il ne voyait pas. Il fut stoppé en plein élan et tomba à la renverse. Anton se tâta le front où une bosse commençait à pousser. Il se tourna vers le cercle de sorcières qui s'était élargi pour le laisser passer.

— Laquelle d'entre vous a fait ça ? Ça vous coûtera cher !

Il se releva et repartit d'un pas décidé. Encore une fois, le choc le fit tomber. À genoux, Anton se mit à palper le mur invisible qui s'étendait devant lui.

— Laissez-moi sortir, dit-il. Tout de suite.

Tituba se détacha du cercle et s'avança vers lui, les yeux brillants, le sourire froid.

— Vous êtes en fâcheuse posture, mon ami.

— Laissez-moi partir tout de suite, sinon…

— Sinon quoi ? le coupa Tituba, menaçante. Vous êtes en pleine forêt, entouré de sorcières et de villageois non moins dangereux. Tous se souviennent exactement de ce que vous avez fait subir à leurs familles et à leurs amis. Et… vous êtes seul.

— J'ai prévenu les autres.

— Bien sûr ! Ezra !

Le jeune homme interpellé s'avança, des cordes apparurent dans sa main. Il allongea Anton à terre, face contre le sol, tira ses deux bras derrière et les ficela solidement, puis fit de même avec ses pieds.

— Arrête ! Tu serres trop fort ! gémit Anton.

Ezra tira d'un coup sec sur la corde et l'observa s'enfoncer dans la chair tendre des chevilles du prisonnier. Il releva ce dernier sans cérémonie et le poussa en avant.

— Qu'allons-nous faire de lui ? demanda-t-il à Tituba.

— Un appât.

Les sorcières et Ezra laissèrent Anton aux hommes qui s'en chargèrent. Tous s'installèrent autour du feu pour tenir conseil.

— Tuons-le, proposèrent les jumelles.

— Non ! s'exclama Abigail Hobbs.

— Tu as pitié de lui après ce qu'il a voulu te faire ? demanda Betty, incrédule.

— Je n'ai pas pitié de lui, il me dégoûte. Mais ne jouons pas le jeu des inquisiteurs. Nous ne sommes pas des tueuses.

— Que proposez-vous, miss Parris ? l'interrogea Tituba.

— Emmenons-le loin d'ici. Faisons-le disparaître. Ce sera toujours un inquisiteur de moins.

— Peut-être recommencera-t-il ailleurs, et dans ce cas, nous serons responsables de ses actions.

— Mais peut-être aussi que cela lui servira de leçon !

— Miss Abigail, votre bonté vous perdra, railla Tituba. Soit. Tout le monde est d'accord pour exiler ce vermisseau ? Bien. La question maintenant est : qui l'accompagnera ?

Ezra se leva.

— Non, pas toi ! Nous avons besoin de toi ici.

— J'irai, déclara Deliverance Hobbs.

— Et je l'accompagnerai, continua sa sœur.

— Bien, très bien, susurra Tituba. La discussion est close. Plus vite il partira, mieux ce sera. Patton se rendra compte de sa disparition tôt ou tard. Nous

devrons y faire face. Préparez-vous au voyage, dit-elle aux sœurs Hobbs.

Tituba se dirigea vers Anton qui tremblotait, assis seul par terre. Ses mains attachées dans le dos le forçaient à se pencher en une attitude grotesque.

— Écoute-moi bien, misérable ! Si cela n'avait tenu qu'à moi, je t'aurais tué sur-le-champ. Or, tu as de la chance. La petite que tu traquais a fait preuve d'une grande générosité à ton égard, ce que tu ne mérites pas. Nous t'enverrons loin ! Si je te recroise un jour, je t'écraserai comme une vulgaire fourmi. Suis-je bien claire ?

Anton ne répondit pas. Deliverance et Abigail Hobbs arrivaient, vêtues de capes et de chauds bonnets de laine.

— Savez-vous où aller ? leur demanda Tituba.

— Nous pensons descendre le long de la côte. Ce serait agréable de voir la mer. Rien ne peut être pire que ce qui se passe ici.

— Soyez prudentes. Ne perdez pas cet homme de vue !

Tous regardèrent les sœurs s'emparer du jeune homme, lui attacher une longe à son cou, et s'enfoncer dans les bois. Tituba souffla. Le pire avait été évité. À peine se fit-elle cette réflexion qu'un cri retentit dans les fourrés. Elle se précipita, aussitôt suivie de Betty, Abigail et Ezra. Deliverance était allongée dans la neige, pestant haut et fort et se tenant le nez qui ruisselait de sang. Sa sœur se tenait le ventre en gémissant.

— Il s'est enfui, dit-elle. Par là !

Ezra courut dans la direction indiquée par Abigail, suivi de Tituba. Au loin, Anton courait comme un dératé. Tituba arrêta brutalement Ezra et tendit le bras vers Anton. Celui-ci s'écroula, raide.

— Qu'avez-vous fait ?

— Je nous ai sauvé la vie. À tous !

— Ou vous n'avez fait qu'empirer les choses ! Il est mort, déclara Ezra touchant le jeune homme.

— Évidemment. Je sais encore quel sort je jette !

— Nous étions convenus de le laisser vivant.

— Il s'est enfui, Ezra ! tonna Tituba. Ce pourceau savait ce qui l'attendait s'il tentait de s'échapper. Je n'ai rien fait de plus que ce que je lui avais promis.

— Est-ce censé me consoler ? Qu'allons-nous faire de son cadavre ?

Abigail et Betty, qui les avaient rejoints, étouffèrent un cri devant le corps sans vie d'Anton. Tous les gens qui peuplaient la clairière se pressèrent autour d'eux. Les mères cachèrent les yeux de leurs enfants et des chuchotements parcoururent l'assemblée.

— Enterrons-le, proposa Abigail.

— Laissons-le en pâture aux bêtes !

— Abandonnons-le loin dans la forêt !

— Taisez-vous, vociféra Tituba. Nous allons nous servir de lui pour montrer aux inquisiteurs de quoi nous sommes capables. Ils nous redouteront peut-être

pour cet acte. Nous avons besoin qu'ils nous donnent cette force.

— J'irai porter le corps, dit Ezra.

— Je t'accompagnerai.

Betty le regarda droit dans les yeux. Ezra se pencha sur le mort et l'empoigna sous les aisselles. La jeune fille s'empressa d'attraper les pieds, en réprimant sa répulsion. Tous trois devinrent invisibles. Sur le chemin qui les menait vers la prison, aucun des deux sorciers ne parlait. Betty s'efforçait de ne pas ressentir la peau molle et sans vie des jambes du jeune homme.

— Laissons-le là, chuchota Ezra en désignant la porte du bureau de Patton.

Betty ne se fit pas prier et lâcha le corps, puis se frotta les mains sur sa robe. Ils s'éloignèrent. Ezra se retourna une dernière fois.

— La guerre est déclarée!

15

Le jeune inquisiteur se tenait, balbutiant, face à Patton qui commençait à perdre patience.

— Je ne comprends rien à ce que tu dis, Dawlish. Et quand bien même je comprendrais, je doute que cela soit très intéressant. Tu m'as toujours paru tellement falot !

— Je veux dire, sir Patton, qu'il y a un cadavre devant la porte. Je suis tombé en butant dessus. Et je crois qu'il s'agit d'Anton.

Patton cessa de rire pour le regarder sérieusement. Il se précipita vers la porte et l'ouvrit violemment. Dans une pose grotesque, Anton reposait sur les marches, les doigts bleuis de froid et le corps raide. Il était mort depuis longtemps. On l'avait sans doute déposé cette nuit devant le quartier général des inquisiteurs. Patton regarda à droite et à gauche sans savoir pourquoi. Le responsable ne s'était sûrement pas attardé. Il regarda à nouveau le jeune homme puis se pencha pour le retourner. Son visage lui apparut, les traits déformés par la surprise, la peur ou la souffrance. Ses cils avaient gelé, de légers cristaux blancs le vieillissaient prématurément. Patton respira profondément. La mort d'Anton ne le chagrinait pas vraiment, il ne l'avait jamais aimé.

LES SORCIÈRES DE SALEM

Au contraire, elle lui paraissait de bon augure. Il pouvait enfin prendre les choses en main.

— Envoie une missive à Craig Dorson, dit-il à son bras droit. Dis-lui de nous envoyer des renforts. Elles ont tué un des nôtres, elles sont dangereuses.

Il sourit en fixant la cime des arbres au loin. Anton les avait trouvées, cet imbécile avait enfin fait quelque chose d'utile. Patton ne s'était même pas souillé les mains pour le faire disparaître. La journée s'annonçait belle, mais le travail à accomplir restait important. Cela ne faisait que commencer. Il rentra dans son bureau pour se réchauffer et s'installa, rêveur. La frustration et la colère des derniers jours laissaient place à une avidité qui ne présageait rien de bon pour les sorcières. Ce ne serait pas facile de toutes les attraper, mais il comptait sur les nouveaux arrivants.

— Sir, je viens d'envoyer le message. Le coursier est parti sur-le-champ. Une réponse ne devrait pas tarder.

— Merci, Harford !

— Sir, pardonnez-moi mais… Savez-vous où elles se cachent ?

— Bien sûr. Elles sont exactement là où Anton l'avait dit. Il ne jurait que par cette clairière. Et il les a trouvées cette nuit. S'il était encore vivant, je le décorerais !

Il éclata d'un rire malfaisant.

— Tu crois que c'était une bonne idée ? demanda Betty à Abigail.

— Bien sûr que non. Ils croient maintenant que nous sommes des tueuses. Ils ne reculeront devant rien pour nous arrêter.

— Tituba a cru bien faire.

— Non, elle savait parfaitement ce que cela allait déclencher !

— Elle ne veut pas qu'on se batte ! Pourquoi nous aurait-elle mis sciemment en danger ?

— Je ne sais pas.

Abigail se rendit compte qu'elle ne voulait pas en parler avec Betty. Son cœur se serra à cette pensée. Betty et elle partageaient tout avant, elles ne se cachaient rien. Elle aurait aimé voir Ezra et discuter avec lui mais il avait encore disparu. La veille, Betty était rentrée seule du village. Elle avait dit à Abigail qu'Ezra était fatigué et qu'il rentrait se reposer. Abigail lui avait demandé s'il lui avait parlé d'elle et avait aussitôt rougi de se voir si égoïste. Betty venait de transporter un cadavre à travers la forêt. Elle s'était excusée et sa cousine l'avait rassurée en lui disant qu'il ne l'avait pas évoquée car le moment était mal choisi. Mais elle ne doutait pas qu'il en mourait d'envie.

Le froid avait envahi leur clairière et Tituba ne pouvait plus rien faire. Les couvertures apportées par les époux Proctor se révélèrent utiles mais insuffisantes. Les feux germaient de partout et tous étaient accroupis autour d'eux, les mains tendues, frissonnants mais ne se plaignant pas. La nourriture vint aussi à manquer. Susannah Post faisait apparaître des fruits, mais les récoltes étaient trop maigres pour

nourrir toute la communauté. Abigail avait essayé de reproduire le sort qui avait fait apparaître à manger pour Emma il y a quelque temps, mais elle fut incapable de créer une seule miche de pain. Croyant qu'elle était trop fatiguée, elle demanda à Betty d'essayer mais celle-ci se révéla tout aussi impuissante. Prenant son courage à deux mains, Abigail alla voir Ezra.

— Je pense que cela ne marche pas car la famine s'est étendue alentour. Lorsque tu prononçais ce sort, cela devait prendre de la nourriture dans un endroit proche. Tu ne la créais pas vraiment. Or, il n'y a plus rien nulle part.

— Nous allons mourir de faim.

— Je ne sais pas. Nous avons de l'eau en abondance, Susannah nous gave de fruits et les racines poussent par milliers dans cette forêt.

— Mais l'hiver est bien avancé maintenant, Tituba n'arrive même plus à contrer le froid. Que vont devenir les enfants ?

— Je n'ai jamais dit que ce serait facile, miss Parris.

Ce nom dans la bouche d'Ezra lui fit mal, déchirant et labourant ses entrailles. Le regard flamboyant du jeune homme l'acheva. Elle s'éloigna, la tête basse, sûre d'y avoir décelé du mépris. Les craintes d'Abigail étaient fondées. Le lendemain, deux nourrissons furent retrouvés morts. De froid, de faim, on ne savait pas. La famille en deuil hurla sa peine pendant ce qui sembla des heures aux membres de la Confrérie.

— Voilà deux bouches de moins à nourrir, déclara Tituba.

— Vous êtes cruelle! s'emporta Abigail. Ce n'étaient que des enfants.

— Vous ne comprendrez donc jamais que la guerre réclame des sacrifices, et que les plus faibles doivent s'en aller en premier pour permettre aux autres de vaincre? Je ne dis pas ça de gaieté de cœur, voyez-vous. Si j'avais su dans quel pétrin je m'embarquais en vous enseignant mon art, croyez bien que je ne l'aurais pas fait. Cessez de me harceler avec votre morale! Vous n'êtes pas ma conscience!

Abigail fulminait. Pouvait-il exister une femme plus maléfique que Tituba? Elle sentit sur son épaule la main de sa cousine.

— Ne lui en veux pas, elle a toujours été brusque! Je crois qu'elle essaie réellement d'aider. Elle est la plus expérimentée de tous ici, nous avons besoin d'elle. Une fois que tout sera terminé, tu pourras régler tes comptes avec elle, mais en attendant, soutenons-nous.

La jeune fille s'éloigna rapidement et sortit de la clairière. Elle fit apparaître quelques fées qui voletèrent autour d'elle au cas où un danger se présenterait. Elle marcha, s'enlisant dans la neige, écartant d'un bras rageur les obstacles sur sa route. Après avoir parcouru une longue distance, elle regarda autour d'elle sans reconnaître les lieux.

— Il ne manquerait plus que je sois perdue et que je passe la nuit en dehors de la clairière, maugréa-t-elle.

Abigail décida d'avancer encore. Sa mère lui avait toujours dit de continuer tout droit lorsqu'elle se perdait. Tôt ou tard, elle tomberait sur un chemin, une

trouée, une maison ou quoi que ce soit d'autre. Moins de cinq minutes plus tard, elle se retrouva au pied d'une montagne dont elle ignorait totalement l'existence. Abigail commençait à perdre son sang-froid et, face à la falaise, elle ignorait s'il valait mieux aller à droite, à gauche ou l'escalader. Elle se décida pour la droite. Pour dissimuler sa peur, elle chantonna, la main glissant sur la paroi de pierre. À la lumière environnante, elle comprit que la nuit n'allait pas tarder à tomber. Elle pressa le pas. Une voix retentit au-dessus d'elle et elle hurla de frayeur. Abigail leva la tête et aperçut la chevelure ébouriffée d'Ezra.

— Je t'ai demandé ce que tu faisais là…

— Je… je me suis perdue. J'ai marché à l'aveuglette et je n'ai pas réussi à retrouver mon chemin. Et toi, pourquoi es-tu ici ?

— La sage et prudente Abigail Parris s'est perdue, railla le jeune homme.

— Si c'est pour te moquer de moi, je m'en vais. Je n'ai pas besoin de ton aide.

Abigail espéra qu'Ezra allait la retenir car elle ignorait complètement le chemin à prendre pour rejoindre la clairière, et la perspective d'errer seule dans les bois la nuit ne la réjouissait pas. La démarche fière, les épaules raides pour camoufler les tremblements, elle s'éloigna.

— Ce n'est pas par là, jeta laconiquement Ezra.

Elle changea aussitôt de direction vers les bois.

— Par là non plus, continua le jeune homme qui ne parvenait pas à rester calme.

— Tu ne veux pas m'aider ? Très bien ! Mais laisse-moi tranquille !

— Allons, Abi, dit Ezra en riant, viens me rejoindre ! Tu passeras la nuit ici et dès demain je te réexpédierai vers cette clairière.

Abigail fut soulagée. Elle allait passer la nuit dans la grotte avec Ezra. Frissonnante de plaisir, elle sentit ses joues chauffer. Oh non ! Pas question qu'elle se présente au jeune homme les joues rouges. Elle se frotta vigoureusement la peau avec des poignées de neige, grimaçant à ce contact. Escaladant tant bien que mal les rochers, elle arriva hors d'haleine devant l'entrée de la grotte où crépitait un bon feu. Abigail s'y précipita et tendit les mains vers la chaleur bienfaisante. Ezra s'affairait, étendant une couverture sur un lit en branchages. Abigail l'observa.

— Je peux te poser une question ? demanda le garçon.

— Bien sûr ! Vas-y !

— Tu es une sorcière, n'est-ce pas ?

— Oui, répondit la jeune fille sans comprendre où il voulait en venir.

— Je t'ai vue t'échiner à grimper jusqu'ici. Ne sais-tu pas voler ?

Abigail sursauta et sentit aussitôt ses joues la brûler. De honte ! Comment avait-elle pu être stupide au point d'en oublier ses pouvoirs ?

— Et je suppose que si tu sais voler, tu aurais pu retrouver ton chemin en retournant à la clairière par le ciel…

— Eh bien, je… j'aime me sentir normale de temps à autre. Je ne vois pas ce qu'il y a de mal à cela.

— Oh voyons, Abigail ! Quand avoueras-tu que tu as fait une erreur ? Quand oseras-tu dire que tout est de ta faute, et que tu t'excuses pour cela ? Est-ce si difficile ?

La soudaine colère d'Ezra la surprit.

— On ne parle pas que de mon égarement, n'est-ce pas ? lui demanda-t-elle.

— Tu crois toujours que tu es meilleure que tout le monde, que ta bonté devrait être égalée par tous, que ton intelligence fait de toi quelqu'un de bien. Tu as eu quinze ans, non ?

— Oui.

— Tu ne crois pas qu'il est temps de grandir et d'assumer tes responsabilités, tes fautes ? Tu vis tout ça comme si tu n'avais pas eu le choix, comme si tu étais une pauvre victime égarée au milieu de ce désastre ! tonna Ezra, dominant Abigail, à genoux près du feu. J'avais une si haute estime de toi ! Jusqu'à ce que tu me trahisses ! Et tu ne t'es même pas excusée !

— Je l'ai fait !

— Non ! Tu as seulement dit que c'était arrivé et voilà tout. Juste ces mots venant de toi, « Je m'excuse », et tout aurait été pardonné. Tu es trop fière, Abigail, je ne te connaissais pas comme ça.

Il rentra dans la grotte et s'enfonça dans l'obscurité.

— Tu peux prendre mon lit pour ce soir, je dormirai sur la couverture.

Abigail écrasa une larme sur sa joue.

Le lendemain, Ezra montra la direction de la clairière à Abigail puis lui tourna le dos pour vaquer à ses occupations. Elle le regarda longtemps sans oser lui dire ce qu'il attendait. Abigail sentait que c'était trop tard. Au pied de la falaise, elle entra dans le sous-bois puis s'envola sans jeter un œil en arrière. Arrivée à la clairière, Betty se jeta sur elle.

— Tu m'as fait une peur bleue ! J'ai cru que tu avais été attrapée. Je suis allée avec Candy à la prison, j'ai guetté les inquisiteurs toute la nuit pour surprendre ton nom. Mais rien ! Je me suis fait un sang d'encre ! Où étais-tu ?

— Je… me suis promenée.

— Toute la nuit ?

— Je n'ai pas vu le temps passer.

— Abi ?

— Tout va bien, ne t'inquiète pas. Pardonne-moi de t'avoir causé du souci.

Betty la regarda, suspicieuse.

— Alice, Mary, Tituba et moi avons eu une idée, commença-t-elle.

— Ah oui, laquelle ? demanda Abigail, faisant un effort pour avoir l'air intéressée.

— Nos troupes perdent le moral et les gens s'enfoncent de plus en plus dans la tristesse et le désespoir. Tituba craint que certains d'entre eux ne flanchent et ne retournent au village pour nous dénoncer.

— Tituba pense ça ?

— Abi !

— Quelle est votre idée, Betty ?

— Des veillées.

— Des veillées ? répéta Abigail, incrédule.

— Pour amuser et détendre tout le monde. Tu te souviens de celles auxquelles nous assistions avec papa, sur la place ? Nous aimions tellement les conteurs, les magiciens et les jongleurs ! Papa disait toujours qu'une bonne veillée sous la neige guérissait tous les maux.

Abigail ne trouvait pas l'idée mauvaise, bien au contraire. C'était de cela dont ils avaient tous besoin. De rires, de chaleur et d'espoir. Et surtout d'être ensemble pour imaginer un meilleur avenir.

— Qu'en penses-tu ?

— C'est une très bonne idée.

— Je suis soulagée car j'ai besoin de toi.

— Pour quoi faire ?

— Un spectacle de lumières ! Toi et tes fées, moi et mes papillons !

Betty souriait comme une enfant émerveillée. Abigail sentit l'émotion la gagner et elle accepta l'offre de sa cousine.

— Peut-être qu'Ezra voudra bien nous raconter des histoires, comme avant, continua-t-elle. Tu ne l'as pas vu ?

Une main de fer serra le cœur d'Abigail à le briser. D'une voix étranglée, elle lui répondit que non. Surexcitée, Betty la laissa là et se dirigea vers d'autres personnes, gesticulant dans tous les sens. À son approche, les villageois souriaient de la voir si exaltée et dès qu'elle exposait leur projet, ils applaudissaient, la serraient contre elle. Les enfants couraient dans ses jambes, voulant son attention. Betty prodiguait une caresse à droite, un baiser à gauche. « Nous avons tellement changé », pensa Abigail.

— Avez-vous trouvé ce que vous cherchiez, miss Abigail ? demanda Tituba qui était apparue à ses côtés.

— Je ne vois pas de quoi vous parlez !

— D'humilité, ma chère. Votre cousine a fait de bien grands progrès, mais il semble qu'elle vous ait laissée en arrière. Mais Ezra vous en a sans doute déjà parlé.

La jeune fille ne répondit pas et s'éloigna pour rejoindre Betty.

— Nous ferons la première ce soir ! cria cette dernière de joie. John Proctor sait jongler, les sœurs Parker et les sœurs Hobbs s'occuperont de faire des tours drôles et,

pour ce qui est de la magie, tout le monde s'en chargera chacun son tour. Ezra a même accepté de reprendre son rôle de conteur. C'est merveilleux !

Abigail tourna la tête de tous les côtés pour apercevoir Ezra. Celui-ci se tenait un peu en retrait et l'observait. La jeune fille baissa la tête, honteuse, et lui tourna le dos.

Le soir venu, tous s'installèrent autour du foyer gigantesque. Les enfants, impatients, se blottirent contre leurs parents pour se protéger du froid. Ezra s'avança.

— Connaissez-vous Boston ? demanda-t-il.

Un murmure négatif envahit l'assistance.

— J'y ai vécu longtemps avant d'arriver parmi vous. Je vivais dans un orphelinat, un lieu affreux et hanté du nom de Crackwick. Le nom seul fait frémir. Là-bas, j'étais insouciant mais vigilant. Nos maîtres ne rêvaient que de nous faire disparaître. Mais les enfants ont du talent à revendre et une formidable envie de vivre. C'est pourquoi je suis là, maintenant.

Il observa un silence travaillé. Abigail vint s'asseoir aux côtés de Betty. Ezra surprit un mouvement et posa ses yeux sur la jeune fille qui, figée, s'immobilisa. Puis il reprit.

— J'avais quatre amis dans cet orphelinat. Les meilleurs que l'on puisse avoir. Ed, Joshua, Harvey et Jack.

À ces noms, les deux cousines se serrèrent la main, heureuses de retrouver ces amis inconnus.

— Nous faisions toutes sortes de bêtises ensemble, c'était le bon temps. Les corrections ne nous arrêtaient jamais. Un soir où la nuit était particulièrement noire, nous avons entendu des craquements dans l'escalier qui menait à nos dortoirs. D'un bond, nous nous sommes tous les cinq retrouvés dehors. Une silhouette sombre descendait doucement. Nous l'avons suivie. Les pierres étaient froides et les tableaux lugubres accrochés aux murs semblaient nous observer.

Abigail regarda l'auditoire. Les enfants étaient subjugués par la voix chaude d'Ezra, et même les parents le regardaient avec intérêt. Il n'avait rien perdu de son talent. Abigail se perdit aussi dans les intonations connues d'Ezra et laissa son esprit dériver durant toute l'histoire. Elle ne se rendit compte qu'il avait terminé que lorsqu'une salve d'applaudissements vint briser le silence. Ezra, retrouvant son insouciance, se prosterna devant son public, un large sourire aux lèvres. Ce fut au tour de Betty et d'Abigail d'exécuter leur numéro. Elles n'avaient rien répété pour laisser la place à l'imprévu. Abigail fit apparaître ses fées argentées tandis que Betty invoquait ses papillons dorés. Et le ballet commença. Les deux jeunes filles leur firent faire de gracieuses arabesques, d'amples mouvements qui les faisaient se perdre dans la foule. Les enfants criaient de joie, essayant de les attraper de leurs petits poings potelés. Les êtres magiques virevoltaient dans les airs, malicieux. Abigail se sentit mieux et elle osa envoyer une de ses fées se lover dans les épais cheveux d'Ezra. Celui-ci ne la délogea pas et esquissa même un sourire à la jeune fille qui se sentit plus légère.

Le spectacle se termina tard dans la nuit. Ezra raconta une nouvelle histoire qui fit frémir les enfants.

Un sombre conte à propos de squelettes trouvés dans la cave de l'orphelinat. Les jumelles Parker firent rire tout le monde avec un numéro de danse chaotique, Mary Black fit fureur en se métamorphosant en dizaines d'animaux et John Proctor remporta un vif succès lorsqu'il se mit à jongler avec cinq torches. Dans la clairière régnait une ambiance chaleureuse et festive qui les rendit tous oublieux des événements à venir.

Harford entra dans le bureau de Patton, une missive à la main.

— Craig Dorson a répondu. Il vous envoie une vingtaine d'hommes. Ils seront là demain. Comment allons-nous procéder ?

— J'ai mon idée.